Elementary Practical Organic Chemistry

Part 2: Qualitative Organic Analysis

SECOND EDITION

BY THE SAME AUTHOR

A Text-Book of Practical Organic Chemistry
including Qualitative Organic Analysis
3rd Edition

'Although it is only eight years since this text-book first appeared, it has become widely accepted as a valuable practical guide to the student of organic chemistry.... The position that "Vogel" has reached in the teaching of practical organic chemistry is proof of the value of the book and this has been enhanced in the new enlarged edition. It is well worth its price.' *Chemistry and Industry*

'Here, in one textbook, is probably the most complete and up to date presentation of practical organic chemistry that has been written to date. Dr. Vogel presents, in this massive volume, not only an excellent series of organic syntheses ranging from those suitable for the beginner to ones complex enough for the advance or graduate student, but also a well organized discussion of the theory and use of the various experimental techniques, and a better than average procedure for the qualitative analysis of organic compounds.... In the opinion of the reviewer this book will very quickly become one of the classics amongst preparatory organic chemistry texts, and on this basis it must be highly recommended to students, teachers, and even research students in the field.'
Journal of the Franklin Institute (U.S.A.)

A Text-Book of Macro and Semimicro Qualitative Inorganic Analysis
4th Edition

'As a text-book for undergraduates, the treatise has already proved its value and as a book of reference it must find a place in every library.' *Science Progress*

'This excellent volume represents an extension and modernisation of the third edition (1945) ... the book appears eminently teachable, and any student familiar with the work will have a very sound background in inorganic and analytical chemistry.' *Science (U.S.A.)*

A Text-Book of Quantitative Inorganic Analysis
Including Elementary Instrumental Analysis
3rd Edition

'The text of the second edition has been revised and expanded making the present edition about 300 pages longer. Nine new chapters are included ... slightly less than half the book is now taken up by instrumental methods of analysis. ...
'The book should have a strong appeal to teachers and students of all grades, as well as being an essential volume for the reference library.' *Chemical Age*

Elementary Practical Organic Chemistry

Part 2: Qualitative Organic Analysis

ARTHUR I. VOGEL
D.Sc. (Lond.), D.I.C., F.R.I.C.

Head of Chemistry Department, Woolwich Polytechnic
Sometime Beit Scientific Research Fellow of the Imperial College, London

SECOND EDITION

John Wiley & Sons Inc
New York, N. Y.

Published throughout the world except the United States by
Longmans, Green & Co. Ltd.

Second Edition © Arthur I. Vogel 1966

First published 1957
Second impression 1959
Third impression 1960
Fourth impression 1961
Fifth impression 1962
Second Edition 1966

Elementary Practical Organic Chemistry, Part 1
Small Scale Preparations (Second Edition)
Elementary Practical Organic Chemistry, Part 3
Quantitative Organic Analysis

PRINTED IN GREAT BRITAIN BY
SPOTTISWOODE, BALLANTYNE AND CO. LTD
LONDON AND COLCHESTER

Preface

THE text has been exhaustively revised, extended and reset in improved type, and now provides a complete text-book of elementary qualitative organic analysis. The most important addition is that of a new Chapter entitled 'The Use of Spectroscopic Methods in Qualitative Organic Analysis', which includes the essentials, from a practical viewpoint, of Ultraviolet and Visible Spectroscopy, Infrared Spectroscopy, Nuclear Magnetic Resonance Spectroscopy and Mass Spectrometry. These spectroscopic techniques are nowadays of such great importance that no book on qualitative organic analysis can be regarded as complete without their inclusion, albeit and of necessity as elementary and brief accounts. It is hoped that sufficient has been given to illustrate the great value of these techniques and to encourage the student to extend his knowledge by consulting specialist texts.

The opportunity has been taken of rearranging the order of the Chapters in a manner which conforms better with experience in the laboratory. The new and old Chapter headings are tabulated below.

New Chapter Number		*Old Chapter Number*
I	Determination of Physical Constants	VI
II	Qualitative Analysis for the Elements	VIII
III	The Solubility Classes	IX
IV	Reactions and Characterization of Selected Classes of Organic Compounds	VII
V	Class Reactions (Reactions for Functional Groups)	X
VI	The Preparation of Derivatives	XI
VII	Qualitative Analysis of Mixtures of Organic Compounds	XII
VIII	The Use of Spectroscopic Methods in Qualitative Organic Analysis	New Chapter
IX	Physical Constants of Organic Compounds. Tables of Derivatives	XIII

The book is now complete on its own and independent of Part I: *Small Scale Preparations*, Second Edition (1966).

The new additions include the following:

Chapter I   A brief reference to optical rotatory dispersion.
Chapter II   The lanthanum chloranilate test for fluoride ion.

Chapter III	This Chapter has been completely revised and simplified.
Chapter IV	(*a*) Mechanisms are given *inter alia* for the addition of bromine to alkenes, the isocyanide test for primary amines, the ninhydrin test, and the reaction of boric acid with polyhydric alcohols. (*b*) Derivatives of alkenes with 2,4-dinitrophenylsulphenyl chloride; of alkynes as mercuric alkynides; of aromatic hydrocarbons as sulphonamides, and as adducts with 2,4,7-trinitro-7-fluorenone; of amino acids with 2,4-dinitrofluorobenzene; of thiols as mercury salts. (*c*) Differentiation of primary, secondary and tertiary alcohols with chromic acid and by the chromic anhydride test.
Chapter VI	An up-to-date account of the examination of the literature for the selection of derivatives.
Chapter VII	Reference to modern methods for the separation of mixtures of organic compounds.
Chapter IX	Some new physical constants have been added and the names of many compounds have been revised to conform with the current practice of the Chemical Society (London) and/or the American Chemical Society.
Appendix	Table of reciprocals (for use with data for infrared spectroscopy).

The book should continue to meet the requirements of all examinations calling for a knowledge of qualitative organic analysis: these include the B.Sc. General and B.Sc. Special (or Honours) degrees in Chemistry of the universities, the B.Sc. Honours and Ordinary degrees in Applied Chemistry of the Council for National Academic Awards, the Graduate Membership examination of the Royal Institute of Chemistry, and the Higher National Certificate in Chemistry. It is also hoped that beginners in organic research will find the volume (and also Part I: *Small Scale Preparations*) of value.

The author's thanks are due to Drs. C. W. N. Cumper, G. H. Jeffery, P. W. G. Smith and A. R. Tatchell for reading the proofs, for help in checking some of the new procedures and for a number of useful suggestions; also to V. Kyte for some of the diagrams.

Criticisms, information concerning errors, and also suggestions for improving the book from lecturers and others will continue to be welcomed by the author. The latter would also welcome information concerning the melting points of derivatives and also of physical constants not included in the text (Chapter IX).

ARTHUR I. VOGEL

Woolwich Polytechnic, London, S.E.18.
November 1965.

Preface to the First Edition

THE appeal of courses in qualitative organic analysis to students is probably due to the interest aroused in the identification of a compound given as an 'unknown.' Such courses have immense educational value in that knowledge acquired in the lecture room and by private study may be utilized for the solution of problems encountered in the laboratory: they also provide valuable training in accurate observation and deductive reasoning. Furthermore, qualitative organic analysis gives excellent practice in small scale experimental work.

The author's experience in teaching the subject extends over a quarter of a century and it is with the object of placing this long experience at the disposal of students of all grades that this book has been written. The subject-matter has been drawn largely (but not exclusively) from the writer's larger work *A Text-Book of Practical Organic Chemistry including Qualitative Organic Analysis*, Third Edition. Special attention has been given to the requirements of beginner students in Chapter VII where the reactions and characterization of selected classes of organic compounds are discussed in great detail. Elementary students may carry out a number of these reactions under the guidance of the teacher and thus establish firm foundations upon which the subsequent study of qualitative organic analysis proper may be based.

It is pertinent now to refer to the main Chapters constituting the book. Chapter VI deals with the determination of physical constants with apparatus that should be available in every laboratory. Chapter VII is concerned with the reactions and characterization of selected classes of organic compounds; although this Chapter is valuable for beginners, many of the procedures for the preparation of derivatives will be utilized subsequently in the routine qualitative analysis of organic compounds. Chapter VIII is devoted to qualitative analysis for the elements. The applications of determinations of solubilities in various media are discussed in Chapter IX: whilst it is fully appreciated that solubility tests are only *preliminary* tests for functional groups, the view is held that such tests provide valuable experience in small scale laboratory work and also encourage the student to apply his knowledge of general organic chemistry. In Chapter X the various class reactions (reactions for functional groups) are described fully. Chapter XI is concerned with the preparation of derivatives, whilst methods for the qualitative analysis of mixtures of organic compounds are discussed in Chapter XII. The physical constants of organic compounds, including tables of derivatives, are collected together in Chapter XIII. The tables are perhaps more comprehensive than would be expected in an elementary text. It is the author's experience that the average student does not readily turn to the larger reference books and to the original literature for further information on derivatives or preparational procedures: he prefers, if possible, to find all that he requires in one laboratory text. The time saved in library practice can be transferred to the laboratory to acquire additional experience in the characterization of a greater number and variety of unknown compounds and in the separation of mixtures.

It will be noted that no original literature references are given in the text. This is because the inclusion of such references would have increased the length and therefore the price of the book appreciably, and thus defeated the author's object of providing a text-book which all, including elementary, students could afford. References to the literature may be obtained from the standard works listed in Section **XI,3.**

The book will be found to meet the requirements of all examinations requiring a knowledge of qualitative organic analysis: these include the Ordinary and Higher National Certificates in Chemistry, the Diploma in Technology (Applied Chemistry), the Graduate Membership examination of the Royal Institute of Chemistry, the B.Sc. General and the B.Sc. Special (or Honours) degrees in Chemistry of the universities.

The author's thanks are due to Messrs. W. T. Cresswell, B.Sc., C. M. Ellis, M.Sc., R. Grzeskowiak, B.Sc., Dr. S. R. Landor and particularly to Dr. G. H. Jeffery, F.R.I.C., for reading the proofs and for a number of useful suggestions.

Criticisms, information concerning errors, and also suggestions for improving the book from lecturers and others are welcome.

ARTHUR I. VOGEL

Woolwich Polytechnic, London, S.E.18.
March 1957.

Contents

CHAPTER I
Determination of Physical Constants

		PAGE
I,1	Basis of qualitative organic analysis	1
I,2	Experimental determination of the melting point	3
I,3	Experimental determination of the boiling point	12
I,4	Calibration of thermometers.	16
I,5	Determination of density and of refractive index	18
I,6	Determination of the optical rotatory power	25
I,7	Determination of molecular weight	31

CHAPTER II
Qualitative Analysis for the Elements

II,1	Ignition test	33
II,2	Carbon and hydrogen.	34
II,3	Nitrogen, sulphur and halogens	34
II,4	The sodium carbonate-zinc method for the detection of nitrogen, sulphur and halogens in organic compounds	41

CHAPTER III
The Solubility Classes

III,1	The solubilities of organic compounds. General discussion	44
III,2	Summary of solubility behaviour	48
III,3	The solubility groups	53
III,4	Determination of the solubilities of organic compounds (*for group tests*)	57

CHAPTER IV
Reactions and Characterization of Selected Classes of Organic Compounds

IV,1	Introduction	61
IV,2	Saturated aliphatic hydrocarbons (alkanes)	61
IV,3	Olefinic hydrocarbons (alkenes)	62
IV,4	Aromatic hydrocarbons (arenes)	66
IV,5	Aliphatic alcohols	71
IV,6	Aromatic alcohols	80

Contents

IV,7	Phenols	80
IV,8	Enols	85
IV,9	Polyhydric alcohols	87
IV,10	Carbohydrates (sugars)	89
IV,11	Alkyl halides	96
IV,12	Halogenated aromatic hydrocarbons	100
IV,13	Aliphatic ethers	102
IV,14	Aromatic ethers	104
IV,15	Aliphatic aldehydes	106
IV,16	Acetals	110
IV,17	Aromatic aldehydes	111
IV,18	Aliphatic ketones	114
IV,19	Aromatic ketones	120
IV,20	Aliphatic carboxylic acids	120
IV,21	Aromatic carboxylic acids	126
IV,22	Acid chlorides of aliphatic acids	126
IV,23	Anhydrides of aliphatic acids	127
IV,24	Acid chlorides of aromatic acids	128
IV,25	Aliphatic esters	129
IV,26	Aromatic esters	136
IV,27	Primary aliphatic amides	137
IV,28	Primary aromatic amides	140
IV,29	Substituted aromatic amides	141
IV,30	Aliphatic nitriles (cyanides)	142
IV,31	Aromatic nitriles	146
IV,32	Primary and secondary aliphatic amines	147
IV,33	Primary, secondary and tertiary aromatic amines	151
IV,34	Amino acids	162
IV,35	Aromatic nitro compounds	168
IV,36	Aliphatic nitro compounds	171
IV,37	Mercaptans and thiophenols (thiols)	172
IV,38	Aromatic sulphonic acids and their salts	175
IV,39	Aromatic sulphonamides	180
IV,40	Quinones	181

CHAPTER V
Class Reactions
(Reactions for Functional Groups)

V,1	Unsaturated hydrocarbons. Tests for unsaturation	184
V,2	Saturated hydrocarbons	185
V,3	Reactivities of halogen compounds	186
V,4	Aldehydes and ketones	188
V,5	Esters and anhydrides	190
V,6	Alcohols and ethers	195
V,7	The iodoform test	198
V,8	Polyhydric alcohols and the polyhydroxy aldehydes and ketones (sugars)	199
V,9	The periodic acid test	201
V,10	Carboxylic acids and phenols	202
V,11	Amines (basic nitrogen compounds)	203
V,12	Acidic and neutral nitrogen compounds	206

V,13	Sulphur compounds	211
V,14	Phosphorus compounds	214
V,15	Summary of the more important class reactions . .	215

CHAPTER VI

The Preparation of Derivatives

VI,1	General discussion	217
VI,2	Summary of the more useful derivatives of selected classes of organic compounds	218
VI,3	Reference works for qualitative organic analysis . .	221

CHAPTER VII

Qualitative Analysis of Mixtures of Organic Compounds

VII,1	General discussion	223
VII,2	Preliminary examination of a mixture . . .	227
VII,3	Separation of a mixture of water-insoluble compounds .	230
VII,4	Separation of a mixture of water-soluble compounds .	233
VII,5	Other methods for separation of mixtures of compounds	236

CHAPTER VIII

The Use of Spectroscopic Methods in Qualitative Organic Analysis

VIII,1	The electromagnetic spectrum. Units . . .	239

ULTRAVIOLET SPECTROSCOPY

VIII,2	General considerations	241
VIII,3	Law of light absorption. Nomenclature . .	242
VIII,4	Solvents for ultraviolet spectroscopy . . .	243
VIII,5	General discussion of ultraviolet spectra of selected organic compounds	244
VIII,6	Identification of functional groups from a knowledge of positions of ultraviolet absorption maxima . .	247
VIII,7	Instruments	252
	Selected bibliography	257

INFRARED SPECTROSCOPY

VIII,8	Elementary theory	258
VIII,9	Uses of infrared spectroscopy	261
VIII,10	Instrumentation and sample handling . . .	262
VIII,11	Group and bond frequencies	273
VIII,12	Some characteristic infrared bands of common functional groups	275
	Selected bibliography	279

Contents

NUCLEAR MAGNETIC RESONANCE SPECTROSCOPY

VIII,13	General principles	280
VIII,14	Nuclear magnetic resonance spectrometers	284
VIII,15	Chemical shifts	287
VIII,16	Spin-spin splitting	290
VIII,17	Some applications of n.m.r. spectroscopy. Typical spectra	292
	Selected bibliography	296

MASS SPECTROMETRY

VIII,18	Elementary principles and apparatus	298
VIII,19	The ionisation process	300
VIII,20	Mass spectra of some classes of organic compounds. Functional group effects	303
VIII,21	Some mass spectra	309
	Selected bibliography	312

CHAPTER IX

Physical Constants of Organic Compounds Tables of Derivatives

IX,1	Preface to tables	313
IX,2	Saturated aliphatic hydrocarbons	316
IX,3	Unsaturated aliphatic hydrocarbons	317
IX,4	Aromatic hydrocarbons	318
IX,5	Aliphatic alcohols	320
IX,6	Aromatic alcohols	324
IX,7	Phenols	326
IX,8	Enols	331
IX,9	Polyhydric alcohols	332
IX,10	Carbohydrates (sugars)	333
IX,11	Aliphatic halogen compounds	334
IX,12	Aromatic halogen compounds	339
IX,13	Aliphatic ethers	343
IX,14	Aromatic ethers	344
IX,15	Aliphatic aldehydes	347
IX,16	Acetals	349
IX,17	Aromatic aldehydes	350
IX,18	Aliphatic ketones	352
IX,19	Aromatic ketones	354
IX,20	Aliphatic carboxylic acids	357
IX,21	Aromatic carboxylic acids	359
IX,22	Acid chlorides (aliphatic)	363
IX,23	Acid anhydrides (aliphatic)	364
IX,24	Acid chlorides and acid anhydrides of aromatic acids	365
IX,25	Aliphatic esters	366
IX,25A	Esters of inorganic acids	372
IX,26	Aromatic esters	373
IX,27	Primary aliphatic amides	377
IX,28	Primary aromatic amides	378
IX,29	Substituted aromatic amides	379

Contents

IX,30	Aliphatic nitriles (cyanides)	381
IX,31	Aromatic nitriles.	383
IX,32	Primary and secondary aliphatic amines	384
IX,33A	Primary aromatic amines	387
IX,33B	Secondary aromatic amines	392
IX,33C	Tertiary amines	394
IX,34	Amino acids	397
IX,35	Aromatic nitro compounds	399
IX,36	Aliphatic nitro compounds	400
IX,37	Mercaptans (thiols)	401
IX,38	Sulphonic acids	402, 404
IX,39	Aromatic sulphonamides	404, 405
IX,40	Quinones	406
IX,41	Imides	407
IX,42	Nitroso, azo, azoxy and hydrazo compounds	408
IX,43	Miscellaneous sulphur compounds	410
IX,44	Miscellaneous phosphorus compounds	412

APPENDIX

A,1	Laboratory accidents and first aid	413
A,2	Reciprocals	418
A,3	Table of relative atomic weights, 1961	420
	INDEX	421

Plates

Fig. *IV*, 10, 1 (osazones)—between pp. 92 and 93.

Fig. *VIII*, 7, 1 (Unicam SP. 800 ultraviolet and visible recording spectrophotometer)—facing p. 253.

Fig. *VIII*, 10, 1 (Unicam SP. 200G recording infrared spectrophotometer)—facing p. 263.

Fig. *VIII*, 14, 2 (Perkin–Elmer n.m.r. spectrometer, Model R.10)—facing p. 286.

Fig. *VIII*, 18, 2 (A.E.I. mass spectrometer, Model MS9)—facing p. 300.

CHAPTER I

Determination of Physical Constants

I, 1 Basis of Qualitative Organic Analysis
Although more than 500,000 organic compounds have been recorded in the literature, most of these may be grouped into a comparatively small number of homologous series or of classes of organic substances. By identifying the class to which an organic compound belongs, the problem of characterization is enormously simplified. For purposes of qualitative organic analysis, the following admittedly incomplete scheme will be adopted in this book for the identification of an organic compound. It must be emphasized, however, that, unlike systematic inorganic analysis,* the scheme is merely intended as a rough guide to the method of attack of the problem; the student must be prepared to apply his knowledge of organic chemistry at all points, and must be alert at all times to the significance of any observations which may throw light on the analysis.

1. **Determination of the physical constants and the establishment of the purity of the compound.** For a solid, the melting point is of great importance: if recrystallization does not alter it, the compound may be regarded as pure. For a liquid, the boiling point is first determined: if most of it distils over a narrow range (say, 1–2°), it is reasonably pure. (Constant boiling point mixtures are, however, known.) The refractive index and the density, from which the molecular refractivity may be calculated, are also valuable constants for liquids.

2. **Qualitative analysis for the elements.** This includes an examination of the effect of heat upon the substance—a test which *inter alia* will indicate the presence of inorganic elements—and qualitative analysis for nitrogen, halogens and sulphur and, if necessary, other inorganic elements. It is clear that the presence or absence of any or all of these elements would immediately exclude from consideration certain classes of organic compounds.

3. **Study of the solubility behaviour of the compound.** A semi-quantita-

---

* See, for example, the author's *Text Book of Macro and Semimicro Qualitative Inorganic Analysis*, Fourth Edition, 1954 (Longmans, Green and Co. Ltd.).

tive study of the solubility of the substance in a limited number of solvents (water, ether, dilute sodium hydroxide solution, dilute hydrochloric acid, sodium bicarbonate solution and concentrated sulphuric acid) will, if intelligently applied, provide valuable information as to the presence or absence of certain classes of organic compounds.

4. **Application of class reactions.** The application of selected reactions that indicate the presence or absence of certain functional groups, with due regard to the indications provided by tests 1, 2 and 3, will locate the class (or classes) to which the compound belongs, or will, at least, serve to eliminate all but a few classes to which the compound can be assigned.

5. **Location of the compound within a class (or homologous series) of compounds.** Reference to tables of the physical properties of the class (or classes) of organic compounds to which the substance has been assigned or reference to the literature, will generally locate a number of compounds which boil or melt within 5° of the value observed for the unknown. If other physical properties (*e.g.*, refractive index and density for a liquid) are available, these will assist in deciding whether the unknown is identical with one of the known compounds. In general, however, it is more convenient in practice to prepare one, but preferably two, crystalline derivatives of the substance.

6. **Preparation of derivatives.** If two distinct crystalline derivatives of the unknown have the same melting point (or other physical properties) as those of a compound described in the literature (see Section **VI**,3) (or in the tables in Chapter IX), the identity of the two compounds may be assumed. Further confirmation may be obtained, if desired, by mixed melting point determinations.

Spectroscopic methods, comprising ultraviolet and visible absorption spectroscopy, infrared absorption spectroscopy, nuclear magnetic resonance spectroscopy and mass spectrometry, have greatly simplified the identification of organic compounds, particularly in establishing the presence of functional groups. These are relatively rapid and require only very small amounts of material. Unfortunately, all these methods involve the use of complex and expensive instruments, and there is also the question of maintenance and of a skilled operator for the n.m.r. and the mass spectrometers. Nevertheless, it should be possible for most laboratories to have at least one recording ultraviolet and visible spectrophotometer and one recording infrared spectrophotometer; the prices of both of these instruments are now such as to render their purchase within the means of any reasonably equipped laboratory. Practice in the use of these two instruments must now be regarded as essential in the training of any chemist. It is hoped that the brief treatment given in Chapter VIII will serve as an introduction to spectroscopic methods and encourage the student to extend his knowledge of the subject with the aid of the books detailed in the various bibliographies.

In the following chapters the application of the various steps in the scheme outlined above to the characterization of organic compounds will be described in detail. Chapter I deals with the determination of the more useful physical properties of organic compounds. Chapter II deals with qualitative analysis for the elements. Chapter III discusses the solubility classes and includes a brief account of the relationship between solubility and structure. Chapter IV is devoted to a general account of the reactions and characterization of selected classes of organic compounds: this will provide *inter alia* an introduction to the subject and also includes full experimental details for the preparation of most derivatives. Chapter V is concerned with the various class reactions that are used to detect the characteristic functional groups in organic compounds. Chapter VI deals in general terms with the preparation of derivatives; many of the experimental procedures are given in Chapter IV. Chapter VII is concerned with the separation of mixtures of organic compounds. The physical properties, together with distinguishing derivatives where available, of the commoner members of the different classes of organic compounds are collected in Chapter IX for convenience of reference. Chapter VIII deals with the use of spectroscopic methods in qualitative organic analysis.

I, 2 Experimental Determination of the Melting Point

A pure crystalline organic compound has, in general, a definite and sharp melting point, that is, the melting point range (the difference between the temperature at which the collapse of the crystals is first observed and the temperature at which the sample becomes completely liquid) does not exceed about $0.5°$. The presence of small quantities of miscible, or partially miscible, impurities will usually produce a marked increase in the melting point range and cause the commencement of melting to occur at a temperature lower than the melting point of the pure substance. The melting point is therefore a valuable criterion of purity for an organic compound.

A sharp melting point is usually indicative of the high purity of a substance. There are, however, some exceptions. Thus a eutectic mixture of two or more compounds may have a sharp melting point, but this melting point may be changed by fractional crystallization from a suitable solvent or mixture of solvents. The number of exceptions encountered in practice is surprisingly small, hence it is reasonable to regard a compound as pure when it melts over a range of about 0·5° (or less) and the melting point is unaffected by repeated fractional crystallization.

In addition to the use of a melting point determination as a criterion of purity, an equally valuable application is for the identification of organic compounds. If the melting point is known within one degree, the major proportion of possible substances is immediately eliminated from consideration. The study of the general chemical properties of the compound and a mixed melting point determination (see discussion at end of this section) will largely establish the identity of the compound.

The experimental method in most common use is to heat a small amount (about 1 mg.) of the substance in a capillary tube attached to a thermometer which is immersed in a suitable bath of liquid, and to determine the temperature at which melting occurs. The **capillary melting point tubes are prepared** either from soft glass test-tubes or from wide glass tubing (*ca.* 12 mm. diameter).* A short length of glass tubing or glass rod is firmly fused to the closed end of the test-tube. The test-tube (or wide glass tubing) must first be thoroughly washed with distilled water to remove dust, alkali and products of devitrification which remain on the surface of the glass, and then dried. The closed end of the test-tube is first heated whilst being slowly rotated in a small blowpipe flame; the glass rod or tube is simultaneously heated in the same manner (Fig. *I*, 2, 1, *a*). When the extremities of both pieces of glass are red hot, they are firmly fused together, twisting of the joint being avoided, and then removed momentarily from the flame until the seal is just rigid enough that no bending occurs. The test-tube is then immediately introduced into a large 'brush' flame (Fig. *I*, 2, 1, *b*) so that a length of about 5 cm. is heated, and the tube is rotated *uniformly* in the flame. When the heated portion has become soft and slightly thickened as the result of the heating, the tube is removed from the flame and, after a second or two, drawn, slowly at first and then more rapidly, as far apart as the arms will permit (or until the external

---

* Pyrex glass is preferable, but this requires an oxy-coal gas blowpipe for manipulation. Suitable melting point tubes may be purchased from dealers in scientific apparatus or chemicals. It is, however, excellent practice, and an essential part of his training, for the student to learn to prepare his own capillary tubes.

diameter of the tube has been reduced to 1–2 mm.). If the operation has been successfully performed, a long capillary of regular bore throughout most of its length will be obtained. The long thin tube is then cut into lengths of about 8 cm. by touching it *lightly* with a file and then tapping gently with the flat portion of the file; after a little practice, no difficulty should be experienced in dividing the long capillary into suitable lengths without crushing the fragile tubing. It will be found that a short length of tubing ('glass spindle'), sufficiently rigid to act as a holder, will remain attached to the test-tube after the long capillary has been cut off. The operation may then be repeated. When the test-tube becomes too short to be handled at the open end, a piece of glass tubing or rod may be fused on, in the manner previously described, to act as a convenient handle. In this way a large number of capillary

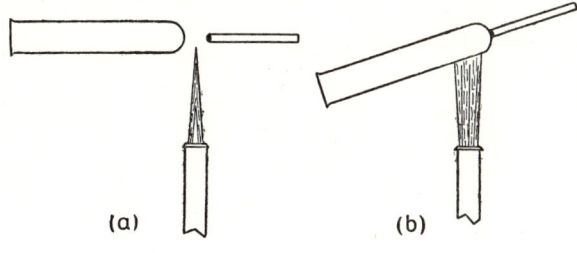

Fig. *I*, 2, 1.

tubes may be prepared from one test-tube. One end of each of the capillary tubes should be sealed by inserting it horizontally into the extreme edge of a small Bunsen flame for a few seconds, and the capillary tube rotated meanwhile; the formation of a glass bead at the end of the tube should be avoided. The prepared capillary tubes should be stored either in a large specimen tube or in a test-tube closed with a cork.

The capillary tube is then filled as follows. About 0·1 gram of the dry substance is placed on a glass slide or upon a fragment of clean porcelain plate and finely powdered with a clean metal or glass spatula, and then formed into a small mound. The open end of the capillary tube is pushed into the powder, 'backing' the latter, if necessary, with a spatula. The solid is then shaken down the tube by tapping the closed end on the bench or by gently drawing the flat side of a triangular file (a pocket 'nail file' is quite effective) along the upper end of the tube. The procedure is repeated until the length of lightly packed material is 3–5 mm. Any substance adhering to the outside of the tube must be wiped off so that it will not discolour the bath.

The filled melting point tube is now attached to the lower end of a calibrated theremometer (see Section I,4) in such a way that the substance is at the level of the middle of the mercury bulb (which has previously been wetted with the bath liquid); the moistened capillary is then slid into position. Advantage is taken of the surface tension of the bath liquid to hold the melting point tube in position by capillary attraction; the use of a thin rubber band, prepared by cutting narrow rubber tubing, to attach the capillary tube near the open end to the thermometer is not recommended. The thermometer, with the tube attached, is inserted into the centre of the bath; the melting point tube should extend about as far above the liquid surface as it does in the liquid in order to ensure that the capillary force will be large enough to hold it to the thermometer.

Two convenient forms of bath are shown in Fig. *I, 2, 2, a* and *b*. The former consists of a long-necked, round-bottomed flask (a long-necked Kjeldahl flask of 100 ml. capacity is quite satisfactory) supported by means of a clamp near the upper part of the neck. The thermometer is fitted through a cork, a section of the cork being cut away (see inset) so that the thermometer scale is visible and also to allow free expansion of the air in the apparatus. The bulb is about three-quarters filled with concentrated sulphuric acid.* The apparatus of Fig. *I, 2, 2, b* consists of a small Pyrex beaker (*e.g.*, of 250 ml. capacity) containing the bath liquid, which may be stirred by means of

---

* The bath liquid generally employed is concentrated sulphuric acid: this may be heated to a temperature of 250–280° in the apparatus of Fig. *I, 2, 2, a*, but only to 200–220° in the open beaker heating bath owing to the excessive fuming above this temperature range. By boiling together in a fume cupboard either 70 parts by weight of concentrated H_2SO_4 and 30 parts by weight of K_2SO_4 or 55 parts by weight of concentrated sulphuric acid with 45 parts by weight of $KHSO_4$ until the solid has dissolved (5–10 minutes), a bath liquid, possessing the consistency of glycerine and which does not fume badly, is obtained; this may be employed in an open beaker for temperatures between 220° and 320° (Mulliken). If the sulphuric acid becomes discoloured, the addition of a few crystals of sodium or potassium nitrate will restore the original colour.

Another convenient heating liquid is medicinal paraffin; it has a low specific heat, is non-inflammable and is non-corrosive, but it can only be safely heated to about 220°; above this temperature it begins to decompose slightly.

A mixture of equal parts of cottonseed oil and castor oil, containing about 1 per cent of hydroquinone as an anti-oxidant, is a useful bath liquid which can be heated up to about 250°.

The highly stable and heat-resistant Silicone oils are very satisfactory. Midland Silicone or Dow-Corning fluid 550 or 500 is recommended. Their only drawback is their high cost.

a small glass stirrer *A* so placed that its shaft is in the glass tube *B*. The thermometer and glass tube are held together by passing through holes in the corks *C* and *D*. The stirrer is connected by a length of string through the tube *B* as shown, and is prevented from falling to the

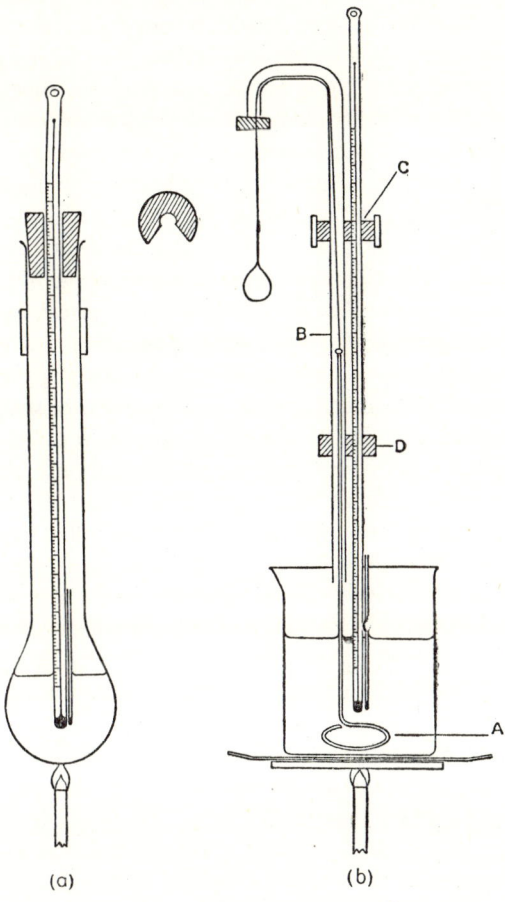

Fig. *1, 2, 2.*

bottom of the beaker by a small cork or knot at the extreme end. This melting point apparatus is supported on a gauze-covered ring attached to a retort stand, which also holds the thermometer and tube in a clamp round the cork *C*. Stirring of the bath liquid is effected by suitable manipulation of the string, and should be conducted at a regular rate throughout the heating.

The melting point apparatus is heated comparatively rapidly with a small flame until the temperature of the bath is within 15° of the melting point of the substance, and then slowly and regularly at the rate of about 2° per minute until the compound melts completely. The temperature at which the substance commences to liquefy and the temperature at which the solid has disappeared, *i.e.*, the melting point range, are observed. For a pure compound, the melting point range should not exceed 0·5–1°; it is usually less. Any sintering or softening below the melting point should be noted as well as any evolution of gas or any other signs of decomposition.* If the approximate melting point is not known, it is advisable to fill two capillaries with the substance. The temperature of the bath may then be raised fairly rapidly using one capillary tube in order to determine the melting point approximately; the bath is then allowed to cool about 30°, the second capillary substituted for the first and an accurate determination made.

It should be noted that a second determination of the melting point should not be made as the bath liquid cools by observing the temperature at which the molten material in the capillary tube solidifies, or by reheating the bath after the solidification has occurred. This is because, in many cases, the substance may partially decompose, and, in some instances, it may undergo a change into another crystalline form possessing a different melting point. A freshly filled capillary tube should always be employed for each subsequent determination. Substances which sublime readily are sometimes heated in melting point capillaries sealed at both ends. For compounds which melt with decomposition, difficulties sometimes arise in the melting point determination; it is best to insert the capillary tube into the bath when the temperature is only a few degrees below the melting and decomposition point of the material. This avoids decomposition, with consequent lowering of the melting point during the time that the temperature of the bath liquid is being raised.

After the melting point has been determined, the thermometer reading is corrected by reference to the calibration chart of the thermometer. Methods for calibrating a thermometer are described in Section **I,4**.

The melting point of a substance which melts either slightly above or below the laboratory temperature is conveniently determined in the

---

* A substance which commences to soften and pull away from the sides of the capillary tube at (say) 120°, with the first appearance of liquid at 121° and complete liquefaction at 122° with bubbling, would be recorded as m.p. 121–122° (decomp.), softens at 120°.

apparatus illustrated in Fig. *I*, 2, 3. It consists of a test-tube supported in a slightly larger test-tube by means of a cork (thus forming an air jacket and preventing too rapid a change of temperature) and cooled in a suitable bath, *e.g.*, of crushed ice. The inner test-tube is provided with a thermometer and a stirrer (preferably of glass), and is supported by means of a clamp. Sufficient substance is introduced to cover the bulb of the thermometer when completely molten. The compound is first melted, *e.g.*, by immersing the tube in warm water, the apparatus set up as in the figure, and the appropriate cooling mixture placed in the beaker (cold water, ice or a freezing mixture, according to the melting point of the substance) so that the rate of cooling is about 0·5° per minute. Both the liquid substance and the cooling bath are kept well stirred, and temperature readings are taken at half-minute or one-minute intervals; this is continued until the compound has fully solidified. Upon plotting temperatures (ordinates) against time (abscissae), a horizontal portion will be obtained in the cooling curve if the substance is pure; this corresponds to the **freezing (or setting) point**. It is advisable to determine the melting point also. The cooling bath is removed and replaced, if the substance melts above room temperature, by a bath of warm water. Stirring is continued as before and temperatures are observed at regular intervals until the substance is completely fluid. Upon plotting the temperature-time graph (heating curve), the break in the curve (hori-

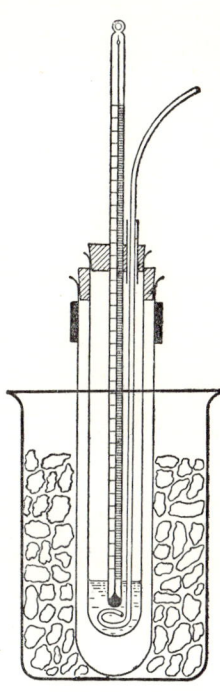

Fig. *I*, 2, 3.

zontal portion for a pure substance) takes place at the **melting point**. For pure compounds the melting point and freezing point are identical. It must be emphasized that the above method applies only to substances which melt without decomposition.

A liquid heating bath may be dispensed with by the use of an apparatus employing electrical heating. An electrically-heated aluminium or copper block is very convenient for this purpose. The essential features of a commercial apparatus* are shown in Fig. *I*, 2, 4.

* The apparatus marketed by A. Gallenkamp and Co. Ltd., Christopher Street, London, E.C.2 is both relatively inexpensive and very satisfactory.

The large hole at the centre is for the thermometer and the three smaller holes are for melting point capillaries which can be observed simultaneously. The block is heated electrically and the rate of heating can be controlled from the front of the apparatus. The melting point tubes are illuminated from two sides, making observation of the melting point by means of the lens housed in the eye-piece very easy. With this apparatus, it is important to raise the temperature slowly near the melting point since heat transfer is less efficient than with liquid baths.

The **Kofler hot bench*** (Fig. *I*, 2, 5) enables melting points to be determined very rapidly (in *ca.* one minute) in the range +50° to 260°C. It consists of a metal alloy band (with corrosion-free steel surface), 36 cm. long and 4 cm. wide, so designed and electrically heated that there is an almost constant temperature gradient. Temperatures are read on a scale on the front of the instrument with lines at every 2° and a reading device. The substance is placed directly on the surface of the hot bench. With pure substances a sharp border line between the liquid and the solid phase forms rapidly and the pointer (which is attached to the temperature scale) is now placed over this border. The hot bench should be calibrated before use with the aid of standard substances: these are obtainable from the manufacturers.

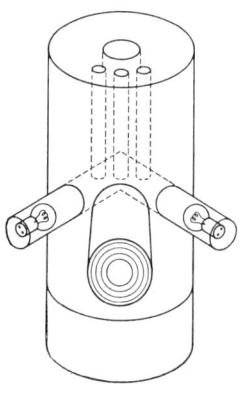

Fig. *I*, 2, 4.

The **microscope hot stage** type of melting point apparatus (essentially an electrically-heated block on a microscope stage) is of particular value when the melting point of a very small amount (*e.g.*, of a single crystal) has to be determined. Further advantages include the possibility of observation of the behaviour of crystals before, during and after melting, and of changes in colour and of crystal form. The main features of a commercial form of apparatus† are shown in Fig. *I*, 2, 6. This incorporates a polarizer: observation of the melting point is very easy in polarized light. The rate of heating is controlled by means of a rheostat.

---

* Manufactured by C. Reichert Optische Werke AG, Wien XVII, and available from Shandon Scientific Co. Ltd.
† Manufactured by C. Reichert Optische Werke AG, Wien XVII, and obtainable from Shandon Scientific Co. Ltd., 65 Pound Lane, London, E.C.2.

A considerably simplified version is also available commercially* ('micro melting point apparatus'). The 'hot stage' may be fitted on any standard microscope and the rate of heating is controlled by a transformer unit. Observations may be made to 325° C; the sample is placed on a cover glass on the surface of the block.

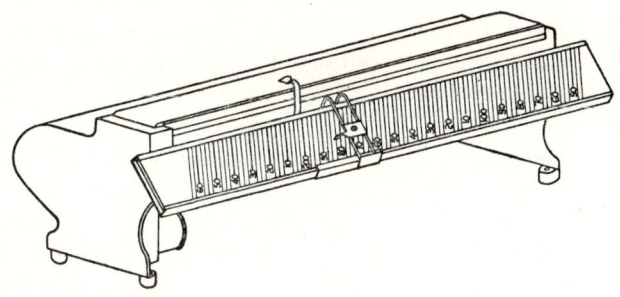

Fig. *I*, 2, 5.

Mixed melting points. In general, the melting point of a compound is lowered and its melting range increased when it is mixed with another substance. Use is made of this fact in testing for the identity of two solids with similar melting points. Thus if an unknown compound is believed to be identical with a known compound, approximately equal amounts are powdered and *intimately mixed* on a small

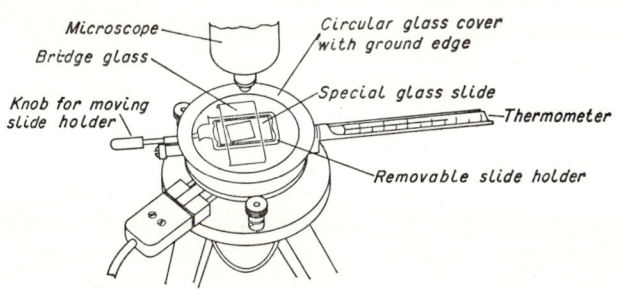

Fig. *I*, 2, 6.

watch glass or a microscope slide and the melting point of the mixture is determined. If the two samples are different, the melting point of the mixture is usually lower than that of either sample by as much as 20° and usually by at least 5–6° and, furthermore, the melting range is increased. If the two samples are identical, no depression in melting

* From A. Gallenkamp and Co. Ltd., London, E.C.2.

point will be observed and the melting range will be as sharp as with the known compound.

A few pairs of substances are known which exhibit no depression in melting point upon admixture, e.g., naphthalene picrate, m.p. 151°, and thionaphthene picrate, m.p. 149°; mixed m.p. 149°. Frequently the failure to secure a depression in melting point occurs only at certain compositions: it is therefore advisable to determine the melting points of mixtures of several compositions. The following simple procedure may be used. Form two small piles of approximately equal sizes of the two compounds (A and B) being examined. Mix one half of pile A with one half of pile B. Now divide the mixture of A and B into three equal parts. To the first add the remainder of A, and to the third add the remainder of B. Three mixtures with compositions 50 per cent A, 50 per cent B; 80 per cent A, 20 per cent B; and 20 per cent A and 80 per cent B are obtained. The melting points of all the three mixtures are determined.

The rule of mixed melting points is not free from exceptions but fortunately it is of wide applicability. It may therefore be stated that identity of melting point provides good evidence for the identity of two compounds although it cannot be regarded as absolute proof.

I, 3 Experimental Determination of the Boiling Point

A sharp boiling point at constant pressure may serve as a criterion of purity for liquids. It must be remembered, however, that constant boiling point mixtures (azeotropic mixtures) also have sharp boiling points so that this physical property is not always indicative of a single pure substance; however, such mixtures are comparatively rare and for purposes of qualitative organic analysis a constant boiling point will be a useful constant not only to establish purity but also for identification. For our immediate purpose it will suffice to state that if the boiling range is small (1–2°), the liquid may be assumed to be fairly pure.

The usual method for the determination of the boiling point of a liquid is to distil a small volume, say 5 ml. Before carrying out the distillation, one should ascertain whether the compound boils without decomposition. About 0·5 ml. of the sample is heated in a test-tube over a low flame. If a nearly colourless vapour and relatively little residue are obtained, the distillation may be undertaken. If decomposition is evident (development of fumes, formation of a dark-coloured substance) or a very high temperature is required, the distillation should be conducted under reduced pressure; experimental details for the latter are given in the author's *Elementary Practical Organic Chemistry*, Part 1: *Small Scale Preparations*.

For distillation at atmospheric pressure a 10 ml. distillation or Claisen flask with long side arm is highly satisfactory; if the boiling point of the liquid is below about 140°, part of the long side arm should be fitted with a short water condenser (Fig. *I*, 3, 1). It is important to arrange that the bulb of the thermometer is opposite to, or preferably slightly below, the side tube of the distilling or Claisen flask.

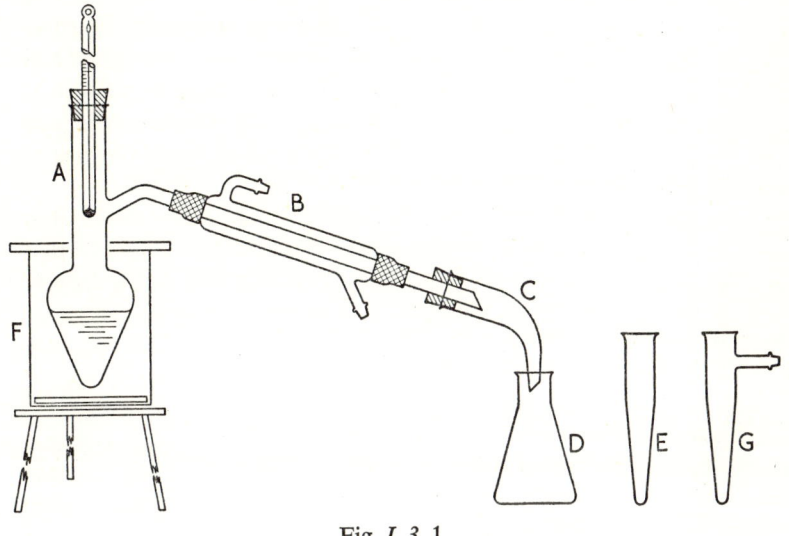

Fig. *I*, 3, 1.

Fit up the apparatus shown in Fig. *I*, 3, 1. *A* is a 10 ml. distilling flask with long side arm, fitted with a condenser jacket *B*. *F* is an air bath; the distillate is collected via the adapter *C* in the small conical flask *D* or in a 3 ml. centrifuge tube *E* supported in a stand (not shown). Pour about 5 ml. of the liquid into the distilling flask, preferably through a small funnel, the stem of which extends below the side arm. Add a few tiny fragments of unglazed porous porcelain or of carborundum ('boiling stones,' 'boiling chips' or 'porous pot'). Place the thermometer in position with the bulb very slightly below the side arm of the distilling flask. The 'boiling stones' will promote regular ebullition in the subsequent heating; they should *never* be added to the hot liquid. Heat the flask in the air bath *F* or, less effectively, on an asbestos-centred wire gauze. Heating may be rather rapid until boiling commences; the flame must then be decreased and adjusted so that the distillate is collected at the rate of one or two drops per second. It must be borne in mind that at the commencement of the distillation it takes an appreciable time for the vapour to heat the upper part of the flask and the thermometer. The distillation should not be conducted too slowly, for the thermometer may momentarily cool from lack of a constant supply of fresh vapour on the bulb, and an irregular boiling point will result; on the other hand, the flame should not be too large for it may heat directly a part of the vapour as well as the liquid, and superheating may occur.

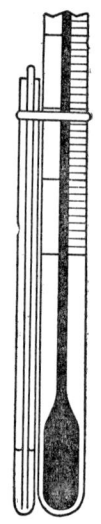

It will be found that the temperature will first rise rapidly until it is near the boiling point of the liquid, then slowly, and finally will remain practically constant. It is a good plan to watch for the ring of condensing vapour in the neck of the flask and to attempt to hold this at least about 1 cm. above the side arm of the flask by appropriately controlling the flame. The distillation should be continued until only a small volume of liquid remains in the flask; the temperature is noted at regular intervals. If the liquid is pure, most of it will pass over at constant temperature (within 0·5°); this constant temperature is **the boiling point of the liquid.** Towards the very end of the distillation the temperature may rise slightly owing to superheating. The necessary correction to the thermometer, as determined from the calibration chart, should be applied in order to obtain the correct boiling point.

Fig. *I*, 3, 2.   When the boiling point of the liquid is above 140–150°, an air condenser may replace the water condenser (jacket removed from water condenser in Fig. *I*, 3, 1, the long side arm acting as an air condenser); in most cases an equivalent result is achieved by emptying the water from the condenser jacket. If the liquid is inflammable, the conical flask may be replaced by a small filter or suction flask, a test-tube with side arm or a centrifuge tube with side arm (*G* in Fig. *I*, 3, 1), attached to *C* by means of a cork.

When only small volumes (0·5–1 ml.) of liquid are available, **Siwoloboff's method** (1886) for the determination of boiling points may be used. Two tubes, closed at one end, are required; one, an ordinary melting point capillary, 90–110 mm. long and 1 mm. in diameter, and the other, 80–100 mm. long and 4–5 mm. in diameter.

The latter may be prepared from 4–5 mm. glass tubing and, if desired, a small thin bulb, not exceeding 6 mm. in diameter, may be blown at one end. A small quantity of the liquid, 0·25–0·5 ml. (depending upon the boiling point), is placed in the wider tube, and the capillary tube, with sealed end uppermost, is introduced into the liquid. The tube is then attached to the thermometer by a rubber band (Fig. *I*, 3, 2), and the thermometer is immersed in the bath of a melting point apparatus (see Fig. *I*, 2, 2). As the bath is gradually heated there will be a slow escape of air bubbles from the end of the capillary tube, but when the boiling point of the liquid is attained, a rapid and continuous escape of air bubbles will be observed. The reading of the thermometer when a rapid and continuous stream of air bubbles first emerges from the capillary tube is the boiling point of the liquid. Unless the temperature is raised very slowly in the vicinity of the boiling point of the liquid, the first determination may be slightly in error. A more accurate result is obtained by removing the source of heat when the rapid stream of bubbles rises from the end of the capillary tube; the speed at which bubbles are given off will slacken and finally, when the last bubble makes its appearance and exhibits a tendency to suck back, the thermometer is read immediately. This is the boiling point of the liquid because it is the point at which the vapour pressure of the liquid is equal to that of the atmosphere. As an additional check on the latter value, the bath is allowed to cool a few degrees and the temperature *slowly* raised; the thermometer is read when the first continuous series of air bubbles is observed. The two thermometer readings should not differ by more than 1°.

The atmospheric pressure should be recorded at the time the boiling point is being determined. For barometric pressures that do not differ

BOILING POINT °C	CORRECTION IN °C FOR 10 MM. DIFFERENCE IN PRESSURE	
	NON-ASSOCIATED LIQUIDS	ASSOCIATED LIQUIDS
50	0·38	0·32
100	0·44	0·37
150	0·50	0·42
200	0·56	0·46
300	0·68	0·56

from 760 mm. by more than 30 mm., the approximate correction to the observed boiling point in order to convert it to a pressure of 760 mm. may be obtained from the preceding Table.

Non-associated liquids include hydrocarbons, alkyl halides, ethers and esters; associated liquids include water, alcohols and carboxylic acids. It is evident that small deviations in pressure from 760 mm., such as 5–10 mm., may be neglected.

I, 4 Calibration of Thermometers

The comparatively inexpensive long-scale thermometer (250–300 mm. long) is usually calibrated by the manufacturers for complete immersion of the mercury column in the vapour or liquid. When such a thermometer is employed for boiling point or melting point determinations, the entire column is neither surrounded by the vapour nor completely immersed in the liquid. The part of the mercury column exposed to the cooler air of the laboratory is obviously not expanded as much as the bulk of the mercury and hence the reading will be *lower* than the true temperature. The error thus introduced is not appreciable up to about 100°, but it may amount to 3–5° at 200° and 6–10° at 250°. The error due to the column of mercury exposed above the heating bath can be corrected by adding a **stem correction,** calculated by the formula:

$$\textit{Stem correction} \text{ (in degrees)} = KN(t_1 - t_2)$$

where K = the apparent expansion coefficient of mercury in glass;
N = the length, measured in degrees, of the part of the thermometer not heated to the temperature of the bulb, *i.e.*, the length of the exposed column;
t_1 = the observed temperature; and
t_2 = the mean temperature of the exposed mercury column (determined on an auxiliary thermometer placed alongside with its bulb at the middle of the exposed thread).

The value of K varies slightly with the nature of the glass and the range of temperature used, but a value of 0·00016 may be used for the stem correction.

In addition to the error due to the exposed stem, ordinary chemical thermometers of low cost are subject to errors due to irregularities in the bore and sometimes the scale graduations may not be very accurate. It is therefore essential to check the thermometer at several temperatures against the melting points of pure solids or the boiling points of pure liquids as described below. The application of an exposed steam correction will of course be unnecessary if the thermometer is calibrated in this way. A calibration curve may then be drawn upon 'graph' paper from the data thus obtained. Temperatures at intervals of about 20° are marked as abscissae and the corrections to be added or subtracted as ordinates; the points thus obtained are then connected by a smooth curve. The thermometer correction at any temperature may be read directly from the curve.

In practice, it is generally more convenient to use thermometers which have been graduated for *partial immersion* for a short and convenient length of the stem. A special mark is usually etched on the stem to indicate the depth of immersion and, provided that this is approximately adhered to, no serious error due to exposed stem will be present in the resulting reading of the thermometer. A convenient depth of immersion is 5 cm.

For most small scale work (but not including melting point determinations) a thermometer with a short scale and 'micro' (or 'pin head') bulb is recommended (Fig. *I, 4*, 1). The dimensions are 175–190 mm. long, 4·5–5 mm. external diameter; the scale reading is 20°–300° calibrated in 2° for a 5 cm. immersion*.

Fig. *I, 4*, 1.

Full experimental details for the determination of melting and boiling points are given in Sections **I,2** and **I,3** respectively. Table I, 4, 1 lists suitable substances for the calibration of thermometers by melting point or boiling point determinations. It need hardly be emphasized that only compounds of the highest purity (*e.g.*, Analytical Reagent quality, when available) should be employed. The boiling point is at 760 mm.: the change in b.p. for every 10 mm. variation in mercury pressure at 760 ± 20 mm. may be assumed to be 0·5°.

The zero point is best determined with an intimate mixture of distilled water and pure ice made from distilled water. About 20 ml. of distilled water are placed in a boiling tube (150×25 mm.) and frozen partially by immersion in an ice-salt mixture; during the freezing the mixture is stirred with a glass rod until a thick slush is obtained. The boiling tube is then removed from the freezing mixture, the ther-

* These small-scale thermometers are manufactured by H. J. Elliott Ltd., Treforest Industrial Estate, Pontypridd, Glam., Wales.

mometer immersed in the slush so that the zero point is just visible; the mixture is stirred gently with the thermometer and the reading taken after the temperature has become constant (2–3 minutes).

Table I, 4, 1. Reference Temperatures for Calibration of Thermometers

MELTING POINT, °C		BOILING POINT, °C AT 760 MM.	
Water-ice	0·0	Acetone	56·1
Diphenylamine	53·5	Benzene	80·2
m-Dinitrobenzene	89·5	Water	100·0
Benzoic acid	122	Ethylene dibromide	131·7
Salicylic acid	159	Bromobenzene	156·2
Succinic acid	185	Aniline	184·4
3,5-Dinitrobenzoic acid	205	Nitrobenzene	210·9
p-Nitrobenzoic acid	239	Quinoline	237·5
s-Di-p-tolylurea	268	Biphenyl	255·5
		1-Bromonaphthalene	281·1
		Benzophenone	305·9

I, 5 Determination of Density and of Refractive Index

The density and the refractive index of a liquid will frequently be of value in assisting its characterization.

Density. The density of a liquid is conveniently determined with the aid of a pycnometer (Fig. *I*, 5, 1).* The bulb has a capacity of 1 or 2 ml. and the arms, constructed with precision bore capillary tubing, have a bore of about 0·5 mm.; a mark *A* is made with a fine file or diamond (in the position indicated) for the adjustment of the level of the liquid in the pycnometer. A thin silver or platinum wire loop is provided for supporting the pycnometer on the hook over the balance pan. This pycnometer is readily filled by means of the device shown in Fig. *I*, 5, 2 (colloquially known as a 'snake'); it consists of a short length of narrow (about 3 mm. bore) rubber tubing into one end of which is fitted a piece of glass tubing shaped as shown in the figure. The liquid is placed in a small glazed crucible (3–5 ml. capacity) and the rubber tubing is fitted over the longer arm of the pycnometer. By holding the pycnometer almost vertically so that the short capillary end is below the surface of the liquid in the crucible, and applying *gentle* suction at

---

* Manufactured by H. J. Elliott Ltd., E-Mil Works, Treforest Industrial Estate, Pontypridd, Glam., Wales, and obtainable from laboratory supply houses.

the glass tube of the 'snake' by means of the mouth,* the pycnometer is completely filled slightly beyond the file mark A. The pycnometer is then returned to the normal position (no air bubbles should be present if the pycnometer has been carefully filled) and the short arm touched with filter paper. This will cause the liquid to move along the capillary; immediately it reaches the mark A, the filter paper is sharply removed. With a little practice, no difficulty will be experienced in filling the pycnometer accurately to the mark A. After polishing the outside with a clean linen cloth and then weighing the pycnometer, the liquid is emptied into the crucible or other vessel by attaching the snake to the

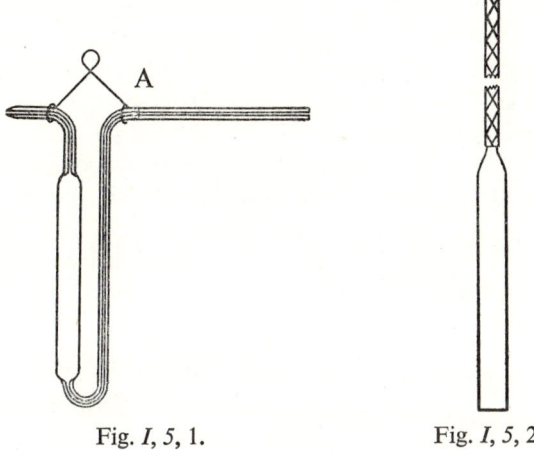

Fig. *I*, 5, 1.   Fig. *I*, 5, 2.

longer arm and blowing gently. The pycnometer is then cleaned by charging the crucible with rectified spirit and then filling the pycnometer; the alcohol is emptied into the 'ALCOHOL RESIDUES' bottle and the pycnometer is then filled again. The process is repeated with sodium-dried ether; finally a stream of air is drawn through the pycnometer by attaching the 'snake' through a filter flask trap to a water pump for 10–15 minutes. The outside of the pycnometer is again wiped with a clean linen cloth and weighed empty.

The density determination may be carried out at the temperature of the laboratory. The liquid should stand for at least one hour and a thermometer placed either in the liquid (if practicable) or in its immediate vicinity. It is usually better to conduct the measurement at a temperature of 20° or 25°; throughout this text-book a standard

* An empty wash-bottle, equipped with a two-holed cork, may be interposed between the mouth and the pycnometer for corrosive or poisonous liquids.

temperature of 20° will be adopted. To determine the density of a liquid at 20°, a clean, corked test-tube containing about 5 ml. of the liquid is immersed for about three-quarters of its length in a water thermostat at 20° for about 2 hours. An empty test-tube and a shallow beaker (*e.g.*, a 'Baco' beaker) are also supported in the thermostat so that only the rims protrude above the surface of the water; the pycnometer is supported by its capillary arms on the rim of the test-tube, and the small crucible is placed in the beaker, which is covered with a clock glass. When the liquid has acquired the temperature of the thermostat, the small crucible is removed, charged with the liquid, the pycnometer rapidly filled and adjusted to the mark. With practice, the whole operation can be completed in about half a minute. The error introduced if the temperature of the laboratory differs by as much as 10° from that of the thermostat does not exceed 1 mg.; if the temperature of the laboratory is adjusted so that it does not differ by more than 1–2° from 20°, the error is negligible. The weight of the empty pycnometer and also filled with distilled (preferably conductivity) water at 20° should also be determined. The density of the liquid can then be computed.

The specific gravity ($d_{t°}^{t°}$) of a liquid may be defined as the ratio of the weight of the liquid to that of an equal volume of water at the same temperature. Thus:

Specific gravity, $d_{20°}^{20°} = \dfrac{\text{Weight of liquid at 20°}}{\text{Weight of an equal volume of water at 20°}} = \dfrac{W_l^{20°}}{W_w^{20°}}$

The density ($d_{4°}^{20°}$) may be regarded as the specific gravity referred to an equal volume of water at 4°, *i.e.*,

$$d_{4°}^{20°} = \frac{W_l^{20°}}{W_w^{20°}} \times D^{20°} = W_l^{20°} \times \left(\frac{0.9982}{W_w^{20°}}\right)$$

where $D^{20°}$ is the density of water at 20°, *i.e.*, 0·9982. The quantity enclosed in the bracket is the constant for the pycnometer and should be recorded permanently. In all subsequent determinations of the density, only the weight of the liquid filling the pycnometer will be required. It is advisable, however, to redetermine the constant periodically.

Refractive index. The refractive index of a liquid is conveniently determined with an **Abbe refractometer.** This refractometer possesses the following advantages:

(*a*) The refractive index (1·3000 to 1·7000) may be read directly on a scale with accuracy of about 0·0002.

(b) It requires only a drop of the sample.

(c) A source of monochromatic light is not essential; by means of a 'compensator' the observed refractive index corresponds to that obtained with the D line of sodium even though white light is used as a source of illumination.

(d) Provision for temperature control of prism and sample is incorporated.

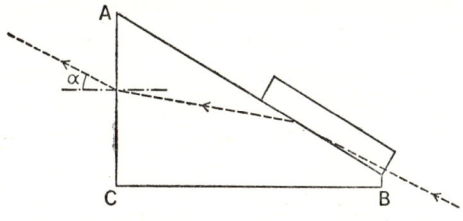

Fig. *I*, 5, 3.

The principle of the instrument is the observation of the 'critical angle' for total reflection between glass of high refractive index (*e.g.*, flint glass, n_D 1·75) and the substance to be examined. The glass is in the form of a right-angled prism upon the hypotenuse face *AB* of which

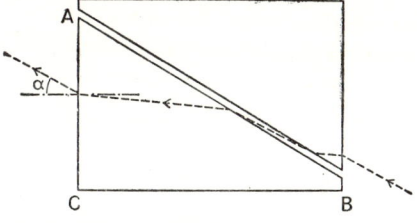

Fig. *I*, 5, 4.

the compound to be investigated is placed. If the compound is a solid, optical contact with the prism is made by means of a liquid of higher refractive index than the solid (*e.g.*, methylene iodide); if it is a liquid (as is usual in qualitative organic analysis), it is enclosed as a thin film (about 0·15 mm. thick) between two similar prisms (Fig. *I*, 5, 4). The face *AC* of the prism plays a part in the refraction of the light, and it is the angle of emergence (α) from this face which is measured, the scale of the instrument being, however, divided to read the refractive index directly. The ray shown in Fig. *I*, 5, 3, and in Fig. *I*, 5, 4, is that which enters the face AB at grazing incidence, and corresponds to the edge of the dark part of the field of view of the instrument. The direction of the ray after entering the face AB depends upon its wavelength, and thus the scale of refractive index will vary with the light employed. That selected is for sodium light, but in order to permit the use of white light, the resultant dispersion of the light emerging from the face AC is neutralized by means of a dispersion 'compensator' situated at the base of the telescope. It consists of two direct vision prisms, made accurately direct for the D sodium line, which are capable of rotation at equal rates and in opposite directions about the axis of the telescope of the refractometer. They form a system of variable dispersion which can be made equal in amount and of opposite direction to the resultant dispersion (D) of the refractometer prism and the substance investigated.

Fig. *I*, 5, 5* is a drawing of the Hilger Abbe refractometer, whilst Fig. *I*, 5, 6* is a line diagram showing the essential parts of the instrument.

To determine the refractive index of a liquid at 20°, circulate water at 20° from a thermostat through the jacket surrounding the two prisms until the temperature on the thermometer has remained steady for at least 10 minutes. Separate the prism jackets by opening the clamp, and move the index arm, if necessary, until the face of the prism is horizontal. Wipe the latter with a clean linen cloth, place a drop or two of the liquid on the smooth glass prism face and then clamp it to the upper polished prism. Focus the cross-wires of the telescope by rotating the eyepiece, and then adjust the mirror so as to give good illumination from a suitably placed frosted electric lamp. By means of the rack and pinion controlling the arm at the side of the apparatus, turn the prism box until the field of view becomes partly light and partly dark. When white light is used, the edge of the light band will show a coloured fringe. By means of the milled screw head at the base of the telescope, rotate the dispersion 'compensator' until the coloured fringe disappears and the light (or dark) band is bounded by a sharp edge. Now rotate the prism box slowly until the sharp edge coincides with the intersection of the cross wires in the telescope, and read off directly the refractive index for the sodium D line on the divided arc

---

* The author is indebted to Messrs. Hilger and Watts Ltd. for these two figures. A detailed description of the instrument will be found in their booklet, *Instructions for the Use of the Abbe Refractometer*, and to which the reader is referred for further particulars. Excellent Abbe refractometers are available from Bellingham and Stanley Ltd., Bausch and Lomb Optical Co., and Carl Zeiss (Jena).

by means of the magnifying lens. Immediately the determination has been completed, wipe off the organic liquid with filter paper or cotton wool, and clean the prism surfaces with cotton wool soaked in acetone. The accuracy of the instrument may be checked by measuring

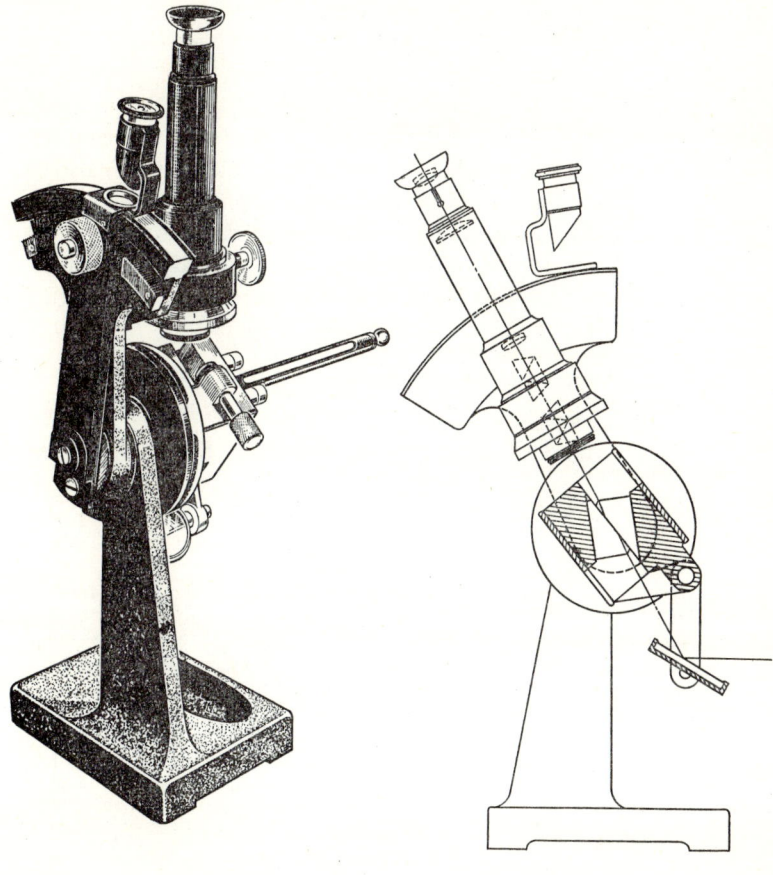

Fig. *I*, 5, 5.   Fig. *I*, 5, 6.

the refractive index of distilled water ($n_D^{10°}$ 1·3337, $n_D^{20°}$ 1·3330, $n_D^{30°}$ 1·3320, $n_D^{40°}$ 1·3307).

The refractive index of a liquid is recorded as $n_D^{t°}$ where t is the temperature at which the measurement is made, and D refers to the wavelength of the D line of sodium. As already pointed out, it is usual to determine both the refractive index and the density of the liquid at 20°; in any case they should be determined at the same temperature.

These two constants are useful in assisting the characterization of a pure liquid; they are particularly valuable for aliphatic hydrocarbons and similar compounds where the methods of characterization by the formation of solid derivatives are not entirely satisfactory. The **molecular refractivity** can be computed from the Lorenz and Lorentz equation:

$$[R_L]_D = \frac{n_D^2 - 1}{n_D^2 + 2} \cdot \frac{M}{d}$$

where n is the refractive index, d is the density at the same temperature, and M is the molecular weight. The molecular refractivity may also be *calculated* from the structural formula by the summation of either the atomic and structural constants or the bond refractions. Agreement between the observed and calculated values of the molecular refractivity constitutes powerful evidence for the correctness of the structural formula from which $[R_L]_D$ was calculated.

Table I, 5A. Atomic and Structural Constants (D-Line)

CH_2	4·647	CO (methyl ketones)	4·76
H (in CH_2)	1·028	COO (esters)	6·20
C (in CH_2)	2·591	COOH	7·23
CH_3	5·65	OH (aliphatic alcohols)	2·55
C_2H_5	10·30	SH (alkyl thiols)	8·76
n-C_3H_7	14·97	S (dialkyl sulphides)	7·92
iso-C_3H_7	14·98	S_2 (dialkyl disulphides)	16·05
n-C_4H_9	19·59	Double bond (C=C)	1·58
iso-C_4H_9	19·62	Triple bond (C≡), terminal	1·98
sec-C_4H_9	19·42	Triple bond (C≡), non-terminal	2·35
tert-C_4H_9	19·85	3-membered carbon ring	0·61
n-C_5H_{11}	24·25	4-membered carbon ring	0·32
iso-C_5H_{11}*	24·20	NH_2 (primary aliphatic amines)	4·44
iso-C_5H_{11}†	24·28	NH (secondary aliphatic amines)	3·61
n-C_6H_{13}	28·86	NH (secondary aromatic amines)	4·68
n-C_7H_{15}	33·55	N (tertiary aliphatic amines)	2·74
n-C_8H_{17}	38·14	N=N (azo)	6·19
C_3H_5 (allyl)	14·52	CN (aliphatic nitriles)	5·46
C_6H_5	25·36	NO_2 (aliphatic nitro compounds)	6·71
Cl	5·84	O.NO (aliphatic nitrites)	7·24
Br	8·74	NO (nitroso)	5·20
I	13·95	SCN (aliphatic thiocyanates)	13·40
F	0·81	NCS (aliphatic isothiocyanates)	15·62
O (ethers)	1·76	CO_3 (dialkyl carbonates)	7·70
O (acetals)	1·61	SO_3 (dialkyl sulphites)	11·34
CO (ketones)	4·60	PO_4 (trialkyl phosphates)	10·77

* From synthetic isoamyl alcohol.
† From fermentation isoamyl alcohol.

Table I, 5B.   Bond Refractions at 20° (D-Line)

Bond	Refraction	Bond	Refraction
C—H	1·676	C=S	11·91
C—C	1·296	C—N	1·57
C=C	4·17	C=N	3·76
C≡C (terminal)	5·87	C≡N	4·82
C≡C (non-terminal)	6·24	O—H (alcohols)	1·66
C—C (3-ring)	1·49	O—H (acids)	1·80
C—C (4-ring)	1·37	S—H	4·80
C—C (5-ring)	1·26	S—S	8·11
C—C (6-ring)	1·27	S—O	4·94
C—F	1·55	S→O	−0·20
C—Cl	6·51	N—NH	1·76
C—Br	9·39	N—O	2·43
C—I	14·61	N→O	1·78
C—O (ethers)	1·54	N=O	4·00
C—O (acetals)	1·46	N—N	1·99
C=O	3·32	N=N	4·12
C=O (methyl ketones)	3·49	C_{ar}—C_{ar}	2·69
C—S	4·61		

Note
In the calculation of the molecular refractivity of esters, the C—O value for acetals is employed.

The values for the sodium D line of the atomic and structural constants and of the bond refractions, as determined by the author, are collected in Tables I, 5A and I, 5B respectively.

I, 6 Determination of the Optical Rotatory Power

The optical rotation is determined only if the list of possible compounds for the unknown (*e.g.*, carbohydrates and osazones) contain optically active substances. Many sugars exhibit the property of mutarotation, *i.e.*, the value of the specific rotation (see below) changes on standing in solution and reaches a constant value after a few hours. This constant value is attained rapidly upon addition of a trace of ammonia solution (0·1 per cent). Specific rotations for sugars usually refer to the anhydrous compound: due regard should therefore be paid to water of crystallization, if any.

When a beam of light is passed through a crystal of Iceland spar, two beams are transmitted, each vibrating in a plane which is perpendicular to the other. A **Nicol prism** is composed of two sections of Iceland spar so cut, and again sealed with Canada balsam, that one of the rays is refracted to the side and absorbed so that all the light which passes through is vibrating in one plane only. The light is said to be **plane polarized.** If this polarized light is examined by means of another

Nicol prism, it will be found that on rotating the latter, the field of view appears alternately light and dark and the minimum of brightness follows the maximum as the prism is rotated through an angle of 90°: the field of view will appear dark when the axes of the two prisms are at right angles to one another. The prism by which the light is polarized is termed the **polarizer**, and the second prism, by which the light is examined, is called the **analyzer**.

If, when the field of view appears dark, a tube containing a solution of cane sugar (sucrose) is placed between the two prisms, the field lights up; one of the prisms must be turned through a certain angle α before the original dark field is restored. The solution of cane sugar has therefore the power of turning or rotating the plane of polarized light through a certain angle, and is accordingly said to be **optically active**. Since the plane of vibration of polarized light may be rotated either clockwise or anti-clockwise, it is necessary to observe a convention regarding the sign of rotation. When, in order to obtain darkness, the analyzer has to be turned clockwise (*i.e.*, to the right), the optically active substance is said to be **dextro-rotatory**; it is **laevo-rotatory** when the analyzer must be rotated anti-clockwise (*i.e.*, to the left).

The obvious disadvantage of the above simple instrument (**polarimeter**) is the difficulty of determining the precise 'end point' or the point of maximum darkness. The human eye is a poor judge of absolute intensities, but is capable of matching the intensities of two fields viewed simultaneously with great accuracy. For this reason all precision polarimeters are equipped with an optical device that divides the field into two or three adjacent parts (half-shadow or triple-shadow polarimeter) such that when the 'end point' is reached the sections of the field become of the same intensity. A very slight rotation of the analyzer will cause one part to become lighter and the other darker. The increase in sensitivity so attained is illustrated by the fact that an accuracy of at least $\pm 0.01°$ is easily obtained with the use of an 'end point' device, whereas with the unaided eye the settings are no more accurate than ± 4–$5°$.

A **half-shadow polarimeter** (Lippich type)* is illustrated diagrammatically in Fig. *I*, 6, 1. Here two polarized rays are produced by

---

* For further details and a description of the triple shadow polarimeter, see any good text-book of practical physical chemistry. The Microptic Polarimeter M412 (Hilger and Watts Ltd., 98 St. Pancras Way, London, N.W.1) is a satisfactory and inexpensive instrument for routine work.

Photoelectric spectropolarimeters are available but are expensive; these are means of the main Nicol prism P and a small Nicol prism P'; the latter covers half the field of the large polarizer P and its plane of polarization is slightly inclined to that of P. The angles between the planes of polarization may be altered by a slight rotation of the polarizer P. Upon rotating the analyzer A, a position will be found at which one beam will be completely, the other only partially, extinguished; the one half of the field of view will therefore appear dark, while the other will still remain light (as in Fig. $I, 6, 2, a$). Upon rotating the analyzer

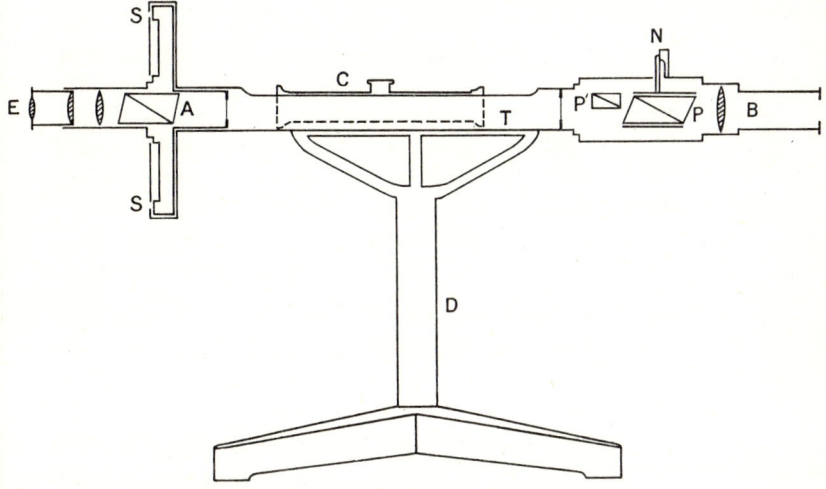

Fig. $I, 6, 1$.

A still further, a second position will be found at which only the second beam will be extinguished and the field will have the appearance shown in (c). When, however, the analyzer occupies an intermediate position, the field of view will appear of uniform brightness (as in b) and this is the position to which the analyzer must be set. In Fig. $I, 6, 1, B$ is a collimator tube, P the polarizer, P' the subsidiary Nicol prism, N is a

highly sensitive (*ca.* 0·001° arc) and rotations may be indicated by a pointer type meter, pen recorder or digital voltmeter. The wavelength of the light beam can be varied continuously from the visible to the ultraviolet: such polarimeters are therefore used for studies of optical rotatory dispersion.

The instruments available include: Photoelectric polarimeter and monochromator (a manual instrument; supplied by W. F. Stanley and Co. Ltd., New Eltham, London, S.E.9). Polarmatic 62 (manual or recording; supplied by Bellingham and Stanley Ltd., 61 Markfield Road, London, N.15 or by Bendix Electronics Ltd., New Basford, Nottingham). Rudolph photoelectric spectropolarimeter (manual from O. C. Rudolph and Sons Inc., Caldwell, N.J.; recording from Rudolph Instrument Engineering Inc., New Jersey, U.S.A.).

device for moving P and thus altering the 'half-shadow angle,' T the trough (shown without cover) which houses the polarimeter tube, C, A is the analyzer, E the eyepiece, S the circular scale fitted with vernier, and D the heavy support stand for the apparatus. Two forms of **polarimeter tube** are shown in Fig. *I*, 6, 3. The common type (*a*) consists of a tube of thick glass with accurately ground ends: the tube is closed by means of circular plates of glass with parallel sides, which are pressed together against the ends of the tube by means of screw

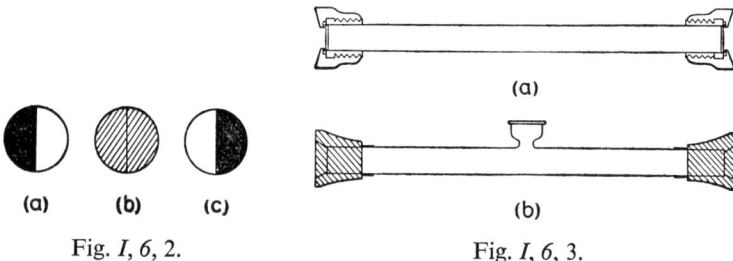

Fig. *I*, 6, 2. Fig. *I*, 6, 3.

caps. The caps must not be screwed so tightly as to cause strain since this may cause a rotation; the glass plates at the end must be clear and the exposed surfaces must be dry. In a modification, the tube is surrounded by a jacket to permit the circulation of water at constant temperature by means of a pump. Tube (*b*) has the opening at the side. The unit of length in polarimetry is 1 dm., hence the tubes are generally made in lengths which are fractions or multiples of this quantity, *e.g.*, 0·5, 1, 2 or 4 dm.

The magnitude of the optical rotation depends upon (i) the nature of the substance, (ii) the length of the column of liquid through which the light passes, (iii) the wavelength of the light employed, (iv) the temperature, and (v) the concentration of the optically active substance, if a solute. In order to obtain a measure of the rotatory power of a substance, these factors must be taken into account. As a rule the wavelength employed is either that for the sodium D line, 5893 Å (obtained with a sodium vapour lamp) or the mercury green line, 5461 Å (produced with a mercury vapour lamp provided with a suitable filter). The temperature selected is 20°, or that of the laboratory t°C. The **specific rotation for a homogeneous active liquid** at a temperature t for the sodium D line is given by:

$$[\alpha]_D^t = \frac{\alpha}{ld}$$

where α is the angular rotation, l is the length of the column of liquid in decimetres and d is the density at temperature t. The **specific rotation for a solution of an optically active substance** is likewise given by:

$$[\alpha]_D^t = \frac{100\alpha}{lc} = \frac{100\alpha}{lpd}$$

where l is the length of the column of liquid in decimetres, c is the number of grams of the substance dissolved in 100 ml. of the solution, p is the number of grams of the substance dissolved in 100 g. of the solution and d is the density of the solution at the temperature t. In expressing the specific rotation of a substance in solution, the concentration and the solvent (which has an influence on the rotation) must be clearly stated. The **molecular rotation** is:

$$[M]_D^t = \frac{[\alpha]_D^t \times M}{100};$$

M is the molecular weight.

The usual **procedure** is to dissolve an accurately weighed sample (0·1–0·5 g.) of the pure compound in 25 ml. of solvent in a volumetric flask. The solvents commonly used are water, absolute methanol, absolute ethanol, chloroform, and a mixture of ethanol and pyridine. The solution must contain no suspended particles and be clear. If the solution is not clear, prepare 50 ml. and filter through a small dry filter paper into a dry flask; set aside the first 25 ml. and use the second 25 ml. of the solution for the determination.

SPECTROPOLARIMETRY: OPTICAL ROTATORY DISPERSION

The specific rotation of a compound is a function of the wavelength. A plot of the optical rotation against the wavelength over the visible and ultraviolet region of the spectrum is more useful than the rotation at a single wavelength. Close relationships have been established between the shape of the optical rotatory dispersion curve and the stereochemistry of optically active compounds. Measurements of rotatory dispersion are therefore of value in the determination of the configurations and conformations of optically active substances, particularly of natural products.

As a simple illustration of the value of optical rotatory dispersion in structure determination, the rotatory dispersion curves in dioxan for *cis*-10-methyl-2-decalone (full line) and *trans*-10-methyl-2-decalone (broken line) are shown in Fig. *I*, 6, 4. Only a small rotation is obtained for each substance at the wavelength of the sodium D line (5893 Å) compared with the rotations between 2600 Å and 4560 Å: the remarkable difference between the curves for the *cis* and *trans* forms is noteworthy.

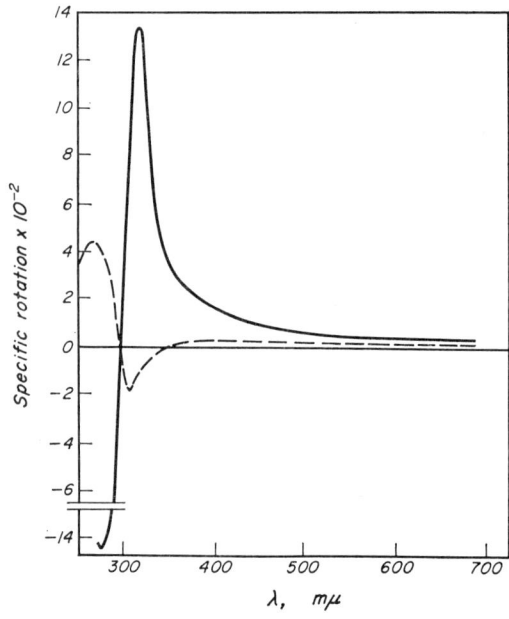

Fig. *I*, 6, 4.

For further information, the following books may be consulted:
C. Djerassi, *Optical Rotatory Dispersion: Applications to Organic Chemistry*. McGraw-Hill Book Co., New York, 1960.
W. C. Klyne and A. C. Parker, *Optical Rotatory Dispersion* in A. Weissberger (Editor), *Technique in Organic Chemistry*, Volume I, Part III. Interscience Publishers, New York, 1960.
G. G. Lyle and R. E. Lyle, *Optical Rotatory Dispersion* in F. C. Nachod and W. D. Phillips (Editors), *Determination of Organic Structures*, Volume 2. Academic Press, New York, 1962.
S. F. Mason, *Optical Rotatory Power* in *Quarterly Reviews*, 1963, **17**, 20.
P. Crabbé, *Optical Rotatory Dispersion and Circular Dichroism in Organic Chemistry*. Holden-Day, San Francisco, 1965.

I, 7 Determination of Molecular Weight

The determination of the molecular weight of a compound is rarely necessary in qualitative organic analysis. Occasionally a knowledge of the molecular weight may be useful, particularly in those cases where a derivative cannot easily be prepared or is unknown. The usual methods of determining molecular weights are too cumbersome and too time-consuming for characterization work. The high freezing point depression of natural *d*-camphor permits the use of an ordinary melting point apparatus, thus enabling the molecular weight to be determined rapidly (**Rast's camphor method**).

Support a small clean test-tube (*e.g.*, 75×10 mm.) in a hole bored in a cork so that it will stand conveniently on the pan of a balance. Weigh the tube. Introduce about 50 mg. of the compound of which the molecular weight is to be determined, and weigh again. Then add 500–600 mg. of pure, resublimed camphor (*e.g.*, the micro-analytical reagent, B.D.H.) and weigh again. Stopper the test-tube loosely and melt the contents by placing it in an oil bath previously heated to about 180°*; stir the liquid with a platinum wire, but do not heat the liquid for more than one minute or camphor will sublime from the solution. Allow to cool, transfer the solid to a clean watch glass and powder the solid. Introduce some of the powder into a thin capillary tube of which the closed end is carefully rounded: press the solid down into the closed end with the aid of a platinum wire or with a closed capillary tube of smaller diameter. The height of the solid should not exceed 2 mm. Determine the melting point of the mixture using, preferably, a 100–200° thermometer graduated in 0·1° or 0·2°; good illumination is essential. The melting point is taken as that temperature at which the last fragment of solid disappears. To make sure that the mixture is homogeneous, repeat the melting point determination with a second sample; if the two differ appreciably, prepare a new mixture. Then determine the melting point of the original camphor. The difference in melting points gives the depression of the melting point of camphor

---

* If very great care is taken, the mixture may be melted by heating over a *very small* flame for about 30 seconds; the technique described in the text is to be preferred.

It is advisable to standardize the camphor by carrying out a molecular weight determination on a pure substance, such as naphthalene (mol. wt. 128) or acetanilide (mol. wt. 135). The method cannot be used for substances which are insoluble in camphor, react with it chemically, or decompose when heated to the m.p. of camphor. For compounds which tend to decompose at the high m.p. of camphor, camphene (m.p. 49°; molecular depression constant, 31·1) has been suggested.

caused by the addition of the compound. The molecular weight M can then be calculated from the formula:

$$M = \frac{K \times w \times 1000}{\Delta T \times W}$$

where K is the molecular depression constant of camphor (39·7)
    w is the weight of the compound
    W is the weight of the camphor
and ΔT is the depression of the melting point.

Note

The solute concentration should be above $0·2M$; in dilute solution K increases from 39·7 to about 50.

CHAPTER II
Qualitative Analysis for the Elements

The most commonly occurring elements in organic compounds are carbon, hydrogen, oxygen, nitrogen, sulphur and the halogens; less common elements are phosphorus, arsenic, antimony, mercury, or other metals which may be present as salts of organic acids. There is no direct method for the detection of oxygen.

It is usually advisable to carry out the ignition test first. This will provide useful information as to the general properties of the compound and, in particular, the residue may be employed for the detection of any inorganic elements which may be present.

II, 1 Ignition Test

Before conducting the ignition test, the substance should be subjected to a preliminary examination and the following noted: colour, odour, crystalline form (if a solid), and viscosity (if a liquid).

Place about 0·1 g. of the compound in a porcelain crucible or crucible cover or small Pyrex test-tube. Heat it gently at first and finally to dull redness. Observe:

(*a*) Whether the substance melts (if a solid), is explosive, or is inflammable and the nature of the flame.

(*b*) Whether gases or vapour are evolved and their odour (*CAUTION!*).

(*c*) Whether the residue fuses.

If an appreciable amount of residue remains, note its colour. Add a few drops of water and test the solution (or suspension) with litmus or with Universal indicator paper. Then add a little dilute hydrochloric acid and observe whether effervescence occurs and the residue dissolves. Apply a flame test with a platinum wire on the hydrochloric acid solution to determine the metal present. (In rare cases, it may be necessary to subject a solution of the residue to the methods of qualitative inorganic analysis to identify the elements or metal ions present.) If the flame test indicates sodium or potassium, repeat the ignition of the substance on platinum foil.

Heating with soda lime is often a useful preliminary test. Mix thoroughly about 0·2 g. of the substance with about 1 g. of powdered soda lime. Place the mixture in a Pyrex test-tube; close the tube by a cork and delivery tube. Incline the test-tube so that any liquid formed in the reaction cannot run back on the hot part of the tube. Heat the test-tube gently at first and finally ignite strongly. Collect any condensate produced in a test-tube containing 2–3 ml. of water. Nitrogenous compounds will usually evolve ammonia or vapours alkaline to litmus and possessing characteristic odours; hydroxybenzoic acids yield phenols; formates and acetates yield hydrogen; simple carboxylic acids yield hydrocarbons (methane from acetic acid, benzene from benzoic or phthalic acid, etc.); amine salts and aromatic amino carboxylic acids yield aromatic amines; etc.

II, 2   Carbon and Hydrogen

Evidence of the organic nature of the substance may be provided by the behaviour of the compound when heated on porcelain or platinum or other comparatively inert metal (*e.g.*, nickel): the substance is inflammable, burns with a more or less smoky flame, chars and leaves a black residue consisting largely of carbon (compare *Ignition Test* above).

If it is desired to test directly for the presence of carbon and hydrogen in a compound, mix 0·1 g. of the substance with 1–2 g. of ignited, fine copper oxide powder* in a dry test-tube, and fit the latter with a cork carrying a tube bent at an angle so that the escaping gases can be bubbled below the surface of lime water contained in a second test-tube. Clamp the test-tube containing the mixture near the cork. Heat the mixture gradually. If carbon is present, carbon dioxide will be evolved which will produce a turbidity in the lime water. If hydrogen is present, small drops of water will collect in the cooler part of the tube.

II, 3   Nitrogen, Sulphur and Halogens

In order to detect these elements in organic compounds, it is necessary to convert them into ionizable inorganic substances so that the ionic tests of inorganic qualitative analysis may be applied. This conversion may be accomplished by several methods, but the best

---

* Copper oxide powder, prepared by grinding copper oxide (wire form), is heated to dull redness in a porcelain basin, allowed to cool partially in the air and finally in a desiccator.

procedure is to fuse the organic compound with metallic sodium (**Lassaigne's test**). In this way sodium cyanide, sodium sulphide and sodium halides are formed, which are readily identified. Thus:

Organic compound containing C,H,O,N,S,Hal. + Na $\xrightarrow{\text{Heat}}$
$NaCN + Na_2S + NaHal. + NaOH$

It is essential to use an excess of sodium, otherwise if sulphur and nitrogen are both present sodium thiocyanate, NaSCN, may be produced; in the test for nitrogen it may give a red coloration with ferric iron but no Prussian blue since there will be no free cyanide ions. With excess of sodium the thiocyanate, if formed, will be decomposed:

$$NaSCN + 2Na \rightarrow NaCN + Na_2S$$

The filtered alkaline solution, resulting from the action of water upon the sodium fusion, is treated with ferrous sulphate and thus forms sodium ferrocyanide:

$$FeSO_4 + 6NaCN \rightarrow Na_4[Fe(CN)_6] + Na_2SO_4$$

Upon boiling the alkaline ferrous salt solution, some ferric ions are inevitably produced by the action of the air; upon the addition of dilute sulphuric acid, thus dissolving the ferrous and ferric hydroxides, the ferrocyanide reacts with the ferric salt producing ferric ferrocyanide (Prussian blue):

$$3Na_4[Fe(CN)_6] + 2Fe_2(SO_4)_3 \rightarrow Fe_4[Fe(CN)_6]_3 + 6Na_2SO_4$$

Hydrochloric acid should not be used for acidifying the alkaline solution since the yellow colour, due to the ferric chloride formed, causes the Prussian blue to appear greenish. For the same reason, ferric chloride should not be added—as is frequently recommended: a sufficient concentration of ferric ions is produced by atmospheric oxidation of the hot alkaline solution. The addition of a little dilute potassium fluoride solution may be advantageous in assisting the formation of Prussian blue in a readily filterable form.

Sulphur, as sulphide ion, is detected by precipitation as black lead sulphide with lead acetate solution and acetic acid or with sodium plumbite solution (an alkaline solution of lead acetate). Halogens (excluding fluoride) are detected as the characteristic silver halides by the addition of silver nitrate solution and dilute nitric acid: the interfering influence of sulphide and cyanide ions in the latter tests are discussed under the individual elements.

Support a small, soft glass test-tube (50 × 8–12 mm.)* in a clamp or insert the tube through a small hole in a piece of asbestos board (or of

---

* If preferred, suitable ignition tubes may be prepared by the student from soft glass tubing: it is important that the thickness of the glass at the closed end be uniform, otherwise the tube is likely to crack when heated. The simplest procedure is to blow a small bulb of uniform wall thickness at the end of the tube. The small test-tubes are available from all laboratory supply dealers.

'uralite') so that the tube is supported by the rim. Place a cube (*ca.* 4 mm. side = 0·04 g.) of freshly cut sodium* in the tube. Have in readiness about 0·05 g. of the compound on a spatula or the tip of a knife blade; if the compound is a liquid, charge a capillary dropper or a melting point capillary with two to three drops of the liquid. Heat the ignition tube, gently at first to prevent cracking, until the sodium melts and the vapour rises 1–2 cm. in the tube. Drop the substance, preferably portionwise, directly on to the molten sodium (*CAUTION:* there may be a slight explosion, particularly with chloroform, carbon tetrachloride, nitroalkanes, organic azides, diazonium salts, and azo compounds). Remove the tube from its support and hold it by means of a pair of tongs. Heat it carefully at first, then strongly until the entire end of the tube is red hot and maintain it at this temperature for a minute or two. Plunge the tube while still hot into an evaporating basin† containing about 10 ml. of distilled water, and cover the dish *immediately* with a clean wire gauze. The tube will be shattered and the residual sodium will react with water. When the reaction is over, heat to boiling, and filter. The filtrate should be water-clear and alkaline. If it is dark coloured, decomposition was probably incomplete: repeat the entire sodium fusion.

The following *alternative procedure* is recommended and it possesses the advantage that the same tube may be used for many sodium fusions. Support a Pyrex test-tube (150 × 12 mm.) vertically in a clamp lined with asbestos cloth or with sheet cork. Place a cube (*ca.* 4 mm. side = 0·04 g.) of freshly cut sodium in the tube and heat the latter until the sodium vapour rises 2–3 cm. in the test-tube. Drop a small amount (about 0·05 g.) of the substance, preferably portionwise, directly into the sodium vapour (*CAUTION:* there may be a slight explosion); then heat the tube to redness for about 1 minute. Allow the test-tube to cool, add 3–4 ml. of methyl alcohol to decompose any

---

* *CAUTION:* Handle sodium with great care. Small pieces for sodium fusions may be kept in a small dry bottle. Larger quantities and pieces are better kept under solvent naphtha or xylene. Do not handle the metal with the fingers: use tongs or pincers or a penknife. If the sodium is stored under naphtha or xylene, dry it quickly with filter paper immediately before use. Any residual sodium should be placed in the bottle for '*Sodium Residues.*' Never throw small pieces of residual sodium in the sink or into water: if you wish to destroy sodium residues, use methylated spirit.

† An alternative technique is as follows. Plunge the hot tube into about 10 ml. of water contained in a small, clean mortar and cover the latter immediately with a clean wire gauze. When the reaction is over, grind the mixture of solution and broken glass to ensure thorough extraction of the sodium salts. Transfer with the aid of a little water to a porcelain basin, heat to boiling, and filter.

unreacted sodium, then half-fill the tube with distilled water and boil gently for a few minutes. Filter and use the clear, colourless filtrate for the various tests detailed below. Keep the test-tube for sodium fusions; it will usually become discoloured and should be cleaned from time to time with a little scouring powder.

Nitrogen. Pour 2–3 ml. of the filtered 'fusion' solution into a test-tube containing 0·1–0·2 g. of powdered ferrous sulphate crystals. Heat the mixture gently with shaking until it boils, then, without cooling, add just sufficient dilute sulphuric acid to dissolve the iron hydroxides and give the solution an acid reaction. {The addition of 1 ml. of 5 per cent potassium fluoride solution is beneficial (possibly owing to the formation of potassium ferrifluoride $K_3[FeF_6]$) and usually leads to a purer Prussian blue.} A Prussian blue precipitate or coloration indicates that nitrogen is present. If no blue precipitate appears at once, allow to stand for 15 minutes, filter through a small filter and wash the paper with water to remove all traces of coloured solution: any Prussian blue present will then become perceptible in the cone of the filter paper. If in doubt, repeat the sodium fusion, preferably using a mixture of the compound with pure sucrose or naphthalene. In the absence of nitrogen, the solution should have a pale yellow colour due to iron salts.

If sulphur is present, a *black* precipitate of ferrous sulphide is obtained when the ferrous sulphate crystals dissolve. It is usually unnecessary to filter off the black precipitate. Heat the 'fusion filtrate' containing 0·1–0·2 g. of ferrous sulphate crystals for about 30 seconds, add just sufficient dilute sulphuric acid to dissolve the precipitate and give the solution an acid reaction. A Prussian blue precipitate indicates that nitrogen is present (see previous paragraph).

Sulphur. This element may be tested for by any one of the following three methods:

(*a*) Prepare a **solution of sodium plumbite** by adding 10 per cent sodium hydroxide solution to a few drops of about N lead acetate solution until the white precipitate of lead hydroxide initially formed just redissolves to a clear solution. Add 1 ml. of the 'fusion' solution: the presence of sulphur is indicated by a black precipitate of lead sulphide.

(*b*) Acidify 2 ml. of the 'fusion' solution with dilute acetic acid, and add a few drops of lead acetate solution. A black precipitate of lead sulphide indicates the presence of sulphur.

(*c*) To 2 ml. of the 'fusion' solution add 2–3 drops of a freshly prepared dilute solution (*ca.* 0·1 per cent) of sodium nitroprusside

Na$_2$[Fe(CN)$_5$NO]. (The latter may be prepared by adding a minute crystal of the solid to about 2 ml. of water.) An intense purple coloration indicates sulphur; the coloration slowly fades on standing.

Halogens. If nitrogen and/or sulphur are present, the addition of silver nitrate to the acidified 'fusion' solution will precipitate silver cyanide and/or silver sulphide in addition to the silver halides. The removal of hydrogen cyanide and/or hydrogen sulphide before precipitation of the silver halides is effected by boiling the 'fusion' solution, just acidified with dilute nitric acid, in an evaporating basin until it has been reduced to half its original volume. Cool, dilute with an equal volume of water and add a few drops of silver nitrate solution. A white or pale yellow precipitate, which darkens rapidly upon exposure to light, indicates the presence of halogen.

An alternative method is to add a little dilute nickel nitrate solution to the 'fusion' solution, the precipitated nickel cyanide and/or nickel sulphide is filtered off, the filtrate is acidified with dilute nitric acid and tested for halogens as above.

(A) **Nitrogen and sulphur absent.** (i) *Silver nitrate test.* Acidify with dilute nitric acid and add excess of silver nitrate solution. A precipitate indicates the presence of a halogen. Decant the mother liquor and treat the precipitate with dilute aqueous ammonia solution. If the precipitate is white and readily soluble in the ammonia solution, chlorine is present; if it is pale yellow and difficultly soluble, bromine is present; if it is yellow and insoluble, then iodine is indicated. Iodine and bromine should be confirmed by the tests (ii) or (iii).

If one or more halogens may be present, use any of the following procedures:

(ii) Acidify 1–2 ml. of the 'fusion' solution with a moderate excess of glacial acetic acid and add 1 ml. of carbon tetrachloride. Then introduce 20 per cent sodium nitrite solution drop by drop with constant shaking. A purple or violet colour in the organic layer indicates the presence of iodine. The reaction is:

$$2NaI + 2NaNO_2 + 4CH_3COOH \rightarrow$$
$$I_2 + 2NO + 4CH_3COONa + 2H_2O$$

This solution may also be employed in the test for bromine. If iodine has been found, add small amounts of sodium nitrite solution, warm slightly and shake with fresh 1 ml. portions of carbon tetrachloride until the last extract is colourless; boil the acid solution until no more nitrous fumes are evolved and cool. If iodine is absent, use 1 ml. of the 'fusion' solution which has been strongly acidified with glacial acetic acid. Add a small amount of lead dioxide, place a strip of fluorescein paper across the mouth of the tube, and warm the solution. If bromine is present, it will colour the test paper rose-pink (eosin).

Fluorescein test paper is prepared by dipping filter paper into a dilute solution of fluorescein in ethyl alcohol; it dries rapidly and is then ready for use. The test paper has a lemon yellow colour.

Lead dioxide in acetic acid solution gives lead tetra-acetate which oxidizes hydrogen bromide (and also hydrogen iodide), but has practically no effect under the above experimental conditions upon hydrogen chloride:

$$2NaBr + PbO_2 + 4CH_3COOH \rightarrow$$
$$Br_2 + (CH_3COO)_2Pb + 2CH_3COONa + 2H_2O$$

(iii) Acidify 1–2 ml. of the 'fusion' solution with dilute sulphuric acid, cool, and add 1 ml. of carbon tetrachloride. Prepare the equivalent of 'chlorine water' by acidifying 10 per cent sodium hypochlorite solution with one-fifth of its volume of dilute hydrochloric acid. Add this solution dropwise (use a dropper) with vigorous shaking to the mixture. If iodine is present, the organic phase first becomes purple in colour. As the addition of the 'chlorine water' is continued, the purple colour disappears (owing to the oxidation of the iodine to iodate) and, if bromine is present, is replaced by a brown or reddish colour. If bromine is absent, the organic layer will be colourless. It is, of course, evident that if the carbon tetrachloride layer remains uncoloured, the halogen present is chlorine.

(iv) Acidify 1–2 ml. of the 'fusion' solution with glacial acetic acid, add a slight excess of pure lead dioxide (say, 0·5 g.) and boil gently until all the iodine and bromine are liberated. Dilute, filter off the excess of lead dioxide, and test for chloride with dilute nitric acid and silver nitrate solution.

$$2NaBr(I) + PbO_2 + 4CH_3COOH \rightarrow$$
$$Br_2(I_2) + (CH_3COO)_2Pb + 2CH_3COONa + 2H_2O$$

(B) **Nitrogen and/or sulphur present.** Just acidify 2–3 ml. of the 'fusion' solution with dilute nitric acid, and evaporate to half the original volume in order to expel hydrogen cyanide and/or hydrogen sulphide which may be present. Dilute with an equal volume of water. If only one halogen is present, proceed as in tests (i) or (iii). If one or more halogens may be present, use tests (ii), (iii) or (iv).

Alternatively, add 1–2 drops of 5 per cent nickel nitrate solution to

2–3 ml. of the 'fusion' solution, filter off the nickel cyanide and/or nickel sulphide, acidify the filtrate with 2N nitric acid and test for halides as above.

The detection of the following elements, which occur infrequently in organic compounds, is included here for the sake of completeness.

Fluorine. Use either of the following tests.

(*a*) Strongly acidify about 2 ml. of the 'fusion' filtrate with glacial acetic acid, and boil until the volume is reduced by about one half. Cool. Place one drop of the solution upon zirconium-alizarin red S test paper. A yellow colour on the red paper indicates the presence of fluoride.

Large amounts of sulphates and phosphates behave similarly. Sulphate is removed by adding benzidine hydrochloride to the test solution: then place the benzidine sulphate suspension on the reagent paper. In the presence of fluoride, a yellow colouration appears on the red paper and is easily seen on the underside of the paper.

Prepare the *zirconium-alizarin red S paper* as follows. Soak dry filter paper in a 5 per cent solution of zirconium nitrate in 5 per cent hydrochloric acid and, after draining, place it in a 2 per cent aqueous solution of sodium alizarin sulphonate (B.D.H. 'Alizarin Red S'). The paper is coloured red-violet by the zirconium lake. Wash the paper until the wash water is nearly colourless and then dry in the air.

(*b*) If nitrogen and/or sulphur present, acidify 3–4 ml. of the 'fusion' solution with dilute nitric acid and evaporate to half the original volume in order to expel any HCN and/or H_2S which may be present. If nitrogen and/or sulphur are absent, proceed directly with 2 ml. of the sodium fusion filtrate. Render the solution just neutral to litmus by the addition of dilute (5M) aqueous ammonia solution, then add 5 drops of 5M acetic acid and 20 mg. of lanthanum chloranilate*, and shake intermittently for 10–15 minutes. Filter. A pink-violet coloration of the filtrate is a positive test for fluorine.

Phosphorus. The presence of phosphorus may be indicated by a smell of phosphine during the sodium fusion and the immediate production of a jet-black colour when a piece of filter paper moistened with silver nitrate solution is placed over the mouth of the ignition tube after the sample has been dropped on the hot sodium. Treat 1·0 ml. of the 'fusion' solution with 3 ml. of concentrated nitric acid and boil for one minute. Cool and add an equal volume of ammonium molybdate reagent. Warm the mixture to 40–50°, and allow to stand. If phosphorus is present, a yellow crystalline precipitate of ammonium phosphomolybdate will separate.

It is usually preferable to oxidize the compound directly as follows. Intimately mix 0·02–0·05 g. of the compound with 3 g. of sodium peroxide and 2 g. of anhydrous sodium carbonate in a nickel crucible. Heat the crucible and its contents with a small flame, gently at first,

---

* 2,5-Dichloro-3,6-dihydroxy-*p*-benzoquinone, lanthanum salt.

afterwards more strongly until the contents are fused, and continue heating for a further 10 minutes. Allow to stand, extract the contents of the crucible with water, and filter. Add excess of concentrated nitric acid to the filtrate and test with ammonium molybdate reagent as above. A yellow precipitate indicates the presence of phosphorus. It must be borne in mind that the above treatment will convert any arsenic present into arsenate.

Arsenic. The presence of arsenic in an organic compound is generally revealed by the formation of a dull grey mirror of arsenic on the walls of the test-tube when the compound is fused with sodium in the Lassaigne test. Usually sufficient arsenic is found in the 'fusion' solution to give a yellow precipitate of arsenic trisulphide when the solution is acidified with hydrochloric acid and treated with hydrogen sulphide.

It is recommended that the compound be fused with a mixture of sodium carbonate (2 parts) and sodium peroxide (1 part) as in the test for *Phosphorus*. Extract the fused mass with water, filter, and acidify with dilute hydrochloric acid. Pass hydrogen sulphide through the hot solution; arsenic is precipitated as yellow arsenic sulphide. If **antimony is present,** it will be precipitated as orange antimony trisulphide.

Mercury. Upon heating a mixture of the compound with soda lime in a long test-tube, a bright metallic mirror and, finally, drops of the metal will form in the upper part of the tube if mercury is present.

II, 4 The Sodium Carbonate-Zinc Method for the Detection of Nitrogen, Sulphur and Halogens in Organic Compounds

The Lassaigne procedure for detecting nitrogen in organic compounds frequently gives unsatisfactory results with explosive compounds (diazonium salts, nitro-alkanes, organic azides, azo compounds, polynitro compounds and the like) and with certain volatile nitrogenous substances, such as bases, their acyl derivatives or their salts. These difficulties may often be surmounted either by mixing the compound with pure naphthalene or sucrose, or by mixing the substance with sodium and placing a layer of soda lime above the mixture. Difficulties are also sometimes experienced in the sodium fusion test with liquids of low boiling point, such as ethyl bromide. Satisfactory results are obtained by heating the organic compounds with sodium carbonate and zinc powder. The latter method has been proposed for the detection of the common elements in all organic compounds. It is doubtful, however, whether it is to be preferred to the sodium fusion procedure in routine testing for elements, although it may be recommended for those relatively few cases in which the Lassaigne test is not entirely satisfactory.

When an organic compound is heated with a mixture of zinc powder and sodium carbonate, the nitrogen and halogens are converted into sodium cyanide and sodium halides respectively, and the sulphur into zinc sulphide (insoluble in water). The sodium cyanide and sodium halides are extracted with water and detected as in Lassaigne's method, whilst the zinc sulphide in the residue is decomposed with dilute acid and the hydrogen sulphide is identified with sodium plumbite or lead acetate paper. The test for nitrogen is thus not affected by the presence of sulphur: this constitutes an advantage of the method.

Prepare the **zinc powder-sodium carbonate mixture** by grinding together in a dry, clean mortar 2·5 g. of A.R. anhydrous sodium carbonate and 5·0 g. of the purest obtainable zinc powder. The reagent is unlikely to contain nitrogen, but traces of sulphur and halogens may be present. It is therefore essential to carry out a blank or control test for sulphur and halogens with every fresh batch of the mixture.

Place about 0·1 g. of the powdered compound in a small dry test-tube, add sufficient of the reagent to give a column about 1 cm. high, and then shake the closed tube until the contents are well mixed. Now add more reagent, without mixing with the material already in the tube, until the total height is about 3 cm. If the compound is a liquid, introduce 2–3 drops into a small dry test-tube, add sufficient of the mixture to form a column about 1 cm. long, and allow the liquid to soak well into the reagent. Then add more reagent, without mixing, until a total height of about 3 cm. is secured. Hold the tube horizontally (use tongs or special test-tube holder) and, by means of a *small* flame, heat a 1 cm. length of the mixture gently near the open end. Gradually increase the size of the flame until the mixture is red hot at the end. Extend the heating gradually and cautiously towards the closed end of the tube until the whole of the mixture is red hot. (The extension of the heating towards the closed end of the tube must be carried out with great care, otherwise the mixture may be projected from the tube; if the mixture tends to be pushed out of the tube by the evolution of gas, stop the heating momentarily and rotate the tube while still in a horizontal position in order to redistribute the contents.) Finally heat the tube to redness in a vertical position for a minute or two and, while the end of the tube is still red hot, plunge the tube into about 10 ml. of water in a porcelain dish. Boil the contents of the dish gently for 1–2 minutes and filter. (If the filtrate is not colourless, repeat the whole process.) Retain the residue in the basin for the sulphur test. Divide the clear filtrate into two portions.

Nitrogen. Treat one portion with 1–2 ml. of 5 per cent sodium hydroxide solution and 0·1 g. of powdered ferrous sulphate. Boil for 1 minute and cool. Cautiously acidify with dilute sulphuric acid (carbon dioxide is evolved). A precipitate of Prussian blue indicates that nitrogen is present.

Halogens. Proceed as described under the Lassaigne test. If nitrogen is present, the cyanide must first be eliminated.

Sulphur. Moisten the centre of a filter paper with sodium plumbite solution. Add about 10 ml. of dilute hydrochloric acid to the residue in the dish and immediately cover it with the prepared filter paper. If zinc sulphide is present in the residue, a dark brown stain, visible on the upper surface of the paper, will be obtained: frequently the presence of hydrogen sulphide can also be detected by its odour.

CHAPTER III

The Solubility Classes

III, 1 The Solubilities of Organic Compounds. General Discussion

The study of the solubility behaviour of an unknown substance in various liquids, *viz.*, water, ether, 5 per cent sodium hydroxide solution, 5 per cent sodium bicarbonate solution, 5 per cent hydrochloric acid and cold concentrated sulphuric acid, provides several general kinds of information about the compound.

1. The presence of functional groups is often indicated. Thus, since hydrocarbons are insoluble in water, the mere fact that an unknown substance, such as diethyl ether, is partially soluble in water indicates that a functional group is present.

2. The solubility in certain solvents often provides specific information about the functional group. For example, *p*-toluic acid is almost insoluble in water (a polar solvent) but it is converted by dilute sodium hydroxide solution into a salt, sodium *p*-toluate, which dissolves readily in water. Here the solubility in 5 per cent sodium hydroxide solution of a water-insoluble compound points to the presence of an acidic functional group.

A further example is provided by *p*-cresol. This compound is sparingly soluble in water, dissolves readily in 5 per cent sodium hydroxide solution but is insoluble in 5 per cent sodium bicarbonate solution. Since *p*-cresol does not dissolve in the weakly basic solvent, 5 per cent sodium bicarbonate solution, it clearly contains a weak acidic functional group. The solubility in dilute sodium hydroxide solution and in dilute sodium bicarbonate solution therefore provides a method for differentiating between relatively strong and weak acidic groups.

3. Deductions about molecular weight may sometimes be made. Thus in many series of mono-functional compounds (*e.g.*, the alcohols), the members with less than about five carbon atoms are soluble in water whilst the higher homologues are insoluble.

When a mixture of a specified amount of a given solute and a specified amount of a given solvent forms a homogeneous liquid, the former is said to be soluble in the latter. The arbitrary standard employed in this book is 0·10 g. of solid or 0·20 ml. of liquid to 3·00 ml.

of solvent. This essentially practical (although arbitrary) definition of solubility forms the basis of various schemes which have been proposed to employ solubility as a basis for the classification of organic compounds.

When solubility in dilute acid or base is being considered, it is important to note whether the unknown is more soluble in aqueous acid or base than it is in water: this increased solubility is the positive test for an acidic or basic functional group. Acidic compounds are detected by their solubility in 5 per cent sodium hydroxide solution. Strong and weak acids are differentiated by the solubility of the former but not the latter in the weakly basic 5 per cent sodium bicarbonate solution. Bases in aqueous solution are detected by their solubility in 5 per cent hydrochloric acid. Many compounds that are neutral even in strong aqueous acid solutions behave as bases in strongly acidic solvents, such as concentrated sulphuric acid; these include compounds that are neutral in water and contain oxygen in any form. The presence of acidic or basic functional groups in water-soluble compounds is detected by testing their aqueous solutions with litmus or other indicator paper.

A detailed discussion of the relationship between solubility and chemical structure is outside the scope of this volume but some general facts may be given which will assist one to predict the solubility behaviour by inspection of the structural formula.

Water has a high dielectric constant (80·4 at 20°) and high hydrogen-bonding ability (leading to association): it may act as an acid and a base. This makes it a good solvent for salts and a poor solvent for non-polar substances. Diethyl ether has a lower dielectric constant (4·34 at 20°), is unassociated, and acts only as a very weak base: this makes it a good solvent for non-polar substances. In general, a polar solvent may be expected to dissolve only polar substances readily, and a non-polar solvent only non-polar solutes easily.

Most organic molecules have both a polar and a non-polar part and it would be expected that the solubility would depend upon their relative proportions. As the hydrocarbon part of the molecule increases, the properties of the compounds approach those of the hydrocarbons from which they may be considered to be derived. This means that the ether solubility increases and the water solubility decreases. Also as the number of polar groups increases, the water solubility will increase. Thus if two or more hydroxyl groups are present in the molecule, the compound becomes more like water in structure and less like the hydrocarbons, consequently the solubility in water increases and the solubility in ether decreases. The following examples may be quoted: ethyl and *n*-propyl alcohol are completely miscible with ether and with water, but ethylene glycol and glycerol whilst very soluble in water are almost insoluble in ether; the carbohydrates, which contain several hydroxyl groups, are very soluble in water but insoluble in ether; succinic acid is sparingly soluble and malic, tartaric and citric acids are insoluble in ether, but all of these polybasic acids are soluble in water. On the other hand, if the number of hydrocarbon (*e.g.*, aromatic) residues in the molecule is increased, the water solubility is decreased and the ether solubility is increased. Thus 1- or 2-naphthol or *p*-hydroxybiphenyl are less soluble in water than is phenol. The phenyl radical when present as a substituent in aliphatic acids, alcohols, aldehydes and similar compounds has an effect on the solubility approximately equal to a four-carbon aliphatic chain: thus the solubilities of benzyl alcohol and *n*-amyl alcohol and of hydrocinnamic acid and *n*-heptoic acid are of the same order in each pair.

The solubility of solid compounds is dependent upon the molecular aggregation in the solid state. The molecular aggregation in the solid state finds some expression in the melting points of the compounds or, otherwise expressed, the melting point of a solid is generally a criterion of the intermolecular cohesive forces. Heat is required to overcome these forces and convert the solid into a liquid; hence the higher the m.p., the greater is the intermolecular attraction. The solution of a solid involves a similar destruction of the intermolecular forces so that, for structurally related compounds, higher melting points are associated with lower solubilities in inert solvents.* The solubilities of some stereoisomers in water and in ethanol are collected in Table III, 1, 1.

Similar relationships are found among the position isomers in benzene derivatives, but some abnormal results are encountered. Among compounds of a homologous series, high melting points often correspond to lower solubilities. Thus with the aliphatic dibasic acids $HOOC(CH_2)_nCOOH$, the 'even' acid has the higher melting point and lower solubility in water than the next higher homologue ('odd' acid). This can be clearly seen from an examination of Table III, 1, 2.

An interesting illustration is urea $CO(NH_2)_2$, m.p. 132°, which is very soluble in water, and oxamide $(CONH_2)_2$, m.p. 420°, which is sparingly soluble in water.

---
* This does not apply to salts; these are highly polar compounds, dissociate in aqueous solution, and are usually very soluble.

Table III, 1, 1. Solubilities of Stereoisomers in Water and in Ethanol

COMPOUND	M.P.	SOLUBILITY IN 100 G. SOLVENT AT 20°	
		WATER	ETHANOL
Maleic acid (*cis*)	135°*	60 g.	51 g.
Fumaric acid (*trans*)	286	0·6 g.	5 g.
D-Tartaric acid	170	139 g.	27 g. (25°)
L-Tartaric acid	170	139 g.	27 g. (25°)
DL-Tartaric acid	206	20 g.	2 g. (25°)

* The m.p. depends upon the rate of heating: the pure acid has m.p. 143°, but commercial samples usually melt at a slightly lower temperature.

Table III, 1, 2. Melting Points and Solubilities of Dibasic Acids, $HOOC(CH_2)_nCOOH$

ACID	M.P.	SOLUBILITY (G./100 G. OF H_2O) AT 20°
Oxalic ($n = 0$)	189°	9·5
Malonic ($n = 1$)	135	73·5
Succinic ($n = 2$)	185	6·9
Glutaric ($n = 3$)	98	63·9
Adipic ($n = 4$)	152	1·5
Pimelic ($n = 5$)	105	4·9
Suberic ($n = 6$)	142	0·15
Azelaic ($n = 7$)	106	0·24
Sebacic ($n = 8$)	134	0·10

Intermolecular forces are also reflected in the boiling points of liquids. It might be expected from a consideration of the effect of branching of a hydrocarbon chain on the boiling points of the lower homologous series (such as the alcohols) that branching lowers intermolecular forces and decreases intermolecular attraction. Hence it is not surprising that a compound having a branched chain is more soluble in water than the corresponding straight-chain compound. This rule applies to simple aliphatic compounds. Thus the solubility of isobutyl alcohol differs appreciably from that of *n*-heptanol. The

Elementary Practical Organic Chemistry [III

position of the functional group in the carbon chain also affects solubility; thus 3-pentanol is more soluble than 2-pentanol, which in turn is more soluble than 1-pentanol. Some quantitative figures for the pentanols, illustrating some of these points, are collected in Table III, 1, 3.

Table III, 1, 3.   Solubilities of the Pentanols in Water at 20°

ALCOHOL	FORMULA	B.P.	SOLUBILITY (G./100 G. OF H_2O)
1-Pentanol	$CH_3(CH_2)_4OH$	138°	2·4
3-Methyl-1-butanol	$(CH_3)_2CHCH_2CH_2OH$	134	2·8
2-Methyl-1-butanol	$CH_3CH_2CH(CH_3)CH_2OH$	129	3·2
2,2-Dimethyl-1-propanol	$(CH_3)_3CCH_2OH$	113	3·7
2-Pentanol	$CH_3CH_2CH_2CH(OH)CH_3$	120	4·9
3-Pentanol	$CH_3CH_2CH(OH)CH_2CH_3$	116	5·6
3-Methyl-2-butanol	$(CH_3)_2CHCH(OH)CH_3$	114	6·1
2-Methyl-2-butanol	$(CH_3)_2C(OH)CH_2CH_3$	102	12·2

An increase in molecular weight leads to an increase in intermolecular forces in a solid. Polymers and other compounds of high molecular weight generally have low solubilities in water. Thus, whilst formaldehyde (CH_2O), glucose ($C_6H_{12}O_6$) and methyl acrylate (CH_2=$CHCOOCH_3$) are readily soluble in water, the polymers—paraformaldehyde $HO(CH_2O—)_nH$; starch, cellulose and glycogen $(C_6H_{10}O_5)_x$; and methyl acrylate polymer—are insoluble in water. Some exceptions are known.

The effect of structure upon acidity and basicity, which is obviously related to solubility in dilute acids and bases, is explained by the electronic and steric influences of substituent groups. The subject is fully discussed in text-books on organic chemistry and need not therefore be given here.

III, 2   Summary of Solubility Behaviour

Solubility in water. Since water is a polar compound, it is a poor solvent for hydrocarbons of all types. Salts are usually extremely polar; most encountered in organic analysis are generally water-soluble. Other compounds fall between these two extremes; these include alcohols, esters, aldehydes, ketones, acids, ethers, amides, nitriles and amines. Acids and amines are generally more soluble than neutral compounds.

For homologous series of mono-functional alcohols, esters, aldehydes, ketones, acids, ethers, amides, nitriles and amines, the upper limit of water solubility is found at about the member containing four carbon atoms. The solubility in water is due largely to the polar group and as the homologous series is ascended, the hydrocarbon (non-polar) part of the molecule increases whilst the polar function remains substantially unchanged; this accounts for the decrease in solubility in polar solvents such as water. This behaviour is an illustration of a general rule that increased structural similarity between the solute and the solvent results in increased solubility in that solvent.

It must be emphasized that the particular region (that of the member containing four carbon atoms) of water solubility for many homologous series is determined by the arbitrary proportions of solute and solvent chosen for our scheme of separation. The limit would be elsewhere for a different ratio of solute to solvent.

Solubility in ether. Non-polar and slightly polar compounds will, in general, dissolve in ether because they are largely unassociated. Ionic compounds, such as salts, are not soluble in ether. The solubility of a polar compound in ether will depend upon the influence of the polar group or groups relative to that of the non-polar part of the molecule. Usually, compounds that have one polar group per molecule will dissolve in ether unless they are highly associated or of extreme polarity (*e.g.*, the sulphonic acids).

Many organic compounds that are insoluble in water dissolve in ether. Hence the solubility in ether is not a good criterion for classification by solubility except for those substances that are also soluble in water. If a compound is soluble in both ether and water, it probably (i) is non-ionic, (ii) contains five or less carbon atoms, (iii) has a functional group that is polar and capable of forming hydrogen bonds, and (iv) does not contain more than one strongly polar group. If a compound dissolves in water but not in ether, it may (i) be ionic (a salt) or (ii) contain two or more polar groups but not more than four carbon atoms per polar group. There are, of course, exceptions to these statements.

Solubility in dilute hydrochloric acid. Most compounds that are soluble in dilute hydrochloric acid contain a basic nitrogen atom (incorporating an unshared electron pair) in the molecule. Thus most aliphatic amines (primary, secondary and tertiary) form salts (polar, water-soluble compounds) with hydrochloric acid. Aryl groups reduce the basicity of the nitrogen atom. Primary aromatic amines (*e.g.*, aniline), although more weakly basic than primary aliphatic amines, are soluble, but in secondary and tertiary purely aromatic amines (*e.g.*, diphenylamine, carbazole and triphenylamine) the basic character of the nitrogen atom has been diminished to such an extent that they do not form salts with dilute hydrochloric acid and consequently do not dissolve. Alkylarylamines (containing not more than one aryl group) and alicyclic amines, however, do dissolve. A few types of oxygen-containing compounds (such as the pyrones and the anthocyanidin pigments of certain flowers) which form oxonium salts dissolve in dilute hydrochloric acid. Amides, $RCONH_2$ and $RCONHR'$, which are insoluble in water, are generally unaffected by 5 per cent hydrochloric acid but may dissolve in higher concentrations (10–20 per cent) of acid: this emphasizes the importance of employing the correct strength of acid in the solubility tests. Many disubstituted amides ($RCONR'R''$), which are of sufficiently high molecular weight to be water-insoluble, dissolve in 5 per cent hydrochloric acid.

It may be noted that some amines react with 5 per cent hydrochloric acid to form insoluble hydrochlorides: such compounds are best classified as soluble. Thus certain aromatic amines, such as 1-naphthylamine, form hydrochlorides which are sparingly soluble in dilute hydrochloric acid; the latter sometimes dissolve upon warming slightly and diluting with water. The appearance of the solid will usually show whether the arylamine has undergone a change: the solid should be separated and its melting point compared with that of the original compound. A test with ethanolic silver nitrate solution would indicate the formation of a hydrochloride.

Solubility in dilute sodium hydroxide solution and in dilute sodium bicarbonate solution. Carboxylic acids (RCOOH), sulphonic acids (RSO_3H), sulphinic acids (RSO_2H), phenols (ArOH), thiophenols (ArSH), mercaptans (RSH), imides (RCONHCOR), aryl sulphonamides ($ArSO_2NH_2$), arylsulphonyl derivatives of primary amines ($ArSO_2NHR$), oximes (RCH=NOH), primary and secondary nitro compounds (RCH=NOOH and RR'C=NOOH, *aci* forms), and some enols (*e.g.*, of 1,3-diketones RCH(OH)=CHCOR or β-keto esters RCH(OH)=CHCOOR') dissolve in dilute sodium hydroxide solution, *i.e.*, contain an acidic group of sufficient strength to react with the alkali. Carboxylic acids, sulphinic acids and sulphonic acids are soluble in dilute solutions of sodium bicarbonate: some negatively-substituted phenols (for example, picric acid, 2,4,6-tribromophenol and 2,4-dinitrophenol) are strongly acidic and also dissolve in sodium bicarbonate solution. Primary and secondary nitro compounds, imides, aryl sulphonamides and oximes are insoluble in sodium bicarbonate solution. Some of the sodium salts of highly substituted phenols are insoluble in sodium hydroxide solution but may dissolve upon dilution and warming with water.

Certain substituents (*e.g.*, the amino group) may markedly affect the solubility and other properties of the sulphonic acid or carboxylic acid. Thus such sulphonic acids as the aminobenzenesulphonic acids, pyridine- and quinoline-sulphonic acids exist in the form of **inner salts** or **dipolar ions** that result from the interaction of the basic amino group and the acidic sulphonic acid. Sulphanilic acid, for example, is more accurately represented by formula (I) than by formula (II):

$$^+H_3N\!-\!\!\langle\!\!\bigcirc\!\!\rangle\!-\!SO_3^-\ (I) \qquad H_2N\!-\!\!\langle\!\!\bigcirc\!\!\rangle\!-\!SO_3H\ (II)$$

These aminosulphonic acids possess the high melting points usually associated with salts and are sparingly soluble or insoluble in water. They all dissolve readily in dilute alkali but not in dilute acid, *i.e.*, they appear to exhibit the reactions of the sulphonic acid group but not of the amino group. The aliphatic aminocarboxylic acids, because of the presence of the strongly basic amino group, exist as dipolar ions:

$$\begin{array}{cc} NH_2 & NH_3^+ \\ | & | \\ RCHCOOH & RCHCOO^- \end{array}$$

they are soluble in water but not in ether, and dissolve in both dilute acid and dilute alkali but do not react with dilute sodium bicarbonate solution. The carboxyl derivatives of the arylamines (*e.g.*, *p*-aminobenzoic acid) are also amphoteric, but the diminution of the basic character of the amino group because of its attachment to the aryl group prevents the formation of inner salts to any degree.

The presence of an aryl group on the nitrogen atom diminishes the basicity to such an extent that these compounds are soluble even in sodium bicarbonate solution. This applies also to such compounds as $C_6H_5NHCH_2CO_2H$ and $C_6H_5N(CH_3)CHRCOOH$. If two aryl groups are attached to the nitrogen atom, the compound behaves simply as a strong acid, *e.g.*, $(C_6H_5)_2NCH_2COOH$.

Solubility in concentrated sulphuric acid. The paraffin hydrocarbons, cycloparaffins, the less readily sulphonated aromatic hydrocarbons (benzene, toluene, etc.) and their halogen derivatives, and the diaryl ethers are generally insoluble in concentrated sulphuric acid. Polyalkylbenzenes, which sulphonate easily, dissolve in the concentrated acid.

Concentrated sulphuric acid is used with neutral, water-insoluble compounds containing no elements other than carbon, hydrogen, and oxygen. It is a very effective proton donor and can protonate very weak bases, such as ethers. Also, because of the equilibrium

$$2H_2SO_4 \rightleftharpoons SO_3 + HSO_4^- + H_3O^+$$

the strong Lewis acid, SO_3, is present and can convert easily sulphonated aromatic hydrocarbons to the ionic sulphonic acids. Sulphuric acid has a high dielectric constant and so favours electrolytic dissociation of ionic products produced in its reaction with solutes.

Unsaturated hydrocarbons dissolve through the formation of soluble alkyl hydrogen sulphates:

$$RCH{=}CHR' + H_2SO_4 \rightarrow [RCH_2{-}\overset{+}{C}HR'] \xrightarrow{HSO_4^-} RCH_2{-}\underset{OSO_3H}{CHR'}$$

Polyalkylated aromatic hydrocarbons and alkyl phenyl ethers are sulphonated:

$$H_3C{-}\underset{CH_3}{\overset{CH_3}{C_6H_3}} + 2H_2SO_4 \rightarrow H_3C{-}\underset{CH_3}{\overset{CH_3}{C_6H_2}}{-}SO_3H + HSO_4^- + H_3O^+$$

Mesitylene

$$CH_3O{-}C_6H_5 + 2H_2SO_4 \rightarrow CH_3O{-}C_6H_4{-}SO_3H + HSO_4^- + H_3O^+$$

Anisole

The most important group of compounds which are soluble in concentrated sulphuric acid are those containing oxygen. The solubility of these compounds is due to the basic character of one or more of the oxygen atoms that are present in the molecules. Organic oxygen compounds exhibit the same wide variations in basicity that are found in nitrogen compounds. With diaryl ethers, the basicity of the oxygen is so much reduced by the two aryl groups that the oxygen is no longer able to ionize the sulphuric acid and in consequence they are insoluble in this reaction solvent. Some examples follow:

$$RCH_2OH + 2H_2SO_4 \rightarrow RCH_2OSO_3H + HSO_4^- + H_3O^+$$
$$RR'CHOH + 2H_2SO_4 \rightarrow RR'CHOSO_3H + HSO_4^- + H_3O^+$$
$$\begin{cases} (RCH_2)_3COH + H_2SO_4 \rightarrow (RCH_2)_3COH_2^+ + HSO_4^- \\ (RCH_2)_3COH_2^+ \rightarrow (RCH_2)_3C^+ + H_2O \\ (RCH_2)_3C^+ \rightarrow (RCH_2)_2C=CHR + H^+ \\ (RCH_2)_3C^+ + HSO_4^- \rightarrow (RCH_2)_3COSO_3H \end{cases}$$
$$R_2O + H_2SO_4 \rightarrow R_2OH^+ + HSO_4^-$$
$$(C_6H_5)_3COH + 2H_2SO_4 \rightarrow (C_6H_5)_3C^+ + 2HSO_4^- + H_3O^+$$
$$(C_6H_5)_2C=O + H_2SO_4 \rightarrow (C_6H_5)_2\overset{+}{C}OH + HSO_4^-$$
$$C_6H_5\overset{O}{\underset{\|}{C}}-OH + H_2SO_4 \rightarrow C_6H_5\overset{OH}{\underset{+}{\underset{|}{C}}}-OH + HSO_4^-$$

$$\underset{\text{Mesitoic acid}}{H_3C-\underset{CH_3}{\overset{CH_3}{\bigcirc}}-CO_2H} + 2H_2SO_4 \rightarrow$$

$$H_3C-\underset{CH_3}{\overset{CH_3}{\bigcirc}}-\overset{+}{C}=O + 2HSO_4^- + H_3O^+$$

The purpose of the reagent is merely to ascertain whether the substance is soluble in the concentrated acid or not. For this reason, the attendant disadvantages of the reagent—the production of more fundamental changes with certain oxygen-containing compounds than mere dissolution or oxonium salt formation—are of secondary importance provided careful distinction is made between the solubility of the original compound and the insolubility of the *products* of the reaction. Thus certain unsaturated hydrocarbons yield insoluble polymers, and benzyl alcohol affords an insoluble polybenzyl alcohol of the average composition

$$C_6H_5CH_2(C_6H_4CH_2)_9C_6H_4CH_2OH.$$

III, 3 The Solubility Groups

It has been found convenient to place organic compounds into seven solubility groups on the basis of:

(a) their solubility behaviour towards water, ether, 5 per cent aqueous sodium hydroxide solution, 5 per cent hydrochloric acid and cold concentrated sulphuric acid, and

(b) the elements, other than carbon and hydrogen, that they contain. The resulting groups are:

Group I. Compounds soluble in both water and ether.

Group II. Compounds soluble in water, but insoluble in ether.

Group III. Compounds insoluble in water, but soluble in dilute sodium hydroxide. This group may be further subdivided into **Group IIIA**—soluble in dilute sodium hydroxide and soluble in dilute 5 per cent sodium bicarbonate; and **Group IIIB**—soluble in dilute sodium hydroxide but insoluble in dilute sodium bicarbonate.

Group IV. Compounds insoluble in water, but soluble in dilute hydrochloric acid.

Group V. Hydrocarbons and compounds containing C, H and O that are not in Groups I–IV and are soluble in concentrated sulphuric acid.

Group VI. All compounds, not containing N or S, that are insoluble in concentrated sulphuric acid.

Group VII. Compounds that contain N or S which are not in Groups I–IV. Many of the compounds in this group are soluble in concentrated sulphuric acid.

It will be observed that halogen compounds are not listed separately, but appear in each of the seven groups in accordance with their solubility behaviour. Similarly, certain compounds containing N or S will fall in Groups I–IV (see preceding Section).

Table III, 3, 1 shows this grouping of organic compounds, together with the commoner classes of compounds that fall into the respective solubility groups.

NOTES ON TABLE III, 3, 1

Group I. This includes the lower members of the various homologous series (4–5 atoms in a normal chain) that contain oxygen and/or nitrogen in their structures: they are soluble in water because of their low carbon content. If the compound is soluble in both water and ether, it would also be soluble in other solvents so that further solubility tests are generally unnecessary: the test with sodium bicarbonate solution should, however, be performed (see Section **III,4**).

Group II. The classes 1 to 5 are usually soluble in dilute alkali and acid. Useful information may, however, be obtained by examining the

Table III, 3, 1. Division of Organic Compounds into Solubility Groups

GROUP I Soluble in Both Ether and Water	GROUP II Soluble in Water but Insoluble in Ether	GROUP III Soluble in 5% Sodium Hydroxide Solution	GROUP IV Soluble in 5% Hydrochloric Acid	GROUP V Not Containing N or S. Soluble only in Concentrated Sulphuric Acid	GROUP VI Not Containing N or S. Insoluble in Concentrated Sulphuric Acid	GROUP VII Containing N or S Compounds not in Groups I to IV
The lower members of the homologous series of: 1. Alcohols 2. Aldehydes 3. Ketones 4. Acids 5. Esters 6. Phenols 7. Anhydrides 8. Amines 9. Nitriles 10. Polyhydroxy phenols	1. Polybasic acids and hydroxy acids 2. Glycols, polyhydric alcohols, polyhydroxy aldehydes and ketones (sugars) 3. Some amides, amino acids, di- and poly-amino compounds, amino alcohols 4. Sulphonic acids 5. Sulphinic acids 6. Salts	1. Acids 2. Phenols 3. Imides 4. Some primary and secondary nitro compounds; oximes 5. Mercaptans and thiophenols 6. Sulphonic acids, sulphinic acids, aminosulphonic acids, and sulphonamides 7. Some diketones and β-keto esters	1. Primary amines 2. Secondary aliphatic and aryl-alkyl amines 3. Aliphatic and some aryl-alkyl tertiary amines 4. Hydrazines	1. Unsaturated hydrocarbons 2. Some polyalkylated aromatic hydrocarbons 3. Alcohols 4. Aldehydes 5. Ketones 6. Esters 7. Anhydrides 8. Ethers and acetals 9. Lactones 10. Acyl halides	1. Saturated aliphatic hydrocarbons 2. Cyclic paraffin hydrocarbons 3. Aromatic hydrocarbons 4. Halogen derivatives of 1, 2 and 3 5. Diaryl ethers	1. Nitro compounds (tertiary) 2. Amides; derivatives of aldehydes and ketones 3. Nitriles 4. Negatively substituted amines 5. Nitroso, azo, hydrazo, and other intermediate reduction products of nitro compounds 6. Sulphones, sulphonamides of secondary amines, sulphates and other sulphur compounds

behaviour of *Salts* to alkaline or acidic solvents. With a salt of a water-soluble base, the characteristic odour of an amine is usually apparent when it is treated with dilute alkali: likewise, the salt of a water-soluble, weak acid is decomposed by dilute hydrochloric acid or by concentrated sulphuric acid. The water-soluble salt of a water-insoluble acid or base will give a precipitate of either the free acid or the free base when treated with dilute acid or dilute alkali. The salts of sulphonic acids and of quaternary bases (R_4NOH) are unaffected by dilute sodium hydroxide or hydrochloric acid.

Group III. Carboxylic and sulphonic acids (also *sym*-tribromophenol, 2,4-dinitrophenol and picric acid) are also soluble in dilute sodium bicarbonate solution.

Group IV. The student should remember that the hydrochlorides of some bases are sparingly soluble in cold water and should therefore not be misled by an apparent insolubility of a compound (containing N) in dilute hydrochloric acid. The suspension in dilute hydrochloric acid should always be filtered and the filtrate made alkaline. A

Table III, 3, 2. **Outline of Solubility Classification Procedure**

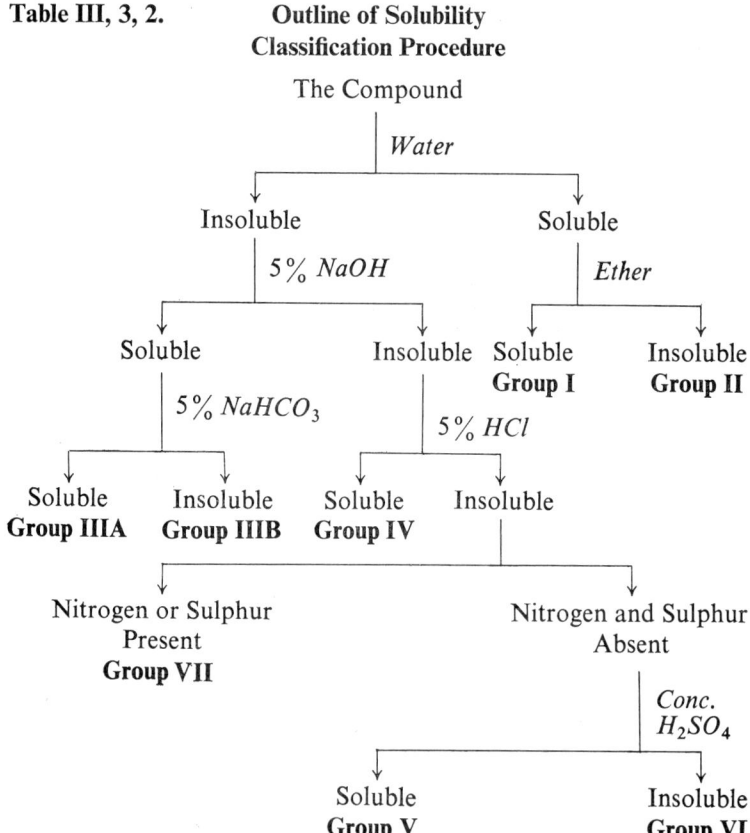

precipitate will indicate that the compound should be placed in Group IV: if no precipitate is formed, the compound is relegated to Group VII.

Group V. This group includes all the water-insoluble hydrocarbons and oxygen compounds that do not contain N or S and are soluble in cold concentrated sulphuric acid. Any changes—colour, excessive charring, evolution of gases or heat, polymerization and precipitation of an insoluble compound—attending the dissolution of the substance should be carefully noted.

Group VI. Concentrated sulphuric acid provides a simple test for the differentiation *inter alia* between (*a*) saturated paraffin and cyclic hydrocarbons and also simple aromatic hydrocarbons and (*b*) unsaturated hydrocarbons.

Group VII. This group comprises all compounds containing N or S which are insoluble in water and are 'indifferent' (*i.e.*, insoluble in dilute acid or alkali).

An outline of the solubility classification procedure is given in Table III, 3, 2, whilst the characteristic features of each of the solubility groups are summarized in Table III, 3, 3.

Table III, 3, 3.   Classification of Solubility Groups

GROUP	WATER	ETHER	NaOH	NaHCO$_3$	HCl	H$_2$SO$_4$
I	+ (1)	+				
II	+	−				
IIIA	−		+ (2)	+		
IIIB	−		+ (2)	−		
IV	−		−		+	
V (3)	−		−		−	+
VI (3)	−		−		−	−
VII (4)	−		−			

Notes

(1) + denotes soluble; − denotes insoluble.
(2) If a compound contains nitrogen its solubility in dilute hydrochloric acid should be tested also to ascertain whether it is amphoteric.
(3) These are neutral compounds in which nitrogen and sulphur are *absent*.
(4) These are neutral compounds in which nitrogen or sulphur is *present*.

III, 4   Determination of the Solubilities of Organic Compounds (*for Group Tests*)

All solubility determinations for Group tests are carried out at the laboratory temperature in small test-tubes (*e.g.*, 100 × 12 mm.) but of sufficient size to permit of vigorous shaking of the solvent and the solute. Shaking for not more than 1–2 minutes should suffice.

Amount of material required. It is convenient to employ an arbitrary ratio of 0·10 g. of solid or 0·20 ml. of liquid for 3·0 ml. of solvent. Weigh out 0·10 g. of the *finely-powdered* solid to the nearest 0·01 g.: after some experience, subsequent tests with the *same* compound may be estimated by eye. Measure out 0·20 ml. of the liquid either with a calibrated pipette dropper or a small graduated pipette. Use either a calibrated dropper or graduated pipette to deliver 3·0 ml. of solvent. Rinse the delivery pipette with alcohol, followed by ether each time that it is used.

Much time will be saved if each of the solvents (Water, Ether, 5 per cent Sodium Hydroxide, 5 per cent Sodium Bicarbonate and 5 per cent Hydrochloric Acid) is contained in a 30 or 60 ml. bottle fitted with a cork carrying a calibrated pipette dropper. The concentrated sulphuric acid should be kept in a glass-stoppered bottle and withdrawn with a dropper or pipette as required.

Attention is directed to the fact that if only minute amounts of material are available or if the substance is expensive, considerable economy may be effected by treating an aqueous solution or suspension with the necessary quantity of concentrated sodium hydroxide solution or concentrated hydrochloric acid. Thus if the compound is insoluble in water, 1·0 ml. of 20 per cent sodium hydroxide solution may be added to give 4 ml. of about 5 per cent sodium hydroxide solution: this will provide a fairly accurate measure of its solubility in this reaction solvent.

Solubility in water. Treat a 0·10 g. portion of the solid with successive 1·0 ml. portions of water, shaking vigorously after each addition, until 3·0 ml. have been added. If the compound does not dissolve completely in 3·0 ml. of water, it may be regarded as insoluble in water. When dealing with a liquid, add 0·20 ml. of the compound to 3·0 ml. of water and shake. In either case, test the contents of the small test-tube with litmus (or with Universal indicator) paper: it is best to remove a little of the solution or supernatant liquid with a pipette dropper.

If the solid appears to be insoluble in water at the laboratory temperature, it is sometimes advisable to warm the mixture gently. If solution is effected in this way, the liquid is cooled to room temperature and is shaken to prevent supersaturation; the addition of a small quantity of the solid to 'seed' the cooled solution often serves to prevent supersaturation.

Solubility in ether. Use 0·10 g. of solid or 0·20 ml. of a liquid in a dry test-tube and proceed exactly as in testing the solubility in water, but do not employ more than 3·0 ml. of solvent.

The detection of the boundary line is sometimes difficult when two colourless liquid phases are present. When a liquid unknown appears to have dissolved in the solvent, shake the test-tube vigorously; if two phases are present, the solution generally becomes cloudy.

Solubility in 5 per cent sodium hydroxide solution. Note whether there is any rise in temperature. If the compound appears insoluble, remove some of the supernatant liquid by means of a dropper to a semimicro test-tube (75 × 10 mm.), add 5 per cent hydrochloric acid dropwise until acid, and note whether any precipitate (or turbidity) is formed. The production of the latter will place the compound in Group III.

Heat should not be applied since it might cause hydrolysis to occur.

Solubility in 5 per cent bicarbonate solution. If the compound is soluble in 5 per cent sodium hydroxide solution, test its solubility in a 5 per cent solution of sodium bicarbonate. Observe whether it dissolves and particularly whether carbon dioxide is evolved either immediately (carboxylic acids, sulphonic, acids, negatively substituted phenols) or after a short time (some amino acids).

Solubility in 5 per cent hydrochloric acid. Add the acid to 0·10 g. of the solid or 0·20 ml. of the liquid in quantities of 1·0 ml. until 3·00 ml. have been introduced. Some organic bases (*e.g.*, 2-naphthylamine) form hydrochlorides that are soluble in water but are precipitated by an excess of acid: if solution occurs at any time, the unknown is assigned to Group IV. If the compound appears insoluble, remove some of the supernatant liquid by means of a pipette dropper to a semimicro test-tube (75 × 10 mm.), and add 5 per cent sodium hydroxide solution until basic and observe whether any precipitate is produced: the formation of a precipitate will place the compound in Group IV.

Heat should not be applied as it might cause hydrolysis to occur.

Solubility in concentrated sulphuric acid. Place 3·0 ml. of pure concentrated sulphuric acid in a dry test-tube and add 0·10 g. of a solid or 0·20 ml. of a liquid. Observe any change in colour, charring, evolution of gaseous products, polymerization accompanied by precipitation, etc.

Practice in solubility determinations. It is suggested that the student should carry out solubility determinations with a selection from the following compounds:

Hydrocarbons. Hexane: Toluene: Naphthalene: Cyclohexane: Amylene: Cyclohexene.

Halogen compounds. n-Butyl bromide: Chlorobenzene: Allyl bromide: Benzoyl chloride.

Elementary Practical Organic Chemistry

Alcohols. n-Butyl alcohol: n-Hexyl alcohol: *tert*-Butyl alcohol: Benzyl alcohol: Glycerol: Sucrose.
Aldehydes and ketones. n-Butyraldehyde: Acetone: n-Amyl methyl ketone: Benzaldehyde: Acetophenone: Benzophenone.
Ethers. Di-n-butyl ether: Anisole: Diethyl ether.
Esters. n-Butyl acetate: Ethyl acetate: Ethyl benzoate.
Acids. Acetic acid: n-Caproic acid: Benzoic acid: Phenylacetic acid: Succinic acid: Adipic acid: Anthranilic acid.
Phenols. Phenol: 2-Naphthol.
Anhydrides. Acetic anhydride: Benzoic anhydride.
Enols. Ethyl acetoacetate.
Nitro compounds. Nitromethane: Nitrobenzene: *m*-Dinitrobenzene.
Amides and imides. Acetamide: n-Caproamide: Acetanilide: Benzanilide: Phthalimide.
Amines. Aniline: Benzidine: 1-Naphthylamine: *p*-Nitroaniline: Dimethylaniline.
Nitriles. n-Butyronitrile: Benzyl cyanide.
Salts. Sodium benzoate: Sodium benzenesulphonate: Aniline hydrochloride: Methylamine hydrochloride.

Record your results in tabular form thus:

COMPOUND	SOLUBILITY IN						SOLUBILITY GROUP
	WATER	ETHER	5% NaOH	5% NaHCO$_3$	5% HCl	CONC. H$_2$SO$_4$	
Phloroglucinol	+	+					I
Benzoic acid	−		+	+			IIIA
Aniline	−		−		+		IV
Acetophenone	−		−		−	+	V
n-Hexane	−		−		−	−	VI
Etc.							

CHAPTER IV

Reactions and Characterization of Selected Classes of Organic Compounds

IV, 1. Introduction. There can be little doubt that a knowledge of the reactions and of the methods of characterization of the principal classes of organic compounds provides a sound foundation for the study of qualitative organic analysis. It is hoped that students, under the guidance of the teacher, will be able to carry out some of the reactions and prepare a few selected derivatives of typical members of different classes of organic compounds: the experience and knowledge thus acquired will be of great value, and the time spent on these preliminary studies will be amply repaid by their subsequent progress in the qualitative analysis of simple organic substances and of organic mixtures.

A reasonable choice of derivatives (together with experimental details for their preparation) for the various classes of organic compounds is given in this Chapter. The detailed experimental procedures will be employed frequently in routine qualitative analysis in testing for functional groups and for the preparation of derivatives. For convenience, the tables of derivatives, arranged according to classes, are collected in Chapter IX.

IV, 2 Saturated Aliphatic Hydrocarbons (Alkanes)

Use a sample of *n*-heptane, b.p. 98–99°. Carry out the following tests.

(i) **Action of bromine water.** Place 1 ml. of heptane in each of two test-tubes, and add 3–4 ml. of bromine water. Shake the tubes well, and keep one of them in your locker and out of the light. Expose the other tube to bright sunlight {or hold it close to a bright (150–200 watts) electric bulb}. Compare the tubes after about 15 minutes.

(ii) **Action of bromine dissolved in a non-aqueous solvent.** Repeat experiment (i), but add 0·5 ml. of a solution of bromine in carbon tetrachloride (1) to each of the tubes. After 10–15 minutes (or as soon as a change has occurred), examine each of the tubes. Blow across the mouth of the tube in which a change has taken place and test the vapour with blue litmus paper.

(iii) **Action of potassium permanganate solution.** Treat 1 ml. of the hydrocarbon with 2 ml. of 0·5 per cent potassium permanganate solution and 1 ml. of dilute sulphuric acid. Shake gently for a short time, and observe if the permanganate solution is decolorized.

(iv) **Action of concentrated sulphuric acid.** Add 1 ml. of the hydrocarbon to 2 ml. of concentrated sulphuric acid and shake gently. Observe whether the acid layer is affected in any way.

(v) **Action of concentrated nitric acid.** Add 1 ml. of *n*-heptane *cautiously* to 2 ml. of concentrated nitric acid. Note whether any reaction occurs.

Note
(1) A solution prepared by dissolving 2 g. of bromine in 100 g. of carbon tetrachloride is satisfactory. Carbon tetrachloride is employed because it is an excellent solvent for bromine as well as for hydrocarbons; it possesses the additional advantage of low solubility for hydrogen bromide, the evolution of which renders possible the distinction between decolorization of bromine due to substitution or due to addition.

CHARACTERIZATION OF SATURATED ALIPHATIC HYDROCARBONS

Because of the chemical inertness of the paraffin hydrocarbons and of the closely related cycloparaffins, no satisfactory crystalline derivatives can be prepared. Reliance is therefore placed upon the physical properties (boiling point, density, and refractive index) of the redistilled samples. These are collected together in Table IX, 2 (Chapter IX).

IV, 3 Olefinic Hydrocarbons (Alkenes)

Carry out the following tests (compare Section **IV**,2) with redistilled cyclohexene.*

(i) **Action of bromine water.** Shake 1 ml. of cyclohexene with 2 ml. of bromine water, and note the result.

(ii) **Action of bromine in carbon tetrachloride solution.** To 1 ml. of cyclohexene add 1–2 ml. of the reagent. Observe that no hydrogen bromide is evolved.

* For preparation, see the author's *Elementary Practical Organic Chemistry, Part I, Small Scale Preparations*, Section **III**,7 (Second Edition, 1966).

The addition may be represented as:

$$>C=C< + Br_2 \rightarrow \underset{}{\overset{Br\ Br}{>C-C<}}$$

In a polar solvent such as water or acetic acid, the reaction has been shown to proceed as follows. The first step is the transfer of a bromine cation to the olefine with the formation of a cyclic bromonium ion. The second step is the reaction of the bromonium ion with a bromide ion to give the product. Since the cyclic bromonium ion opens with inversion of configuration, the over-all steric course of the reaction is the addition of two bromine atoms to opposite sides of the plane of the double bond. This is termed *trans* addition of bromine to the double bond.

$$Br-Br + >C=C< \rightarrow Br^- + >\overset{+}{\underset{Br}{C-C}}<$$

$$Br^- + >\overset{+Br}{C-C}< \rightarrow >\underset{Br}{\overset{Br}{C-C}}<$$

(iii) **Action of potassium permanganate solution.** Add 1 ml. of cyclohexene to 2 ml. of 0·5 per cent potassium permanganate solution and 1 ml. of dilute sulphuric acid, and shake. If the reagent is decolorized, add further small quantities.

The reaction may be represented as:

$$>C=C< \xrightarrow[H_2O]{(O)} >\underset{HO\ OH}{C-C}< \xrightarrow{\text{Further oxidation}} >C=O + O=C<$$

In cold dilute aqueous solution, the main product of the action of potassium permanganate on an alkene is the glycol: with excess of the reagent and heating of the reaction mixture, further oxidation occurs and cleavage of the carbon chain takes place.

(iv) **Action of concentrated sulphuric acid.** Add cautiously 1 ml. of cyclohexene to 2 ml. of concentrated sulphuric acid. Shake very gently. Note whether any change in colour and in temperature takes place.

Cool 1 ml. of cyclohexene in ice and add 1 ml. of cold, dilute sulphuric acid (2 acid:1 water), and shake gently until the mixture is homogeneous. Dilute with 2 ml. of water; if an upper layer of the alcohol does not separate immediately, introduce a little sodium chloride into the mixture in order to decrease the solubility of the alcohol. Observe the odour. The unsaturated hydrocarbon is thus largely reconverted into the alcohol from which it may be prepared.

The reaction may be written:

$$\mathord{>}C\mathord{=}C\mathord{<} \xrightarrow{H_2SO_4} \mathord{>}\underset{H}{C}\mathord{-}\underset{OSO_3H}{C}\mathord{<} \xrightarrow{H_2O} \mathord{>}\underset{H}{C}\mathord{-}\underset{OH}{C}\mathord{<}$$

CHARACTERIZATION OF UNSATURATED ALIPHATIC HYDROCARBONS

Unlike the saturated hydrocarbons, unsaturated aliphatic hydrocarbons are soluble in concentrated sulphuric acid and exhibit characteristic reactions with dilute potassium permanganate solution and with bromine. Their characterization is generally based upon a determination of their physical properties (boiling point, density and refractive index). The physical properties of a number of selected unsaturated hydrocarbons are collected in Table IX, 3 (Chapter IX). A few crystalline derivatives are known and these are described below.

CRYSTALLINE DERIVATIVES OF ALKENES

1. **Adducts with 2,4-dinitrophenylsulphenyl chloride** (abbreviated to DPSC). 2,4-Dinitrophenylsulphenyl chloride, $(NO_2)_2C_6H_3S-Cl$, reacts in polar solvents (acetone, ethylene dichloride, acetic acid and dimethylformamide) with alkenes to yield crystalline adducts, for example, β-chloroalkyl-2,4-dinitrophenyl sulphides:

$$RCH{=}CH_2 + O_2N{-}\underset{}{\bigcirc}{-}SCl \;\;{\to}\;\; R\underset{Cl}{C}H{-}CH_2{-}S{-}\underset{}{\bigcirc}{-}NO_2$$

(with NO_2 / O_2N substituents on the rings)

For olefines, addition of the reagent is stereospecific (*trans* addition) and one can thus differentiate between *cis* and *trans* isomers: thus *cis*-butene and *trans*-butene give products of m.p. 129° and 77° respectively. The reagent has also been used for the characterization of alkylbenzenes but the procedure is not as convenient as that involving conversion into sulphonamides (Section **IV,4,***1*).

Heat a solution of 0·2 g. of the reagent and 0·2–0·3 g. of the olefine in glacial acetic acid on the steam bath for 15 minutes or until the potassium iodide test shows that the reaction is complete. Add a drop of the reaction solution to a drop of potassium iodide solution on a spot plate; the presence of unreacted reagent is revealed by the liberation of iodine:

$$2RSCl + 2I^- \rightarrow RSSR + I_2 + 2Cl^-$$

Cool the mixture in ice. If a solid separates, filter it off; if not, pour the reaction mixture on to 5–10 g. of crushed ice. Recrystallize the resulting solid or oil from ethanol.

The melting points of the adducts of some typical olefinic compounds are: 2-pentene, 117°; 1-hexene, 62°; cyclohexene, 117°; 1-methylcyclohexene, 139°; D- or L-limonene, 195°; styrene, 143°; 1,4-dihydronaphthalene, 156°.

Preparation of the reagent. As the reagent is not readily available commercially, some brief details for its preparation may be useful. Prepare bis(2,4-dinitrodiphenyl) disulphide by reaction of 2,4-dinitrochlorobenzene with sodium disulphide, following the procedure described for di-*o*-nitrophenyl disulphide in *Organic Syntheses*, Collective Volume I, p. 220 (1941). Now chlorinate the disulphide with sulphuryl chloride in the presence of pyridine. Suspend 25 g. of the pulverized disulphide (dried for 12 hours at 80–90°) in 150 ml. of carbon tetrachloride in a 250 ml. flask fitted with a reflux condenser. Add 10 ml. of sulphuryl chloride, followed by 1 ml. of pyridine. Reflux the mixture on a steam bath for 1 hour, and add a further 12·5 ml. of sulphuryl chloride in 4 portions (about every 30 minutes) and also 1·5 ml. more of pyridine during the course of the reaction. Continue to reflux for 3–5 hours; the reaction is complete when all the insoluble disulphide has disappeared. Treat the hot reaction mixture with 1 g. of decolorizing carbon and filter through 'filter aid'. Concentrate the filtrate and collect the product which crystallizes on cooling. The yield of yellow crystalline DPSC, m.p. 97–98°, is 24 g.

$$ArSSAr + Cl_2 \rightarrow 2RSCl \text{ where } Ar = 2,4\text{-dinitrophenyl}$$

The reagent keeps for several months. It is known to be explosive when heated to elevated temperatures, hence particular care must be taken to avoid indiscriminate heating of this sulphenyl chloride above 90–100°.

CRYSTALLINE DERIVATIVES OF ALKYNES

1. **Addition products with 2,4-dinitrophenylsulphenyl chloride.** The reagent reacts with symmetrical alkynes as follows:

$$RC{\equiv}CR + ArSCl \rightarrow RC(Cl){=}CR(SAr)$$

where Ar = 2,4-dinitrophenyl.

Experimental details for 2-butyne follow. Dissolve 1·60 g. of the reagent in 15 ml. of ethylene dichloride at 0°C and add 3·0 ml. of ice-cold 2-butyne. Keep at 0° for 2 hours, remove the solvent by aspiration, and keep the clear yellow oil in a refrigerator until crystallization occurs. Dissolve the crystals in 25 ml. of absolute ethanol, decolorize with charcoal, and filter. Concentrate the filtrate, collect the crystals which separate, and recrystallize from ethanol.

The melting points of the adducts of some typical alkynes are: 2-butyne, 75°; 3-hexyne, 65°; diphenylacetylene, 208°.

2. **Mercurides of monosubstituted alkynes (mercuric alkynides).** Monosubstituted alkynes form mercurides which are suitable for identification purposes:

$$2R-C\equiv C-H + K_2[HgI_4] + 2KOH \rightarrow$$
$$(R-C\equiv C)_2Hg + 4KI + 2H_2O$$

The procedure consists in adding a dilute solution of the alkyne in ethanol to an excess of an alkaline mercuric iodide reagent: a white or greyish-white precipitate forms immediately, which is filtered off, washed with dilute ethanol and recrystallized. The yield of mercuride is 85–95 per cent.

The mercuric iodide reagent is *prepared* by dissolving 6·6 g. of mercuric chloride (POISONOUS) in a solution of 16·3 g. of potassium iodide in 16·3 ml. of water and adding 12·5 ml. of 10 per cent sodium hydroxide solution.

Into a cooled dilute solution of 2 equivalents of alkaline mercuric iodide reagent, drop slowly, with mechanical stirring, a solution of 1 equivalent of the monosubstituted alkyne in 20 volumes of 95 per cent ethanol. A white crystalline precipitate separates at once. Stir for 2–3 minutes, filter rapidly with suction, and wash with 50 per cent ethanol. Recrystallize from ethanol or benzene.

The melting points of the 'mercurides' of some typical alkynes are: 1-propyne, 203°; 1-butyne, 162°; 1-pentyne, 118°; 1-hexyne, 99°; 1-heptyne, 61°; 1-decyne, 83°; phenylacetylene, 125°.

IV, 4 Aromatic Hydrocarbons (Arenes)

Unlike aliphatic hydrocarbons, aromatic hydrocarbons can be sulphonated, chlorosulphonated, carboxybenzoylated and nitrated. They also form characteristic addition compounds with 2,4,7-trinitro-9-fluorenone, styphnic acid and 1,3,5-trinitrobenzene: these molecular compounds are now usually regarded as charge-transfer complexes. Polynuclear aromatic hydrocarbons, and many of their derivatives, yield solid addition compounds with picric acid. Picrates vary considerably in their stability; those of the alkylated benzenes are particularly unstable. Many of the reactions of aromatic hydrocarbons will be evident from the following discussion of crystalline derivatives suitable for their characterization.

1. Sulphonamides. Aromatic hydrocarbons react with chlorosulphonic acid to yield the corresponding sulphonyl chlorides (the process is known as *chlorosulphonation*). These do not usually crystallize well and are therefore converted into the sulphonamides by treatment with concentrated ammonia solution or with solid ammonium carbonate.

$$ArH + 2HOSO_2Cl \rightarrow ArSO_2Cl + H_2SO_4 + HCl$$
$$ArSO_2Cl + (NH_4)_2CO_3 \rightarrow ArSO_2NH_2 + NH_4Cl + CO_2 + H_2O$$

Dissolve 1·0 g. of the compound in 5 ml. of dry ($CaCl_2$) chloroform in a dry test-tube, cool it in a beaker of ice, and add 3–5 ml. of chlorosulphonic acid dropwise. When the evolution of hydrogen chloride has subsided, remove the test-tube from the ice bath and allow to stand at room temperature for 20–30 minutes; then pour on to crushed ice (30 g.). Separate the chloroform layer, wash it with water, dry ($CaCl_2$), and evaporate the solvent.

Boil the arylsulphonyl chloride (0·5 g.) with 5 ml. of aqueous ammonia (sp. gr. 0·88) for 10 minutes (FUME CUPBOARD or HOOD). Cool the reaction mixture and dilute it with 10 ml. of water. Filter off the sulphonamide, wash it with water, and recrystallize from dilute ethanol.

Alternatively, heat a mixture of 0·5 g. of the arylsulphonyl chloride with 2·8 g. of dry powdered ammonium carbonate at 100° during 30 minutes. Wash the residue with several portions (10 ml.) of cold water, filter and recrystallize from dilute ethanol.

The melting points of the sulphonamides of some typical hydrocarbons are as follows: benzene, 153°; toluene, 137°; ethylbenzene, 109°; *o*-xylene, 144°; *m*-xylene, 137°; *p*-xylene, 147°; cumene, 146°; mesitylene, 142°; pseudocumene, 181°; durene, 155°; isodurene, 142°.

2. o-Aroylbenzoic acids. Aromatic hydrocarbons react with phthalic anhydride in the presence of anhydrous aluminium chloride producing aroylbenzoic acids in good yields:

$$\text{phthalic anhydride} + ArH \xrightarrow{AlCl_3} \text{o-aroylbenzoic acid (COAr, COOH)}$$

The process is termed *carboxybenzoylation*.

Place a mixture of 1·0 g. of the hydrocarbon, 10 ml. of dry methylene chloride or ethylene dichloride, 2·5 g. of powdered anhydrous aluminium chloride and 1·2 g. of pure phthalic anhydride in a 25–50 ml. round-bottomed flask fitted with a reflux condenser (5" jacket). Heat on a water bath for 30 minutes (or until no more hydrogen chloride fumes are evolved). Cool in ice and add 10 ml. of concentrated hydrochloric acid cautiously and with constant shaking. When the reaction has subsided, add 20 ml. of water and shake vigorously. (All the solid material should pass into solution.) Transfer the two-phase system to a separatory funnel, add 25 ml. of ether, and shake. Discard the lower aqueous phase. Wash the ethereal layer with 25 ml. of 2·5M hydrochloric acid to ensure removal of any aluminium salts present. Shake the ethereal solution cautiously with 25 ml. of M sodium carbonate solution, and run the aqueous phase slowly into 30 ml. of M hydrochloric acid. Collect the aroylbenzoic acid by suction filtration, wash it with 25–50 ml. of water, and recrystallize it from dilute ethanol or from acetic acid. The derivatives prepared from benzene and toluene crystallize with water of crystallization; the latter is removed by drying at 100°.

3. **Nitro derivatives.** No general experimental details for the preparation of nitro derivatives can be given, as the ease of nitration and the product formed frequently depend upon the exact experimental conditions. Moreover, some organic compounds react violently so that nitrations should always be conducted on a very small scale. The derivatives already described are usually more satisfactory.

Three typical nitrations will, however, be described in order to illustrate the results which may be obtained.

Benzene. Add 0·5 ml. of benzene slowly and with shaking and cooling to a mixture of 4 ml. each of concentrated sulphuric and nitric acids. Heat the mixture carefully on a water bath until it just boils, cool and pour into excess of cold water. Filter off the precipitate, wash it free from acid and recrystallize it from dilute ethanol. *m*-Dinitrobenzene, m.p. 90°, is formed.

Toluene. Proceed as for *Benzene* but use 0·5 ml. of toluene and a mixture of 3 ml. of concentrated sulphuric acid and 2 ml. of fuming nitric acid. Warm the mixture on a water bath for 5–10 minutes, cool, and pour into 20 ml. of ice water. Recrystallize the product from dilute ethanol. 2,4-Dinitrotoluene, m.p. 71°, is obtained.

Biphenyl. Reflux a mixture of 1·0 g. of biphenyl, 2 ml. of glacial acetic acid and 0·5 ml. of fuming nitric acid for 10 minutes. Pour into 20 ml.

of cold water, filter off the precipitate, wash it with cold water until free from acid, and recrystallize from ethanol. The product is 4-nitrobiphenyl, m.p. 114°.

4. Oxidation of a side chain by alkaline permanganate. Aromatic hydrocarbons containing side chains may be oxidized to the corresponding acids: the results are generally satisfactory for compounds with one side chain (*e.g.*, toluene or ethylbenzene → benzoic acid; nitrotoluene → nitrobenzoic acid) or with two side chains (*e.g.*, *o*-xylene → phthalic acid).

Suspend in a round-bottomed flask 1·0 g. of the substance in 75–80 ml. of boiling water to which about 1·5 g. of sodium carbonate crystals has been added, and introduce slowly 4 g. of finely-powdered potassium permanganate. Heat under reflux until the purple colour of the permanganate has disappeared (1–4 hours). Allow the mixture to cool and carefully acidify with dilute sulphuric acid. Heat the mixture under reflux for a further 30 minutes and then cool. Remove any excess of manganese dioxide by the addition of a little sodium bisulphite. Filter off the precipitated acid and recrystallize it from a suitable solvent (*e.g.*, benzene, ethanol, dilute ethanol or water). If the acid does not separate from the solution, extract it with ether, benzene or carbon tetrachloride.

5. Addition compounds with 2,4,7-trinitro-9-fluorenone (abbreviated to T.N.F.). Aromatic hydrocarbons (and also some polynuclear

(I)

substituted aromatic compounds) react with 2,4,7-trinitro-9-fluorenone (I) to yield crystalline 1,1-adducts.

Dissolve equimolecular proportions of pure T.N.F. and the hydrocarbon separately in absolute ethanol or ethanol-benzene or glacial acetic acid and mix the two hot nearly saturated solutions. Heat for 1 minute and cool. Recrystallize from acetic acid, absolute ethanol, ethanol-benzene or benzene.

The melting points of some typical crystalline adducts are: naphthalene, 153°; 1-methylnaphthalene, 165°; 2-methylnaphthalene, 127°; biphenyl, 132°; anthracene, 194°; phenanthrene, 196°; fluorene,

179°; chrysene, 248°; pyrene, 242°; acenaphthene, 175°; carbazole, 173°; 1-naphthol, 196°; 2-naphthol, 176°.

6. Picrates. Many aromatic hydrocarbons (and other classes of organic compounds) form molecular compounds with picric acid, for example, naphthalene picrate $C_{10}H_8 \cdot C_6H_2(NO_2)_3OH$. Some picrates, *e.g.*, anthracene picrate, are so unstable as to be decomposed by many, particularly hydroxylic, solvents; they therefore cannot be easily recrystallized but may be washed with a little ether and dried on a porous tile. Their preparation may often be accomplished in such non-hydroxylic solvents as chloroform, benzene or ether. The picrates of hydrocarbons can be readily separated into their constituents by warming with dilute ammonia solution and filtering (if the hydrocarbon is a solid) through a moist filter paper. The filtrate contains the picric acid as the ammonium salt, and the hydrocarbon is left on the filter paper.

Picrates are usually prepared by mixing hot solutions of equivalent quantities of the two components in the minimum volume of rectified spirit or benzene and allowing to cool; the derivative separates in a crystalline condition. It is filtered off, washed with a little ether, and pressed on a porous tile. If the picrate is stable, it is recrystallized from ethanol, ethyl acetate, benzene or ether. Do not mistake the recrystallized reagent (m.p. 122°) for a picrate.

The following are typical experimental details for the preparation of naphthalene picrate. Dissolve 0·1 g. of naphthalene and 0·2 g. of picric acid separately in the minimum volume of hot rectified spirit (about 2 ml.), mix the solutions and allow to cool. Filter and wash with 2 ml. of ethanol. Recrystallize from hot ethanol, ethyl acetate or ether.

7. Styphnates. Aromatic hydrocarbons (and also some amines and heterocyclic bases) form 1:1-addition products with styphnic acid (2,4,6-trinitroresorcinol),

$$O_2N-C_6H(NO_2)_2(OH)_2$$

These derivatives do not crystallize quite so well as the corresponding picrates, but are frequently of great value. Benzene and its simple homologues do not give stable derivatives.

Dissolve equimolecular amounts of the hydrocarbon and styphnic acid in the minimum volume of hot acetic acid and allow to cool. Filter off the crystalline derivative which separates, wash it with a little acetic acid and dry in the air. Determine the m.p. Recrystallize from acetic acid and again determine the m.p.

Benzene must be employed as the solvent for anthracene styphnate since most other solvents lead to dissociation.

8. Addition compounds with 1,3,5-trinitrobenzene

$$\underset{\underset{NO_2}{|}}{\underset{|}{O_2N-\bigcirc-NO_2}}$$

This reagent affords compounds (1:1) with aromatic hydrocarbons and other classes of organic compounds (heterocyclic compounds, aromatic ethers, etc.).

Dissolve equimolecular quantities of the hydrocarbon and 1,3,5-trinitrobenzene in hot ethanol, benzene or glacial acetic acid, and allow to cool. Filter off the solid which separates and recrystallize it from one of these solvents.

Data for a number of typical aromatic hydrocarbons are collected in Table IX, 4 (Chapter IX).

IV, 5 Aliphatic Alcohols

Carry out the following simple experiments; these have been selected to illustrate some of the general properties of alcohols.

(i) **Miscibility with water.** Measure out 3·1 ml. (2·5 g.) of *n*-butyl alcohol into a dry 100 ml. conical or flat-bottomed flask provided with a well-fitting stopper. From a burette add distilled water to the alcohol, a few drops at a time and shake vigorously after each addition, until a slight but permanent turbidity is produced. Note the volume of water added and calculate the solubility of water in *n*-butyl alcohol at the temperature of the laboratory. Continue the addition of water, 2–3 ml. at a time and with vigorous shaking, until the contents of the flask are just homogeneous: near the point of homogeneity the additions should be reduced to portions of 1 ml. Note the *total* volume of water which has been added from the burette, and calculate the solubility of *n*-butanol in water at the temperature of the laboratory.

The student will doubtless be aware of the fact that methyl, ethyl, *n*-propyl and isopropyl alcohols are completely miscible with water. The solubilities of the higher alcohols decrease progressively as the carbon content increases. The solubilities of all types of alcohols with five carbon atoms or more are quite small. For the isomeric butyl alcohols the solubilities (g. per 100 g. of water at 20°) are: *n*-butyl, 8; isobutyl, 23; *sec*-butyl, 13; *tert*-butyl, completely miscible.

Divide the saturated solution of *n*-butyl alcohol in water into three approximately equal parts. Treat these respectively with about 2·5 g. of sodium chloride, potassium carbonate and sodium hydroxide, and shake each until the solids have dissolved. Observe the effect of these compounds upon the solubility of *n*-butanol in water. These results illustrate the phenomenon of **salting out** of organic compounds, *i.e.*, the decrease of solubility of organic compounds in water when the solution is saturated with an inorganic compound. The alcohol layer which separates is actually a saturated solution of water in *n*-butyl alcohol.

(ii) **Drying of alcohols.** Place 2 ml. of methyl alcohol, *n*-butyl alcohol and cyclohexanol in three separate test-tubes, and add about 0·5 g. of anhydrous calcium chloride to each. Shake and observe the result (evolution of heat and chemical reaction). Stopper the tubes and leave overnight. Do your results explain why anhydrous calcium chloride cannot be employed for drying alcohols?

(iii) **Reaction with sodium.** Treat 2 ml. of dry *n*-butyl alcohol with a few small thin slices of dry, freshly-cut sodium (handle with tongs or with a penknife). Observe the result. Cool the solution when all the sodium has reacted, and add 2–3 ml. of dry diethyl ether. What is the precipitate?

Apply the test to the following alcohols: absolute methanol, absolute ethanol, *sec*-butyl alcohol, *tert*-butyl alcohol and cyclohexanol. Use dry test-tubes (75 × 10 mm.) and 1·0 ml. of each of the alcohols. Observe the rate of reaction in each case and arrange the alcohols in the order of decreasing reactivity towards sodium.

The reaction with sodium is by no means an infallible practical test for alcohols since, strictly speaking, it is applicable only to pure anhydrous liquids. Traces of water, present as impurities, would give an initial evolution of hydrogen, but reaction would stop after a time if an alcohol were absent. Furthermore thiols (RSH), compounds containing a methylene group adjacent to one or two activating groups, certain esters and methyl ketones evolve hydrogen when treated with sodium. It may, however, be assumed that if no hydrogen is evolved in the test, the substance is not an alcohol.

(iv) **Reaction with acetyl chloride.** Treat 1 ml. of the dry alcohols enumerated in (iii) cautiously with 0·5–0·7 ml. of acetyl chloride. Observe the reaction which occurs. After 2–3 minutes, pour the contents of the various test-tubes into 3 ml. portions of water, neutralize the aqueous layer with solid sodium bicarbonate, and examine the residual liquids for odour and density (relative to water).

(v) **Oxidation with 'chromic acid'.** A primary alcohol is oxidized by 'chromic acid' to the corresponding aldehyde whilst a secondary alcohol yields a ketone: tertiary alcohols are generally unaffected or are decomposed into non-ketonic products. Oxidation therefore provides a method for distinguishing between primary, secondary and tertiary alcohols.

$$RCH_2OH \xrightarrow{[O]} RCHO$$
$$RR'CHOH \xrightarrow{[O]} RR'CO$$

To an ice-cold mixture of 1·0 ml. of concentrated sulphuric acid and 5 ml. of saturated aqueous potassium dichromate solution, add 2 ml. of the alcohol or its concentrated aqueous solution. If the alcohol is not miscible with the reagent, shake the reaction mixture vigorously. After 5 minutes, dilute with an equal volume of water, distil and collect the first few ml. of the aqueous distillate in a test-tube cooled in ice. (Aldehydes and ketones are volatile in steam.) Test a portion of the distillate for a carbonyl compound with 2,4-dinitrophenylhydrazine reagent (Section **IV,18,***1*). If a solid derivative is obtained, indicating that the compound was a primary or secondary alcohol, test a further portion with dimedone reagent (Section **IV,15,***2*) to distinguish between the two possibilities. The derivative may be recrystallized; the m.p. may give a preliminary indication of the identity of the alcohol.

(vi) **Differentiation between primary, secondary and tertiary alcohols (Lucas' test).** The test depends upon the different rates of formation of the alkyl chlorides upon treatment with a hydrochloric acid-zinc chloride reagent* (containing 1 mole of acid to 1 mole of anhydrous zinc chloride) and with hydrochloric acid. It applies only to aliphatic and cycloaliphatic alcohols.

To 1 ml. of the alcohol in a small test-tube, add quickly 6 ml. of Lucas' reagent at 26–27°, close the tube with a cork, shake, and allow to stand. Observe the mixture during 5 minutes. The following results may be obtained:

(*a*) Primary alcohols, lower than hexyl, dissolve; there may be some darkening, but the solution remains clear.

---

* **Lucas' reagent is prepared** by dissolving 68 g. (0·5 mole) of anhydrous zinc chloride (fused sticks, powder, etc.) in 52·5 g. (0·5 mole) of concentrated hydrochloric acid with cooling to avoid loss of hydrogen chloride.

These alcohols are stronger bases than the anions of strong acids (here Cl⁻), hence they may dissolve in the strong acid to form oxonium salts:

$$ROH + H_3O^+ \rightarrow [ROH_2]^+ + H_2O$$

(*b*) Primary alcohols, hexyl and higher, do not dissolve appreciably; the aqueous phase remains clear.

(*c*) Secondary alcohols: the clear solution becomes cloudy owing to the separation of finely-divided drops of the chloride.* A distinct upper layer is visible *after one hour* except for isopropyl alcohol (probably because of the volatility of the chloride).

(*d*) Tertiary alcohols: two phases separate *almost immediately* owing to the formation of the tertiary chloride.

If a turbid solution is obtained, suggesting the presence of a secondary alcohol but not excluding a tertiary alcohol, a further test with concentrated hydrochloric acid must be made. Mix 1 ml. of the alcohol with 6 ml. of concentrated hydrochloric acid, and observe the result:

(*e*) Tertiary alcohols: immediate reaction to form the insoluble chloride which rises to the surface in a few minutes.

(*f*) Secondary alcohols: the solution remains clear.

Carry out the Lucas test with isopropyl alcohol, *n*-butyl alcohol, *sec*-butyl alcohol, cyclohexanol and *tert*-butyl alcohol. Obtain an 'unknown' alcohol from the instructor for test.

(vii) **Rapid method for distinguishing tertiary alcohols from primary and secondary alcohols (chromic anhydride test).** A solution of chromic anhydride in dilute sulphuric acid oxidizes primary and also secondary alcohols almost instantaneously: tertiary alcohols do not react visibly within 2 minutes.

$$3RCH_2OH + 4CrO_3 + 6H_2SO_4 \rightarrow 3RCOOH + 2Cr_2(SO_4)_3 + 9H_2O$$
$$3RR'CHOH + 2CrO_3 + 3H_2SO_4 \rightarrow 3RR'CO + Cr_2(SO_4)_3 + 6H_2O$$

This forms the basis of the test described below.

Prepare the **chromic anhydride reagent** by dissolving 25 g. of chromic anhydride in 25 ml. of concentrated sulphuric acid and pouring slowly and with constant stirring into 75 ml. of distilled water. Cool the deep orange-red solution to room temperature before use.

To 1·0 ml. of A.R. acetone in a small test-tube, add one drop of the liquid alcohol or about 10 mg. of a solid alcohol. Then add 1 drop of the reagent with shaking: note the result *within 2 seconds*. Primary or

---

* Allyl alcohol behaves like a secondary alcohol and reacts within 7 minutes.

secondary alcohols react within 2 seconds to give a precipitate that causes the test solution to become opaque and acquire a greenish (or greenish-blue) tint. Tertiary alcohols give no visible reaction and the solution remains orange in colour. Disregard any changes after 2 seconds.

Positive tests are given by primary and secondary alcohols without restriction of molecular weight. Aldehydes will, of course, react positively and enols may give a positive test. Phenols give dark test solutions.

Crystalline Derivatives of Aliphatic Alcohols

1. **3,5-Dinitrobenzoates.** 3,5-Dinitrobenzoyl chloride reacts with alcohols to form solid esters which possess sharp melting points and are therefore admirably suited for purposes of characterization:

$$O_2N\text{-}C_6H_3(NO_2)\text{-}COCl + HOR \rightarrow O_2N\text{-}C_6H_3(NO_2)\text{-}COOR + HCl$$

The acid chloride is available commercially, but it is more economical to prepare it from the acid as and when required. Furthermore, 3,5-dinitrobenzoyl chloride tends to undergo hydrolysis if kept for long periods, particularly if the stock bottle is frequently opened. The substance may, however, be stored under sodium-dry light petroleum.

Method 1. Mix 1·0 g. of 3,5-dinitrobenzoic acid with 4 ml. of thionyl chloride in a dry 25 ml. conical flask; fit a reflux condenser, carrying a plug of cotton wool at the upper end, into the flask and heat on a water bath for 15–30 minutes. Remove the condenser and heat the flask in a boiling water bath (*FUME CUPBOARD!*) until the excess of thionyl chloride has evaporated. Use all the resulting 3,5-dinitrobenzoyl chloride (about 1·0 g.) immediately.

Add 0·5 ml. of the alcohol, cork the flask loosely, and heat on a water bath for 10 minutes: secondary and tertiary alcohols require longer heating (up to 30 minutes). Cool the mixture, add 10 ml. of 5 per cent (or saturated) sodium bicarbonate solution, break up the resulting solid ester with a stirring rod (alternatively, stir until crystalline), and filter at the pump; wash with a little sodium bicarbonate solution, followed by water, and then suck as dry as possible. Dissolve the crude ester in the minimum volume of hot rectified (or methylated) spirit. Add hot water, drop by drop, with agitation, until the solution *just* develops a slight turbidity that does not disappear on shaking; immerse the mixture in a hot water bath during the recrystallization. Allow to cool slowly (in order to avoid the formation of oily drops with esters of low melting point). Filter off the crystals, and dry them upon a few thicknesses of filter paper or upon a piece of porous plate. Determine the melting point of the crystals when thoroughly dry. Carbon tetrachloride or light petroleum may also be employed for recrystallization.

The above procedure may also be carried out in the presence of dry pyridine, and this is preferred for higher alcohols, glycols and tertiary alcohols: the acid chloride must be in excess.

Treat a mixture of 0·5 ml. of the alcohol and 1 ml. of anhydrous pyridine with a solution of 3,5-dinitrobenzoyl chloride (*ca.* 1·0 g.) in 5 ml. of dry benzene. When any initial reaction has subsided, heat the mixture under reflux on a water bath for 5 minutes (with tertiary alcohols, 30 minutes), and pour into water. Extract the product with ether, wash the extract successively with small volumes of dilute hydrochloric acid, sodium carbonate solution, and finally with water; dry with anhydrous magnesium sulphate and evaporate the solvent. Recrystallize the ester from aqueous ethanol, carbon tetrachloride, benzene or light petroleum (b.p. 40–60°).

Method 2. Mix 1·0 g. of 3,5-dinitrobenzoic acid with 1·5 g. of phosphorus pentachloride in a small, dry test-tube. Warm the mixture gently over a small smoky flame to start the reaction; when the reaction has subsided (but not before), boil for 1–2 minutes or until the solid matter has dissolved. Pour the mixture while still liquid on a dry watch glass (*CAUTION:* the fumes are irritating to the eyes). When the product has solidified, remove the liquid by-product (phosphorus oxychloride) by transferring the pasty mixture to a pad of several thicknesses of filter paper or to a small piece of porous tile. Spread the material until the liquid has been absorbed and the residual solid is dry. Transfer the 3,5-dinitrobenzoyl chloride immediately to a test-tube, add 0·5 ml. of the alcohol, and continue as in *Method 1*.

2. *p*-**Nitrobenzoates.** Alcohols react readily with *p*-nitrobenzoyl chloride to yield *p*-nitrobenzoates:

$$p\text{-}NO_2C_6H_4COCl + ROH \rightarrow p\text{-}NO_2C_6H_4COOR + HCl$$

The melting points of these esters are usually much lower than those of the corresponding 3,5-dinitrobenzoates: their preparation, therefore, offers no advantages over the latter except for alcohols of high molecular weight and for polyhydroxy compounds. The reagent is, however, cheaper than 3,5-dinitrobenzoyl chloride; it hydrolyses in the air so that it should either be stored under dry light petroleum or be prepared from the acid, when required, by the thionyl chloride or phosphorus pentachloride method.

The experimental technique is similar to that given under *1* above.

3. **Benzoates.** Alcohols react with benzoyl chloride in the presence of pyridine or of sodium hydroxide solution to produce esters of benzoic acid:

$$C_6H_5COCl + ROH \rightarrow C_6H_5COOR + HCl$$

These derivatives are generally liquids and hence are of little value for characterization; the polyhydric alcohols, on the other hand, afford solid benzoates. Thus the benzoates of ethylene glycol, trimethylene glycol and glycerol melt at 73°, 58°, and 76° respectively.

The experimental technique is similar to that given under *Aromatic Amines*, Section **IV,33,**2. The following alternative method may also be used. Mix together 0·5–0·8 ml. of the polyhydroxy compound, 5 ml. of pyridine and 2·5 ml. of redistilled benzoyl chloride in a 50 ml. flask, and heat under reflux for 30–60 minutes. Add 25 ml. of 5 per cent sodium bicarbonate solution to the cold reaction mixture and cool in ice until the precipitate solidifies. Filter and wash with a little water. Recrystallize from dilute ethanol as detailed under *1* above.

4. **Phenyl- and 1-naphthyl-urethanes (Phenyl- and 1-naphthyl-carbamates).** Both phenyl isocyanate and 1-naphthyl isocyanate react with alcohols to yield phenylurethanes and 1-naphthylurethanes respectively:

$$C_6H_5N{=}C{=}O + ROH \rightarrow C_6H_5NHCOOR$$
$$(1{-}C_{10}H_7)N{=}C{=}O + ROH \rightarrow (1{-}C_{10}H_7)NHCOOR$$

If the alcohol is not anhydrous, reaction also occurs between the water and the reagent to produce diphenylurea (m.p. 242°) and di-1-naphthylurea (m.p. 297°) respectively, for example:

$$2C_6H_5N{=}C{=}O + H_2O \rightarrow C_6H_5NHCONHC_6H_5 + CO_2$$

The ureas are less soluble than the corresponding urethanes, but their separation is not always easy. For this reason the urethanes are generally prepared from alcohols which are insoluble in water and can therefore be easily obtained in the anhydrous condition.

1-Naphthyl isocyanate is usually preferred to phenyl isocyanate for the following reasons:—(*a*) it is much less lachrymatory; (*b*) it is not so readily decomposed by cold water and thus possesses better keeping qualities; and (c) the melting points of the 1-naphthylurethanes are generally higher than those of the corresponding phenylurethanes. Furthermore, with primary alcohols, which react readily in the cold, only small amounts of the urea are produced and these may be removed by taking advantage of the extreme insolubility of di-1-naphthylurea in hot ligroin.

Place 1·0 g. of the anhydrous alcohol in a dry test-tube and add 0·5 ml. of 1-naphthyl isocyanate* (if the molecular weight is known, use a 10 per cent excess of the reagent); insert a loose plug of cotton wool in the mouth of the tube. If no solid separates after shaking and standing for 5 minutes, warm on a water bath for 5–10 minutes, and then cool in ice. If no solid is now obtained, 'scratch' the sides of the tube with a glass rod to induce crystallization. Extract the solid with 5–10 ml. of boiling ligroin (light petroleum, b.p. 100–120°)†; this rapidly dissolves the 1-naphthylurethane but not the di-1-naphthylurea. Remove the urea (if any) by filtration and allow the hot ligroin solution to cool. If the urethane does not crystallize out, evaporate the solution to half its original volume, and allow to cool. Collect the crystals on a filter, dry, and determine the melting point. If the latter is not sharp, recrystallize from light petroleum (b.p. 100–120°), ethanol, chloroform or carbon tetrachloride.

5. Hydrogen 3-nitrophthalates. 3-Nitrophthalic anhydride, a yellow crystalline powder of m.p. 163–164°, reacts with alcohols to yield acid esters of 3-nitrophthalic acid:

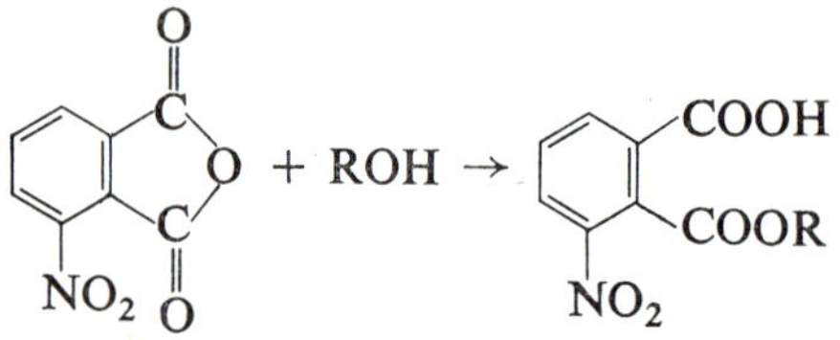

Although two isomeric esters are theoretically possible, the main product is the 2-ester (formulated above); traces of the isomeric 1-ester are eliminated during purification. These derivatives possess a free carboxyl group; their equivalent weights may therefore be determined by titration with standard alkali and thus serve as an additional check upon the identity of the compound.

The reagent must be carefully protected from moisture as it is

* The procedure for phenyl isocyanate is similar, but great care must be taken to protect both the reagent and the reaction mixture from moisture.
† Carbon tetrachloride is sometimes a satisfactory solvent.

comparatively easily hydrated to the acid, m.p. 217–218° (sealed capillary tube). It may be recrystallized from acetic anhydride. Dilute aqueous solutions of an alcohol should be treated with solid potassium carbonate and the alcohol layer used for the test.

Phthalic anhydride reacts similarly, but the acid phthalates are somewhat more difficult to isolate and the melting points are considerably lower.

For alcohols of b.p. below 150°, mix 0·5 g. of 3-nitrophthalic anhydride and 0·5 ml. (0·5 g.) of the dry alcohol in a test-tube fitted with a short condenser, and heat under reflux for 10 minutes after the mixture liquefies. For alcohols boiling above 150°, use the same quantities of reactants, add 5 ml. of dry toluene, heat under reflux until all the anhydride has dissolved and then for 20 minutes more: remove the toluene under reduced pressure (suction with water pump). The reaction product usually solidifies upon cooling, particularly upon rubbing with a glass rod and standing. If it does not crystallize, extract it with dilute sodium bicarbonate solution, shake the extract with ether, and acidify. Recrystallize from hot water, or from 30 to 40 per cent ethanol or from toluene. It may be noted that the m.p. of 3-nitrophthalic acid is 218°.

6. 3,4,5-Triiodobenzoates. The derivatives enumerated above are unsatisfactory for alcohol-ethers, *e.g.*, the mono-ethers of ethylene-glycol ('cellosolves') and the mono-ethers of diethylene-glycol ('carbitols') (see Table IX, 9). **Crystalline derivatives of alcohol-ethers** are readily obtained with 3,4,5-triiodobenzoyl chloride, for example:

$$\text{I}_3\text{C}_6\text{H}_2\text{COCl} + \text{HOCH}_2\text{CH}_2\text{OR} \rightarrow \text{I}_3\text{C}_6\text{H}_2\text{COOCH}_2\text{CH}_2\text{OR} + \text{HCl}$$

Place 0·5 g. of 3,4,5-triiodobenzoyl chloride in a small test-tube, add 0·25 ml. of the alcohol-ether and heat the mixture gently over a micro burner until the evolution of hydrogen chloride ceases (3–5 minutes). Pour the molten mass into 10 ml. of 20 per cent ethanol to which crushed ice has been added. Some derivatives solidify instantly;

those which separate as oils change to solids in a few minutes without further manipulation. Recrystallize from rectified spirit (use 50 per cent ethanol for esters of methyl and butyl 'carbitol').

The following melting points have been recorded:—methyl cellosolve, 152°; cellosolve, 128°; isopropyl cellosolve, 80°; butyl cellosolve, 85°; phenyl cellosolve, 145°; benzyl cellosolve, 104°; methyl carbitol, 82°; ethyl carbitol, 76°; butyl carbitol, 54°.

The melting points of derivatives of selected alcohols are collected in Table IX, 5 (Chapter IX).

IV, 6 Aromatic Alcohols

Aromatic alcohols are insoluble in water and usually burn with a smoky flame. Their boiling points are comparatively high; some are solids at the ordinary temperature. Many may be oxidized to the corresponding aldehyde by cautious addition of dilute nitric acid; upon neutralization of the excess of acid, the aldehyde may be isolated by ether extraction or steam distillation, and then identified as detailed under *Aromatic Aldehydes*, Section **IV**,17.

Most aromatic alcohols exhibit the majority of the reactions given under *Aliphatic Alcohols*, Section **IV**,5, and may be converted into crystalline derivatives as there described.

Table IX, 6 (Chapter IX), contains the melting points of the derivatives of a number of commonly occurring aromatic alcohols.

IV, 7 Phenols

Most phenols are crystalline solids; notable exceptions are *m*-cresol and *o*-bromophenol. The monohydric phenols generally have characteristic odours. The solubility in water increases with the number of hydroxyl groups in the molecule.

(i) **Ferric chloride solution.** Dissolve about 0·05 g. of the compound in 5 ml. of water; if the compound is sparingly soluble, prepare a hot, saturated aqueous solution, filter and use 1 ml. of the cold filtrate. Place the solution in a 75 × 10 mm. test-tube. Add 1 drop of 'neutral' 1 per cent ferric chloride solution* and observe the colour; add another drop after 2–3 seconds. If a transient or permanent coloration (usually purple, blue or green) other than yellow or orange-yellow is observed, the substance is probably a phenol (or an enol). If no coloration is obtained, repeat the test as above but substitute absolute ethanol for water as solvent.

(ii) **Sodium bicarbonate solution.** Phenols do not usually liberate

* For preparation, see Section **IV**,8.

carbon dioxide from 5 per cent sodium bicarbonate solution {for details, see under *Aliphatic Carboxylic Acids*, Section **IV,20,**(i)}. They will dissolve, however, in sodium hydroxide solution. Add 0·1 g. of the substance to 1 ml. of 5 per cent sodium hydroxide solution and shake or stir. Observe whether the material dissolves and/or a coloration is produced (*e.g.*, a brown coloration from *o*- and *p*-polyhydric phenols): if only partial solution takes place or another substance appears to form, dilute with 1 ml. of water and shake. The latter procedure is necessary for sparingly soluble sodium salts (*e.g.*, sodium methyl salicylate).

(iii) **Bromine water.** Many phenols (with the exception of those with strong reducing properties) yield crystalline bromination products; these are often useful for purposes of characterization. Dissolve or suspend 0·25 g. of the compound in 10 ml. of dilute hydrochloric acid or of water, and add bromine water dropwise until decolorization is slow: a white precipitate of the bromophenol may form. Recrystallize and determine the m.p.

An alternative procedure, more suitable for the preparation of somewhat larger quantities of the bromo derivative, is the following. Dissolve 1·0 g. of the compound in 10–15 ml. of glacial acetic acid, cautiously add a solution of 3–4 ml. of liquid bromine in 10–15 ml. of glacial acetic acid until the colour of bromine persists, and allow the mixture to stand for 15–20 minutes. Pour into 50–100 ml. of water, filter off the bromo compound at the pump, and wash with a little cold water. Recrystallize from dilute ethanol.

CRYSTALLINE DERIVATIVES OF PHENOLS

1. **Acetates.** The acetates of monohydric phenols are usually liquids, but those of di- and tri-hydric phenols and also of many substituted phenols are frequently crystalline solids. They may be prepared with acetic anhydride as detailed under *Aromatic Amines*, Section **IV,33,***1*.

Acetates may also be prepared by adding acetic anhydride to somewhat dilute solutions of compounds containing hydroxyl (or amino) groups in aqueous caustic alkalis. The amount of alkali used should suffice to leave the liquid slightly basic at the end of the operation; so much ice should be added that a little remains unmelted, and the acetic anhydride should be added quickly.

Dissolve 0·01 mol (or 1·0 g. if the molecular weight is unknown) of the compound in 5 ml. of 3N sodium hydroxide solution, add 10–20 g.

of crushed ice followed by 1·5 g. (1·5 ml.) of acetic anhydride. Shake the mixture vigorously for 30–60 seconds. The acetate separates in a practically pure condition either at once or after acidification by the addition of a mineral acid. Collect the acetyl derivative, and recrystallize it from hot water or from dilute ethanol.

2. **Benzoates.** The benzoates of a few phenols (*e.g.*, *o*-cresol) are liquids. Many phenols do, however, yield crystalline benzoyl derivatives: these are useful for purposes of characterization.

The Schotten–Baumann method of benzoylation with benzoyl chloride in the presence of aqueous sodium hydroxide may be used. Full details are given under *Aromatic Amines*, Section **IV,33,**2. Alternatively, dissolve 1·0 g. of the phenol in 3 ml. of dry pyridine and add 0·5 g. of benzoyl chloride. After the initial reaction has subsided, warm the mixture over a small flame for a minute or two and pour, with vigorous stirring, into 10–15 ml. of water. Allow the precipitate to settle, decant the supernatant liquid, stir the residue thoroughly with 5–10 ml. of N sodium carbonate solution, filter, and recrystallize from ethanol or from light petroleum.

3. ***p*-Nitrobenzoates and 3,5-dinitrobenzoates.** Both *p*-nitrobenzoyl chloride and 3,5-dinitrobenzoyl chloride react with phenols, best in pyridine solution, to yield crystalline *p*-nitrobenzoates and 3,5-dinitrobenzoates respectively:

$$p\text{-}NO_2C_6H_4COCl + ArOH \rightarrow p\text{-}NO_2C_6H_4COOAr + HCl$$
$$3:5\text{-}(NO_2)_2C_6H_3COCl + ArOH \rightarrow 3,5\text{-}(NO_2)_2C_6H_3COOAr + HCl$$

For properties of these reagents and their preparation from the corresponding acids, see under *Aliphatic Alcohols*, Section **IV,5,***1* and *2*.

Dissolve 0·5 g. of the phenol in 4–5 ml. of dry pyridine, add 1·3 g. of 3,5-dinitrobenzoyl chloride and reflux for 25–30 minutes. Pour the cold reaction mixture into 40 ml. of *ca.* 2N hydrochloric acid. Decant the supernatant aqueous liquid from the precipitated solid or oil and stir it vigorously with about 10 ml. of N sodium carbonate solution. Filter off the solid derivative and wash it with water. Recrystallize from ethanol, dilute ethanol, benzene-acetone or benzene-light petroleum (b.p. 60–80°).

4. **Aryloxyacetic acids.** Phenols, in the presence of alkali, react with chloroacetic acid to give aryloxyacetic acids:

$$ArONa + ClCH_2COONa \longrightarrow ArOCH_2COONa + NaCl$$
$$\xrightarrow{HCl} ArOCH_2COOH + 2NaCl$$

These are crystalline compounds with sharp melting points, and possess the further advantage that their equivalent weights may be determined by dissolving in dilute ethanol and titrating with standard alkali. Nitrophenols, however, give unsatisfactory derivatives.

To a mixture of 1·0 g. of the compound and 3·5 ml. of 33 per cent sodium hydroxide solution in a test-tube, add 2·5 ml. of 50 per cent chloroacetic acid solution. If necessary, add a little water to dissolve the sodium salt of the phenol. Stopper the test-tube loosely and heat on a gently-boiling water bath for an hour. After cooling, dilute with 10 ml. of water, acidify to Congo Red with dilute hydrochloric acid, and extract with 30 ml. of ether. Wash the ethereal extract with 10 ml. of water, and extract the aryloxyacetic acid by shaking with 25 ml. of 5 per cent sodium carbonate solution. Acidify the sodium carbonate extract (to Congo Red) with dilute hydrochloric acid, collect the aryloxyacetic acid which separates, and recrystallize it from hot water or from dilute ethanol.

5. **Diphenylurethanes.** Phenols react with diphenylcarbamyl chloride to yield diphenylurethanes (or aryl N,N-diphenylcarbamates):

$$(C_6H_5)_2NCOCl + HOAr \xrightarrow{C_5H_5N} (C_6H_5)_2NCOOAr + HCl$$

The reagent is unsuitable for a number of phenolic acids.

Dissolve 0·5 g. of the phenol in 2·5 ml. of pyridine, and add one equivalent of diphenylcarbamyl chloride (or 0·4–0·5 g. if the molecular weight is uncertain). Reflux the mixture for 30–60 minutes on a boiling water bath, and then pour into about 25 ml. of water. Filter the derivative, wash with a little sodium bicarbonate solution, and recrystallize from ethanol, benzene, light petroleum (b.p. 60–80°) or carbon tetrachloride.

6. **1-Naphthylurethanes (1-naphthylcarbamates).** 1-Naphthyl isocyanate reacts smoothly with monohydric, but not with polyhydric, phenols to give 1-naphthylurethanes (or N-1-naphthylcarbamates):

$$(1-C_{10}H_7)N=C=O + ArOH \rightarrow (1-C_{10}H_7)NHCOOAr$$

(compare *Aliphatic Alcohols*, Section **IV,5,4**). Some phenols, *e.g.*, nitrophenols and halogenophenols, react with difficulty with the reagent alone; the addition of a few drops of pyridine or 1 drop of an ethereal solution of trimethylamine or triethylamine generally results in the rapid formation of the urethane.

Place 0·25 g. of the phenol together with an equal weight of 1-naphthyl isocyanate in a *dry* test-tube closed with a stopper carrying a calcium chloride or cotton wool guard tube. If a spontaneous reaction does not occur, boil the mixture gently for 2–3 minutes, and cool; if the reaction mixture does not solidify, rub the walls of the tube vigorously with a glass rod. If no crystalline solid is obtained, add 2 drops of dry pyridine or 1 drop of an ethereal solution of triethylamine, and warm on a water bath for 5 minutes. Extract the contents of the tube with boiling light petroleum (b.p. 80–100° or 100–120°) or with carbon tetrachloride to separate any insoluble di-1-naphthyl urea. Recrystallize the crystals which separate on cooling from the same solvent.

The following alternative method may be used. Dissolve 0·01 mol of the phenol and 0·01 mol of 1-naphthyl isocyanate in 20 ml. of light petroleum (b.p. 60–80°), add 2 drops of triethylamine (or, less satisfactorily, 2 drops of pyridine), reflux for 5 minutes, and allow to crystallize. Filter off the crystalline solid through a sintered glass funnel.

7. *p*-Toluenesulphonates. *p*-Toluenesulphonyl chloride condenses readily with phenols to yield *p*-toluenesulphonates:

$$p\text{-}CH_3C_6H_4SO_2Cl + ArOH \rightarrow p\text{-}CH_3C_6H_4SO_2OAr + HCl$$

Mix 1·0 g. of the phenol with 2·5 ml. of pyridine, add 2 g. of *p*-toluenesulphonyl chloride, and heat on a water bath for 15 minutes. Pour into 25 ml. of cold water and stir until the oil solidifies. Filter, wash with cold dilute hydrochloric acid (to remove pyridine), then with cold dilute sodium hydroxide solution (to remove any phenol present) and finally with cold water. Recrystallize from methyl or ethyl alcohol.

8. **2,4-Dinitrophenyl ethers.** 2,4-Dinitrochlorobenzene reacts with the sodium salts of phenols to yield crystalline 2,4-dinitrophenyl ethers:

$$O_2N\text{-}C_6H_3(NO_2)\text{-}Cl + ArONa \rightarrow O_2N\text{-}C_6H_3(NO_2)\text{-}OAr + NaCl$$

Dissolve 1·0 g. (or 0·01 mol) of the phenol in a solution of 0·40 g. of sodium hydroxide in 5 ml. of water. Add the resulting solution to 2·0 g. of 2,4-dinitrochlorobenzene dissolved in 30 ml. of 95 per cent ethanol; add more alcohol, if necessary, to effect solution. Heat the solution under reflux on a water bath until the colour (usually red) is discharged and a copious precipitate of sodium chloride appears (30–60 minutes). Dilute the reaction mixture with an equal volume of water, filter off the precipitated 2,4-dinitrophenyl ether, wash with water, and recrystallize from ethanol.

Note

The 2,4-dinitrochlorobenzene must be handled cautiously: it is a skin irritant. If any touches the skin, wash it immediately with methylated spirit.

9. **Bromo derivatives.** The presence of the hydroxyl group in phenols facilitates the substitution of the nuclear hydrogen atoms by halogen; the number and position of the substituent atoms vary with the nature of the phenol. This method is an indirect means of identification, as the formation of a substitution derivative is not a characteristic reaction of the phenol group but of the benzene nucleus. Phenol reacts with bromine to give 2,4,6-tribromophenol:

$$C_6H_5OH + 3Br_2 \rightarrow C_6H_2Br_3OH + 3HBr.$$

Bromo derivatives are often difficult to prepare, particularly in the case of polyhydroxy phenols which oxidize easily.

The method of preparation is given under (iii) above. The following alternative procedure may be used. Dissolve 1·0 g. of the phenol in water, ethanol or acetone and add slowly, with constant shaking, just sufficient of a bromine solution (prepared by adding 5 g. of bromine to a solution of 7·5 g. of potassium bromide in 50 ml. of water) to impart a yellow colour to the mixture. Allow to stand for 5 minutes. Add about 50 ml. of water, and shake vigorously to break up any lumps. Filter and wash the bromo derivative with a dilute solution of sodium bisulphite. Recrystallize from ethanol or from dilute ethanol.

The melting points of the derivatives of a number of selected phenols are collected in Table IX, 7 (Chapter IX).

IV, 8 Enols

Enols may be divided into (*a*) β-keto esters and (*b*) 1,3-diketones. Two simple **tests for enols** may be given here.

(i) *Ferric chloride solution.* Add a few drops of neutral ferric chloride solution to a solution of 0·1 g. of the compound in water or in methanol. Most enols give a red coloration.

Prepare the **neutral ferric chloride solution** (*i.e.*, free from hydrochloric acid) by adding dilute sodium hydroxide solution to the bench reagent until a slight precipitate of ferric hydroxide is formed. Filter off the precipitate and use the clear filtrate for the test.

(ii) *Copper derivative.* Shake 0·2 g. of the substance vigorously with a little cold, saturated, aqueous copper acetate solution. Many enols give a solid, green or blue, copper derivative, which can be crystallized from ethanol and often has a definite m.p. (*e.g.*, from ethyl acetoacetate, m.p. 192°; from ethyl acetonedicarboxylate, m.p. 142°).

With 5 per cent sodium hydroxide solution a β-keto ester yields the salt of the corresponding acid which, when heated with dilute hydrochloric acid, is decarboxylated to a ketone:

$$RCOCHR'COOR'' + NaOH \rightarrow R''OH + RCOCHR'COONa$$
$$RCOCHR'COONa + HCl \rightarrow RCOCH_2R' + CO_2 + NaCl$$

A 1,3-diketone under similar conditions affords a ketone and the salt of an acid:

$$RCOCH_2COR' + NaOH \rightarrow RCOCH_3 + R'COONa$$

These ketones (also produced by direct hydrolysis with boiling dilute acid) may be characterized by the usual ketone derivatives (Section **IV,18**); carbonyl derivatives (*e.g.*, semicarbazones) may be prepared directly from β-keto esters. Heating with an equivalent amount of phenylhydrazine often yields characteristic derivatives. Thus β-keto esters afford pyrazolones:

$$CH_3\underset{\underset{O}{\|}}{C}CH_2COOC_2H_5 + H_2N-NHC_6H_5 \xrightarrow{-H_2O} \underset{\underset{C_6H_5}{\overset{|}{NH}}}{\underset{N}{\overset{CH_3C-CH_2}{\overset{\|}{}\overset{|}{COOC_2H_5}}}} \xrightarrow{-C_2H_5OH}$$

$$\underset{C_6H_5}{\underset{\underset{N}{\overset{|}{}}}{\overset{CH_3C-CH_2}{\overset{\|}{}\overset{|}{CO}}}}$$

3-Methyl-1-phenylpyrazolone

whilst 1,3-diketones yield 1-phenylpyrazoles:

$$C_6H_5COCH_2COCH_3 + H_2NNHC_6H_5 \rightarrow \underset{C_6H_5N-N}{\overset{C_6H_5C=CH}{\overset{|}{}}}\!\!\!\!\!>\!CCH_3$$

Benzoylacetone

1,5-Diphenyl-3-methylpyrazole

Heat a mixture of 0·5 g. of ethyl acetoacetate and an equivalent amount of phenylhydrazine in an oil bath at 100–110° for 2 hours. Water and alcohol vapours are evolved. Cool and recrystallize the product from ethanol. The resulting methylphenylpyrazolone has m.p. 127°.

For 1,3-diketones, excellent results are obtained by refluxing the reactants in ethanolic solution for 2–3 hours; the product separates on cooling.

The physical properties as well as the melting points of the derivatives of a number of enols (β-keto esters and 1,3-diketones) are given in Table IX, 8 (Chapter IX).

IV, 9 Polyhydric Alcohols

Some characteristic reactions of polyhydric alcohols are given below:

(i) They are colourless viscous liquids (or crystalline solids) freely soluble in water, but insoluble in anhydrous ether.

(ii) Upon heating with a little potassium hydrogen sulphate, they may yield aldehydes (*e.g.*, ethylene glycol yields acetaldehyde; glycerol gives the irritating odour of acrolein, CH_2=CHCHO), which can be identified with Schiff's reagent and with dimedone (*Aliphatic Aldehydes*, Section **IV,15**,*2*).

(iii) Upon adding a few drops of phenolphthalein to a 1 per cent solution of borax, a pink coloration is produced: the addition of a polyhydric alcohol causes the pink colour to disappear, but it reappears on warming and vanishes again upon cooling.

This reaction is due to the combination of the hydroxy compound with the boric acid to form a much stronger monobasic acid:

Three of the hydroxyl groups are esterified with the three hydroxyl groups of boric acid. The fourth hydroxyl group is so situated spatially that it can supply an electron pair to the empty boron orbital and close the second ring. The resulting oxonium salt is a stronger acid than the boric acid. This reaction with boric acid occurs only when two hydroxyl groups in the compound are *cis* to each other: it is only the *cis*-diols that can form ionized cyclic compounds with boric acid.

(iv) **Periodic acid test.** Periodic acid has a selective oxidizing action upon 1,2-glycols and upon α-hydroxy aldehydes and ketones (*Malaprade reaction*):

$$RCHOH.CHOHR' + HIO_4 \rightarrow RCHO + R'CHO + H_2O + HIO_3$$
$$RCHOH.COR' + HIO_4 \rightarrow RCHO + R'COOH + HIO_3$$
$$RCO.COR' + HIO_4 + H_2O \rightarrow RCOOH + R'COOH + HIO_3$$

Add 1 drop (0·05 ml.) of concentrated nitric acid to 2·0 ml. of a 0·5 per cent aqueous solution of paraperiodic acid (H_5IO_6) contained in a small test-tube and shake well. Then introduce 1 drop or a small crystal of the compound. Shake the mixture for 15 seconds and add 1–2 drops of 5 per cent aqueous silver nitrate. The immediate production of a *white* precipitate (silver iodate) constitutes a positive test and indicates that the organic compound has been oxidized by the periodic acid. The test is based upon the fact that silver iodate is sparingly soluble in dilute nitric acid whereas silver periodate is very soluble; if too much nitric acid is present, the silver iodate will not precipitate.

An alternative procedure for the above test is as follows. Mix 2–3 ml. of 2 per cent aqueous paraperiodic acid solution with 1 drop of dilute sulphuric acid (*ca.* 2·5N) and add 20–30 mg. of the compound. Shake the mixture for 5 minutes, and then pass sulphur dioxide through the solution until it acquires a pale yellow colour (to remove the excess of periodic acid and also iodic acid formed in the reaction). Add 1–2 ml. of Schiff's reagent (Section **IV,15**): the production of a violet colour constitutes a positive test.

CRYSTALLINE DERIVATIVES

1. **Benzoates.** The preparation of benzoates of polyhydric alcohols may be illustrated by reference to glycerol. They are usually crystalline solids.

Method 1. Place in a test-tube or small flask 1·3 g. of glycerol and 30 ml. of 10 per cent sodium hydroxide solution; add gradually, with simultaneous shaking, 1·2 g. of benzoyl chloride. Stopper the vessel, shake for several minutes and allow to stand. Decant the solution from the pasty solid and wash the latter with cold water by decantation. Recrystallize the solid tribenzoate from dilute rectified (or methylated) spirit or from light petroleum, b.p. 40–60°; the pure compound has m.p. 76°.

Method 2. Add gradually 2·5 ml. of benzoyl chloride to a solution of 0·5 g. of glycerol in 5 ml. of pure pyridine, cooled in ice; then reflux for 1 hour. Treat the cold mixture with dilute sulphuric acid; this dissolves the pyridine salt and precipitates the glycerol tribenzoate. Wash it with sodium bicarbonate solution, followed by water, and recrystallize as in *Method 1*.

Derivatives of higher melting point may be obtained with *p*-nitrobenzoyl chloride; the experimental details are similar to those given above for benzoyl chloride. 3,5-Dinitrobenzoyl chloride (*Aliphatic Alcohols*, Section **IV,5,***1*) may also be used; glycerol gives unsatisfactory results with this reagent.

2. **1-Naphthylcarbamates (or 1-naphthylurethanes).** Full details are given in Section **IV,5,***4*.

The melting points of a few derivatives of selected polyhydric alcohols are collected in Table IX, 9 (Chapter IX).

IV, 10 Carbohydrates (Sugars)

Mono- and di-saccharides are colourless solids or syrupy liquids, which are freely soluble in water, practically insoluble in ether and other organic solvents, and neutral in reaction. Polysaccharides possess similar properties, but are generally insoluble in water because of their high molecular weights. Both poly- and di-saccharides are converted into monosaccharides upon hydrolysis.

(i) **Molisch's test.** This is a general test for carbohydrates. Place 5 mg. of the substance in a test-tube containing 0·5 ml. of water and mix it with 2 drops of a 10 per cent solution of 1-naphthol in ethanol or in chloroform. Allow 1·0 ml. of concentrated sulphuric acid to flow down the side of the inclined tube (it is best to use a dropper pipette) so that the acid forms a layer beneath the aqueous solution without mixing with it. If a carbohydrate is present, a red ring appears at the interface of the two liquids: the colour quickly changes on standing or shaking, a violet solution being formed. Shake and allow the mixture to stand for 2 minutes, then dilute with 5 ml. of water. In the presence of a carbohydrate, a dull-violet precipitate will appear immediately.

For practice, the student should apply the test to glucose, lactose, sucrose, starch and paper fibres.

(ii) **Barfoed's reagent.** This reagent may be used as a general test for monosaccharides. Heat a test-tube containing 1 ml. of the reagent and 1 ml. of a dilute solution of the carbohydrate in a beaker of boiling water. If red cuprous oxide is formed within 2 minutes, a monosaccharide is present. Disaccharides on prolonged heating (about 10 minutes) may also cause reduction, owing to partial hydrolysis to monoses.

Barfoed's reagent is prepared by dissolving 13·3 g. of crystallized neutral copper acetate in 200 ml. of 1 per cent acetic acid solution. The reagent does not keep well.

For practice, the student should apply the test to glucose and lactose.

(iii) **Fehling's solution.** Place 5 ml. of Fehling's solution, prepared by mixing equal volumes of Fehling's solution No. 1 (copper sulphate solution) and solution No. 2 {alkaline tartrate solution—see *Aliphatic Aldehydes*, Section **IV**,15,(ii)}, in a test-tube and heat to gentle boiling. Add a solution of 0·1 g. of the carbohydrate in 2 ml. of water and continue to boil gently for a minute or two, and observe the result. A yellow or red precipitate of cuprous oxide indicates the presence of a reducing sugar. An alternative method of carrying out the test is to add the hot Fehling's solution dropwise to the boiling solution of the carbohydrate; in the presence of a reducing sugar (*e.g.*, glucose, fructose, mannose, lactose and maltose) the blue colour will disappear and a yellow precipitate, changing to red, is thrown down.

Of the common disaccharides sucrose does not reduce Fehling's solution. If the sucrose is hydrolysed by boiling it with dilute acid and the solution is neutralized with aqueous sodium hydroxide, the reduction of Fehling's solution occurs readily.

(iv) **Benedict's solution.** This is a modification of Fehling's solution and consists of a single test solution which does not deteriorate appreciably on standing. To 5 ml. of Benedict's solution add 0·4 ml. of a 2 per cent solution of the carbohydrate, boil for 2 minutes and allow to cool spontaneously. If no reducing sugar is present, the solution remains clear; in the presence of a reducing sugar, the solution will contain cuprous oxide. The test may also be carried out according to the experimental details given under (iii).

Benedict's solution is prepared as follows. Dissolve 86·5 g. of crystallized sodium citrate ($2Na_3C_6H_5O_7,11H_2O$) and 50 g. of anhydrous sodium carbonate in about 350 ml. of water. Filter, if necessary. Add a solution of 8·65 g. of crystallized copper sulphate in 50 ml. of water with constant stirring. Dilute to 500 ml. The resulting solution should be perfectly clear: if it is not, pour it through a fluted filter paper.

The citrate ion forms a chelate complex which decreases the copper ion concentration below that necessary for the precipitation of cupric hydroxide. The complex salt may be formulated:

$$\left[\begin{array}{c} {}^-OOC-CH_2 \\ {}^-OOC-CH_2 \end{array} \!\!C\!\! \begin{array}{c} O \\ C=O \\ O^- \end{array} \!\!\!\!\! \begin{array}{c} O^- \\ | \\ O \\ Cu \\ O \end{array} \!\!\!\!\! \begin{array}{c} O=C \\ C \\ O \end{array} \!\!C\!\! \begin{array}{c} CH_2-COO^- \\ CH_2-COO^- \end{array} \right] 6Na^+$$

For practice, the student should apply tests (iii) and (iv) to glucose, lactose, maltose and sucrose.

CHARACTERIZATION OF CARBOHYDRATES (SUGARS)

The melting points (more accurately termed the decomposition points) of sugars and some of their derivatives, *e.g.*, osazones, are not so definite as those of other classes of organic compounds: they vary with the rate of heating and the differences between individual members are not always large. There are, however, a number of reactions and derivatives which will assist in the characterization of the simple sugars normally encountered by the student in his training in qualitative organic analysis.

1. **Osazone formation.** The carbohydrates containing an aldehyde or keto group ('potential' in the cyclic form) react with one molecular proportion of phenylhydrazine in the cold to form the corresponding phenylhydrazones (compare *Aliphatic Ketones*, Section **IV,18**); these are usually soluble in water and consequently are of little value for purposes of separation and identification. If, however, they are heated at 100° in the presence of excess (3–4 mols) of phenylhydrazine, the $\rangle$CHOH in an aldose or the —CH$_2$OH in a ketose adjacent to the phenylhydrazone group are converted by one molecule of phenylhydrazine into a keto or aldehyde group respectively, which condense with a further molecule of phenylhydrazine to give a bis-phenylhydrazone or **osazone.**

Glucose and fructose (and also mannose) form the same osazone. The osazones are usually yellow, well-defined crystalline compounds and are sparingly soluble in cold water. The characteristic crystalline

$$
\begin{array}{c}
\text{RCHOH} \\
| \\
\text{CHO} \\
\text{or} \\
\text{RCO} \\
| \\
\text{CH}_2\text{OH}
\end{array}
\xrightarrow{\text{C}_6\text{H}_5\text{NHNH}_2}
\left[
\begin{array}{c}
\text{RCHOH} \\
| \\
\text{CH}=\text{NNHC}_6\text{H}_5 \\
\text{or} \\
\text{RC}=\text{NNHC}_6\text{H}_5 \\
| \\
\text{CH}_2\text{OH}
\end{array}
\right]
\xrightarrow[(-2\text{H})]{\text{C}_6\text{H}_5\text{NHNH}_2}
$$

$$
\left[
\begin{array}{c}
\text{RCO} \\
| \\
\text{CH}=\text{NNHC}_6\text{H}_5 \\
\text{or} \\
\text{RC}=\text{NNHC}_6\text{H}_5 \\
| \\
\text{CHO}
\end{array}
\; + \text{C}_6\text{H}_5\text{NH}_2 \;\; + \text{NH}_3
\right]
\xrightarrow{\text{C}_6\text{H}_5\text{NHNH}_2}
\begin{array}{c}
\text{RC}=\text{NNHC}_6\text{H}_5 \\
| \\
\text{CH}=\text{NNHC}_6\text{H}_5
\end{array}
$$

forms of the osazones of the commonly occurring sugars, when examined under the microscope, may be employed for their identification; the melting or decomposition points are less satisfactory since these depend to a marked degree on the rate of heating.

Certain carbohydrates (sugars) may be identified by the length of time required to form osazones upon treatment with phenylhydrazine under standard experimental conditions. Monosaccharides give precipitates at 100° within 20 minutes. The di-saccharides maltose and lactose give no osazone at 100° even after 2 hours, but osazones are obtained on cooling after 10–15 minutes heating. With sucrose an osazone commences to separate after about 30 minutes, due to gradual hydrolysis into glucose and fructose, but no osazone is produced on cooling after heating for 10–15 minutes.

Place 0·20 g. of the carbohydrate, 0·40 g. of pure *white* phenylhydrazine hydrochloride (*e.g.*, of A.R. quality), 0·60 g. of crystallized sodium acetate and 4·00 ml. of water in a dry test-tube. (Weigh the quantities with an accuracy of 0·01 g.) Stopper the tube *loosely* with a cork, and stand or clamp it upright in a beaker containing boiling water. Note the time of immersion and the time when the osazone first separates. Shake the tube occasionally (without removing it from the boiling water) in order to prevent supersaturation. The precipitate separates quite suddenly: duplicate experiments should

GLUCOSAZONE

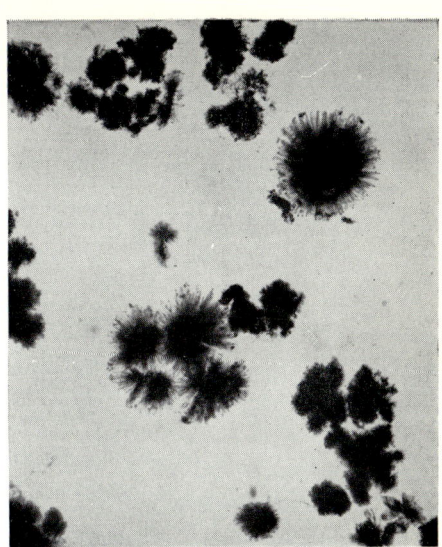
GALACTOSAZONE

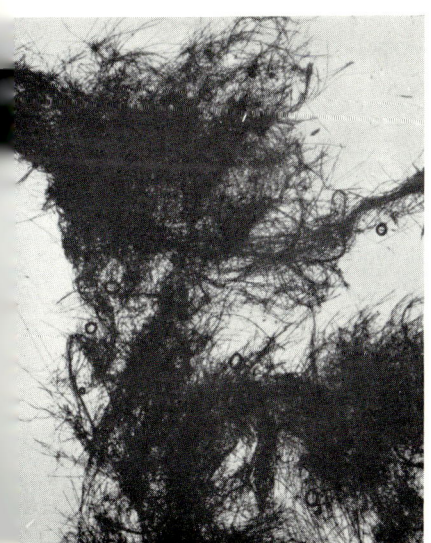
ARABINOSAZONE

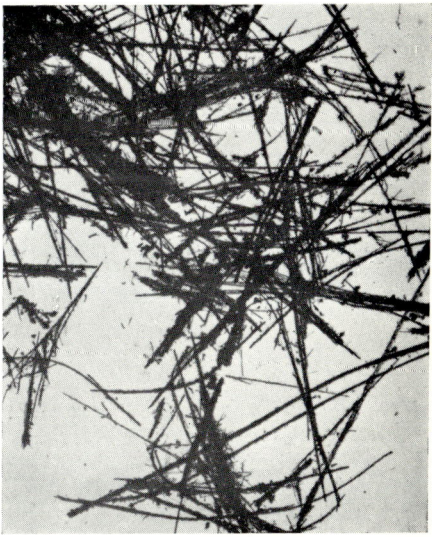
XYLOSAZONE

Fig. *IV*, *10*, 1.

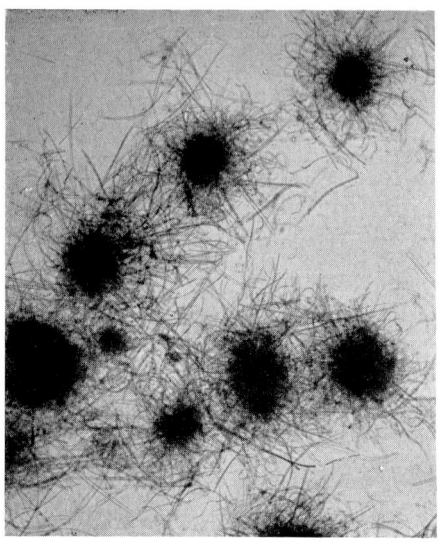 LACTOSAZONE

MALTOSAZONE

 CELLOBIOSAZONE

 SORBOSAZONE

Fig. *IV*, *10*, 1.

agree within 0·5 minute. Note whether the precipitate is white (mannose), yellow or orange-yellow, and whether it is crystalline or 'oily.'

The approximate times of osazone formation in minutes are given in Table IX, 10 (Chapter IX). The product from mannose is the simple hydrazone and is practically white. Arabinose osazone separates first as an oil, whilst that from galactose is highly crystalline. Lactose and maltose give no precipitate from hot solution.

For practice, the student should prepare the osazones from glucose and fructose. He should also use the same technique for lactose and maltose, but the solution should be cooled after boiling for 10–15 minutes. The resulting osazones should be examined under the microscope: this is most simply done by withdrawing a small quantity of the crystalline suspension with a dropper pipette on to a microscope slide, and viewing under the microscope. It may be necessary to recrystallize the osazone in order to obtain the best results. The precipitate should be filtered off on a small filter paper, washed with a little cold water, and then recrystallized from hot water or from 60 per cent ethanol or from dilute pyridine. The crystal forms should be compared with those given in Fig. *IV, 10*, 1 (plate facing this page).*
The crystal forms of the osazones are more trustworthy for identification purposes than the melting points.

2. **Acetates.** Complete acetylation of all the hydroxyl groups is desirable in order to avoid mixtures. In some cases, the completely acetylated sugars may be obtained in the α- or β-forms depending upon the catalyst, *e.g.*, zinc chloride or sodium acetate, that is employed in the acetylation.

The β-acetate is usually obtained by the following procedure. Dissolve the powdered carbohydrate (1·0 g.) and powdered, fused sodium acetate (1·0 g.) in 10 ml. of acetic anhydride by heating on a water bath under reflux (*ca.* 30 minutes), and continue the heating for a further 2 hours. Pour the hot reaction mixture cautiously and with stirring into 50 ml. of ice-cold water: stir vigorously for several minutes to decompose the excess of acetic anhydride. Filter the solid product, wash it with cold water, and recrystallize from ethanol.

The β-acetate may be converted into the α-acetate as follows. Add 0·5 g. of the β-acetate to a 2 per cent solution of anhydrous zinc chloride in acetic anhydride (2·5 ml.), and heat the resulting solution

---

* The photographs of the osazones were kindly supplied by Thomas Kerfoot and Co. Ltd., of Vale of Bardsley, Ashton-under-Lyne, the well-known manufacturers of sugars.

under reflux on a water bath for 30 minutes. Allow to cool. Pour the solution into 25 ml. of ice-cold water, and stir until the acetic anhydride has been decomposed. Collect the product and recrystallize it from ethanol.

3. *p*-Nitrophenylhydrazones. This reagent has been used in the characterization of a number of monosaccharides.

Heat 0·25 g. of the compound with 3 ml. of ethanol, add 0·25 g. of *p*-nitrophenylhydrazine, and heat the suspension until the reaction appears complete. The *p*-nitrophenylhydrazone soon separates. Filter, preferably after standing overnight, wash with a little cold ethyl alcohol, and then recrystallize from ethanol.

4. Benzoates. Benzoyl chloride has a very limited application as a reagent in the sugar series, but it is useful for the preparation of a crystalline derivative of glucose and of fructose.

In a 50–100 ml. conical flask place a solution of 0·5 g. of glucose in 5 ml. of water, 12–15 ml. of 10 per cent sodium hydroxide solution and 1 ml. of benzoyl chloride, cork tightly, and shake until the odour of benzoyl chloride has disappeared and a crystalline (frequently sticky) solid has separated. Filter off the solid, wash it with a little water, and recrystallize it from ethyl or *n*-butyl alcohol. (If the product is sticky, it should be removed, and spread on a porous tile before recrystallization.) Glucose pentabenzoate has m.p. 179°. Fructose pentabenzoate, m.p. 78–79°, may be similarly prepared.

The following simple test distinguishes fructose from all other carbohydrates. Upon heating a little fructose with dilute cobalt chloride solution, cooling and treating with a little ammonia solution, a violet to purple colour is developed; the colour gradually fades and must be observed immediately after the addition of the ammonia solution. Green cobalt hydroxide is formed with all other carbohydrates.

5. Methylphenylosazones. *as*-Methylphenylhydrazine does not form osazones with aldoses presumably because the base or more probably the methylphenylhydrazonium ion $[C_6H_5NCH_3NH_3]^+$ will oxidize a —CH_2OH but not a >$CHOH$ group: it readily forms osazones with ketoses, thus providing an excellent reagent for fructose.

Dissolve 0·2 g. of fructose in 10 ml. of water, add 0·6 g. of *as*-methylphenylhydrazine and sufficient rectified spirit to give a clear solution. Since the fructose may not be quite pure, warm the mixture slightly, allow to stand, preferably overnight, so that any insoluble hydrazones may separate; if present, remove them by filtration. Add 4 ml. of 50 per cent acetic acid to the filtrate; it will become yellow in colour. Heat the solution on a water bath for 5–10 minutes, and allow to stand in the dark until crystallization is complete; it may be necessary to 'scratch' the walls of the vessel to induce crystallization. Filter off the crystals and wash with water, followed by a little ether. Recrystallize the orange-coloured methylphenylosazone from benzene: m.p. 152°.

The properties of a number of sugars are collected in Table IX, 10 (Chapter IX); the specific rotations in water are included for reference purposes.

Notes on the Identification of Polysaccharides

Most polysaccharides are insoluble or sparingly soluble in cold water, insoluble in cold ethanol and ether, and rarely possess melting points. Exceptionally inulin melts at about 178° (dec.) after drying at 130°.

Starch. A few centigrams rubbed to a thin cream with cold water and then gradually stirred into 100 ml. of boiling water dissolve to give a nearly clear solution. This gives a deep blue coloration with a dilute solution of iodine in potassium iodide solution, temporarily decolorized by heat or by traces of free alkali, but restored on cooling or upon acidifying. It is hydrolysed by boiling with dilute hydrochloric acid to give products (largely glucose) which reduce Fehling's or Benedict's solution.

Cellulose. This is insoluble in water, hot and cold. It dissolves in a solution of Schweitzer's reagent (precipitated cupric hydroxide is washed free from salts and then dissolved in concentrated ammonia solution), from which it is precipitated by the addition of dilute acids. Cellulose is not hydrolysed by dilute hydrochloric acid.

Inulin. This polysaccharide melts with decomposition at about 178°. It is insoluble in cold but dissolves readily in hot water giving a clear solution which tends to remain supersaturated. It does not reduce Fehling's or Benedict's solution. Inulin gives no coloration with iodine solution.

Glycogen. It dissolves easily in water to an intensely opalescent solution; the opalescence is not destroyed by filtration, but is removed by the addition of acetic acid. Glycogen gives a wine coloration with iodine solution; the coloration disappears on heating and reappears on cooling. The compound does not reduce Fehling's or Benedict's solution: upon boiling with dilute acid glucose is produced and the resulting solution, when neutralized, therefore reduces Fehling's or Benedict's solution.

IV, 11 Alkyl Halides

The following are some of the most important reactions of alkyl halides which will assist in their identification.

(i) **Beilstein's test.** This test serves to detect the presence of halogens in many organic compounds. It consists in heating the substance in contact with pure copper oxide in the Bunsen flame: the corresponding copper halide is formed, which, being volatile, imparts an intense green or bluish-green colour to the mantle of the flame.

Push one end of a length of 20 cm. of stout copper wire into a cork (this will serve as a holder); at the other end make two or three turns about a thin glass rod. Heat the coil in the outer mantle of a Bunsen flame until it ceases to impart any colour to the flame. Allow the wire to cool somewhat and, while still warm, dip the coil into a small portion of the substance to be tested and heat again in the non-luminous flame. If the compound contains a halogen element, a green or bluish-green flame will be observed (usually after the initial smoky flame has disappeared). Before using the wire for another compound, heat it until the material from the previous test has been destroyed and the flame is not coloured.

It has been stated that many halogen-free compounds, *e.g.*, certain derivatives of pyridine and quinoline, purines, acid amides and cyano compounds, when ignited on copper oxide impart a green colour to the flame, presumably owing to the formation of volatile cuprous cyanide. The test is therefore not always trustworthy. The test is not given by fluorides since copper fluoride is not volatile.

(ii) **Ethanolic silver nitrate solution.** Shake 0·1 g. of the substance with 2 ml. of ethanolic silver nitrate solution. Alkyl iodides usually yield silver iodide instantly; alkyl bromides react rapidly, but may require warming; alkyl chlorides give very little precipitate in the cold, but a copious precipitate is obtained by warming on a water bath. If a precipitate forms, note its colour. Add 2–3 drops of dilute (5 per cent) nitric acid and observe whether the precipitate dissolves: silver halides are insoluble in dilute nitric acid but silver salts of organic acids dissolve. The order of reactivity is I > Br > Cl and tertiary > secondary > primary.

The **ethanolic silver nitrate solution** consists of a saturated solution of silver nitrate in absolute ethanol (about 1–2 per cent).

(iii) **Ethanolic potassium hydroxide solution.** Boil 0·5 ml. of the compound with 4 ml. of 0·5N ethanolic potassium hydroxide under reflux for 15 minutes. Most alkyl halides give a crystalline precipitate of the potassium halide. Dilute with 5 ml. of water, acidify with dilute nitric acid, and test with silver nitrate solution.

The **0·5N ethanolic potassium hydroxide solution is prepared** by dissolving 16 g. of potassium hydroxide pellets in 500 ml. of ethanol (or industrial spirit) contained in a bottle closed by a cork. After standing for 24 hours, the clear solution is decanted or filtered from the residue of potassium carbonate. It is said that a solution in methyl alcohol has better keeping qualities than that in ethyl alcohol.

Crystalline Derivatives of Alkyl Halides

1. **Anilides and 1-Naphthalides.** The Grignard reagents prepared from alkyl halides react with phenyl isocyanate ($C_6H_5N\!=\!C\!=\!O$) or with 1-naphthyl isocyanate $\{(1\!-\!C_{10}H_7)N\!=\!C\!=\!O\}$ to yield addition products that are converted by hydrolysis into anilides and 1-naphthalides respectively:

$$RX + Mg \rightarrow RMgX$$

$$ArN\!=\!C\!=\!O + RMgX \rightarrow ArN\!=\!\underset{\underset{\displaystyle}{|}}{C}\!-\!R \xrightarrow{H_2O}$$

$$\left[ArN\!=\!\underset{\underset{\displaystyle}{|}}{C}\!-\!R\right] + Mg(OH)X \rightarrow ArNH\overset{\overset{\displaystyle O}{\|}}{C}R$$

Phenyl isocyanate is a colourless liquid, b.p. 164° or 55°/13 mm.; its vapour is lachrymatory. The liquid reacts readily with water, yielding diphenylurea, m.p. 242°, and hence must be protected from atmospheric moisture:

$$2C_6H_5NCO + H_2O \rightarrow C_6H_5NHCONHC_6H_5 + CO_2$$

1-Naphthyl isocyanate, b.p. 269–270° or 153°/18 mm., is not quite so irritant and is somewhat more stable towards water (di-1-naphthyl urea has m.p. 297°). It is therefore to be preferred as a reagent; furthermore the 1-naphthalides are less soluble than the corresponding anilides.

In a small dry flask, fitted with a short reflux condenser and a calcium chloride or cotton wool guard tube, place 0·4 g. of dry magnesium turnings, a minute crystal of iodine and a solution of 1·0 ml. (or 0·01 mol) of the alkyl halide in 5–10 ml. of anhydrous ether. If the reaction does not start immediately (as indicated by the disappearance of the iodine colour), warm for a short period in a beaker of warm water; allow the reaction to proceed spontaneously, moderating it if necessary by immersing the flask in cold water. When the reaction has ceased, decant the nearly clear liquid from any solid material into another dry flask, and fit the reflux condenser into it. Add, portion-wise, through the condenser a solution of 0·5 ml. of phenyl- or 1-naphthyl isocyanate in 10 ml. of anhydrous ether, shaking the flask after each addition. Allow the mixture to stand for 10 minutes and then add 30 ml. of N hydrochloric acid dropwise and with vigorous shaking and cooling in ice. (Alternatively, pour the reaction mixture cautiously into 20 ml. of ice water containing 1 ml. of concentrated hydrochloric acid, and shake the mixture well.) Transfer to a separatory funnel, shake well, then discard the lower aqueous layer. Dry the ethereal solution with a little anhydrous magnesium sulphate and distil off the ether. Recrystallize the residue: methyl alcohol, ethyl alcohol, light petroleum, ether or hot water are suitable recrystallization solvents.

If dry apparatus and dry reagents have not been used, diphenylurea (m.p. 241°) or di-1-naphthylurea (m.p. 297°) are obtained.

2. **Alkyl mercuric halides.** Grignard reagents, prepared from alkyl halides, react with a mercuric halide that contains the *same halogen* as the reagent to form alkyl mercuric halides:

$$RMgX + HgX_2 \rightarrow RHgX + MgX_2$$

The reaction is applicable to primary and secondary halides only; tertiary halides do not react.

Filter the Grignard solution, prepared as in *1*, rapidly through a little glass wool into a test-tube containing 4–5 g. of mercuric chloride, bromide or iodide, depending upon the halogen in the original alkyl halide. Shake the reaction mixture vigorously for a few minutes, warm on a water bath for 2–3 minutes, and then evaporate to dryness. Boil the residue with 20 ml. of rectified spirit, filter the solution, dilute it with 10 ml. of distilled water, reheat to dissolve any precipitated solid, and allow to cool. Recrystallize the alkyl mercuric halide from dilute ethanol.

3. ***S*-Alkylthiuronium picrates.** Alkyl bromides or iodides react with thiourea in ethanolic solution to produce *S*-alkylthiuronium salts, which yield picrates of sharp melting point:

$$RX + S{=}C{<}^{NH_2}_{NH_2} \rightarrow \left\{R{-}S{-}C{<}^{NH_2}_{NH_2}\right\}^+ X^-$$

$$\left\{R{-}S{-}C{<}^{NH_2}_{NH_2}\right\}^+ X^- + HPic \rightarrow \left\{R{-}S{-}C{<}^{NH_2}_{NH_2}\right\}^+ Pic^-$$

$$[HPic \equiv HOC_6H_2(NO_2)_3]$$

Alkyl chlorides react slowly and the yield of the derivative is poor. Tertiary halides give anomalous results.

Place a mixture of 0·5 g. of finely powdered thiourea, 0·5 g. of the alkyl halide and 5 ml. of 95 per cent ethanol in a test-tube or small flask equipped with a reflux condenser. Reflux the mixture for a period depending upon the nature of the halide: primary alkyl bromides and iodides, 10–20 minutes (according to the molecular weight); secondary alkyl bromides or iodides, 2–3 hours; alkyl chlorides, 3–5 hours*; polymethylene dibromides or di-iodides, 20–50 minutes. Then add 0·5 g. of picric acid, boil until a clear solution is obtained, and cool. If no precipitate is obtained, add a few drops of water. Recrystallize the resulting S-alkylthiuronium picrate from ethanol.

The derivatives of ethylene dibromide, propylene dibromide, trimethylene dibromide and isobutylene dibromide melt at 260°, 232°, 229° and 223° respectively.

4. **Picrates of alkyl 2-naphthyl ethers.** Alkyl halides react with the sodium or potassium derivative of 2-naphthol in ethanolic solution to yield the corresponding alkyl 2-naphthyl ethers (which are usually low m.p. solids) and the latter are converted by alcoholic picric acid into the crystalline picrates:

$$RX + (2\text{—}C_{10}H_7)ONa \rightarrow (2\text{—}C_{10}H_7)OR + NaX$$

Mix together 1·0 g. of pure 2-naphthol and a solution of 0·3 g. of sodium hydroxide in 12 ml. of rectified spirit, and add 1·0 g. of the alkyl halide. For alkyl chlorides, the addition of 0·3 g. of potassium iodide is recommended. Heat the mixture under reflux for 15–30 minutes and dissolve any sodium halide by the addition of a few drops of water. The 2-naphthyl ether usually crystallizes out on cooling; if it does not, add dilute sodium hydroxide solution, with stirring, until precipitation occurs. Dissolve the 2-naphthyl ether in the minimum volume of hot ethanol and add the calculated quantity of picric acid dissolved in hot ethanol. The picrate separates out on cooling. Recrystallize it from rectified spirit. Some picrates decompose upon recrystallization.

The 2-naphthyl ethers of methylene halides have m.p. 133°, of ethylene halides 217°, and trimethylene halides 148°.

---

* Alkyl chlorides often react more rapidly (5–60 minutes) upon adding 0·5 g. of potassium iodide to the original reaction mixture, followed by sufficient water or ethanol to produce a clear solution at the boiling point. After refluxing, 0·5 g. of picric acid is added, etc.

Di- and poly-halogenated aliphatic hydrocarbons. No general procedure can be given for the preparation of derivatives of these compounds. Reliance must be placed upon their physical properties (b.p., density and refractive index) and upon any chemical reactions which they undergo.

Table IX, 11 (Chapter IX) deals with a number of aliphatic halogen compounds together with their crystalline derivatives. Some aromatic compounds, which simulate the properties of aliphatic halides in some respects, are included.

IV, 12 Halogenated Aromatic Hydrocarbons

The following reactions will assist the student in the identification of halogenated aromatic hydrocarbons.

(i) **Ethanolic silver nitrate solution.** Chlorobenzene and similar nuclear substituted compounds do not react. Benzyl chloride and other aromatic compounds with the halogen in the side chain react rapidly.

For details of test, see under *Alkyl Halides*, Section **IV,11**,(ii).

(ii) **Ethanolic potassium hydroxide solution.** This reagent gives similar results to ethanolic silver nitrate solution.

For details of tests, see under *Alkyl Halides*, Section **IV,11**,(iii).

CRYSTALLINE DERIVATIVES

1. **Nitration products.** Although no general method of nitration can be given, the following procedure is widely applicable.

Add 1·0 g. of the compound to 4 ml. of concentrated sulphuric acid and cautiously introduce, drop by drop, 4 ml. of fuming nitric acid. Warm the mixture on a water bath for 10 minutes, then pour it on to 25 g. of crushed ice (or 25 ml. of ice water). Collect the precipitate by filtration at the pump, and recrystallize it from dilute ethanol.

Twenty per cent oleum may be substituted for the concentrated sulphuric acid for compounds which are difficult to nitrate.

2. **Reaction with chlorosulphonic acid ('chlorosulphonation'). Sulphonamides.** Many aryl halides, either alone or in chloroform solution, when treated with excess of chlorosulphonic acid afford the corresponding sulphonyl chlorides in good yield: the latter may be readily converted into the aryl-sulphonamides by reaction with concentrated ammonia solution or with solid ammonium carbonate (see Sections **IV,4** and **IV,14**).

The following give abnormal results when treated with chlorosulphonic acid alone, preferably at 50° for 30–60 minutes: fluorobenzene (4,4′-difluorobiphenylsulphone, m.p. 98°); iodobenzene (4,4′di-iodobiphenylsulphone, m.p. 202°); o-dichlorobenzene (3,4,3′,4′-tetrachlorobiphenylsulphone, m.p. 176°); and o-dibromobenzene (3,4,3′,4′-tetrabromobiphenylsulphone, m.p. 176–177°). The resulting sulphones may be crystallized from glacial acetic acid, benzene or ethanol, and are satisfactory for identification of the original aryl halide. In some cases sulphones accompany the sulphonyl chloride; they are readily separated from the final sulphonamide by their insolubility in cold $6N$ sodium hydroxide solution; the sulphonamides dissolve readily and are reprecipitated by $6N$ hydrochloric acid.

Procedure 1. Dissolve 1·0 g. of the compound in 5 ml. of dry ($CaCl_2$) chloroform in a test-tube and cool in ice. Add 5 ml. of chlorosulphonic acid (*CAUTION* in handling) dropwise and with shaking. When the initial evolution of hydrogen chloride subsides, remove the reaction mixture from the ice and, after 20 minutes, pour it cautiously into a 50 ml. beaker filled with crushed ice. Separate the chloroform layer, wash it well with water, dry ($CaCl_2$) and evaporate the solvent. Recrystallize the residual aryl sulphonyl chloride from light petroleum (b.p. 40–60°), chloroform or benzene; this is not essential for conversion into the sulphonamide.

Procedure 2. Follow Procedure *1* except that no solvent is employed. Pour the syrupy reaction mixture on to crushed ice, remove the resulting arylsulphonyl chloride or sulphone, if a solid, by filtration with suction and, if a liquid, by means of a small separatory funnel or dropper, and wash with water. Polyhalogen compounds may require heating for 1 hour at 100° under a reflux condenser.

To convert the arylsulphonyl chloride into the sulphonamide, use either of the following methods:—

(i) Boil 0·5 g. with 5 ml. of concentrated ammonia solution, sp. gr. 0·88, for 10 minutes, cool to room temperature, add 10 ml. of cold water, filter with suction, wash well, and recrystallize to constant m.p. from dilute ethanol; dry at 100°.

(ii) Mix the product from the chlorosulphonation (0·5 g.) with 2·0 g. of dry, powdered ammonium carbonate and heat at 100° for 30 minutes. Wash with several 10 ml. portions of cold water, filter, and recrystallize from dilute ethanol.

If the presence of a sulphone is suspected, treat the product with $6N$ sodium hydroxide solution (only the sulphonamide dissolves), filter and reprecipitate the sulphonamide by $6N$ hydrochloric acid.

3. **Oxidation of side chains.** The oxidation of halogenated toluenes

and similar compounds and of compounds with side chains of the type —CH_2Cl and —CH_2OH proceeds comparatively smoothly with alkaline permanganate solution (for experimental details, see under *Aromatic Hydrocarbons*, Section **IV,4,**4 or under *Aromatic Ethers*, Section **IV,14**). The resulting acid may be identified by a m.p. determination and by other tests.

4. Picrates. Some halogen derivatives of the higher aromatic hydrocarbons form picrates (for experimental details, see under *Aromatic Hydrocarbons*, Section **IV,4,**6), for example, 1-chloronaphthalene (m.p. 137°), 1-bromonaphthalene (m.p. 134°), and 2-bromonaphthalene (m.p. 86°).

The properties of a number of aromatic halogen compounds are collected in Table IX, 12 (Chapter IX).

IV, 13 Aliphatic Ethers

Chemically, the ethers are inert compounds. The important reactions are:

(i) After being dried with anhydrous calcium chloride, they do not react with sodium (compare alcohols and esters).

(ii) They are not attacked by dilute acid or by alkali (compare esters).

(iii) They generally dissolve in concentrated sulphuric acid to give *clear* solutions, and are precipitated upon dilution with water. This test is carried out by adding 1 ml. of concentrated sulphuric acid to 1·0 ml. of the ether cooled in ice: observe whether the solution is clear and also whether discoloration occurs. Add the solution to ice water; the original ether should be precipitated and no sulphur dioxide should be apparent.

CAUTION. Ethers that have been stored for long periods, particularly in partly-filled bottles, frequently contain small quantities of highly explosive peroxides. The presence of peroxides may be detected either by the 'perchromic acid' test of qualitative inorganic analysis (addition of an acidified solution of potassium dichromate) or by the liberation of iodine from acidified potassium iodide solution. The peroxides are non-volatile and may accumulate in the flask during the distillation of the ether; the residue is explosive and may detonate, when distilled, with sufficient violence to shatter the apparatus and cause serious personal injury. If peroxides are found, they must first be removed by treatment with acidified ferrous sulphate solution or with sodium sulphite solution or with stannous chloride solution. The common extraction solvents diethyl ether and di-isopropyl ether are particularly prone to the formation of peroxides.

Characterization of Aliphatic Ethers

The low reactivity of aliphatic ethers renders the problem of the preparation of suitable crystalline derivatives a somewhat difficult one. Increased importance is therefore attached to the physical properties (boiling point, density and refractive index) as a means for providing preliminary information. There are, however, two reactions based upon the cleavage of the ethers which are useful for characterization.

1. **Reaction with 3,5-dinitrobenzoyl chloride.** Ethers undergo cleavage with 3,5-dinitrobenzoyl chloride in the presence of zinc chloride:

$$ROR + (NO_2)_2C_6H_3COCl \xrightarrow{ZnCl_2} (NO_2)_2C_6H_3COOR + RCl$$

The resulting alkyl 3,5-dinitrobenzoate may be employed for the characterization of the ether. The method is applicable only to symmetrical or simple ethers; a mixed aliphatic ether ROR' would yield an inseparable mixture of solid esters.

Add 1.0 ml. of the alcohol-free ether to 0·1–0·15 g. of finely powdered anhydrous zinc chloride and 0·5 g. of pure 3,5-dinitrobenzoyl chloride (Section **IV,5,***1*) contained in a test-tube; attach a small water condenser and reflux gently for 1 hour. Treat the reaction product with 10 ml. of 1·5N sodium carbonate solution, heat and stir the mixture for 1 minute upon a boiling water bath, allow to cool, and filter at the pump. Wash the precipitate with 5 ml. of 1·5N sodium carbonate solution and twice with 5 ml. of water. Dry on a porous tile or upon a pad of filter paper. Transfer the crude ester to a test-tube and boil it with 10 ml. of chloroform or carbon tetrachloride; filter the hot solution, if necessary. If the ester does not separate on cooling, evaporate to dryness on a water bath, and recrystallize the residue from 2–3 ml. of either of the above solvents. Determine the melting point of the resulting 3,5-dinitrobenzoate (see Section **IV,5**).

2. **Cleavage of ethers with hydriodic acid.** Aliphatic ethers undergo cleavage when boiled with constant boiling point hydriodic acid:

$$ROR' + 2HI \rightarrow RI + R'I + H_2O$$

If the ether is a simple one ($R = R'$), the identification of the resulting alkyl iodide presents no difficulties. If, however, it is a mixed aliphatic ether, the separation of the two alkyl iodides by fractional distillation is generally difficult unless R and R' differ considerably in molecular weight and sufficient material is available.

Reflux 1·0 ml. of the ether with 5 ml. of freshly distilled, constant boiling point hydriodic acid, b.p. 126–128°, for 2–3 hours. Add 10 ml. of water, distil and collect about 7 ml. of liquid. Decolorize the distillate by the addition of a little sodium bisulphite, and separate the two layers by means of a dropper pipette. Determine the b.p. of the resulting iodide by the Siwoloboff method (Section **I,3**) and prepare a crystalline derivative (Section **IV,11**).

The physical properties of a number of aliphatic ethers are collected in Table IX, 13 (Chapter IX). Some related heterocyclic compounds are included in the Table.

IV, 14 Aromatic Ethers

Purely aromatic ethers (*e.g.*, diphenyl ether), which are commonly encountered, are very limited in number. Most of the aromatic ethers are of the mixed aliphatic-aromatic type. They are not attacked by sodium nor by dilute acids or alkalis. When liquid, the physical properties (b.p., $d_{4°}^{20°}$ and $n_D^{20°}$) are useful constants to assist in their identification. Three important procedures are available for the characterization of aromatic ethers.

1. **Cleavage with hydriodic acid.** Aromatic ethers undergo fission when heated with constant boiling point hydriodic acid:

$$\text{ArOR} + \text{HI} \rightarrow \text{ArOH} + \text{RI}$$

The cleavage products are a phenol and an alkyl iodide, which will serve to characterize the ether.

Experimental details can easily be adapted from those given under *Aliphatic Ethers*, Section **IV,13**,*2*.

To isolate the phenol, treat the residue in the flask with aqueous sodium carbonate until alkaline and extract the mixture with ether. Wash the ethereal extract with saturated aqueous sodium carbonate, and then with 2N sodium hydroxide solution. Acidify the sodium hydroxide solution (to Congo Red paper) and extract the liberated phenol with ether. Identify the phenol as in Section **IV,7**.

2. **Sulphonamides of aryl ethers.** Aromatic ethers react smoothly in chloroform solution with chlorosulphonic acid at 0° to give sulphonyl chlorides, for example:

$$\text{RO-C}_6\text{H}_5 + 2\text{ClSO}_3\text{H} \rightarrow \text{RO-C}_6\text{H}_4\text{-SO}_2\text{Cl} + \text{H}_2\text{SO}_4 + \text{HCl}$$

The sulphonyl chlorides are treated with concentrated ammonia solution or with solid ammonium carbonate to produce sulphonamides, which usually possess sharp melting points and are therefore useful as derivatives, for example:

$$RO\text{—}C_6H_4\text{—}SO_2Cl + 2NH_3 \rightarrow RO\text{—}C_6H_4\text{—}SO_2NH_2 + NH_4Cl$$

Dissolve 1·0 g. of the compound in 5 ml. of dry chloroform in a dry test-tube, cool to 0°, and add dropwise 5 g. (2·8 ml.) of redistilled chlorosulphonic acid. When the evolution of hydrogen chloride subsides, allow the reaction mixture to stand at room temperature for 20 minutes. Pour the contents of the test-tube cautiously on to 25 g. of crushed ice contained in a small beaker. Separate the chloroform layer and wash it with a little cold water. Add the chloroform layer, with stirring, to 10 ml. of concentrated ammonia solution. After 10 minutes, evaporate the chloroform on a water bath, cool the residue and treat it with 5 ml. of 10 per cent sodium hydroxide solution; the sulphonamide dissolves as the sodium derivative,

$$RO.C_6H_4.SO_2NHNa.$$

Filter the solution to remove any insoluble matter (sulphone, etc.), acidify the filtrate with dilute hydrochloric acid, and cool in ice water. Collect the sulphonamide and recrystallize it from dilute ethanol.

3. Picrates of aromatic ethers. Many phenolic ethers react with picric acid in chloroform or ethanolic solution to yield crystalline picrates (compare *Aromatic Hydrocarbons*, Section **IV**,4,*1*).

Dissolve 0·01 mol of the phenolic ether in 10 ml. of warm chloroform, and also (separately) 0·01 mol of picric acid plus 5 per cent excess (0·241 g.) in 10 ml. of hot chloroform. Stir the picric acid solution and pour in the solution of the phenolic ether. Set the mixture aside in a 100 ml. beaker and allow it to crystallize. Recrystallize the picrate from the minimum volume of chloroform. In most cases equally satisfactory results may be obtained by conducting the preparation in rectified spirit (95 per cent C_2H_5OH). The m.p. should be determined immediately after recrystallization. It must be pointed out, however, that the picrates of aromatic ethers suffer from the disadvantage of being comparatively unstable and may undergo decomposition during recrystallization.

4. Bromo derivatives. These may be prepared as described under *Phenols* in Section **IV**,7,(ii) using glacial acetic acid as solvent. In some cases, carbon tetrachloride is a satisfactory solvent; the carbon tetrachloride is separated by distillation and the residue is recrystallized from dilute ethanol.

5. Nitro derivatives. These may be prepared as detailed under *Halogenated Aromatic Hydrocarbons* (Section **IV,12**,*3*), except that concentrated nitric acid replaces fuming nitric acid.

When aromatic ethers possess an aliphatic side chain, a satisfactory derivative may frequently be obtained by **oxidation of the side chain to a carboxyl group.** The general procedure may be illustrated by the oxidation of *p*-cresyl methyl ether *p*-$CH_3C_6H_4OCH_3$ to anisic acid *p*-$HOOCC_6H_4OCH_3$. Prepare a solution of 6 g. of potassium permanganate in a mixture of 20 ml. of 5 per cent sodium hydroxide solution and 150 ml. of water, add 2·0 g. of *p*-cresyl methyl ether, and heat under reflux for 2–3 hours. If any permanganate remains at the end of this period, destroy it by the addition of a few drops of ethanol. Remove the precipitated manganese dioxide by filtration at the pump, evaporate the filtrate to a volume of 25–30 ml., and acidify it (to Congo Red) with dilute sulphuric acid. Anisic acid, m.p. 183–184°, crystallizes out on cooling.

Table IX, 14 (Chapter IX) contains data referring to a number of selected aromatic ethers.

IV, 15 Aliphatic Aldehydes

The following reactions are characteristic of aliphatic aldehydes; those which are shared by ketones, due to the presence of the carbonyl group, are given under *Aliphatic Ketones* (Section **IV,18**).

Use acetaldehyde (or *n*-butyraldehyde*) for the following tests.

(i) **Reduction of ammoniacal silver nitrate solution.** Add a few drops of a dilute solution of the aldehyde to 2–3 ml. of an ammoniacal solution of silver nitrate {this contains the ion $[Ag(NH_3)_2]^+$} in a clean test-tube. A silver mirror is deposited on the walls of the tube either in the cold or upon warming in a beaker of boiling water.

$$RCHO + 2[Ag(NH_3)_2]OH \rightarrow RCOONH_4 + 2Ag + 3NH_3 + H_2O$$

Note

Do not heat the silver solution or allow it to stand even for a few hours, since explosive silver fulminate may be formed. The **ammoniacal solution of silver nitrate is prepared** by treating 3 ml. of 0·1N silver nitrate solution with very dilute ammonia solution dropwise until the precipitate which is first formed just redissolves.

It is preferable to use **Tollen's ammoniacal silver nitrate reagent**, which is **prepared** as follows: Dissolve 3·0 g. of silver nitrate in 30 ml. of water (solu-

---

* If the temperature of the laboratory is above 20°, *n*-butyraldehyde should be employed for all the tests.

tion *A*) and 3·0 g. of sodium hydroxide in 30 ml. of water (solution *B*). When the reagent is required, mix equal volumes (say, 1 ml.) of solutions *A* and *B* in a *clean* test-tube, and add dilute ammonia solution drop by drop until the silver oxide is just dissolved. Great care must be taken in the preparation and use of this reagent, which must not be heated. Only a small volume should be prepared just before use, any residue washed down the sink with a large quantity of water, and the test-tubes rinsed with dilute nitric acid.

(ii, *a*) **Reduction of Fehling's solution.** Place 4 ml. of freshly prepared Fehling's solution [made by mixing equal volumes of Fehling's solution No. 1 (copper sulphate solution) and solution No. 2 (alkaline tartrate solution)] in a test-tube. Add 2–3 drops of acetaldehyde or of *n*-butyraldehyde and boil the solution. A bright red precipitate of cuprous oxide is ultimately formed.

$$RCHO + 2CuO \rightarrow RCOOH + Cu_2O$$

Preparation of Fehling's solution. *Solution No. 1.* Dissolve 34·64 g. of A.R. copper sulphate crystals in water containing a few drops of dilute sulphuric acid, and dilute the solution to 500 ml.

Solution No. 2. Dissolve 60 g. of pure sodium hydroxide and 173 g. of pure Rochelle salt (sodium potassium tartrate) in water, filter if necessary through a sintered glass funnel, and make up the filtrate and washings to 500 ml.

Keep the two solutions separately in tightly stoppered bottles and mix exactly equal volumes immediately before use.

The tartrate ion forms a chelate complex which decreases the cupric ion concentration below that necessary for the precipitation of cupric hydroxide. The complex salt may be formulated:

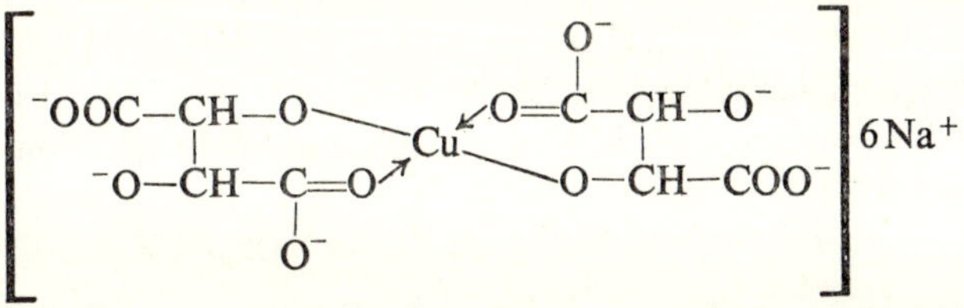
O⁻
⁻OOC—CH—O
O=C—CH—O⁻
Cu
⁻O—CH—C=O
O—CH—COO⁻
O⁻
6Na⁺

(ii, *b*) **Reduction of Benedict's solution.** Place 4 ml. of Benedict's solution in a test-tube, add 2–3 drops of acetaldehyde or of *n*-butyraldehyde, and heat the mixture to boiling. A bright red precipitate of cuprous oxide is rapidly formed.

The preparation of Benedict's solution is described under *Carbohydrates* in Section **IV,10,**(iv). The reaction may be represented as:

$$RCHO + 2Cu^{++} \text{ (as citrate complex)} + 4OH^- \rightarrow RCOOH + Cu_2O + 2H_2O$$

This test is frequently more trustworthy than that with Fehling's solution. It is positive for all aliphatic aldehydes and usually indecisive for aromatic aldehydes: a procedure is thus available for distinguishing between aliphatic and aromatic aldehydes.

(iii) **Test with Schiff's reagent (fuchsin aldehyde reagent).** Add 1 drop of acetaldehyde or of n-butyraldehyde to 2–3 ml. of water in a small test-tube, and to this solution add 1 ml. of Schiff's reagent. Observe the production of a red to violet-purple coloration within a few minutes.

Schiff's reagent is a dilute solution of fuchsin hydrochloride (p-rosaniline) that has been decolorized by sulphur dioxide. This decolorization is the result of a reaction between the p-rosaniline and sulphurous acid that destroys the quinonoid structure of the dye and produces a colourless compound. The colourless compound (a leuco-sulphonic acid) is unstable and loses sulphurous acid when treated with an aldehyde to yield a violet-purple dye.

By way of caution it should be noted that free alkali or the alkali salts of weak acids will redden the reagent like an aldehyde. It is also, of course, reddened by heat or when exposed in small quantities to the air for some time. Mineral acids greatly reduce the sensitivity of the test.

Preparation of Schiff's reagent. *Method 1.* Dissolve 0·2 g. of pure p-rosaniline hydrochloride in 40 ml. of a cold, freshly-prepared, saturated aqueous solution of sulphur dioxide; allow the solution to stand for a few hours until it becomes colourless or pale yellow. Dilute the solution to 200 ml. and keep it in a tightly-stoppered bottle. If the bottle is not adequately stoppered, the reagent will gradually lose sulphur dioxide and the colour will return. The solution keeps well if not unnecessarily exposed to light and air.

Method 2. Add 2 g. of sodium bisulphite to a solution of 0·2 g. of p-rosaniline hydrochloride and 2 ml. of concentrated hydrochloric acid in 200 ml. of water.

(iv) **Sodium bisulphite test.** Aldehydes react with saturated sodium bisulphite solution to yield crystalline bisulphite-addition compounds:

$$RCHO + NaHSO_3 \rightleftharpoons RCH(OH)SO_3Na$$

A condition of equilibrium is reached (70–90 per cent of bisulphite compound with equivalent quantities of the reagents in 1 hour), but by using a large excess of bisulphite almost complete conversion into the addition compound results. Since the reaction is reversible, the aldehyde can be recovered by adding to an aqueous solution of the bisulphite compound sufficient sodium carbonate solution or hydrochloric acid to react with the free sodium bisulphite present in the equilibrium mixture. Bisulphite compounds may therefore be employed for the purification of aldehydes or for their separation from other organic substances.

The most satisfactory reagent is a saturated solution of sodium bisulphite containing some ethanol*; it must be prepared as required since it oxidizes and decomposes on keeping. Frequently, a saturated aqueous solution is used without the addition of ethanol.

Prepare 10 ml. of saturated sodium bisulphite solution and add 4 ml. of the aldehyde: shake thoroughly and observe the rise in temperature. Filter off the crystalline precipitate at the pump, wash it with a little ethanol, followed by ether, and allow it to dry.

Treat a small quantity of the bisulphite addition compound with 5 ml. of 10 per cent sodium carbonate solution, and note the odour. Repeat the experiment with 5 ml. of dilute hydrochloric acid.

Crystalline Derivatives of Aliphatic Aldehydes

1. **2,4-Dinitrophenylhydrazones.** For experimental details, see under *Aliphatic Ketones,* Section **IV,18,***1.*

2. **Dimedone derivatives.** Dimedone or 5,5-dimethylcyclohexane-1,3-dione† in saturated aqueous solution‡ or in 10 per cent ethanolic solution gives crystalline derivatives (I) with aldehydes, but not with ketones. The reaction is:

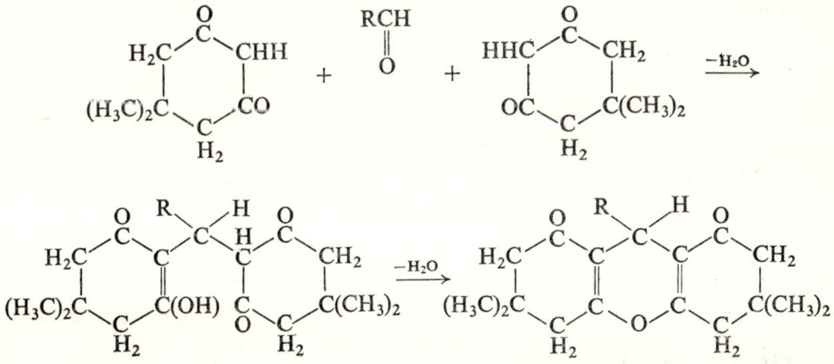

[Chemical reaction scheme showing two dimedone molecules reacting with RCHO to form intermediate (I) which loses water to form (II)]

---

* This **sodium bisulphite reagent is prepared** by treating a saturated aqueous solution of sodium bisulphite with 70 per cent of its volume of rectified (or methylated) spirit, and then adding just sufficient water to produce a clear solution.

The bisulphite solution obtained by passing sulphur dioxide into sodium carbonate solution is not recommended since the resulting yellow solution contains free sulphurous acid which dissolves some bisulphite compounds.

† Also termed dimethyldihydroresorcinol, 5,5-dimethyl-1,3-cyclohexanedione and methone. The derivatives (I) are conveniently termed formaldehyde bis-methone (R=H), etc.

‡ The solubilities in 100 ml. of water are:—19°, 0·40 g.; 25°, 0·42 g.; 50°, 1·19 g.; 80°, 3·02 g.; 90°, 3·84 g.

The condensation products are almost insoluble in water, but can be crystallized from *dilute* ethanol. Dimedone is therefore a good reagent for the detection and characterization of aldehydes.

The alkylidene dimethone (dimedone) (I) upon boiling with glacial acetic acid, acetic anhydride, hydrochloric acid and other reagents frequently loses water and passes into a substituted octahydroxanthene or the 'anhydride' (II), which often serves as another derivative. The derivatives (I) are soluble in dilute alkali and the resulting solutions give colorations with ferric chloride solution; on the other hand, the 'anhydrides' (II) are insoluble in dilute alkali and hence can easily be distinguished from the alkylidene dimedones (I).

Add 0·1 g. of the aldehyde to 4 ml. of a 10 per cent solution of dimedone in 50 per cent aqueous ethanol. If a precipitate does not form immediately, warm for 5 minutes*; if the solution is still clear at the end of this period, add hot water until the mixture is just cloudy and cool to about 5°. Collect the crystalline derivative and recrystallize it from methanol-water or ethanol-water.

To prepare the 'anhydride', boil a solution of 0·1 g. of the dimedone derivative (I) in 5 ml. of 80 per cent ethanol to which 1 drop of concentrated hydrochloric acid has been added for 5 minutes, then add hot water until the mixture is just turbid, cool and collect the 'anhydride' by filtration. Recrystallize it from methanol or aqueous methanol.

3. Semicarbazones. For experimental details, see under *Aliphatic Ketones*, Section **IV,18**, 2.

For the preparation of oximes, phenylhydrazones and *p*-nitrophenylhydrazones (where applicable), see under *Aromatic Aldehydes*, Section **IV,17**,*4–6*.

The melting points of some crystalline derivatives of a number of selected aliphatic aldehydes are collected in Table IX, 15 (Chapter IX).

IV, 16 Acetals

Acetals are usually liquid; they are almost unaffected by alkalis and are not attacked by metallic sodium nor by Fehling's (or Benedict's) solution. They are identified by reference to the alcohol and aldehyde (or ketone if a ketal) which they yield when hydrolysed in acid solution. Hydrolysis proceeds readily in dilute acid solution (*e.g.*, with 2–3 per cent hydrochloric acid):

$$RCH(OR')_2 + H_2O \xrightarrow{H^+} RCHO + 2R'OH$$

* The addition of one drop of piperidine accelerates the reaction.

The rate of hydrolysis depends upon the solubility of the acetal in the hydrolysis medium. Acetals of low molecular weight are completely hydrolysed by refluxing for 5–10 minutes; those of higher molecular weight, and therefore of small solubility, may require 30–60 minutes, but the rate of hydrolysis may be increased by the addition of dioxan which increases the solubility of the acetal.

CAUTION: Acetals, like ethers, may contain explosive peroxides which must be removed before distillation is attempted. The procedure to be adopted is similar to that described under *Aliphatic Ethers* (see Section **IV,13**).

The experimental procedure to be followed depends upon the products of hydrolysis. If the alcohol and aldehyde are both soluble in water, the reaction product is divided into two parts. One portion is used for the characterization of the aldehyde by the preparation of a suitable derivative (*e.g.*, the 2,4-dinitrophenylhydrazone, semicarbazone or dimedone compound—see Sections **IV,15** and **IV,18**). The other portion is employed for the preparation of a 3,5-dinitrobenzoate, etc. (see Section **IV,5**): it is advisable, first, to concentrate the alcohol by distillation or to attempt to salt out the alcohol by the addition of solid potassium carbonate. If one of the hydrolysis products is insoluble in the reaction mixture, it is separated and characterized. If both the aldehyde and the alcohol are insoluble, they are removed from the aqueous layer; separation is generally most simply effected with sodium bisulphite solution (compare Section **IV,18**), but fractional distillation may sometimes be employed.

The formulae and physical properties of a number of common acetals are collected in Table IX, 16 (Chapter IX).

IV, 17 Aromatic Aldehydes

Aromatic aldehydes usually have relatively high boiling points, but distil with little or no decomposition. The vapours burn with a smoky flame. They are easily oxidized on standing in the air into the corresponding acids; the odours are often pleasant and characteristic. Aromatic aldehydes, by virtue of their high molecular weight, yield crystalline derivatives with phenyl-hydrazine and hydroxylamine—these reagents are not generally recommended for aliphatic aldehydes since they give derivatives which are either liquids or solids of low m.p.

Aromatic aldehydes react with the dimedone reagent (Section **IV,15,***2*). All aromatic aldehydes (i) reduce ammoniacal silver nitrate solution and (ii) restore the colour of Schiff's reagent; many react with sodium bisulphite solution. They do not, in general, reduce Fehling's solution or Benedict's solution. Unlike aliphatic aldehydes, they usually undergo the Cannizzaro reaction under the influence of sodium hydroxide solution. For full experimental details of the above tests, see under *Aliphatic Aldehydes*, Section **IV,15**. They are easily oxidized by dilute alkaline permanganate solution at the ordinary temperature: after removal of the manganese dioxide by sulphur dioxide or by sodium bisulphite, the acid can be obtained by acidification of the solution.

CRYSTALLINE DERIVATIVES

1. **Dimedone derivatives.** For experimental details, see under *Aliphatic Aldehydes*, Section **IV,15,***2*.

2. **2,4-Dinitrophenylhydrazones.** For experimental details, see under *Aliphatic Ketones*, Section **IV,18,***1*.

3. **Semicarbazones.** See Section **IV,18,***2*.

4. **Oximes** (compare Section **IV,18,***B*). The following procedure has wide application. Dissolve 0·5 g. of hydroxylamine hydrochloride in 2 ml. of water, add 2 ml. of 10 per cent sodium hydroxide solution and 0·2 g. of the aldehyde (or ketone). If the latter is insoluble, add just sufficient ethanol to the mixture to give a clear solution. Heat the mixture under reflux for 10–15 minutes, and then cool in ice. If crystals separate, filter these off, and recrystallize from ethanol, dilute ethanol, benzene or light petroleum (b.p. 60–80°). If no solid separates on cooling, dilute with 2–3 volumes of water, filter off the precipitated solid, and recrystallize.

5. **Phenylhydrazones** (compare Section **IV,18,***C*). Dissolve 0·5 g. of *colourless* phenylhydrazine hydrochloride and 0·8 of sodium acetate in 5 ml. of water, and add a solution of 0·2–0·4 g. of the aldehyde (or ketone) in a little ethanol (free from aldehydes and ketones). Shake the mixture until a clear solution is obtained and add a little more ethanol, if necessary. Warm on a water bath for 10–15 minutes and cool. Filter off the crystalline derivative, and recrystallize it from dilute ethanol or water; sometimes benzene or light petroleum (b.p. 60–80°) may be used.

The use of liquid phenylhydrazine in the preparation of phenylhydrazones is not recommended for beginners because of the highly poisonous character of the liquid. A phenylhydrazine reagent may, however, be used.

The **phenylhydrazine reagent may be prepared** by either of two methods.

Method A. Dissolve 25 ml. of light-coloured phenylhydrazine (redistil, if necessary) in 250 ml. of 10 per cent acetic acid, add 0·5 g. of decolorizing carbon, shake and filter into a dark bottle.

Method B. Dissolve 25 g. of colourless phenylhydrazine hydrochloride (recrystallize, if necessary) in 250 ml. of water; warming may be required. Add 45 g. of crystallized sodium acetate to the cold solution and shake until dissolved. Add 0·5 g. of decolorizing carbon, shake, and filter into a dark bottle. The reagent should not be kept for longer than 1 month.

6. p-Nitrophenylhydrazones (compare Section **IV,18,***1*). Reflux a mixture of 0·5 g. of *p*-nitrophenylhydrazine, 0·5 g. of the aldehyde (or ketone), 10–15 ml. of ethanol and 2 drops of glacial acetic acid for 10 minutes. Add more ethanol if the boiling solution is not homogeneous. Cool the clear solution, filter off the *p*-nitrophenylhydrazone, and recrystallize it from ethanol or acetic acid.

Alternatively, dissolve approximately equivalent amounts of the aldehyde (or ketone) and the solid reagent in the minimum volume of cold glacial acetic acid, and reflux for 15 minutes. The *p*-nitrophenylhydrazone separates on cooling or upon careful dilution with water.

Note

All aldehydes, and also those ketones which have two different groups attached to the carbonyl grouping, are capable of yielding two stereoisomeric oximes, hydrazones or semicarbazones. As a general rule, however, one of the stereoisomerides is formed in much greater amount than the other, and no doubt therefore arises as to the purity of the ketonic compound under investigation; occasionally a mixture of stereoisomerides is obtained, which may be difficult to separate by recrystallization. The formation, therefore, of one of the above derivatives of indefinite melting point and obvious heterogeneity does not necessarily imply the presence of an impure ketonic substance.

7. **2,4-Dinitrophenylhydrazones.** The following procedure for the preparation of 2,4-dinitrophenylhydrazones is alternative to those given in Section **IV,18,***1*.

To the clear solution obtained by warming 0·25 g. of 2,4-dinitrophenylhydrazine, 0·5 ml. of concentrated hydrochloric acid and 4–5 ml. of ethanol, add 0·1–0·2 g. of the aldehyde dissolved in a small volume of ethanol (if insoluble in water) and heat just to boiling. Allow to cool to room temperature, filter off the 2:4-dinitrophenylhydrazone and recrystallize it from ethanol or glacial acetic acid.

8. **Azines.** Aldehydes react with hydrazine to yield azines: the reaction cannot usually be arrested at the hydrazone stage. This reaction may be illustrated by the preparation of *benzalazine* from benzaldehyde:

$$2C_6H_5CHO + N_2H_4,H_2SO_4 \xrightarrow[NH_3]{Aq.}$$
$$C_6H_5CH=N-N=CHC_6H_5 + H_2SO_4 + 2H_2O$$

Stir a mixture of 2·4 g. of powdered hydrazine sulphate, 18 ml. of water and 2·4 ml. of concentrated aqueous ammonia (sp. gr. 0·88), and add 4·6 g. (4·4 ml.) of benzaldehyde (free from benzoic acid) dropwise, with stirring, over a period of 30–60 minutes. Stir the mixture for a further hour, collect the solid by suction filtration and wash it with water. Recrystallize from 8 ml. of rectified spirit. The yield of benzalazine (yellow needles), m.p. 92–93°, is 3·6 g.

The melting points of the various derivatives of a number of typical aromatic aldehydes are collected in Table IX, 17 (Chapter IX).

IV, 18 Aliphatic Ketones

Ketones, unlike aldehydes (Section **IV,15**), do not (*a*) reduce ammoniacal solutions of silver salts, (*b*) reduce Fehling's solution, (*c*) react with Schiff's reagent, (*d*) yield resins with strong sodium hydroxide solution and (*e*) do not react with the dimedone reagent. Most ketones which contain the —COCH$_3$ grouping (*e.g.* acetone) {excluding those possessing the phenyl (C$_6$H$_5$) grouping} or those which contain the $>$CO grouping as part of a ring (*e.g.*, cyclohexanone) react with sodium bisulphite solution to an appreciable extent. Aldehydes and those ketones which combine appreciably with sodium bisulphite react with hydrogen cyanide to form **cyanohydrins**:

$$>\!\!C\!=\!O + HCN \rightarrow \;>\!\!C(OH)CN$$

The carbonyl compound may be mixed with an aqueous solution of sodium or potassium cyanide and mineral acid added, or the bisulphite compound may be treated with an equivalent quantity of sodium cyanide, for example:

$$CH_3COCH_3 \xrightarrow{NaHSO_3} (CH_3)_2C(OH)SO_3Na \xrightarrow{NaCN} (CH_3)_2C(OH)CN$$
Acetone cyanohydrin

Most of the characteristic reactions of ketones (RR'CO) depend upon condensation with substituted amines. The reactions occur between the carbonyl group and the —NH_2 group of the substituted amine, and hence are also shared by aldehydes RCHO:

$$>C=O + H_2N- \rightarrow >C=N- + H_2O$$

Many of these are crystalline compounds of sharp m.p. and are therefore useful for identification and characterization. These include the condensation products with:

(i) **Hydroxylamine** (NH_2OH). The substance formed is termed an **oxime**, for example:

$$(CH_3)_2CO + H_2NOH \rightarrow (CH_3)_2C=NOH + H_2O$$
$$\text{Acetoxime}$$

(ii) **Hydrazine** (NH_2NH_2). The product formed is called a **hydrazone**, but since this derivative possesses a free amino group it can condense with another molecule of the carbonyl compound to yield an **azine**:

$$RR'CO + H_2NNH_2 \rightarrow RR'C=NNH_2 \xrightarrow{RR'CO} RR'C=NN=CRR'$$
$$\qquad\qquad\qquad\qquad\qquad\text{Hydrazone} \qquad\qquad\qquad \text{Azine}$$

This double condensation is prevented by the use of substituted hydrazines.

Ketazines are usually liquids for aliphatic ketones but solids for alkyl-aryl and for diaryl ketones.

(iii) **Phenylhydrazine** ($C_6H_5NHNH_2$). Carbonyl compounds react with phenylhydrazine to give **phenylhydrazones.** These derivatives are largely oils (or possess low melting points) for many aliphatic aldehydes and ketones, but are generally crystalline for aromatic carbonyl compounds and also for cycloaliphatic and heterocyclic aldehydes and ketones, for example:

$$H_2C\begin{smallmatrix}CH_2-CH_2\\CH_2-CH_2\end{smallmatrix}CO + H_2NNHC_6H_5 \longrightarrow$$
$$\text{Cyclohexanone}$$

$$H_2C\begin{smallmatrix}CH_2-CH_2\\CH_2-CH_2\end{smallmatrix}C=NNHC_6H_5$$
$$\text{Cyclohexanone phenylhydrazone}$$

(iv) **2,4-Dinitrophenylhydrazine** ($O_2N-C_6H_3(NO_2)-NHNH_2$). The **2,4-dinitrophenylhydrazones** formed with this reagent are generally highly crystalline and almost insoluble in water (because of their high molecular weight) and are therefore eminently suitable for the detection and characterization of carbonyl compounds.

(v) **Semicarbazide hydrochloride** ($NH_2CONHNH_2,HCl$). This is one of the best reagents for the characterization of carbonyl compounds since the derivatives, known as **semicarbazones**, are readily formed, are highly crystalline, possess sharp melting points, and are easily crystallized (*e.g.*, from alcohol or acetone):

$$RR'C{=}O + H_2NNHCONH_2 \rightarrow \underset{\text{Semicarbazone}}{RR'C{=}NNHCONH_2} + H_2O$$

The reagent is, however, more expensive than 2,4-dinitrophenylhydrazine.

In order to obtain practice in the preparation of the above derivatives, experimental details for a few typical examples will be given.

A. Purification of commercial cyclohexanone through the bisulphite compound

Prepare a saturated solution of sodium bisulphite at the laboratory temperature from 20 g. of finely powdered sodium bisulphite: about 35 ml. of water are required. Measure the volume of the resulting solution and treat it with 70 per cent of its volume of rectified spirit (or methylated spirit); add sufficient water (about 23 ml.) to just dissolve the precipitate which separates. Introduce 10 g. of commercial cyclohexanone into the aqueous-ethanolic bisulphite solution with stirring and allow the mixture to stand for 30 minutes; stir or shake occasionally. Filter off the crystalline bisulphite compound at the pump, and wash it with a little methylated spirit.

Transfer the bisulphite compound to a separatory funnel and decompose it with 40 ml. of 10 per cent sodium hydroxide solution. Remove the liberated cyclohexanone, saturate the aqueous layer with salt and extract it with 15 ml. of ether. Combine the ether extract with the ketone layer and dry with 2 g. of anhydrous magnesium or sodium sulphate. Filter the dried ethereal solution into a 25 ml. distilling flask (1), attach a condenser, add a few fragments of porous porcelain, and distil off the ether from a water bath; take the usual precautions against fire. Distil the residual cyclohexanone using an air bath or an asbestos-centred wire gauze, and collect the fraction, b.p. 153–155°. The yield of pure cyclohexanone is 8–9 g., depending upon the purity of the sample of ketone employed.

Note

(1) Alternatively—and this procedure is recommended—remove the ether by flash distillation. A slightly improved yield is obtained if a short fractionating column is used.

B. Acetoxime

Dissolve 2·5 g. of hydroxylamine hydrochloride in 5 ml. of water in a small conical flask and add a solution of 1·5 g. of sodium hydroxide in 5 ml. of water. Cool the solution in cold or ice water, and add 3·0 g. (3·8 ml.) of acetone slowly. Cool the flask, shake well, and leave overnight, during which time the oxime may crystallize out. If no crystals appear, cork the flask and shake vigorously when the acetoxime usually separates as colourless crystals. Filter off the crystals at the pump, dry rapidly between filter paper (yield: 2·5 g.) and determine the m.p. (59°). Extract the filtrate with two 10 ml. portions of ether, and remove the solvent: a further 0·3 g. of acetoxime (m.p. 60°) is obtained. Recrystallize from light petroleum, b.p. 40–60° (*CAUTION:* inflammable) to obtain the pure acetoxime, m.p. 60°. Acetoxime sublimes when left exposed to the air.

B'. Cyclohexanone Oxime

Dissolve 2·5 g. of hydroxylamine hydrochloride and 4 g. of crystallized sodium acetate in 10 ml. of water in a small flask or in a test-tube. Warm the solution to about 40° and add 2·5 g. of cyclohexanone. Stopper the vessel securely with a cork and shake vigorously for a few minutes: the oxime soon separates as a crystalline solid. Cool in ice, filter the crystals at the pump, and wash with a little cold water. Recrystallize from light petroleum, b.p. 60–80°, and dry the crystals upon filter paper in the air. The yield of pure cyclohexanone oxime, m.p. 90°, is 2·5 g.

C. Cyclohexanone Phenylhydrazone

Prepare a solution of phenylhydrazine by dissolving 1·0 g. of phenylhydrazine hydrochloride and 1·5 g. of crystallized sodium acetate in 10 ml. of water;* if the resulting solution is turbid, filter.

---

* The reagent may also be prepared by dissolving 1.0 ml. of phenylhydrazine in a solution of 1 ml. of glacial acetic acid and 10 ml. of water. This procedure is not so convenient as that from the solid hydrochloride because of the poisonous character of phenylhydrazine (both liquid and vapour). If the liquid is accidentally spilled on the skin, wash it at once with dilute acetic acid, followed by soap and water.

Add a solution of 0·5 ml. of cyclohexanone in 8 ml. of water to the reagent contained in a test-tube, cork the tube, and shake vigorously until the phenylhydrazone has crystallized. Filter off the crystals at the pump and wash well with water. Recrystallize from dilute ethanol. M.p. 77°.

D. Acetone Semicarbazone

Prepare a solution of 1·0 g. of semicarbazide hydrochloride ($NH_2CONHNH_2,HCl$) and 1·5 g. of crystallized sodium acetate in 10 ml. of water in a test-tube. Add 1·0 ml. of acetone, close the tube with a cork and shake vigorously. Allow the mixture to stand, with occasional vigorous shaking, for 10 minutes: it is advantageous to cool in ice. Filter the crystals, wash with a little cold water, and recrystallize from water or dilute ethanol. The m.p. of acetone semicarbazone is 187°.

CRYSTALLINE DERIVATIVES OF ALIPHATIC ALDEHYDES AND KETONES

1. **2,4-Dinitrophenylhydrazones.** Suspend 0·25 g. of 2,4-dinitrophenylhydrazine in 5 ml. of methanol and add 0·4–0·5 ml. of concentrated sulphuric acid cautiously. Filter the warm solution and add a solution of 0·1–0·2 g. of the carbonyl compound in a small volume of methanol or of ether. If no solid separates within 10 minutes, dilute the solution carefully with $2N$ sulphuric acid. Collect the solid by suction filtration and wash it with a little aqueous methanol. Recrystallize the derivative from ethanol, dilute ethanol, ethyl acetate, dioxan, acetone, acetic acid, nitromethane, nitrobenzene or xylene.

The following **2,4-dinitrophenylhydrazine reagent** may be used for the routine detection of keto compounds. Suspend 2·0 g. of 2,4-dinitrophenylhydrazine in 100 ml. of methanol; add *cautiously* 4·0 ml. of concentrated sulphuric acid. The mixture becomes warm and the solid usually dissolves to produce a clear solution. Filter, if necessary.

For the preparation of 2,4-dinitrophenylhydrazones, dissolve the carbonyl compound (say, 0·3 g.) in 3 ml. of methanol and add the calculated volume of the reagent. If a precipitate does not form immediately, dilute with a little water. Collect the derivative and recrystallize it as above.

2. **Semicarbazones.** Dissolve 0·5 g. of semicarbazide hydrochloride and 0·8 g. of crystallized sodium acetate in 4–5 ml. of water; add 0·3–0·5 g. of the aldehyde or ketone and shake. If the mixture is turbid, add methanol (acetone-free) or water until a clear solution is obtained; shake the mixture for a few minutes and allow to stand. Usually the semicarbazone crystallizes from the cold solution on standing, the time varying from a few minutes to several hours. The reaction may be accelerated, if necessary, by warming the mixture on a water bath for a few minutes and then cooling in ice water. Filter off the crystals, wash with a little cold water, and recrystallize from water or from methyl or ethyl alcohol either alone or diluted with water.

Note

When semicarbazide is heated in the absence of a carbonyl compound for long periods, condensation to **biurea,** $NH_2CONHNHCONH_2$, m.p. 247–250° (decomp.), may result; occasionally this substance may be produced in the normal preparation of a semicarbazone that forms slowly. Biurea is sparingly soluble in ethanol and soluble in hot water, whereas semicarbazones with melting points in the same range are insoluble in water: this enables it to be readily distinguished from a semicarbazone.

3. **Oximes.** The method given for semicarbazones (see 2) may be employed: use 1 g. of hydroxylamine hydrochloride, 2 g. of crystallized sodium acetate and 0·5 g. of the aldehyde or ketone. It is usually advisable to warm on a water bath for 10 minutes.

For water-insoluble aldehydes or ketones, the following alternative procedure may be used. Reflux a mixture of 0·5 g. of the aldehyde or ketone, 0·5 g. of hydroxylamine hydrochloride, 5 ml. of ethanol and 2·5 ml. of pyridine on a water bath for 15–60 minutes. Remove the solvent either by distillation (water bath) or by evaporation of the hot solution in a stream of air (water pump). Add 5 ml. of water to the cooled residue, cool in an ice bath and stir until the oxime crystallizes. Filter off the solid, wash it with a little water and dry. Recrystallize from ethanol (95 per cent or more dilute), benzene, or benzene-light petroleum (b.p. 60°–80°).

4. **Benzylidene derivatives.** Compounds containing the ketomethylene group ($-CH_2CO-$) react with benzaldehyde to yield benzylidene derivatives:

$RCOCH_2R' + C_6H_5CHO \rightarrow RCOC(=CHC_6H_5)R' + H_2O$

$RCH_2COCH_2R' + 2C_6H_5CHO \rightarrow$
$\quad RC(=CHC_6H_5)COC(=CHC_6H_5)R' + 2H_2O$

Cyclic ketones yield dibenzylidene derivatives.

Dissolve 1·0 g. of the ketomethylene compound and 1·1 g. or 2·2 g. of pure benzaldehyde (according as to whether the compound may be regarded as $RCOCH_2R'$ or as RCH_2COCH_2R') in about 10 ml. of rectified (or methylated) spirit, add 1 ml. of $2N$ sodium hydroxide solution, shake and allow the mixture to stand for about an hour at room temperature. The benzylidene derivative usually crystallizes out or will do so upon 'scratching' the walls of the vessel with a glass rod. Filter off the solid, wash it with a little cold ethanol, and recrystallize it from absolute ethanol (or absolute industrial spirit).

Experimental details for the preparation of oximes, phenylhydrazones and *p*-nitrophenylhydrazones will be found under *Aromatic Aldehydes*, Section **IV,17,***4–6*.

Table IX, 18 (Chapter IX) lists the melting points of derivatives of some selected aliphatic and cycloaliphatic ketones.

IV, 19 Aromatic Ketones

Aromatic ketones usually have relatively high boiling points, but distil with little or no decomposition. Many are solids. The vapours generally burn with a smoky flame. They react with the 2,4-dinitrophenylhydrazine reagent (Section **IV,18,***1*) or with the phenylhydrazine reagent (Section **IV,17,***5*), but are unaffected by the dimedone reagent (Section **IV,15,***2*). The general reactions are similar to those already given under *Aliphatic Ketones* (Section **IV**,18). Owing to their higher molecular weight, such derivatives as oximes and phenylhydrazones are frequently quite satisfactory.

The preparation of crystalline derivatives, including 2,4-dinitrophenylhydrazones, semicarbazones, oximes, phenylhydrazones and *p*-nitrophenylhydrazones can be carried out as described in Sections **IV,17** and **IV,18**.

The melting points of various derivatives of a number of typical aromatic ketones are collected in Table IX, 19 (Chapter IX).

IV, 20 Aliphatic Carboxylic Acids

(i) **Action upon sodium bicarbonate solution.*** Place 1 ml. of 5 per cent sodium bicarbonate solution upon a watch glass; introduce the pure acid (1 drop or a little of the finely powdered solid). Evolution of carbon dioxide indicates the presence of an acid.

Test the solution so obtained for **unsaturation** by adding cold

---

* Potassium bicarbonate solution is sometimes preferred because of the greater solubility of the solid in water.

1 per cent potassium permanganate solution a drop at a time. The immediate disappearance of the purple colour and the formation of a brown turbidity indicate the presence of a double bond (**Baeyer's test**). It must be noted that many substances, not unsaturated, decolorize warm acid or neutral potassium permanganate solution.

Test a small quantity of the aqueous solution or extract of the carboxylic acid with litmus or with Universal indicator paper.

(ii) **Ester formation.** Warm a small amount of the acid with 2 parts of absolute ethyl alcohol and 1 part of concentrated sulphuric acid for 2 minutes. Cool, and pour cautiously into aqueous sodium carbonate solution contained in an evaporating dish, and smell immediately. An acid usually yields a sweet, fruity smell of an ester. (Acids of high molecular weight often give almost odourless esters.)

(iii) **Neutralization equivalent.** It is recommended that the neutralization equivalent (or the **equivalent weight**) of the acid be determined: this is the number expressing the weight in grams of the compound neutralized by one gram equivalent of alkali. Weigh out accurately about 0·2 g. of the acid (finely powdered if a solid), add about 30 ml. of water and, if necessary, just sufficient ethanol to dissolve most of the acid, followed by two drops of phenolphthalein indicator. Titrate with accurately standardized $0 \cdot 1N$ sodium or barium hydroxide solution.* Calculate the equivalent weight from the expression:

$$\text{Neutralization equivalent} = \frac{\text{Grams of acid} \times 1000}{\text{Ml. of alkali} \times \text{Normality of alkali}}$$

Crystalline Derivatives of Aliphatic Carboxylic Acids

1. **Amides, anilides and *p*-toluidides.** The dry acid is first converted by excess of thionyl chloride into the acid chloride:

$$\text{RCOOH} + \text{SOCl}_2 \rightarrow \text{RCOCl} + \text{SO}_2 + \text{HCl}$$

The by-products are both gaseous and the excess of thionyl chloride (b.p. 78°) may be readily removed by distillation. Interaction of the

---

* For further details as to the standardization of the alkali and the storage of standard alkali solutions, see A. I. Vogel. *A Text Book of Quantitative Inorganic Analysis including Elementary Instrumental Analysis.* Third Edition, 1961 (Longmans, Green and Co. Ltd.). Run a blank on the solvent and use the same amount of indicator.

acid chloride with ammonia solution, aniline or *p*-toluidine yields the amide, anilide or *p*-toluidide respectively:

$$RCOCl + 2NH_3 \rightarrow RCONH_2 + NH_4Cl$$
$$RCOCl + 2R'NH_2 \rightarrow RCONHR' + R'NH_2,HCl$$

Stopper the side arm of a 10 or 25 ml. distilling flask with long side arm and attached condenser (Fig. *I*, 3, 1), and fit a vertical water condenser into the neck. Place 0·5 g. of the dry acid (finely powdered if it is a solid) or its sodium salt into the flask, add 2·0–2·5 ml. of redistilled thionyl chloride and reflux gently for 30 minutes; it is advisable to place a plug of cotton wool* in the top of the reflux condenser to exclude moisture. Remove the reflux condenser and distil off the excess of thionyl chloride† (b.p. 78°). The residue in the flask consists of the acid chloride and can be converted into any of the derivatives given below.

(*a*) **Amides.** Treat the acid chloride cautiously with about 20 parts of concentrated ammonia solution (sp. gr. 0·88) and warm for a few moments. If no solid separates on cooling, evaporate to dryness on a water bath. Recrystallize the crude amide from water or dilute ethanol.

Alternatively, dissolve or suspend the acid chloride in 5–10 ml. of dry ether or dry benzene, and pass in dry ammonia gas. If no solid separates, evaporate the solvent. Recrystallize the amide from water or dilute ethanol.

(*b*) **Anilides.** Dilute the acid chloride with 5 ml. of pure ether (or benzene), and slowly add a solution of 1 g. of pure aniline in 8–10 ml. of the same solvent until the odour of the acid chloride has disappeared; excess of aniline is not harmful. Shake with excess of dilute hydrochloric acid to remove aniline and its salts, wash the ethereal (or benzene) layer with 3–4 ml. of water, and evaporate the solvent [*CAUTION!*]. Recrystallize the anilide from water, dilute ethanol or benzene-light petroleum (b.p. 60–80°).

p-**Bromoanilides** are similarly prepared with *p*-bromoaniline.

(*c*) *p*-**Toluidides.** Proceed as under (*b*), but substitute *p*-toluidine for aniline.

---

* This is more convenient than the conventional calcium chloride guard tube and possesses the advantage of cheapness and hence can easily be renewed for each experiment: it is, of course, removed during distillations.
† If the boiling point of the acid chloride is too near that of thionyl chloride to render separation by distillation practicable, the excess of the reagent can be destroyed by the addition of pure formic acid:

$$HCOOH + SOCl_2 \rightarrow CO + SO_2 + 2HCl$$

Anilides and *p*-toluidides may also be *prepared directly from the acids* by heating them with aniline or *p*-toluidine respectively:

$$RCOOH + R'NH_2 \rightarrow RCONHR' + H_2O$$

Alternatively, the alkali metal salts of the acids may be heated with the hydrochloride of the appropriate base.

Place 1·0 g. of the monobasic acid and 2 g. of aniline or *p*-toluidine in a dry test-tube, attach a short air condenser and heat the mixture in an oil bath at 140–160° for 2 hours: do not reflux too vigorously an acid that boils below this temperature range, and allow only steam to escape from the top of the condenser. For a sodium salt, use the proportions of 1·0 g. of salt to 3·0 g. of the hydrochloride of the base. If the acid is dibasic, employ double the quantity of amine and a reaction temperature of 180–200°: incidentally, the procedure is recommended for dibasic acids since the latter frequently give anhydrides with thionyl chloride. Powder the cold reaction mixture, triturate it with 20–30 ml. of 10 per cent hydrochloric acid, and recrystallize from dilute ethanol.

2. ***p*-Bromophenacyl esters.** *p*-Bromophenacyl bromide reacts with the alkali metal salts of acids to form crystalline *p*-bromophenacyl esters:

$$Br\text{-}C_6H_4\text{-}COCH_2Br + RCOONa \longrightarrow Br\text{-}C_6H_4\text{-}COCH_2OOCR + NaBr$$

When preparing derivatives as detailed under 2, 3 and 4, care must be taken that the original reaction mixture is not alkaline: alkalis cause hydrolysis of the phenacyl halides to phenacyl alcohols.

Dissolve or suspend 0·5 g. of the acid in 5 ml. of water in a small conical flask, add a drop or two of phenolphthalein indicator, and then 4–5 per cent sodium hydroxide solution until the acid is just neutralized. Add a few drops of very dilute hydrochloric acid so that the final solution is *faintly* acid (litmus).* Introduce 0·5 g. of *p*-bromophenacyl bromide (m.p. 109°)† dissolved in 5 ml. of rectified (or methylated) spirit, and heat the mixture under reflux for 1 hour: if

---

* If the sodium salt of the acid is available, dissolve 0·5 g. in 5 ml. of water, add a solution of 0·5 g. of the reagent in 5 ml. of ethanol, and proceed as detailed in the text after just acidifying (litmus) with dilute hydrochloric acid.

† *CAUTION:* phenacyl halides are lachrymatory.

the mixture is not homogeneous at the boiling point or if a solid separates out, add just sufficient ethanol to produce homogeneity. [Di- and tri-basic acids require proportionately larger amounts of the reagent and longer refluxing periods.] Allow the solution to cool, filter off the separated crystals at the pump, wash with a little ethanol and then with water. Recrystallize from dilute ethanol: dissolve the solid in hot ethanol, add hot water until a turbidity just results, clear the latter with a few drops of ethanol, and allow to cool. Acetone may sometimes be employed for recrystallization.

3. *p*-Nitrobenzyl esters. *p*-Nitrobenzyl bromide (m.p. 100°) reacts with the alkali metal salts of acids to give *p*-nitrobenzyl esters:

$$O_2N-C_6H_4-CH_2Br + RCOONa \longrightarrow$$
$$O_2N-C_6H_4-CH_2OOCR + NaBr$$

It is important that the solution of the sodium salt be *faintly* acid in order that the formation of coloured by-products in the subsequent reaction may be prevented. If the molecular weight of the monobasic acid is known, it is desirable to employ a slight excess of the sodium salt, since excess of the latter is more easily removed than the unchanged reagent.

Use the procedure given under *2* for *p*-bromophenacyl esters. If the ester does not crystallize out on cooling, reheat the reaction mixture, and add small portions of hot water to the point of incipient cloudiness and allow to cool.

4. *p*-Phenylphenacyl esters. *p*-Phenylphenacyl bromide reacts with soluble salts of organic acids to yield crystalline *p*-phenylphenacyl esters:

$$p\text{-}C_6H_5C_6H_4COCH_2Br + NaOOCR \rightarrow$$
$$p\text{-}C_6H_5C_6H_4COCH_2OOCR + NaBr$$

The procedure is similar to that given under *2* and *3* above. Add a weighed amount of acid (0·005 mol) to 5 ml. of water in a small conical flask and neutralize it with N sodium carbonate or N sodium hydroxide. The final solution should be faintly acid to litmus (add more of the organic acid or a few drops of dilute hydrochloric acid); unless this precaution is taken, coloured by-products are formed which are very difficult to remove. [If the alkali metal salt is available, dissolve 0·005 mol in 5 ml. of water, and render the solution just acid to litmus by the addition of dilute hydrochloric acid.] Introduce 10 ml. of ethanol, and if the salt of the organic acid is not thrown out of solution, add 0·005 mol* of p-phenylphenacyl bromide: reflux the mixture for periods of up to 1, 2 or 3 hours according to the basicity of the acid. If the salt of the organic acid is precipitated by the ethanol, add more water until the salt dissolves. Some of the esters are sparingly soluble in the reaction mixture and crystallize from the boiling solution; in most cases, however, crystal formation does not occur until the mixture is cooled. In some instances it may be necessary to concentrate the solution before crystallization occurs. Recrystallize the crude p-phenylphenacyl ester from ethanol, dilute ethanol, acetone or benzene.

Certain dibasic acids, of which the sodium or potassium salts are sparingly soluble in dilute ethanol, cause difficulty; these should be neutralized with ethylamine solution.

5. S-Benzylthiuronium salts. S-Benzylthiuronium chloride reacts with the alkali metal salts of organic acids to produce crystalline S-benzylthiuronium salts:

$$\{C_6H_5CH_2\text{—}S\text{—}C(\text{—}NH_2)\text{—}NH_2\}^+ Cl^- + RCOONa \rightarrow$$
$$\{C_6H_5CH_2\text{—}S\text{—}C(\text{—}NH_2)\text{—}NH_2\}^+ RCOO^- + NaCl$$

It is important not to allow the reaction mixture to become appreciably alkaline, since the free base then decomposes rapidly yielding benzyl mercaptan, which has an unpleasant odour.

Dissolve (or suspend) 0·25 g. of the acid in 5 ml. of warm water, add a drop or two of phenolphthalein indicator and neutralize carefully with *ca.* N sodium hydroxide solution. Then add about 2–3 drops of *ca.* $0·1N$ hydrochloric acid to ensure that the solution is almost neutral (*pale* pink colour). (Under alkaline conditions the reagent tends to decompose to produce the evil-smelling benzyl mercaptan.) If the sodium salt is available dissolve 0·25 g. in 5 ml. of water, and add 2 drops of *ca.* $0·1N$ hydrochloric acid. Introduce a solution of 1·0 g. of S-benzylthiuronium chloride in 5 ml. of water *or* in 10 ml. of rectified spirit, and cool in ice until precipitation is complete. Recrystallize the crude derivative from dilute ethanol or from hot water.

With some acids (*e.g.*, succinic acid and sulphanilic acid) more satisfactory results are obtained by reversing the order of mixing,

* Dibasic and tribasic acids will require 0·01 and 0·015 mol respectively.

i.e., by adding the solution of the sodium salt of the acid to the reagent. In view of the proximity of the melting points of the derivatives of many acids, the mixed m.p. test should be applied.

The melting points of the derivatives of a number of selected aliphatic acids are collected in Table IX, 20 (Chapter IX).

IV, 21   Aromatic Carboxylic Acids

Aromatic carboxylic acids are usually crystalline solids, burn with a smoky flame, and are generally sparingly soluble in water. They may be detected and characterized as already described under *Aliphatic Carboxylic Acids* (Section **IV,20**).

An additional useful test is to **distil the acid or its sodium salt with soda lime.** Heat 0·1 of the acid or its sodium salt with 0·2 g. of soda lime in an ignition tube to make certain that there is no explosion. Then grind together 0·5 g. of the acid or its sodium salt with 3 g. of soda lime, place the mixture in a Pyrex test-tube and cover it with an equal bulk of soda lime. Fit a wide delivery tube dipping into an empty test-tube. Clamp the tube near the mouth. Heat the soda lime and then the mixture gradually to a dull-red heat. Examine the product: this may consist of aromatic hydrocarbons or derivatives, *e.g.*, phenol from salicylic acid, anisole from anisic acid, toluene from toluic acid, etc.

The melting points of the derivatives of a number of selected aromatic carboxylic acids are collected in Table IX, 21 (Chapter IX).

IV, 22   Acid Chlorides of Aliphatic Acids

Carry out the following simple experiments with acetyl chloride.

(i) To a test-tube containing about 5 ml. of water add cautiously a few drops of acetyl chloride. Note that the acetyl chloride does not dissolve in the water, but on shaking reaction occurs with the evolution of heat and the formation of acetic acid.

$$CH_3COCl + H_2O \rightarrow CH_3COOH + HCl$$

(ii) To 1 ml. of *absolute* ethyl alcohol in a dry test-tube add 1 ml. of acetyl chloride drop by drop (use a dropper pipette; keep the mixture cold by holding the tube under the tap. Note whether any hydrogen chloride gas is evolved (blow across the mouth of the tube). Pour into 2 ml. of saturated salt solution and observe the formation of an upper layer of ester (ethyl acetate) and also note the odour of the ester; if this does not appear to have a fruit-like odour, add a little sodium carbonate to neutralise the acid and examine again.

$$CH_3COCl + C_2H_5OH \rightarrow CH_3COOC_2H_5 + HCl$$

Repeat the test with 1 ml. of *n*-butyl alcohol.

(iii) Add 1 ml. of acetyl chloride, drop by drop, to 0·5–1 ml. of aniline. After the vigorous reaction is over, dilute the mixture with 5 ml. of water and observe the formation of a solid (acetanilide). Filter this off, recrystallize from a little boiling water, and determine the m.p. after drying. Pure acetanilide melts at 114°.

$$CH_3COCl + 2C_6H_5NH_2 \rightarrow C_6H_5NHCOCH_3 + C_6H_5NH_3Cl$$

The above simple experiments illustrate the more important properties of aliphatic acid chlorides. For **characterization**, the general procedure is to hydrolyse the acid chloride by warming with dilute alkali solution, neutralize the resulting solution with dilute hydrochloric acid (phenolphthalein), and evaporate to dryness on a water bath. The mixture of the sodium salt of the acid and sodium chloride thus obtained may be employed for the preparation of solid esters as detailed under *Aliphatic Carboxylic Acids*, Section **IV,20**. The anilide or *p*-toluidide may be prepared directly from the acid chloride {see (iii) above and Section **IV,20,***1*}.

The physical properties of a number of aliphatic acid chlorides are collected in Table IX, 22 (Chapter IX).

IV, 23 Anhydrides of Aliphatic Acids

Carry out the following simple experiments with redistilled acetic anhydride.

(i) Mix 5 ml. of water in a test-tube with 0·5 ml. of acetic anhydride and shake. Observe that no apparent reaction occurs immediately. Upon warming, however, the acetic anhydride dissolves and acetic acid is formed:

$$(CH_3CO)_2O + H_2O \rightarrow 2CH_3COOH$$

(ii) Mix 2 ml. of absolute ethyl alcohol with 1 ml. of acetic anhydride. No apparent reaction occurs in the cold. Heat the mixture gently for a few minutes: the anhydride slowly passes into solution. Treat with a little sodium carbonate solution; observe the characteristic odour of ethyl acetate. If the ester does not separate from the solution, add a little salt until saturated.

$$(CH_3CO)_2O + C_2H_5OH \rightarrow CH_3COOC_2H_5 + CH_3COOH$$

Repeat the experiment with 2 ml. of *n*-butyl alcohol.

(iii) Heat a mixture of 1 ml. of aniline and 1 ml. of acetic anhydride almost to the boiling point and cool. No solid separates. Add 4–5 ml. of water and rub the walls of the test-tube with a glass rod. Crystals of acetanilide are formed. Recrystallize from a little boiling water and determine the m.p. (114°).

$$(CH_3CO)_2O + C_6H_5NH_2 \rightarrow C_6H_5NHCOCH_3 + CH_3COOH$$

Perform the following experiment with *succinic anhydride*. This illustrates the formation of an **anilic acid**, which is usually an excellent derivative for the characterization of an anhydride of a dibasic acid (particularly if it is a liquid) and indirectly for the dibasic acid itself. Dissolve 0·5 g. of succinic anhydride in 15 ml. of benzene by heating on a water bath, and add a solution of 0·5 ml. of aniline in 3 ml. of benzene. The anilic acid soon separates in a crystalline form.* Cool, filter off the crystals and wash with a little benzene. Recrystallize from dilute ethanol and determine the m.p. Pure succinanilic acid (I) melts at 150°.

$$\begin{array}{l} CH_2CO \\ \diagdown \\ O + H_2NC_6H_5 \rightarrow \\ \diagup \\ CH_2CO \end{array} \quad \begin{array}{l} CH_2COOH \\ | \\ CH_2CONHC_6H_5 \end{array} \quad (I)$$

The above simple experiments illustrate the more important properties of the anhydrides of aliphatic acids. For their **characterization** the reaction with aniline or *p*-toluidine is frequently employed. Alternatively, the anhydride may be hydrolysed with dilute alkali as detailed under *Acid Chlorides*, Section **IV,22**, and the resulting acid characterized as in Section **IV,20**.

The physical properties of a number of acid anhydrides (aliphatic) are given in Table IX, 23 (Chapter IX).

IV, 24 Acid Chlorides of Aromatic Acids

Most aromatic acid chlorides impart a strongly acid reaction when shaken with water (compare Section **IV,20**). All are completely hydrolysed by boiling with solutions of caustic alkalis and yield no product volatile from the alkaline solution (compare *Esters*, Sections

---

* If the anhydride of an unknown acid is being used and the anilic acid does not crystallize after the mixture has been boiled for a short time, cool the solution, wash it with dilute hydrochloric acid to remove the excess of aniline, and evaporate the solvent; the anilic acid will then usually crystallize.

IV,25 and **IV,26**). They may be distinguished from acids by their ease of reaction with alcohols (compare Section **IV,5**), phenols (compare Section **IV,7**), and amines (compare Sections **IV,32** and **IV,33**).

Acyl halides may be identified by: hydrolysis to the corresponding acids (the latter may be further characterized as in Section **IV,21**); conversion into amides (Section **IV,20**), anilides or *p*-toluidides (Section **IV,20**); and conversion into solid esters (Section **IV,26**).

The physical properties of a few typical acid chlorides of aromatic acids are collected in Table IX, 24 (Chapter IX). Some acid anhydrides are also included in this Table (compare Section **IV,23**).

IV, 25 Aliphatic Esters

Hydrolysis (or saponification) of *n*-butyl acetate. Boil 2·0–2·5 g. of *n*-butyl acetate with 25 ml. of 10 per cent sodium hydroxide solution under reflux until the odour of the ester can no longer be detected (about 1 hour). Set the condenser for downward distillation and collect the first 5 ml. of distillate. Saturate it with potassium carbonate, allow to stand for 5 minutes, and withdraw all the liquid into a small pipette or dropper pipette. Allow the lower layer of carbonate solution to run slowly into a test-tube, and place the upper layer in a small test-tube or weighing bottle. Dry the alcohol with about one quarter of its bulk of anhydrous potassium carbonate. Remove the alcohol with a dropper pipette and divide it into two parts; use one portion for the determination of the b.p. by the Siwoloboff method (Section **I,3**) and convert the other portion into the 3,5-dinitrobenzoate (Section **IV,5,*1***) and determine the m.p.

Acidify the residue in the flask with dilute sulphuric acid and distil off 10–15 ml. of the solution. Test a small portion of the distillate for acidity, and also observe the odour. Neutralize the main portion with sodium hydroxide solution (add a drop of phenolphthalein to act as indicator), evaporate to small bulk, and convert the sodium salt into the *p*-bromophenacyl ester or into some other suitable derivative (Section **IV,20**); determine the m.p. of the derivative.

The above example serves to illustrate the basis of the procedure employed for the characterization of aliphatic esters, *viz.*, hydrolysis to, and identification of, the parent acids and alcohols. Most esters are liquids; a notable exception is dimethyl oxalate, m.p. 54°. Many have pleasant, often fruit-like, odours. Many dry esters react with sodium, but less readily than do alcohols: hydrogen is evolved particularly on warming, and a solid sodio derivative may separate on cooling (*e.g.*, ethyl acetate yields ethyl sodioacetoacetate; ethyl adipate gives ethyl sodio cyclopentanonecarboxylate).

In the routine examination of esters it is often a good plan to carry out two hydrolyses, one for the isolation and characterization of the parent acid, and the other for the isolation and identification of the parent alcohol.

1. Drop 1 g. of sodium into 10 ml. of ethyl alcohol (or methanol) in a small flask provided with a small water condenser; heat the mixture until all the sodium has dissolved. Cool, and add 1·0 g. of the suspected ester and 0·5 ml. of water. Frequently the sodium salt of the acid will be deposited either at once or after boiling for a few minutes. If this occurs, filter off the solid at once, wash it with a little absolute ethyl alcohol (or absolute methylated spirit), and convert it into the *p*-bromophenacyl ester, *p*-nitrobenzyl ester or *S*-benzyl-thiuronium salt (for experimental details, see Section **IV,20**). If no solid separates, continue the boiling for 30–60 minutes, boil off the alcohol, allow to cool, render the product just neutral to phenolphthalein with dilute sulphuric or hydrochloric acid, convert the sodium salt present in solution into a crystalline derivative (Section **IV,20**), and determine its melting point.

2. Boil 1·0 g. of the ester with 15 ml. of 10 per cent sodium or potassium hydroxide solution under reflux for at least 1 hour. If the alcohol formed is water (or alkali) soluble, the completion of the hydrolysis will be indicated by the disappearance of the ester layer. Distil off the liquid through the same condenser and collect the first 2–2·5 ml. of distillate. If a distinct layer separates on standing (or upon saturation of half the distillate with potassium carbonate), remove this layer with a capillary dropper, dry it with a little anhydrous potassium carbonate or anhydrous calcium sulphate, and determine the b.p. by the Siwoloboff method (Section **I,3**). Whether an insoluble alcohol separates out or not, prepare a crystalline derivative (*e.g.*, the 3,5-dinitrobenzoate, Section **IV,5,***1*) and determine its m.p.

The residue in the flask will contain the sodium (or potassium) salt of the acid together with excess of alkali. Just acidify with dilute sulphuric acid and observe whether a crystalline acid separates; if it does, filter, recrystallize and identify (Section **IV,20**). If no crystalline solid is obtained, the solution may be just neutralized to phenolphthalein and the solution of the alkali salt used for the preparation of a crystalline derivative. This will confirm, if necessary, the results of hydrolysis by Method 1. If the time factor is important, either

Method 1 or the product of the caustic alkali hydrolysis may be used for the identification of the acid.

The following notes may be useful:

(1) The b.p., density and refractive index are valuable constants for the final characterization of liquid esters.

(2) Some esters, *e.g.*, methyl formate, methyl oxalate, methyl succinate, methyl and ethyl tartrate, are appreciably soluble in water. These are usually easily hydrolysed by alkali.

(3) Of the common esters, methyl oxalate (solid, m.p. 54°) and ethyl oxalate (liquid) give amides almost immediately upon shaking with concentrated ammonia solution. The resulting oxamide, m.p. 417°, is valueless as a derivative. The esters may, however, be easily hydrolysed and identified as above.

(4) If the original ester is a fat or oil and produces an odour of acrolein when heated, it may be a **glyceride.** Esters of ethylene glycol and of glycerol with simple fatty acids are viscous and of high b.p. They are hydrolysed (method 1) and the ethyl alcohol (or methanol) distilled off. The residue is diluted (a soap **may** be formed) and acidified with hydrochloric acid (Congo Red paper). The acid is filtered off or extracted with ether. If no acid can be isolated by these methods, it must be simple and volatile, and should be separated by distillation. The residual aqueous solution of glycol or glycerol is neutralized, evaporated to a syrup on a water bath, and extracted with ethyl alcohol or with ethyl acetate; the alcohol is evaporated and the glycol or glycerol in the residue is identified as usual.

(5) **β-Keto esters** (*e.g.*, ethyl acetoacetate) are soluble in solutions of caustic alkalis but not in sodium carbonate solution. They give colours with freshly prepared ferric chloride solution; a little ethanol should be added to bring the ester into solution. Sodium ethoxide solution reacts to yield sodio compounds, which usually crystallize out in the cold. They are hydrolysed by boiling sulphuric acid to the corresponding ketones, which can be identified as usual (Section **IV,18**). Phenylhydrazine yields pyrazolones.

(6) **Unsaturated esters** decolorize a solution of bromine in carbon tetrachloride and also neutral potassium permanganate solution.

It is frequently advisable in the routine examination of an ester, and before any derivatives are considered, to determine the **saponification equivalent** of the ester. In order to ensure that complete hydrolysis takes place in a comparatively short time, the quantitative saponification is conducted with a standardized ethanolic solution of caustic alkali—preferably potassium hydroxide since the potassium salts of organic acids are usually more soluble than the sodium salts. A knowledge of the b.p. and the saponification equivalent of the unknown ester would provide the basis for a fairly accurate approximation of the size of the ester molecule. It must, however, be borne in mind that certain structures may affect the values of the equivalent: thus aliphatic halogenated esters may consume alkali because of

Elementary Practical Organic Chemistry

hydrolysis of part of the halogen during the determination, nitro esters may be reduced by the alkaline hydrolysis medium, etc.

DETERMINATION OF THE SAPONIFICATION EQUIVALENT OF AN ESTER

The **saponification equivalent** or the **equivalent weight of an ester** is that weight in grams of the ester from which one equivalent weight of acid is obtainable by hydrolysis, *or* that quantity which reacts with one equivalent of alkali. The saponification equivalent is determined in practice by treating a known weight of the ester with a known quantity of caustic alkali used in excess (see also Section **V,5**). The residual alkali is then readily determined by titration of the reaction mixture with a standard acid. The amount of alkali that has reacted with the ester is thus obtained: the equivalent can then be readily calculated.

Obtain a 100 ml. round-bottomed flask and attach an efficient reflux condenser to it by means of a clean rubber stopper. (The rubber stopper is cleaned by warming with dilute alkali, and then thoroughly washing with distilled water.) Place the sample of ester in a weighing bottle fitted with a cork carrying a small dropper pipette, transfer about 0·5 g. of the ester, weighed to an accuracy of 0·001 g., to the flask. Then introduce 25·0 ml. of standard 0·5N alcoholic potassium hydroxide solution by means of a pipette into the flask, add a few chips of broken glass, attach the reflux condenser, and heat the flask gently on a water bath until hydrolysis is complete (1·5–2 hours). When cold, pour about 25 ml. of distilled water through the condenser, add 2–3 drops of phenolphthalein indicator, and titrate the excess of alkali with standard 0·5N or 0·25N hydrochloric or sulphuric acid. The end point should be a faint pink. If too much acid is accidentally added, back titrate the excess of acid with the original alkali. Calculate the saponification equivalent from the expression:

$$\text{Saponification Equivalent} = \frac{\text{Weight of ester} \times 1000}{\text{Ml. of } N \text{ KOH used}}$$

The **0·5N ethanolic potassium hydroxide solution is prepared** by dissolving 8 g. potassium hydroxide pellets in 250 ml. of rectified spirit contained in a bottle closed by a cork; shaking is necessary. After standing for 24 hours, the clear solution is decanted or filtered from the residue of potassium carbonate.

It is essential to standardize the ethanolic potassium hydroxide solution immediately before use by titration with standard 0·5N or 0·25N hydrochloric or sulphuric acid using phenolphthalein as indicator.

Identification of the alcohol components of simple esters. The alcohol components of many simple esters may be identified as the crystalline 3,5-dinitrobenzoates (compare Section **IV,5,***1*) by heating the esters with 3,5-dinitrobenzoic acid in the presence of a little concentrated sulphuric acid:

$$\text{RCOOR}' + \underset{O_2N}{\overset{O_2N}{\bigcirc}}\text{—COOH} \rightleftharpoons \text{RCOOH} + \underset{O_2N}{\overset{O_2N}{\bigcirc}}\text{—COOR}'$$

The reaction does not appear to be applicable if either the R or the R' group of the ester reacts with concentrated sulphuric acid; also esters of high molecular weight (>250) react with difficulty.

Mix 2·0 ml. of the ester with 1·5 g. of 3,5-dinitrobenzoic acid and add 2 drops of concentrated sulphuric acid. If the b.p. of the ester is below 150°, reflux the mixture gently; if the b.p. is above 150° heat the mixture, with frequent shaking at first, in an oil bath at about 150°. If the 3,5-dinitrobenzoic acid dissolves within 15 minutes, heat the mixture for 30 minutes, otherwise 60 minutes heating is required. Allow the reaction mixture to cool, dissolve it in 25 ml. of pure ether, and extract thoroughly with 5 per cent sodium carbonate solution (*ca.* 25 ml.). Wash the ethereal solution with water, and evaporate the ether. Dissolve the residue (which is usually an oil) in 5 ml. of hot ethanol, add hot water cautiously until the 3,5-dinitrobenzoate commences to separate, cool and stir. Recrystallize the derivative from dilute ethanol: the yield is 0·1–0·2 g.

Identification of the acidic components of simple esters. The following procedures may be regarded as alternative to that described above involving hydrolysis of the ester.

Anilides or p-*toluidides of acids from esters.* Esters are converted into the corresponding anilides or *p*-toluidides by treatment with anilino- or with *p*-toluidino-magnesium bromide, which are readily obtained from any simple Grignard reagent and aniline or *p*-toluidine:

$$\text{ArNH}_2 + \text{RMgX} \rightarrow \text{ArNHMgX} + \text{RH}$$

$$2\text{ArNHMgX} + \text{R}'\text{COOR}'' \rightarrow$$

$$\text{R}'\text{C(OMgX)(NHAr)}_2 + \text{Mg(OR}''\text{)X} \xrightarrow{2\text{HCl}}$$

$$\text{R}'\text{CONHAr} + \text{ArNH}_3\text{Cl} + \text{MgClX}$$

This procedure is speedy, economical, and employs materials which are readily available. It is not satisfactory for esters of dibasic acids.

Add 2·0 g. (2·0 ml.) of pure aniline dropwise to a cold solution of ethyl magnesium bromide (or iodide) prepared from 0·5 g. of magnesium, 2·5 g. (1·8 ml.) of ethyl bromide (or the equivalent quantity of ethyl iodide), and 15 ml. of pure, sodium-dried ether. When the vigorous evolution of ethane has ceased, introduce 0·01 mol of the ester in 5 ml. of anhydrous ether, and warm the mixture on a water bath for 10 minutes; cool. Add dilute hydrochloric acid to dissolve the magnesium compounds and excess of aniline. Separate the ethereal layer, dry it with anhydrous magnesium sulphate and evaporate the ether. Recrystallize the residual anilide, which is obtained in almost quantitative yield, from dilute ethanol or other suitable solvent.

Alternatively, add a solution of 4·5 g. of *p*-toluidine in dry ether to the Grignard reagent prepared from 1·0 g. of magnesium as detailed above. Then introduce 1·0 g. (or 0·02 mol) of the ester and proceed as described for anilides.

N-*Benzylamides of acids from esters.* Esters are converted into the *N*-benzylamides of the corresponding acids by heating with benzylamine in the presence of a little ammonium chloride as catalyst:

$$RCOOR' + C_6H_5CH_2NH_2 \rightarrow RCONHCH_2C_6H_5 + R'OH$$

The reaction (which is essentially the direct aminolysis of esters with benzylamine) proceeds readily when R' is methyl or ethyl. Esters of higher alcohols should preferably be subjected to a preliminary methanolysis by treatment with sodium methoxide in methanol:

$$RCOOR' + CH_3OH \xrightarrow{CH_3ONa} RCOOCH_3 + R'OH$$

N-Benzylamides are recommended when the corresponding acid is liquid and/or water-soluble so that it cannot itself serve as a derivative. The benzylamides derived from the simple fatty acids or their esters are not altogether satisfactory (see Table below); those derived from most hydroxyacids and from polybasic acids or their esters are formed in good yield and are easily purified. The esters of aromatic acids yield satisfactory derivatives but the method must compete with the equally simple process of hydrolysis and precipitation of the free acid, an obvious derivative when the acid is a solid. The procedure fails with esters of keto, sulphonic and inorganic acids, and with some halogenated aliphatic esters.

Reflux a mixture of 1·0 g. of the ester, 3 ml. of benzylamine and 0·1 g. of powdered ammonium chloride for 1 hour in a Pyrex test-tube fitted with a short condenser. Wash the cold reaction mixture with water to remove the excess of benzylamine. If the product does not crystallize, stir it with a little water containing a drop or two of dilute hydrochloric acid. If crystallization does not result, some unchanged ester may be present: boil with water for a few minutes in an evaporating dish to volatilize the ester. Collect the solid N-benzylamide on a filter, wash it with a little light petroleum, b.p. 100–120°, and recrystallize it from dilute ethanol, ethyl acetate or acetone.

If the ester does not yield a benzylamide by this procedure, convert it into the methyl ester by refluxing 1 g. for 30 minutes with 5 ml. of absolute methanol in which about 0·1 g. of sodium has been dissolved. Remove the methanol by distillation and treat the residual ester as above.

The melting points of the N-benzylamides are collected in the following Table:

N-Benzylamides of some Carboxylic Acids

Formic	60°	Oxalic	223°	Benzoic	106°
Acetic	61	Malonic	142	p-Aminobenzoic	90
Propionic	44	Succinic	206	m-Hydroxybenzoic	142
n-Butyric	38	Glutaric	170	m-Nitrobenzoic	101
Isobutyric	87	Adipic	189	p-Nitrobenzoic	142
n-Valeric	42	Pimelic	154	o-Iodobenzoic	110
Isovaleric	54	Sebacic	167	Phenylacetic	122
n-Caproic	53	Carbonic	169	m-Toluic	75
Lauric	83	Ethylmalonic	138	p-Toluic	133
Palmitic	95	n-Butylmalonic	149	Anisic	132
Myristic	90	D-Tartaric	199	Salicylic	136
Stearic	97	DL-Tartaric	210	Anthranilic	125
Glycollic	104	meso-Tartaric	205	Cinnamic	225
Cyanoacetic	124	D-Malic	157	Hydrocinnamic	85
Crotonic	114	Maleic	150	Phthalic	179
2-Furoic	111	Fumaric	205	Terephthalic	266
Acrylic	237	Citric	170		
		Saccharic	201		

Acid hydrazides from esters. Methyl and ethyl esters react with hydrazine to give acid hydrazides:

$$RCOOCH_3 + H_2NNH_2 \rightarrow RCONHNH_2 + CH_3OH$$

The hydrazides are often crystalline and then serve as useful derivatives. Esters of higher alcohols should be converted first to the methyl esters by boiling with sodium methoxide in methanol (see under N-benzylamides).

Place 1·0 ml. of hydrazine hydrate (*CAUTION:* corrosive chemical) in a test-tube fitted with a short reflux condenser. Add 1·0 g. of the methyl or ethyl ester dropwise (or portionwise) and heat the mixture gently under reflux for 15 minutes. Then add just enough absolute ethanol through the condenser to produce a clear solution, reflux for a further 2–3 hours, distil off the ethyl alcohol, and cool. Filter, off the crystals of the acid hydrazide, and recrystallize from ethanol, dilute ethanol or from water.

The melting points of the hydrazides of some acids are given in Table IX, 20 (Chapter IX).

In Table IX, 25 (Chapter IX) the boiling points, densities and refractive indices of a number of selected esters are collected.

IV, 26 Aromatic Esters

Aromatic esters usually burn with a smoky flame, possess reasonably high boiling points, and are (particularly esters of phenols) sometimes crystalline solids. Phenyl esters usually give phenol upon distillation with soda lime (see *Aromatic Carboxylic Acids*, Section **IV,21** for general details).

The experimental details already given for the detection and characterization of aliphatic esters (determination of saponification equivalents; hydrolysis: *Aliphatic Esters*, Section **IV,25**) apply equally to aromatic esters. A slight modification in the procedure for isolating the products of hydrolysis is necessary for phenolic (or phenyl) esters since the alkaline solution will contain both the alkali phenate and the alkali salt of the organic acid: upon acidification, both the phenol and the acid will be liberated. Two methods may be used for **separating the phenol and the acid:**

1. Acidify the cold alkaline reaction mixture with dilute sulphuric acid (use litmus or Congo Red paper) and extract both the acid and the phenol with ether. Remove the acid by washing the ethereal extract with saturated sodium bicarbonate solution until effervescence ceases; retain the aqueous washings. Upon evaporating the ether, the phenol remains; it may be identified (*a*) by its action upon ferric chloride solution, (*b*) the formation of a crystalline derivative with bromine water, and (*c*) by any of the methods given in Section **IV,7**. Acidify the aqueous washings with dilute sulphuric acid whilst stirring steadily, and investigate the organic acid (Sections **IV,20** and **IV,21**).

2. Add dilute sulphuric acid, with stirring, to the cold alkaline solution until the solution is acid to litmus or Congo Red paper, and the acid, if a solid, commences to separate as a faint permanent precipitate. Now add dilute sodium carbonate solution until the solution is alkaline (litmus paper) and any precipitate has completely redissolved. Extract the clear solution twice with ether: evaporate or distil the ether from the ethereal solution on a water bath (*CAUTION: no flames may be near*) and identify the residual phenol as under *1*. Remove the dissolved ether from the aqueous solution by boiling, acidify with dilute sulphuric acid and identify the organic acid present (see Sections **IV,20** and **IV,21**).

The student is recommended to carry out **the hydrolysis of phenyl benzoate.** Place a mixture of 2·0 g. of phenyl benzoate and 25 ml. of 10 per cent aqueous sodium hydroxide solution in a 100 ml. flask fitted with a reflux condenser. Boil until the ester has completely disappeared (about 1 hour). If any unchanged ester volatilizes in the steam and crystallizes in the condenser, pour about 5 ml. of 10 per cent sodium hydroxide solution down the condenser in order to return the ester to the flask. Cool the clear solution in ice and, when cold, add dilute sulphuric acid with stirring until a faint but permanent precipitate is formed: test with litmus or Congo Red paper to ensure that the solution is acidic. Then add dilute sodium carbonate solution with vigorous stirring until the precipitate just redissolves and the solution is alkaline to litmus paper. Extract the solution twice with ether, dry the combined ethereal extracts with anhydrous magnesium sulphate or potassium carbonate and distil off most of the ether. Pour the remainder while still hot into an evaporating or crystallizing dish; the phenol will crystallize when all the ether has evaporated. Prepare a crystalline derivative of the phenol. Acidify the aqueous solution from the ether extraction with dilute sulphuric acid, filter off the benzoic acid with suction, wash with water, and recrystallize from boiling water. Confirm the identity of the acid by a mixed m.p. determination.

Table IX, 26 (Chapter IX) summarizes the physical properties of a few selected aromatic esters.

IV, 27 Primary Aliphatic Amides

The student should carry out the following simple experiments with acetamide or with any other aliphatic amide, *e.g.*, *n*-caproamide; they illustrate some of the general reactions of primary aliphatic amides.

(i) Boil 0·5 g. of acetamide with 3 ml. of 10 per cent sodium hydroxide solution. Note that ammonia is evolved. Acidify and test for acetic acid in the solution.

$$CH_3CONH_2 + NaOH \rightarrow CH_3COONa + NH_3$$

(ii) Boil 0·5 g. of acetamide with 3 ml. of dilute hydrochloric acid (1:1) or, better, with 10 per cent sulphuric acid. Observe that acetic acid is evolved.

$$CH_3CONH_2 + HCl + H_2O \rightarrow CH_3COOH + NH_4Cl$$

(iii) Dissolve 1 g. of acetamide in 2 ml. of water, add about 0·1 g. of yellow mercuric oxide, and warm gently. The mercuric oxide passes into solution, and a water-soluble, non-ionic mercury derivative (NN'-mercuribisacetamide) is produced:

$$2CH_3CONH_2 + HgO \rightarrow (CH_3CONH)_2Hg + H_2O$$

CHARACTERIZATION

Aliphatic amides may be hydrolysed by boiling with 10 per cent sodium hydroxide solution to the corresponding acid (as the sodium salt). The alkaline solution should be acidified with dilute sulphuric acid; any water-soluble acid may then be distilled from the solution. Alternatively, hydrolysis may be effected with 10–20 per cent sulphuric acid. The resulting aliphatic acid (usually a liquid) may be characterized as detailed in Section **IV,20.**

Crystalline derivatives may be prepared with xanthydrol (9-hydroxyxanthen), but the reagent is comparatively expensive. Xanthydrol reacts with primary amides with the formation of crystalline **xanthylamides** or **9-acylamidoxanthens**:

Xanthydrol + RCONH$_2$ → Xanthylamide + H$_2$O

Commercial xanthydrol may be used, but the pure white product, m.p. 120–121°, obtained by the reduction of xanthone with sodium amalgam gives better results.

1. **Xanthylamides.** Dissolve 0·25 g. of xanthydrol in 3·5 ml. of glacial acetic acid; if an oil separates (as is sometimes the case with commercial material), allow to settle for a short time and decant the supernatant solution. Add 0·25 g. of the amide, shake and allow to stand. If a crystalline derivative does not separate in about 10 minutes, warm on a water bath for a period not exceeding 30 minutes, and allow to cool. Filter off the solid xanthylamide (9-acylamidoxanthen) and recrystallize it from dioxan-water or from acetic acid-water, dry at 80° for 15 minutes and determine the m.p.

Some amides do not dissolve in the acetic acid; in such cases a mixture of 2 ml. of glacial acetic acid and 3 ml. of water may be used as a solvent for the reaction.

Di- and tri-chloroacetamide, oxamide, guanidine, and cyanoguanidine (dicyanodiamide) do not give satisfactory results.

The melting points of the xanthylamides of a number of aliphatic primary amides are collected in Table IX, 27 (Chapter IX).

Reactions of Urea

The student should carry out the following reactions of urea:

(i) **Solubility.** Confirm that urea is very soluble in water and dissolves in hot methyl, ethyl and amyl alcohols, but is almost insoluble in ether.

(ii) **Sodium hydroxide solution.** Dissolve 0·2 g. of urea in 5 ml. of dilute sodium hydroxide solution and warm. Observe that ammonia is evolved.

$$CO(NH_2)_2 + 2NaOH \rightarrow Na_2CO_3 + 2NH_3$$

(iii) **Nitrous acid.** Dissolve 0·2 g. of urea in 2–3 ml. of dilute hydrochloric acid and add 3 ml. of dilute (about 5 per cent) sodium nitrite solution. Effervescence occurs, and nitrogen and carbon dioxide are evolved:

$$CO(NH_2)_2 + 2HNO_2 \rightarrow CO_2 + 2N_2 + 3H_2O$$

(iv) **Sodium hypobromite (or hypochlorite) solution.** Dissolve 0·5 g. of urea in 3 ml. of water and add 5–10 ml. of dilute sodium hypochlorite or hypobromite solution.* Nitrogen is evolved.

$$CO(NH_2)_2 + 3NaOBr + 2NaOH \rightarrow$$
$$N_2 + 3H_2O + Na_2CO_3 + 3NaBr$$

(v) **Urea nitrate.** Dissolve 0·5 g. of urea in 3 ml. of water and add 1 ml. of concentrated nitric acid. White crystals of urea nitrate $\{CO(NH_2)_2, HNO_3\}$, m.p. 163°, separate immediately.

(vi) **Urea oxalate.** Dissolve 0·5 g. of urea in 3 ml. of water and add a solution of 0·6 g. of oxalic acid in 7 ml. of water. Upon stirring urea oxalate $\{2CO(NH_2)_2, H_2C_2O_4\}$, m.p. 171°, crystallizes out.

Urea oxalate is also sparingly soluble in amyl alcohol and since urea is soluble in this alcohol, the property may be utilized in separating urea from mixtures. An aqueous extract of the mixture is rendered slightly alkaline with sodium hydroxide solution and extracted with ether; this removes all the basic components, but not urea. The residual aqueous solution is

---

* The hypobromite solution may be prepared by treating 2 ml. of bromine water with dilute sodium hydroxide solution, dropwise, until the bromine colour is just discharged.

extracted with amyl alcohol (to remove the urea): upon adding this extract to a solution of oxalic acid in amyl alcohol crystalline urea oxalate is precipitated.

(vii) **Biuret reaction.** Place 0·5 g. of urea in a dry test-tube and heat gently just above the m.p. for 1–2 minutes. Ammonia is first evolved and the residue solidifies with the formation of biuret:

$$CO(NH_2)_2 \rightarrow NH_3 + HN{=}C{=}O$$
$$HN{=}C{=}O + H_2NCONH_2 \rightarrow H_2NCONHCONH_2 \text{ (biuret)}$$

The latter may be identified by dissolving the residue in a few ml. of warm 10 per cent sodium hydroxide solution, cooling and adding 1 drop of very dilute copper sulphate solution. A purple or violet coloration is obtained. Carry out a blank test and compare the result.

This colour reaction is also given by malonamide and oxamide.

(viii) **Xanthydrol reaction.** Add a solution of 0·1 g. of urea in 2 ml. of acetic acid to 1–2 ml. of a 5 per cent solution of xanthydrol in acetic acid or in methyl alcohol and warm. Filter off the dixanthydryl urea and recrystallize it from aqueous dioxan; wash with a little ethanol and ether, and dry at 80°. Determine the m.p. (274°).

IV, 28 Primary Aromatic Amides

Primary aromatic amides are crystalline solids with definite melting points. Upon boiling with 10–20 per cent sodium or potassium hydroxide solution, they are hydrolysed with the evolution of ammonia (vapour turns red litmus paper blue and mercurous nitrate paper black) and the formation of the alkali metal salt of the acid:

$$RCONH_2 + NaOH \rightarrow RCOONa + NH_3$$

The acid is liberated upon acidification. Hydrolysis may also be effected (but less readily and usually not quite so satisfactorily) by boiling with dilute hydrochloric acid (1:1) or 20 per cent sulphuric acid:

$$RCONH_2 + H_2O + HCl \rightarrow RCOOH + NH_4Cl$$

The **hydrolysis by alkali** is illustrated by the foll)wing experimental details for benzamide. Place 1·5 g. of benzamide and 25 ml. of 10 per cent sodium hydroxide solution in a 100 ml. conical or round-bottomed flask equipped with a reflux condenser. Boil the mixture gently for 30 minutes; ammonia is freely evolved. Detach the condenser and continue the boiling in the open flask for 3–4 minutes to expel the residual ammonia. Cool the solution in ice, and add concentrated hydrochloric acid until the mixture is strongly acid; benzoic acid separates immediately. Leave the mixture in ice until cold, filter at the pump, wash with a little cold water and drain well. Recrystallize the benzoic acid from hot water. Determine the m.p., and confirm its identity by a mixed m.p. test.

The characterization of a primary aromatic amide is based upon its own m.p. and the identification of the acid (see Section **IV,21**) produced on hydrolysis. A crystalline derivative may be prepared directly with xanthydrol (for experimental details, see Section **IV,27,*1***).

The melting points of a few selected primary aromatic amides (together with those of the xanthylamides, where known) are collected in Table IX, 28 (Chapter IX). A more detailed list will be found in the column headed *Amides* in Table IX, 21 (*Aromatic Carboxylic Acids*).

IV, 29 Substituted Aromatic Amides

This group comprises substances of the type ArCONHR and ArCONRR′, *i.e.*, substituted amides of the aromatic series or aroyl derivatives of primary and secondary amines. They are all well-defined crystalline solids, sparingly soluble in cold but often appreciably soluble in hot water and moderately soluble in ether; they are generally neutral or feebly basic in reaction.

Upon warming with 10–20 per cent sodium or potassium hydroxide solution, no ammonia is evolved (distinction from primary amides). The base, however, is usually liberated upon **fusion with soda lime** (for experimental details see *Aromatic Carboxylic Acids*, Section **IV,21**) and at the same time the aroyl group yields a hydrocarbon. Thus benz-*p*-toluidide affords *p*-toluidine and benzene.

Carry out a preliminary soda lime fusion test to determine whether the base is liberated under these conditions; if it is, repeat the experiment with 1·0 g. of the substance. Identify the base (amine) by its m.p. (if a solid) and the preparation of a solid derivative (Section **IV,33**).

Hydrolysis of the original compound will confirm its identity. Boil 0·5–1·0 g. of the original substance with 10–20 ml. of concentrated hydrochloric acid under reflux for 2 hours:

$$ArCONHR + H_2O + HCl \rightarrow ArCOOH + RNH_3^+Cl^-$$

The solution will then contain the free acid and the hydrochloride of the base; either of these may separate if sparingly soluble. If a solid crystallizes from the cold solution, filter, test with sodium bicarbonate solution {see Section **IV,20,(i)**} and compare the m.p. with that of the original compound. If it is a hydrolysis product, examine it separately.

Otherwise, render the filtrate alkaline with sodium hydroxide solution and extract the base with ether; if the presence of the unchanged aroyl compound is suspected, extract the base with weak acid. Identify the base in the usual manner (see Section **IV,33**). The acid will be present as the sodium salt in the alkaline extract and may be identified as described under *Aromatic Carboxylic Acids* in Section **IV,21**.

Benzanilide and similar compounds are hydrolysed very slowly by concentrated hydrochloric acid; hydrolysis is quite rapid with 60–70 per cent sulphuric acid (experimental details for benzanilide are given below). In the preliminary experiment boil 0·5–1·0 g. of the compound with 10–20 ml. of dilute sulphuric acid (1:1 by volume) under reflux for 20–30 minutes. Dilute with 10 ml. of water and filter off any acid which may be precipitated; if the acid is liquid and volatile, distil it directly from the reaction mixture. Render the residue alkaline and isolate the base as above.

Hydrolysis of benzanilide. Place 2·5 g. of benzanilide and 25 ml. of 70 per cent sulphuric acid* in a small flask fitted with reflux condenser, and boil gently for 30 minutes. Some of the benzoic acid will vaporize in the steam and solidify in the condenser. Pour 30–35 ml. of hot water down the condenser; this will dislodge and partially dissolve the benzoic acid. Cool the flask in ice water; filter off the benzoic acid (aniline sulphate does not separate at this dilution), wash well with water, drain, dry upon filter paper, and identify by m.p. (121°). Render the filtrate alkaline by cautiously adding 10 per cent sodium hydroxide solution, cool and isolate the aniline by ether extraction. Recover the ether and test the residue for aniline (Section **IV,33**).

$$C_6H_5NHCOC_6H_5 + H_2SO_4 + H_2O \rightarrow$$
$$(C_6H_5NH_3)^+(HSO_4)^- + C_6H_5COOH$$

The melting points of some typical substituted aromatic amides are collected in Table IX, 29 (Chapter IX). Other examples will be found in the appropriate columns of Tables IX, 33A and B (*Primary and Secondary Aromatic Amines*) and of Table IX, 21 (*Aromatic Carboxylic Acids*).

IV, 30 Aliphatic Nitriles (Cyanides)

Aliphatic nitriles are usually liquids or low melting point solids. The most important reaction of a nitrile is its hydrolysis either by an

---

* Seventy per cent sulphuric acid is prepared by adding 20 ml. of the concentrated acid cautiously and with stirring and cooling to 15 ml. of water.

alkali or by an acid to the corresponding aliphatic acid: characterization of the acid enables the identity of the original nitrile to be established.

(i) **Hydrolysis with alkali.** When nitriles are treated with 20–40 per cent sodium or potassium hydroxide solution, there is no reaction in the cold; upon prolonged boiling hydrolysis proceeds comparatively slowly (compare primary amides which are rapidly hydrolysed) to the sodium salt of the acid and ammonia. The reaction is complete when ammonia is no longer evolved:

$$RCN + H_2O + NaOH \rightarrow RCOONa + NH_3$$

The excess of alkali is then neutralized to phenolphthalein or to Congo Red with dilute hydrochloric acid and the solution is evaporated to dryness on the water bath. The acid may then be characterized as the S-benzylthiuronium salt or as the p-bromophenacyl ester (Section **IV,20**). In many instances the derivative may be prepared directly from the neutralized solution.

(ii) **Hydrolysis with acid.** Most nitriles are hydrolysed by boiling with 5–8 times the weight of 50–75 per cent sulphuric acid under reflux for 2–3 hours:

$$2RCN + H_2SO_4 + 4H_2O \rightarrow 2RCOOH + (NH_4)_2SO_4$$

The acid, if monobasic, can usually be distilled directly from the reaction mixture. If this procedure is not possible, the reaction mixture is poured into excess of crushed ice, and the acid is isolated by ether extraction or by other suitable means. The acid is then characterized (Section **IV,20**). The addition of hydrochloric acid (as sodium chloride; say, 5 per cent of the weight of sulphuric acid) increases the rate of the reaction.

For those nitriles which yield water-insoluble amides (*e.g.*, the higher alkyl cyanides), *conversion to the amide* often leads to a satisfactory derivative. The hydration is effected by warming a solution of the nitrile in concentrated sulphuric acid for a few minutes, cooling and pouring into water; an imino-sulphate is probably formed intermediately and this is hydrolysed:

$$RC \equiv N \xrightarrow{HOSO_3H} \underset{OSO_3H}{RC=NH} \xrightarrow{HOH} \left[\underset{OH}{RC=NH} \right] \rightarrow \underset{O}{RC-NH_2}$$

Warm a solution of 0·5 g. of the nitrile in 2 ml. of concentrated sulphuric acid to 80–90° and allow the solution to stand for 5 minutes. Cool under the tap and pour the sulphuric acid solution into 20 ml.

of cold water. Filter off the precipitated solid and stir it with 5 ml. of cold 5 per cent sodium hydroxide solution. Collect the insoluble crude amide and recrystallize it from dilute ethanol.

For practice, the student should carry out both alkaline and acid hydrolysis of acetonitrile, n-valeronitrile (n-butyl cyanide) and n-capronitrile (n-amyl cyanide).

CRYSTALLINE DERIVATIVES OF ALIPHATIC NITRILES (CYANIDES)

1. Acyl phloroglucinols. Crystalline derivatives may be prepared by an application of the Hoesch reaction. Equimolecular proportions of phloroglucinol (I) and the nitrile react in dry ethereal solution in the presence of anhydrous zinc chloride and hydrogen chloride to give an imine hydrochloride (II), which is converted into a solid alkyl trihydroxyphenyl ketone (III) by hydrolysis:

$$\text{(I)} + RC \equiv N + HCl \xrightarrow{ZnCl_2}$$

$$\text{(II)} \xrightarrow[H_2O]{\text{Hydrolysis}} \text{(III)} + NH_4Cl$$

The alkyl 2,4,6-trihydroxyphenyl ketones are usually highly crystalline solids of sharp melting point and are purified by recrystallization from hot water. Many contain water of crystallization which can be removed by drying 'in vacuo' at about 100°; the melting points of both the hydrated and anhydrous compounds should be determined.

Add 0·4 g. of powdered, anhydrous zinc chloride to a solution of 1·1 g. of anhydrous phloroglucinol in 25 ml. of sodium-dried ether, and introduce the nitrile (0·01 g. mol) dissolved in 5 ml. of dry ether. Pass a steady stream of dry hydrogen chloride through the solution for 25–30 minutes; it becomes turbid after 2–3 minutes but the turbidity subsequently disappears. Decant the supernatant liquid, dissolve the residual oil or crystals in 25 ml. of water, and shake the aqueous solution with two 20 ml. portions of ether. Concentrate the aqueous layer to about 10–12 ml. The hydroxy ketone separates upon cooling; recrystallize it from hot water and dry in the air. The hydrate is thus produced.

2. **Reduction to primary amines** and conversion into substituted phenylthioureas. Reduction of a nitrile with sodium and alcohol yields the primary amine, which may be identified by direct conversion into a substituted phenylthiourea.

$$RCN + 2H_2 \xrightarrow[ROH]{Na,} RCH_2NH_2$$

Dissolve 1·0 g. of the nitrile in 20 ml. of absolute ethanol in a dry 200 ml. round-bottomed flask fitted with a reflux condenser. Add through the top of the condenser 1·5 g. of clean sodium (previously cut into small pieces) at such a rate that the reaction, although vigorous, remains under control. When all the sodium has reacted (10–15 minutes), cool the reaction mixture to about 20°, and add 10 ml. of concentrated hydrochloric acid dropwise through the condenser whilst swirling the contents of the flask vigorously: the final solution should be acid to litmus. Transfer to a 100 ml. distilling flask connected to a condenser, and distil off about 20 ml. of liquid (dilute ethanol). Cool the flask and fit a small dropping funnel into the neck of the distilling flask. Place 15 ml. of 40 per cent sodium hydroxide solution in the dropping funnel, attach an adapter to the end of the condenser and so arrange it that the end dips into about 3 ml. of water contained in a 50 ml. conical flask. Add the sodium hydroxide solution dropwise and with shaking: a vigorous reaction ensues. When all the alkali has been added, separate the amine by distillation until the contents of the flask are nearly dry.

Add 0·5 ml. of phenyl isothiocyanate to the distillate and shake the mixture vigorously for 3–4 minutes. If no derivative separates, crystallization may be induced by cooling the flask in ice and 'scratching' the walls with a glass rod. Filter off the crude product, wash it with a little 50 per cent ethanol, and recrystallize from hot dilute ethanol.

3. **α-Iminoalkylmercaptoacetic acid hydrochlorides.** Mercaptoacetic acid (thioglycollic acid) reacts with nitriles in the presence of hydrogen chloride to give α-iminoalkylmercaptoacetic acid hydrochlorides:

$$RCN + HSCH_2COOH + HCl \rightarrow RC\begin{smallmatrix}\nearrow NH,HCl \\ \searrow SCH_2COOH\end{smallmatrix}$$

These salts have sharp and reproducible decomposition temperatures but no true melting points. They act as dibasic acids when titrated with standard alkali, thymol blue being used as indicator.

Dissolve 1·0 g. of the nitrile and 2·0 g. of mercaptoacetic acid in 25 ml. of sodium-dried ether in a dry test-tube or small flask. Cool the solution in ice and saturate it with dry hydrogen chloride (5–10 minutes). Stopper the test-tube or flask and keep it at 0° until crystallization is complete (15–60 minutes). Collect the crystals by suction filtration, wash with anhydrous ether and dry in a vacuum desiccator over potassium hydroxide pellets (to remove hydrogen chloride) and paraffin wax shavings (to remove ether).

The physical properties, and also the melting points of a number of derivatives, of aliphatic nitriles are collected in Table IX, 30 (Chapter IX).

IV, 31 Aromatic Nitriles

Aromatic nitriles are generally liquids or low melting point solids, and usually have characteristic odours. They give no ammonia with aqueous sodium hydroxide solution in the cold. These nitriles are hydrolysed by boiling aqueous alkali but more slowly than primary amides:

$$RCN + NaOH + H_2O \rightarrow RCOONa + NH_3$$

When distilled with soda lime (*Aromatic Carboxylic Acids*, Section **IV,21**), nitriles yield some ammonia, but pass over, in part, unchanged. They are identified by the b.p. and by hydrolysis to, and characterization of, the corresponding acid.

Hydrolysis may be effected with 10–20 per cent sodium hydroxide solution or with 10 per cent methyl alcoholic sodium hydroxide. For difficult cases, *e.g.*, 1-naphthonitrile, a mixture of 50 per cent sulphuric acid and glacial acetic acid may be used. In alkaline hydrolysis the boiling is continued until no more ammonia is evolved. In acid hydrolysis 2–3 hours boiling is usually sufficient: the reaction product is poured into water, and the organic acid is separated from any unchanged nitrile or from amide by means of sodium carbonate solution. The resulting acid is identified as detailed in Section **IV,21.**

Nitriles may often be converted (hydrated) into the amides (RCN→ RCONH$_2$) by concentrated sulphuric acid or by concentrated hydrochloric acid, usually in the cold or at 40° (see Section **IV,30**). The resulting amide is, of course, a useful derivative. The experimental details for a typical hydration follow.

Phenylacetamide from benzyl cyanide. Dissolve 1·0 g. of benzyl cyanide (phenylacetonitrile) in 4 ml. of concentrated sulphuric acid, warm to 80–90°, and allow the solution to stand for 5 minutes. Cool under the tap and pour the solution into 20 ml. of cold water. Filter off the precipitate, stir the wet solid with 20 ml. of cold 10 per cent aqueous sodium hydroxide solution, filter, and recrystallize from benzene or dilute ethanol. The resulting phenylacetamide (0·8 g.) has m.p. 156°.

The physical properties of some typical aromatic nitriles are collected in Table IX, 31 (Chapter IX).

IV, 32 Primary and Secondary Aliphatic Amines

The more important reactions of aliphatic amines, which will assist in their detection, are given below.

Salts of amines are generally soluble in water. Upon treatment with 10 per cent sodium hydroxide solution, the amine will separate if it is insoluble or sparingly soluble in water; if the amine is water-soluble, it can be partially volatilized by gentle warming and its presence will be suggested by a characteristic odour.

PRIMARY AMINES

(i) **Reaction with nitrous acid.** Dissolve 0·2 g. of the substance in 5 ml. of $2N$ hydrochloric acid; cool in ice and add 2 ml. of ice-cold 10 per cent aqueous sodium nitrite solution. Warm gently upon a water bath, when nitrogen will be freely evolved:

$$RNH_2 + HNO_2 \rightarrow ROH + N_2 + H_2O$$

If desired, the alcohol may be identified as the 3,5-dinitrobenzoate (*Aliphatic Alcohols,* **IV,5**); it is then best to repeat the experiment on a larger scale and to replace the dilute hydrochloric acid by dilute sulphuric acid. It must, however, be pointed out that the reaction is not always so simple as indicated in the above equation. Olefine formation and production of alcohols sometimes occur: thus *n*-propylamine yields *n*-propyl alcohol, isopropyl alcohol and propylene, evidently due to the intermediate formation of a carbonium ion.

(ii) **Rimini's test.** To a suspension or solution of 1 drop of the compound or to an equivalent quantity of its solution in 5 ml. of water, add 1 ml. of pure acetone and 1 drop of freshly prepared 1 per cent aqueous solution of sodium nitroprusside. A violet-red colour will develop within 1 minute.

(iii) **Carbylamine (isocyanide) test.** To 1 ml. of $0.5N$ ethanolic potassium hydroxide solution (or to a solution prepared by dissolving a fragment of potassium hydroxide half the size of a pea in 1 ml. of ethanol), add 0·01 g. of the amine and 2 drops of chloroform, and heat to boiling. A carbylamine (isocyanide) is formed and will be readily identified by its nauseating odour:

$$RNH_2 + CHCl_3 + 3KOH \rightarrow RNC + 3KCl + 3H_2O$$

This test must be performed in a fume cupboard (hood) with a good draught. After the reaction, do *not* pour away the reaction mixture at once but add concentrated hydrochloric acid and wait until the smell has disappeared. Then pour the contents of the test-tube carefully down the main drain and not into the laboratory sink. The test is so sensitive that it is apt to be misleading; it will often detect traces of primary amines in secondary and tertiary amines. It must therefore be used with due regard to this and other factors. The obnoxious and persistent smell makes the test unsuitable for general use.

The *mechanism* of the reaction probably involves conversion of the chloroform by the strong base into the reactive intermediate, dichlorocarbene. The latter is a strong electrophile and reacts immediately with the amine: loss of two molecules of hydrogen chloride yields the isocyanide.

$$Cl_3C:H + HO^- \rightarrow Cl_3\bar{C}: + H_2O$$

$$Cl_3\bar{C}: \rightarrow Cl_2C: + Cl^-$$

$$R-\underset{H}{\overset{H}{N}}: + \ddot{C}Cl_2 \rightarrow R-\underset{H}{\overset{H}{N^+}}:\bar{C}-Cl \xrightarrow{HO^-}$$
$$ Cl$$

$$R-\underset{H}{N^+}=\bar{C}: \xrightarrow{HO^-} R-\overset{+}{N}\equiv\bar{C}:$$
$$ Cl$$

SECONDARY AMINES

(iv) **Reaction with nitrous acid.** Oily nitrosoamines (compare Section **IV,33**) are generally formed: no nitrogen is evolved {see (i)}.

(v) **Carbon disulphide reagent test.** This test is based upon the formation from a secondary amine and carbon disulphide of a dialkyldithiocarbamate; the latter readily forms a nickel derivative with a solution of a nickel salt:

$$R_2NH + CS_2 \xrightarrow[\text{aq.}]{NH_3} R_2N-\overset{\displaystyle S}{\underset{\|}{C}}-SNH_4 \xrightarrow{NiCl_2} (R_2N-\overset{\displaystyle S}{\underset{\|}{C}}-S-)_2Ni$$

To 5 ml. of water add 1–2 drops of the secondary amine; if it does not dissolve, add a drop or two of concentrated hydrochloric acid. Place 1·0 ml. of the reagent (1) in a test-tube, add 0·5–1 ml. of concentrated ammonia solution, followed by 0·5–1 ml. of the above amine solution. A precipitate indicates a secondary amine. A slight turbidity points to the presence of a secondary amine as an impurity. The test is very sensitive; it is not given by primary amines.

Note

1. The **carbon disulphide reagent is prepared** by adding to a solution of 0·5 g. of crystallized nickel chloride in 100 ml. of water enough carbon disulphide so that after shaking a globule of carbon disulphide is left at the bottom of the bottle. The reagent is stable for long periods in a well-stoppered bottle. If all the carbon disulphide evaporates, more must be added.

CRYSTALLINE DERIVATIVES OF PRIMARY AND SECONDARY ALIPHATIC AMINES

1. **Benzenesulphonyl or *p*-toluenesulphonyl derivatives.** These are generally very satisfactory. For experimental details, see under *Aromatic Amines*, Section **IV,33,3**.

2. **Phenylthioureas.** Primary and secondary amines react with phenyl isothiocyanate to yield phenylthioureas:

$$C_6H_5N{=}C{=}S + RNH_2 \longrightarrow C_6H_5NHCSNHR$$
$$C_6H_5N{=}C{=}S + R_2NH \longrightarrow C_6H_5NHCSNR_2$$

Phenyl isothiocyanate is not sensitive to water; the reaction may be carried out with an aqueous solution of an amine.

Dissolve equivalent quantities of the reagent and of the amine in a small amount of rectified spirit. If no reaction appears to take place in the cold, reflux the mixture for 5–15 minutes. Upon cooling (and 'scratching' with a glass rod, if necessary) the crystalline phenylthiourea separates. Recrystallize it from rectified spirit or from 60–80 per cent ethanol.

Alternatively, mix equal amounts (say, 0·2 g. of each) of the amine and phenyl isothiocyanate in a test-tube and shake for 2 minutes.

If no reaction occurs, heat the mixture gently for 2 minutes and then cool in ice until the mass solidifies. Powder the solid, wash it with a little light petroleum (b.p. 100–120°), and recrystallize from rectified spirit.

1-Naphthyl isothiocyanate yields crystalline 1-naphthylthioureas and is similarly employed.

3. **Picrates.** Picric acid combines with amines to yield molecular compounds (picrates), which usually possess characteristic melting points. Most picrates have the composition 1 mol amine:1 mol picric acid. The picrates of the amines, particularly of the more basic ones, are generally more stable than the molecular complexes formed between picric acid and the hydrocarbons (compare Section **IV,4,6**).

If the amine is soluble in water, mix it with a slight excess (about 25 per cent) of a saturated solution of picric acid in water (the solubility in cold water is about 1 per cent). If the amine is insoluble in water, dissolve it by the addition of 2–3 drops of dilute hydrochloric acid (1:1) for each 2–3 ml. of water, then add a slight excess of the reagent. If a heavy precipitate does not form immediately after the addition of the picric acid solution, allow the mixture to stand for some time and then shake vigorously. Filter off the precipitated picrate and recrystallize it from boiling water, ethanol or dilute ethanol, boiling 10 per cent acetic acid, chloroform or, best, benzene.

The following alternative procedure may sometimes be employed. Dissolve 0·5 g. of the amine in 5 ml. of rectified spirit and add 5 ml. of a cold saturated solution of picric acid in alcohol. Warm on a *water bath* for 5 minutes and allow to cool. Collect the precipitated picrate and recrystallize it as above.

4. *N*-**Substituted phthalimides.** Phthalic anhydride reacts with primary amines only to yield *N*-substituted phthalimides:

$$\text{C}_6\text{H}_4(\text{CO})_2\text{O} + \text{RNH}_2 \rightarrow \text{C}_6\text{H}_4(\text{CO})_2\text{NR} + \text{H}_2\text{O}$$

Dissolve 0·5 g. of the primary amine and 0·5 g. of pure phthalic anhydride in 5 ml. of glacial acetic acid and reflux for 20–30 minutes. (If the amine salt is used, add 1 g. of sodium acetate.) The *N*-substituted phthalimide separates out on cooling. Recrystallize it from ethanol or from glacial acetic acid.

Experimental details for the preparation of **acetyl derivatives** (substituted acetamides), **benzoyl derivatives** (substituted benzamides) and **3-nitrophthalamic acids** are given under *Aromatic Amines*, Section **IV,33,***1, 2* and *7* respectively.

The melting points of the derivatives of some primary and secondary aliphatic amines are collected in Table IX, 32 (Chapter IX).

Tertiary aliphatic amines are discussed under *Aromatic Amines* in Section **IV,33**.

IV, 33 Primary, Secondary and Tertiary Aromatic Amines

Those reactions which are common to both aliphatic and aromatic amines and have been described under *Aliphatic Amines* (Section **IV,32**) will not be repeated in this Section except where differences in experimental technique occur.

PRIMARY AMINES

(i) **Carbylamine (isocyanide) test.** See Section **IV,32**,(iii). The following alternative technique may be employed. Add 1 small drop of the liquid (or 0·02 g. of the solid) amine to 2 ml. of ethanol. Place 1 drop of the resulting *ca.* 1 per cent solution in a small test-tube with 1 drop of chloroform and 4 ml. of 10 per cent sodium hydroxide solution; heat the solution gently. The unpleasant odour of an isocyanide will be apparent with a primary amine. For special precautions associated with this test, see Section **IV,32**,(iii).

(ii) **Reaction with nitrous acid and the formation of an azo dye.** Dissolve 1·0 ml. (1·0 g.) of aniline (or the equivalent quantity of any other primary aromatic amine) in 3 ml. of concentrated hydrochloric acid and 5 ml. of water, and cool the solution to 0–5°. Add a cold solution of 1·0 g. of sodium nitrite in 5 ml. of water slowly (preferably by means of a dropper) and with stirring until, after standing for 3–4 minutes, an immediate positive test for nitrous acid is obtained. Remove 1 drop of the solution, dilute with 4–5 drops of water, and apply to potassium iodide-starch paper; an immediate blue coloration should be obtained. Divide the resulting diazonium solution into two parts. To a cold solution of 0·4 g. of 2-naphthol in 4 ml. of 5 per cent sodium hydroxide solution, add the cold diazonium solution slowly and with stirring. A coloured (*e.g.*, orange-red) dye is formed; this may be filtered off and recrystallized from ethanol or glacial acetic acid. Warm the other half of the solution: nitrogen is evolved and a phenol is produced; note the odour.

Elementary Practical Organic Chemistry [IV

Some primary aromatic diamines cannot be diazotized (tetrazotized) and coupled normally. Thus *o*-phenylenediamine yields a triazole derivative and *m*-phenylenediamine gives an azo dye (Bismarck brown) by self-coupling.

SECONDARY AMINES

(iii) **Carbylamine (isocyanide) test.** This is negative if the secondary amine is free from primary aromatic amine.

(iv) **Reaction with nitrous acid.** Nitrosamines are formed; these are usually yellow oils or low m.p. solids, and give the **Liebermann nitroso reaction.** The latter reaction consists in warming the nitrosamine with phenol and concentrated sulphuric acid. The sulphuric acid liberates nitrous acid from the nitrosamine, the nitrous acid reacts with the phenol to form *p*-nitrosophenol, which then combines with another molecule of phenol to give a red indophenol. In alkaline solution the red indophenol yields a blue indophenol anion:

$$R_2NH + HNO_2 \rightarrow R_2NNO \text{ (nitrosamine)} + H_2O$$

$$R_2NNO \xrightarrow{H_2SO_4} HONO \xrightarrow{C_6H_5OH} HO-\!\!\!\left\langle\!\!\!\bigcirc\!\!\!\right\rangle\!\!\!-NO \xrightarrow{C_6H_5OH}$$

p-Nitrosophenol

$$HO-\!\!\!\left\langle\!\!\!\bigcirc\!\!\!\right\rangle\!\!\!-N=\!\!\!\left\langle\!\!\!\bigcirc\!\!\!\right\rangle\!\!\!=O \xrightarrow{NaOH} {}^-O-\!\!\!\left\langle\!\!\!\bigcirc\!\!\!\right\rangle\!\!\!-N=\!\!\!\left\langle\!\!\!\bigcirc\!\!\!\right\rangle\!\!\!=O$$

Indophenol (red)   Indophenol anion (blue)

Dissolve 1·0 g. of the secondary amine in 3–5 ml. of dilute hydrochloric acid or of ethanol (in the latter case, add 1 ml. of concentrated hydrochloric acid). Cool to about 5° and add 4–5 ml. of 10 per cent sodium nitrite solution, and allow to stand for 5 minutes. Add 10 ml. of water, transfer to a small separatory funnel and extract the oil with about 20 ml. of ether. Wash the ethereal extract successively with water, dilute sodium hydroxide solution and water. Remove the ether on a previously warmed water bath: no flames should be present in the vicinity. Apply Liebermann's nitroso reaction to the residual oil or solid thus. Place 1 drop or 0·01–0·02 g. of the nitroso compound in a dry test-tube, add 0·05 g. of phenol and warm together for 20 seconds; cool, and add 1 ml. of concentrated sulphuric acid. An intense green (or greenish-blue) coloration will be developed, which changes to pale red upon pouring into 30–50 ml. of cold water; the colour becomes deep blue or green upon adding excess of sodium hydroxide solution.

TERTIARY AMINES

(v) **Carbylamine (isocyanide) test.** This is negative for pure tertiary amines.

(vi) **Reaction with nitrous acid.** The dialkylanilines yield green solid *p*-nitroso compounds. Thus dimethylaniline reacts with nitrous acid to yield *p*-nitrosodimethylaniline:

$$(CH_3)_2N{-}\!\!\left\langle\right\rangle + HONO \rightarrow (CH_3)_2N{-}\!\!\left\langle\right\rangle{-}NO + H_2O$$

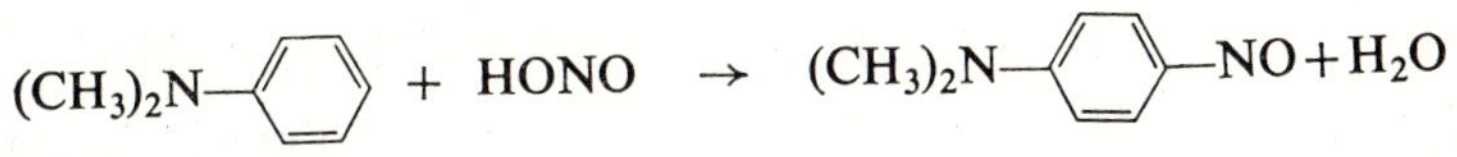

Dissolve 1·0 g. of dimethylaniline in 10 ml. of dilute hydrochloric acid (1:1), cool to 0–5°, and slowly add, with stirring, a solution of 0·70 g. of sodium nitrite in 4 ml. of water. After 20–30 minutes, filter off the precipitated yellow hydrochloride,* and wash it with a little dilute hydrochloric acid. Dissolve the precipitate in the minimum volume of water, add a solution of sodium carbonate or sodium hydroxide to decompose the hydrochloride (*i.e.*, until alkaline), and extract the free base with ether. Evaporate the ether, and recrystallize the residual green crystals of *p*-nitrosodimethylaniline from light petroleum (b.p. 60–80°) or from benzene. The pure compound has m.p. 85°.

The *p*-nitroso compounds do not give Liebermann's nitroso reaction.

(vii) **Separation of primary, secondary and tertiary amines (Hinsberg's method).** When a mixture of primary, secondary and tertiary amines is shaken with benzenesulphonyl chloride in the presence of dilute sodium hydroxide solution, the following reactions occur:

primary amine: $C_6H_5SO_2Cl + H_2NR \xrightarrow{NaOH} [C_6H_5SO_2NR]^-Na^+$
(water soluble)

$\xrightarrow{HCl} C_6H_5SO_2NHR$
(water-insoluble)

secondary amine: $C_6H_5SO_2Cl + HNR'R'' \xrightarrow{NaOH} C_6H_5SO_2NR'R''$
(insoluble in alkali)

---

* The hydrochloride may not separate with other dialkylanilines. Add a slight excess of sodium carbonate or sodium hydroxide to the solution, extract the free base with ether, etc.

tertiary amine: does not react in the presence of water, and may be removed by steam distillation or solvent extraction.

The benzenesulphonyl derivatives are crystalline solids and may be filtered off. They may be identified and separated from one another by taking advantage of the fact that the derivative from the primary amine is soluble in dilute sodium hydroxide solution (since it contains a hydrogen atom attached to nitrogen and activated by the strongly unsaturated sulphonyl group), whilst the derivative of the secondary amine is insoluble in dilute alkali (since it contains no corresponding hydrogen atom):

$$C_6H_5SO_2NHR + NaOH \rightarrow [C_6H_5SO_2NR]^-Na^+ \text{ (soluble)}$$

Upon acidifying the solution of the sodium derivative with hydrochloric acid, the corresponding sulphonamide $C_6H_5SO_2NHR$ is precipitated. By boiling the sulphonamides with 10–12 times the weight of 25 per cent hydrochloric acid or, better, with 80 per cent sulphuric acid, rendering alkaline with sodium hydroxide and extracting with ether, the original primary and/or secondary amines may be recovered:

$$C_6H_5SO_2NHR + H_2O + HCl \rightarrow C_6H_5SO_3H + [RNH_3]^+Cl^-$$
$$C_6H_5SO_2NR'R'' + H_2O + HCl \rightarrow C_6H_5SO_3H + [R'R''NH_2]^+Cl^-$$

Certain primary amines yield disulphonyl derivatives, which are insoluble in alkali and therefore may be confused with the monosulphonyl derivatives of secondary amines.

$$RNH_2 + 2C_6H_5SO_2Cl \xrightarrow{-2HCl} RN(SO_2C_6H_5)_2$$

These may be converted into the monosulphonyl derivatives by boiling for 30 minutes with a 5 per cent solution of sodium ethoxide in ethyl alcohol:

$$RN(SO_2C_6H_5)_2 + NaOC_2H_5 \rightarrow$$
$$[RNSO_2C_6H_5]^-Na^+ + C_2H_5OSO_2C_6H_5$$

There are complications in applying the Hinsberg test to certain amines containing hydroxyl, nitro and carboxyl groups, *e.g.*, *p*-*N*-methylaminobenzoic acid {$CH_3NHC_6H_4COOH$ (1,4)} may behave in this test as a primary amine (soluble in alkali) so that it is essential to consider the properties of the original compound in conjunction with the results of the test.

p-Toluenesulphonyl chloride may replace benzenesulphonyl chloride.

33]   **Reactions and Characterization of Organic Compounds**

The following experimental details will illustrate how the Hinsberg separation of amines may be carried out in practice.

Treat 2·0 g. of the mixture of amines with 40 ml. of 10 per cent sodium hydroxide solution and add 4 g. (3 ml.) of benzenesulphonyl chloride (or 4 g. of *p*-toluenesulphonyl chloride) in small portions. Warm on a water bath to complete the reaction. Acidify the alkaline solution with dilute hydrochloric acid when the sulphonamides of the primary and secondary amines are precipitated. Filter off the solid and wash it with a little cold water; the tertiary amine will be present in the filtrate. To convert any disulphonamide that may have been formed from the primary amine into the sulphonamide, boil the solid under reflux with 2·0 g. of sodium dissolved in 40 ml. of absolute ethyl alcohol for 30 minutes. Dilute with a little water and distil off the alcohol: filter off the precipitate of the sulphonamide of the secondary amine. Acidify the filtrate with dilute hydrochloric acid to precipitate the derivative of the primary amine. Recrystallize the respective derivatives from ethanol or from dilute ethanol, and identify them *inter alia* by a determination of the m.p.

The above reactions will serve to place an amine into its class—primary, secondary or tertiary. For complete characterization, a crystalline derivative should be prepared. A large number of derivatives of amines are available: the following will be found useful.

Crystalline Derivatives of Primary and Secondary Amines

1. **Acetyl derivatives.** Primary and secondary amines are best acetylated with acetic anhydride:

$$RNH_2 + (CH_3CO)_2O \rightarrow CH_3CONHR + CH_3COOH$$
$$R'R''NH + (CH_3CO)_2O \rightarrow CH_3CONR'R'' + CH_3COOH$$

Acetyl chloride is not so satisfactory since an equivalent quantity of the amine hydrochloride is simultaneously produced:

$$2RNH_2 + CH_3COCl \rightarrow CH_3CONHR + \{RNH_3\}^+Cl^-$$

Reflux gently in a test-tube under a short air condenser 1·0 g. of the base with 2·5 mols {or 3·0 g. (3·0 ml.) if the molecular weight is unknown} of redistilled acetic anhydride for 10–15 minutes. Cool the reaction mixture and pour it into 20 ml. of cold water (*CAUTION!*). Either boil to decompose the excess of acetic anhydride, or neutralize with sodium carbonate and, if necessary, stir or shake to decompose the excess of the reagent. When cold, filter off the residual insoluble acetyl derivative and wash it with a little cold water. Recrystallize from water or from dilute ethanol.

Certain *ortho* substituted derivatives of aromatic amines are difficult to acetylate under the above conditions owing to steric hindrance. The process is facilitated by the addition of a few drops of concentrated sulphuric acid which acts as a catalyst, and the use of a large excess of acetic anhydride.

Excellent results may often be obtained by conducting the acetylation with acetic anhydride in aqueous solution in the presence of a slight excess of sodium acetate. Experimental details follow.

Dissolve about 0·5 g. of the base in 30 ml. of 5 per cent hydrochloric acid; add small portions of 5 per cent sodium hydroxide solution until the mixture becomes cloudy and remove the turbidity with a few ml. of 5 per cent hydrochloric acid. Add 5 g. of crushed ice, followed by 4 ml. of redistilled acetic anhydride. Stir the mixture vigorously and then add in one portion a solution of 4 g. of crystallized sodium acetate in 15 ml. of water. Cool in ice. Filter off the precipitated solid and recrystallize it from dilute ethanol.

2. **Benzoyl derivatives.** Both primary and secondary amines form benzoyl derivatives under the conditions of the Schotten-Baumann reaction.

$$RCOCl + R'NH_2 + NaOH \rightarrow RCONHR' + NaCl + H_2O$$

Benzoyl chloride* is the reagent commonly used. This reagent is so slowly hydrolysed by water that benzoylation can be carried out in an aqueous medium. In the **Schotten-Baumann method of benzoylation** the amino compound or its salt is dissolved or suspended in a slight excess of 8–15 per cent sodium hydroxide solution, a small excess (about 10–15 per cent more than the theoretical quantity) of benzoyl chloride is then added and the mixture vigorously shaken in a stoppered vessel (or else the mixture is stirred mechanically). Benzoylation proceeds smoothly and the sparingly soluble benzoyl derivative separates as a solid. The sodium hydroxide hydrolyses the excess of benzoyl chloride, yielding sodium benzoate and sodium chloride, which remain in solution:

$$C_6H_5COCl + 2NaOH \rightarrow C_6H_5COONa + NaCl + H_2O$$

The benzoyl compounds frequently occlude traces of unchanged benzoyl chloride, which thus escapes hydrolysis by the caustic alkali;

---

* This substance has an irritating vapour and should be handled with caution. It is best kept in the fume cupboard (hood).

it is therefore advisable, wherever possible, to recrystallize the benzoyl derivative from methyl or ethyl alcohol or from methylated spirit, since these solvents will esterify the unchanged chloride and so remove the latter from the recrystallized material. Sometimes the benzoyl compound does not crystallize well; this difficulty may frequently be overcome by the use of *p*-nitrobenzoyl chloride or of 3,5-dinitrobenzoyl chloride, which usually give highly crystalline derivatives of high melting point (see under *Phenols*, Section **IV,7**).

Suspend 1·0 g. (or 1·0 ml.) of the substance in 20 ml. of 5 per cent sodium hydroxide solution* in a well-corked boiling tube or small conical flask, and add 2·0 ml. of redistilled benzoyl chloride, *ca.* 0·5 ml. at a time, with constant shaking, and cooling in water (if necessary). Shake vigorously for 5–10 minutes until the odour of the benzoyl chloride has disappeared. Make sure that the mixture has an alkaline reaction. Filter off the solid benzoyl derivative, wash it with a little cold water, and recrystallize it from ethanol or dilute ethanol.

If the benzoyl derivative is soluble in alkali, precipitate it together with the benzoic acid derived from the reagent by the addition of hydrochloric acid: filter and extract the product with cold ether or light petroleum (b.p. 40–60°) to remove the benzoic acid.

The following alternative procedures are sometimes useful.

Benzene method. To a solution of 1·0 g. of benzoyl chloride (or 1·1 g. of *p*-nitrobenzoyl chloride) in 20 ml. of dry benzene, add 1·0 g. of the amine and heat the mixture under reflux for 15 minutes. Filter the cooled solution and wash the precipitate with 5–10 ml. of warm benzene; add the washings to the original filtrate. Wash the benzene solution successively with 10 ml. of 3 per cent sodium carbonate solution, 10 ml. of 3 per cent hydrochloric acid, and 10 ml. of water. Evaporate the benzene and recrystallize the residue from ethanol or dilute ethanol.

Pyridine method. To a solution of 0·5 g. of the amine in 4 ml. of dry pyridine and 10 ml. of dry benzene, add dropwise 0·5 ml. of redistilled benzoyl chloride. Heat the mixture under reflux on a water bath at 60–70° for 20–30 minutes and then pour into 80–100 ml. of water. Separate the benzene layer and extract the aqueous layer with 10 ml. of benzene. Wash the combined benzene solutions with 5 ml. of 5 per cent sodium carbonate solution, followed by 5 ml. of water, and dry with a little anhydrous magnesium sulphate. Filter off the desiccant through a small fluted filter paper and evaporate the benzene

* Potassium hydroxide solution gives a slightly better yield of the benzoyl derivative.

solution to a small volume (3–4 ml.). Stir 15–20 ml. of hexane into the residue: the crystalline benzoyl derivative separates. Filter and wash with a little hexane. Recrystallize from a mixture of cyclohexane with hexane or with ethyl acetate; alternatively, use ethanol or dilute ethanol for recrystallization.

3. **Benzenesulphonyl or *p*-toluenesulphonyl derivatives.** The Hinsberg procedure for the separation of primary, secondary and tertiary amines is given under (vii) above, and this method may be used. The following experimental details may, however, be found useful for the preparation of derivatives of primary and secondary amines.

Treat 1·0 g. (1·0 ml.) of the amine with 4 mols of 10 per cent sodium or potassium hydroxide solution (say, 20 ml.), and add 1·5 mols (or 3·0 g. if the molecular weight is unknown) of benzenesulphonyl or *p*-toluenesulphonyl chloride in small portions with constant shaking. To remove the excess of acid chloride, either shake vigorously or warm gently. Acidify with dilute hydrochloric acid and filter off the sulphonamide. Recrystallize it from ethanol or dilute ethanol.

If the presence of a disulphonyl derivative from a primary amine is suspected (*e.g.*, formation of a precipitate in alkaline solution even after dilution), reflux the precipitate, obtained after acidifying, with a solution of 1 g. of sodium in 20 ml. of rectified spirit for 15 minutes. Evaporate the alcohol, dilute with water, and filter if necessary; acidify with dilute hydrochloric acid. Collect the sulphonyl derivative and recrystallize it from ethanol or dilute ethanol.

It is generally more convenient to employ the solid *p*-toluenesulphonyl chloride (m.p. 69°) rather than the liquid benzenesulphonyl chloride. Moreover, the benzenesulphonamides of certain secondary amines are oils or low melting point solids that may be difficult to crystallize: the *p*-toluenesulphonamides usually have higher melting points and are more satisfactory as derivatives. **Technical *p*-toluenesulphonyl chloride may be purified** by dissolving it in benzene and precipitating with light petroleum (b.p. 40–60°).

Feebly basic amines, *e.g.*, the nitroanilines, generally react so slowly with benzenesulphonyl chloride that most of the acid chloride is hydrolysed by the aqueous alkali before a reasonable yield of the sulphonamide is produced; indeed, *o*-nitroaniline gives little or no sulphonamide under the conditions of the Hinsberg test. Excellent results are obtained by carrying out the reaction in *pyridine solution:*

$$o\text{-}NO_2C_6H_4NH_2 + C_6H_5SO_2Cl + C_5H_5N \rightarrow$$
$$o\text{-}NO_2C_6H_4NHSO_2C_6H_5 + C_5H_5N,HCl$$

Reflux a mixture of 1·0 g. (1·0 ml.) of the amine, 2–3 g. of benzene-sulphonyl chloride and 6 ml. of pyridine for 30 minutes. Pour the reaction mixture into 10 ml. of cold water and stir until the product crystallizes. Filter off the solid and recrystallize it from ethanol or dilute ethanol.

Most amines react so rapidly in pyridine solution that the reaction is usually complete after refluxing for 10–15 minutes.

4. Benzal derivatives. *Primary* aromatic amines generally condense directly with benzaldehyde to form derivatives (**Schiff's bases or anils**):

$$RNH_2 + OCHC_6H_5 \rightarrow RN\!\!=\!\!CHC_6H_5 + H_2O$$

These are often crystalline and therefore useful for the characterization of primary amines. Diamines may, of course, yield di-benzal derivatives.

Heat the amine with one or two mols of redistilled benzaldehyde (according as to whether the base is a monamine or diamine) to 100° for 10 minutes; if the molecular weight is unknown, use 1·0 g. of the base and 1·0 or 2·0 g. of benzaldehyde. Sometimes a solvent, such as ethanol (5 ml.) or acetic acid, may be used. Recrystallize from ethanol, dilute ethanol or benzene.

5. Picrates. Experimental details will be found under *Aliphatic Amines*, Section **IV,32,3**.

6. 2,4-Dinitrophenyl derivatives. The halogen atom in 2,4-dinitrochlorobenzene is reactive and coloured crystalline compounds (usually yellow or red) are formed with primary and with secondary amines:

[2,4-dinitrochlorobenzene] + RNH_2 → [N-substituted 2,4-dinitroaniline] + HCl

Dissolve 1·0 g. (or 1·0 ml.) of the amine and 1·0 g. of 2,4-dinitrochlorobenzene in 5–10 ml. of ethanol, add a slight excess of anhydrous potassium carbonate or of powdered fused sodium acetate, reflux the mixture on a water bath for 20–30 minutes, and then pour into water. Wash the precipitated solid with dilute sodium carbonate solution, followed by dilute hydrochloric acid. Recrystallize from ethanol, dilute ethanol or glacial acetic acid.

Note

Dinitrochlorobenzene must be handled with care: it is a skin irritant. If it touches the skin, wash it off immediately with methylated spirit.

7. Derivatives with 3-nitrophthalic anhydride. 3-Nitrophthalic anhydride reacts with primary and secondary amines to yield nitrophthalamic acids; it does not react with tertiary amines. The phthalamic acid derived from a primary amine undergoes dehydration when heated to 145° to give a neutral *N*-substituted 3-nitrophthalimide. The phthalamic acid from a secondary amine is stable to heat and is, of course, soluble in alkali. The reagent therefore provides a method for distinguishing and separating a mixture of primary and secondary amines.

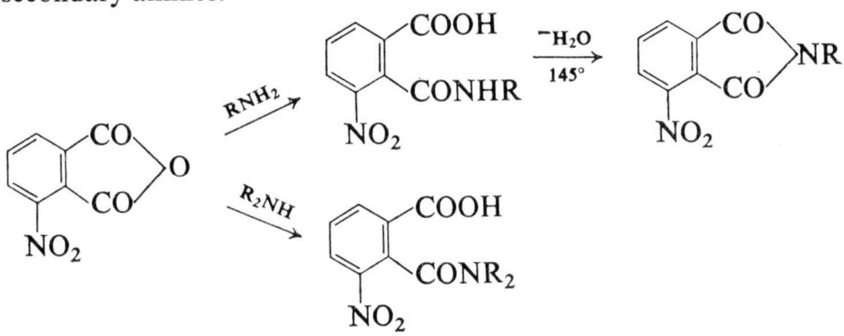

Heat 0·5 g. (or 0·5 ml.) of the amine with 0·5 g. of pure 3-nitrophthalic anhydride in an oil bath at 145–150° for 10–20 minutes, pour the reaction mixture into a small mortar or Pyrex dish, and allow it to solidify. Recrystallize from ethanol, aqueous ethanol or ethanol-acetone.

8. Formyl derivatives. Formic acid condenses with primary and secondary amines to yield formyl derivatives:

$$\text{ArNHR} + \text{HCOOH} \rightarrow \text{ArN(CHO)R} + \text{H}_2\text{O} \quad (\text{R} = \text{H, alkyl, etc.})$$

With *o*-phenylenediamine, benzimidazole is formed, m.p. 170°:

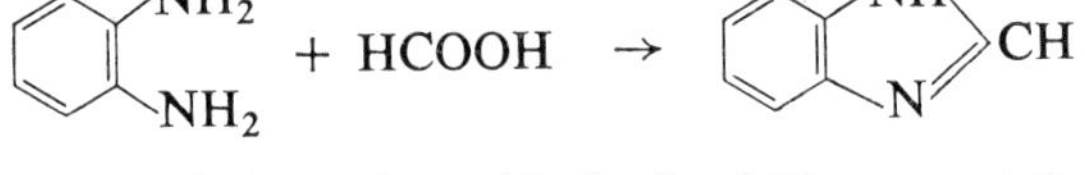

Reflux 0·5 g. of the amine with 5 ml. of 90 per cent formic acid (*CAUTION* in handling) for 10 minutes, and dilute the hot solution with 10 ml. of cold water. Cool in ice and, in some cases, saturate with salt if the derivative does not separate immediately. Filter, wash with cold water, and recrystallize from water, ethanol or light petroleum (b.p. 60–80°).

9. Phenylthioureas. Experimental details are given under *Aliphatic Amines*, Section **IV,32,**2.

The melting points of the derivatives of a number of selected primary and secondary aromatic amines are given in Tables IX, 33A and IX, 33B (Chapter IX) respectively.

Crystalline Derivatives of Tertiary Aromatic Amines

1'. **Picrates.** Experimental details are given under *Aliphatic Amines*, Section **IV,32,**3.

2'. **Methiodides.** Methyl iodide reacts with tertiary amines to form the crystalline quaternary ammonium iodide (methiodide):

$$RR'R''N + CH_3I \rightarrow \{RR'R''NCH_3\}^+I^-$$

Some of these derivatives are hygroscopic.

Allow a mixture of 0·5 g. of the tertiary amine and 0·5 ml. of colourless methyl iodide* to stand for 5 minutes. If reaction has not occurred, warm under reflux for 5 minutes on a water bath and then cool in ice water. The mixture will generally set solid: if it does not, wash it with a little dry ether and 'scratch' the sides of the tube with a glass rod. Recrystallize the solid product from absolute ethyl or methyl alcohol, ethyl acetate, glacial acetic acid or ethanol-ether.

Alternatively, dissolve 0·5 g. of the tertiary amine and 0·5 ml. of methyl iodide in 5 ml. of dry ether or benzene, and allow the mixture to stand for several hours. The methiodide precipitates, usually in a fairly pure state. Filter, wash with a little of the solvent, and recrystallize as above.

The ethiodide is prepared similarly, using ethyl iodide.

3'. **Metho-*p*-toluenesulphonates.** Methyl *p*-toluenesulphonate combines with many tertiary amines to yield crystalline derivatives:

$$RR'R''N + p\text{-}CH_3C_6H_4SO_3CH_3 \rightarrow$$
$$\{RR'R''NCH_3\}^+\{p\text{-}CH_3C_6H_4SO_3\}^-$$

Dissolve 2–3 g. of methyl *p*-toluenesulphonate in 10 ml. of dry benzene, add 1·0 g. of the amine, and boil the mixture for 20–30 minutes. Cool, and filter off the precipitated quaternary salt. Recrystallize by dissolving the solid in the minimum volume of boiling

---

* Keep a coil of copper wire (prepared by winding copper wire round a glass tube) or a little silver powder in the bottle, which should be of brown or amber glass; the methyl iodide will remain colourless indefinitely. Ethyl iodide may sometimes give more satisfactory results.

ethyl alcohol and then adding ethyl acetate until crystallization commences. Filter the cold mixture, dry rapidly on a porous plate, and determine the m.p. immediately.

The benzyl chloride quaternary salts $\{RR'R''NCH_2C_6H_5\}^+Cl^-$ are prepared similarly; 3 g. of redistilled benzyl chloride replaces the methyl p-toluenesulphonate.

4′. p-Nitroso Derivatives. Aromatic tertiary amines, such as dimethylaniline, react with nitrous acid to yield crystalline p-nitroso compounds. For further details, see (vi) above.

The melting points of the derivatives of a number of tertiary amines, both aliphatic and aromatic, are collected in Table IX, 33C (Chapter IX).

IV, 34 Amino Acids

The aliphatic compounds which contain both an amino and a carboxyl group (amino acids) are generally insoluble (or very sparingly soluble) in organic solvents such as ether or benzene, sparingly soluble in ethanol, very soluble in water and are neutral in reaction. They have no true melting points, but decompose on heating at temperatures between 120° and 300°; the apparent melting points vary considerably according to the conditions of heating and are therefore of no great value for precise identification. These properties resemble those of inorganic salts. In an amino acid H_2N—CHR—COOH, which contains both a basic and an acidic group, salt formation can take place between the two groups. Measurements of the crystal structure of amino acids show that in the solid state they exist as internal salts or dipolar ions, $\overset{+}{H_3N}$—CHR—CO_2^-. Even in aqueous solution an amino acid exists predominantly as the dipolar ion, but there is also a minute (almost negligible) quantity of the uncharged molecule present:

$$\overset{+}{H_3N}\text{—CHR—}CO_2^- \rightleftharpoons H_2N\text{—CHR—}CO_2H$$

In aqueous solution, the following equilibria may occur between the dipolar ion and the anion or cation form of the amino acid:

$$H_2N\text{—CHR—}CO_2^- \underset{HO^-}{\overset{H_3O^+}{\rightleftharpoons}} \overset{+}{H_3N}\text{—CHR—}CO_2^- \underset{HO^-}{\overset{H_3O^+}{\rightleftharpoons}}$$

Anion form $\qquad\qquad$ Dipolar ion

$$\overset{+}{H_3N}\text{—CHR—}CO_2H$$

Cation form

The position of equilibrium varies with the amino acid and with the pH of the solution; in strongly basic solution the amino acid is largely in the anion form, whereas in strongly acidic solution it is largely in the cation form.

Amino acids give the following reactions:

(i) They dissolve slowly in 5 per cent sodium bicarbonate solution; the evolution of carbon dioxide may not be apparent until after 2–3 minutes {compare the corresponding test for *Aliphatic Acids*, Section **IV,20,(i)**}.

(ii) They give the 'carbylamine' (or isocyanide) reaction {see under *Aliphatic Amines*, Section **IV,32,(iii)**}.

(iii) They yield nitrogen and a hydroxy acid when treated with nitrous acid (from sodium nitrite and dilute acetic acid), for example:

$$\overset{+}{H_3N}-CHR-CO_2^- \rightleftharpoons H_2N-CHR-CO_2H + HNO_2 \rightarrow$$
$$HO-CHR-CO_2H + N_2 + H_2O$$

(iv) Upon adding an aqueous solution of an amino acid to copper sulphate solution, a deep blue coloration is obtained. The deep blue copper derivative may be isolated by boiling a solution of the amino acid with precipitated copper hydroxide or with copper carbonate, filtering and concentrating the solution. These blue complexes are co-ordination compounds of the structure:

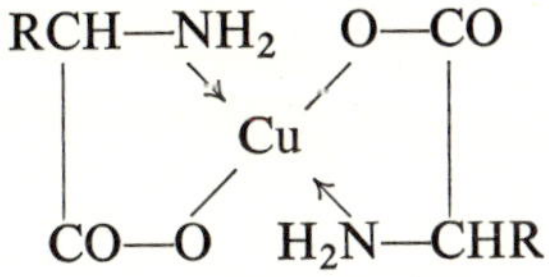

$$\begin{array}{ccc} RCH-NH_2 & & O-CO \\ | & \searrow \nearrow & | \\ & Cu & \\ | & \swarrow \nwarrow & | \\ CO-O & & H_2N-CHR \end{array}$$

(v) Upon warming a solution of an α-amino acid with a few drops of a 0·25 per cent aqueous solution of **ninhydrin** (triketohydrindene hydrate or indane-1,2,3-trione hydrate), a blue-violet coloration is produced (see p. 164 for mechanism of colour formation).

This highly sensitive test is also given by some β-amino acids and by some peptides and proteins, particularly on warming. The colour test is of great value in the characterization of the α-amino acids separated by paper and by thin layer chromatography.

Crystalline derivatives of amino acids are usually produced by reaction at the amino group by treatment with appropriate reagents in alkaline solution:

$$\overset{+}{H_3N}-CHR-CO_2^- + Na^+OH^- \rightarrow$$
$$(H_2N-CHR-CO_2)^-Na^+ + H_2O;$$

the derivative is finally precipitated by acidification of the alkaline mixture.

CRYSTALLINE DERIVATIVES OF AMINO ACIDS

1. **2,4-Dinitrophenyl derivatives.** The reaction between 2,4-dinitrofluorobenzene and amino acids leads to 2,4-dinitrophenyl derivatives: these are often crystalline and possess relatively sharp melting points.

$$O_2N\text{-}C_6H_3(NO_2)\text{-}F + H_2NCHRCOOH \xrightarrow[\text{HCl}]{NaHCO_3} O_2N\text{-}C_6H_3(NO_2)\text{-}NHCHRCOOH + NaF$$

To a solution or suspension of 0·25 g. of the amino acid in 5 ml. of water and 0·5 g. of sodium bicarbonate, add a solution of 0·4 g. of 2,4-dinitrofluorobenzene in 3 ml. of ethanol. Shake the reaction mixture vigorously and allow to stand for 1 hour with intermittent vigorous shaking. Add 3 ml. of saturated sodium chloride solution and extract with ether (2×5 ml.) to remove unchanged reagent. Pour the aqueous layer into 12 ml. of cold 5 per cent hydrochloric acid with vigorous agitation: this mixture should be distinctly acid to Congo Red indicator paper. If the product separates as an oil, try to induce crystallization by 'scratching' or stirring. Collect the derivative by suction filtration and recrystallize it from 50 per cent ethanol.

2. **Benzoates.** Dissolve 0·5 g. of the amino acid in 10 ml. of 10 per cent sodium bicarbonate solution and add 1·0 g. of benzoyl chloride. Shake the mixture vigorously in a stoppered test-tube; remove the stopper from time to time since carbon dioxide is evolved. When the odour of benzoyl chloride has disappeared, acidify with dilute hydrochloric acid to Congo Red and filter. Extract the solid with a little cold ether to remove any benzoic acid which may be present. Recrystallize the benzoyl derivative which remains from hot water or from dilute ethanol.

3. **3,5-Dinitrobenzoates.** The following experimental details are for glycine (aminoacetic acid) and may be easily adapted for any other amino acid. Dissolve 0·15 g. of glycine in 4 ml. of N sodium hydroxide solution and add 0·46 g. of finely powdered 3,5-dinitrobenzoyl chloride. Shake the mixture vigorously in a stoppered test-tube; the acid chloride soon dissolves. Continue the shaking for 2 minutes, filter (if necessary) and acidify with dilute hydrochloric acid to Congo Red. Recrystallize the derivative immediately from water or 50 per cent ethanol.

Excess of the reagent should be avoided, if possible. If excess of dinitrobenzoyl chloride is used, this appears as the acid in the precipitate obtained upon acidification: the acid can be removed by shaking in the cold with a mixture of 5 volumes of light petroleum (b.p. 40–60°) and 2 volumes of ethanol. The glycine derivative is insoluble in this medium. For some amino acids (leucine, valine and phenylalanine) acetic acid should be used for acidification.

4. **1-Naphthylureido acids** (or **1-naphthylhydantoic acids**). Amino acids react in alkaline solution with 1-naphthyl isocyanate to yield the sodium salts of the corresponding 1-naphthylureido acids, which remain in solution: upon addition of a mineral acid, the ureido acid is precipitated.

$$\underset{\text{COONa}}{\text{RCH(CH}_2)_n\text{NH}_2} + (1-\text{C}_{10}\text{H}_7)\text{N}=\text{C}=\text{O} \rightarrow$$

$$\underset{\text{COONa}}{\text{RCH(CH}_2)_n\text{NHCONH}(1-\text{C}_{10}\text{H}_7)} \xrightarrow[\text{HCl}]{\text{Dilute}}$$

$$\underset{\text{COOH}}{\text{RCH(CH}_2)_n\text{NHCONH}(1-\text{C}_{10}\text{H}_7)}$$

Dissolve 0·5 g. of the amino acid in slightly more than the equivalent quantity of N sodium hydroxide solution in a small glass bottle or flask. Add a quantity of 1-naphthyl isocyanate just equivalent to the alkali (if the molecular weight of the compound is not known, use 1·0 g. of the reagent and the corresponding quantity of alkali), stopper the bottle or flask and shake vigorously until the odour of the reagent has disappeared. Filter off any insoluble di-1-naphthylurea (resulting from the action of water upon the excess of the reagent), and acidify the filtrate to Congo Red with dilute hydrochloric acid. Filter the 1-naphthylhydantoic acid at the pump, wash it with a little cold water, and recrystallize from hot water or dilute ethanol.

The phenylhydantoic acid is prepared similarly, using phenyl isocyanate. The latter is more sensitive to water than 1-naphthyl isocyanate and therefore does not keep so well.

5. ***p*-Toluenesulphonates.** Amino acids react with *p*-toluenesulphonyl chloride (compare Section **IV**,33,*3*) under the following experimental conditions to yield, in many cases, crystalline p-toluene-sulphonates.

Dissolve 0·01 g. equivalent (or 1·0 g. if the molecular weight is unknown) of the amino acid in 20 ml. of N sodium hydroxide solution and add a solution of 2·0 g. of p-toluenesulphonyl chloride in 25 ml. of ether; shake the mixture mechanically or stir vigorously for 3–4 hours. Separate the ether layer: acidify the aqueous layer to Congo Red with dilute hydrochloric acid. The derivative usually crystallizes out rapidly or will do so on standing in ice. Filter off the crystals and crystallize from 4–5 ml. of 60 per cent ethanol.

With phenylalanine and tyrosine, the sodium salt of the derivative is sparingly soluble in water and separates during the initial reaction. Acidify the suspension to Congo Red: the salts pass into solution and the mixture separates into two layers. The derivative is in the ethereal layer and crystallizes from it within a few minutes. It is filtered off and recrystallized.

6. **2,4-Dichlorophenoxyacetates.** Amino acids react with 2,4-dichlorophenoxyacetyl chloride to give crystalline derivatives:

2,4-Cl$_2$C$_6$H$_3$OCH$_2$COCl + H$_2$NCHRCOOH $\xrightarrow{-HCl}$ 2,4-Cl$_2$C$_6$H$_3$OCH$_2$CONHCHRCOOH

Dissolve 0·01 g. equivalent of the amino acid in 0·03 g. equivalent of N sodium hydroxide solution and cool to 5° in a bath of ice. Add, with rapid stirring 0·01 g. equivalent of 2,4-dichlorophenoxyacetyl chloride dissolved in 5 ml. of dry benzene at such a rate (5–10 minutes) that the temperature of the mixture does not rise above 15°; if the reaction mixture gels after the addition of the acid chloride, add water to thin it. Remove the ice bath and stir for 2–3 hours. Extract the resulting mixture with ether, and acidify the aqueous solution to Congo Red with dilute hydrochloric acid. Collect the precipitate by filtration and recrystallize it from dilute ethanol.

Commercial 2,4-dichlorophenoxyacetic acid may be recrystallized from benzene; m.p. 138°–139°. Reflux 10 g. of the acid with 15 ml. of thionyl chloride on a steam bath for 1 hour, distil off the excess of thionyl chloride at atmospheric pressure and the residue under reduced pressure: 2,4-dichlorophenoxyacetyl chloride (8 g.) passes over at 155–157°/22–23 mm. It occasionally crystallizes (m.p. 44·5–45·5°), but usually tends to remain as a supercooled liquid.

7. Phthalyl derivatives. Many amino acids condense with phthalic anhydride at 180–185° to yield crystalline phthalyl derivatives:

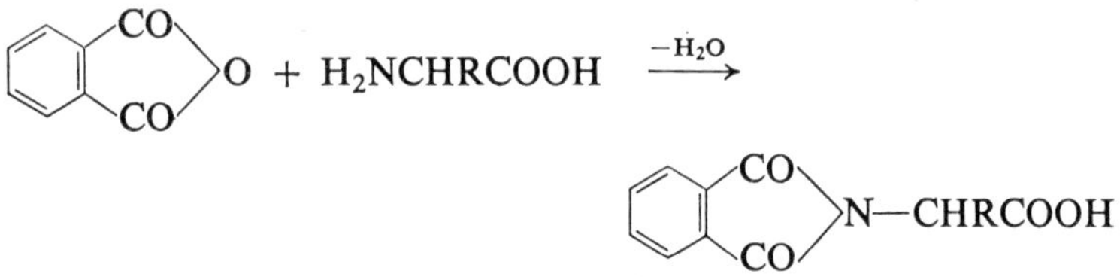

$$\underset{\text{CO}}{\underset{|}{\text{C}_6\text{H}_4}}\!\!<\!\!\underset{\text{CO}}{\overset{\text{CO}}{>}}\!\!\text{O} + \text{H}_2\text{NCHRCOOH} \xrightarrow{-\text{H}_2\text{O}} \underset{\text{CO}}{\underset{|}{\text{C}_6\text{H}_4}}\!\!<\!\!\underset{\text{CO}}{\overset{\text{CO}}{>}}\!\!\text{N}\!-\!\text{CHRCOOH}$$

Place 0·5 g. of the amino acid and 1·0 g. of phthalic anhydride in a Pyrex test-tube and immerse the lower part of the tube in an oil bath, which has previously been heated to 180–185°. Stir the mixture occasionally during the first 10 minutes and push down the phthalic anhydride which sublimes on the walls into the reaction mixture with a glass rod. Leave the mixture undisturbed for 5 minutes. After 15 minutes, remove the test-tube from the bath: when the liquid mass solidifies, invert the test-tube and scrape out the excess of phthalic anhydride on the walls. Recrystallize the residue from 10 per cent ethanol or from water.

The melting points of the derivatives of a number of amino acids are collected in Table IX, 34 (Chapter IX). Most α-amino acids decompose on heating so that the melting points would be more accurately described as decomposition points: the latter vary somewhat with the rate of heating and the figures given are those obtained upon rapid heating.

IV, 35 Aromatic Nitro Compounds

Nitro compounds, when liquid, have characteristic odours, are insoluble in water, highly refractive and with a density greater than unity. Many are crystalline solids. Most nitro compounds are slightly coloured, generally yellow; the intensity of the colour increases with the number of nitro groups. The following reactions will assist in their detection.

(i) **Action of alkali.** Provided acidic groups are absent, simple aromatic nitro compounds are practically unaffected by caustic alkalis, but a pale yellow or orange colour may develop. Aromatic compounds that contain two or more nitro groups in *meta* positions to each other, when treated in ethanol or acetone solution with aqueous alkali, give a red or purple coloration.

(ii) **Reduction to the hydroxylamine.** This is a general test for a nitro group. With a neutral reducing agent, nitro compounds yield the corresponding hydroxylamines which can be detected by their action upon Tollen's reagent {see *Aliphatic Aldehydes*, Section **IV,15,(i)**}:

$$RNO_2 + 4H \rightarrow RNHOH + H_2O$$
$$RNHOH + 2[Ag(NH_3)_2]OH \rightarrow RNO + 2Ag + 4NH_3 + 2H_2O$$

It must be noted, however, that nitroso, azoxy and azo compounds when subjected to the same treatment yield respectively hydroxylamines, hydrazo and hydrazine compounds, all of which reduce ammoniacal silver nitrate solution in the cold.

Dissolve 0·5 g. of the substance in 10 ml. of 50 per cent ethanol, add 0·5 g. of solid ammonium chloride and about 0·5 g. of zinc powder. Heat the mixture to boiling, and allow the ensuing chemical reaction to proceed for 5 minutes. Filter from the excess of zinc powder, and test the filtrate with Tollen's reagent {Section **IV,15,(i)**}. An immediate black or grey precipitate or a silver mirror indicates the presence of a hydroxylamine formed by reduction of the nitro compound. Alternatively, the filtrate may be warmed with Fehling's solution, when cuprous oxide will be precipitated if a hydroxylamine is present. Make certain that the original compound does not affect the reagent used.

(iii) **Ferrous hydroxide test.** Compounds containing one or more nitro groups will oxidize ferrous hydroxide to ferric hydroxide; the colour change is from green to brown:

$$RNO_2 + 6Fe(OH)_2 + 4H_2O \rightarrow RNH_2 + 6Fe(OH)_3$$

Add about 0·01–0·02 g. of the substance to 1·5 ml. of the ferrous sulphate reagent (**A**) in a test-tube, and then introduce 1·0 ml. of the ethanolic potassium hydroxide solution (**B**). Insert a glass tube so that it reaches to the bottom of the test-tube and pass a slow stream of coal gas through the tube for about 30 seconds in order to remove air. Stopper the test-tube rapidly and shake. A positive test is indicated by the precipitate turning brown within 1 minute.

Prepare solution **A** by adding 2·5 g. of A.R. ferrous ammonium sulphate crystals and 0·2 ml. of concentrated sulphuric acid to 50 ml. of recently boiled, distilled water. Introduce a little iron wire to retard oxidation by air.

Prepare the solution **B** by dissolving 3·0 g. of potassium hydroxide pellets in 3·0 ml. of distilled water, and adding the solution to 20 ml. of rectified spirit.

The test is given by some but not by all nitroparaffins: thus nitromethane and 2-nitropropane, but not nitroethane and 1-nitropropane, give positive results under the conditions of the test. Positive results are also given by other compounds which oxidize ferrous hydroxide, *e.g.*, nitroso compounds, quinones, hydroxylamines, alkyl nitrates and alkyl nitrites; they are not so common as the nitro compounds and may be identified by other tests.

CRYSTALLINE DERIVATIVES

1. **Reduction with tin and hydrochloric acid and characterization of the resulting primary amine.** Add 10 ml. of concentrated hydrochloric acid in small portions to a mixture of 1·0 g. of the nitro compound and 3 g. of granulated tin contained in a small (say, 50 ml.) flask fitted with a reflux condenser. Shake the flask well to ensure thorough mixing during the addition of the acid. After 10 minutes warm under reflux at 100° with vigorous shaking until the nitro compound has dissolved and its odour is no longer apparent. (If the nitro compound dissolves slowly, add a few ml. of ethanol.) Cool the reaction mixture, and cautiously make it alkaline with 20–40 per cent sodium hydroxide solution. Isolate the liberated amine by steam distillation or by ether extraction. Test a small portion qualitatively for an amine and then identify it as detailed under *Aromatic Amines*, Section **IV,33.**

2. **Oxidation of side chains.** Aromatic nitro compounds that contain a side chain (*e.g.*, nitro derivatives of alkyl benzenes) may be oxidized to the corresponding acids either by alkaline potassium permanganate (*Aromatic Hydrocarbons*, Section **IV,4,***6*) or, preferably, with a sodium dichromate-sulphuric acid mixture in which medium the nitro compound is more soluble.

Mix 1·0 g. of the nitro compound with 4 g. of sodium dichromate and 10 ml. of water in a 50 ml. flask, then attach a reflux condenser to the flask. Add slowly and with shaking 7 ml. of concentrated sulphuric acid. The reaction usually starts at once; if it does not, heat the flask gently to initiate the reaction. When the heat of reaction subsides, boil the mixture, cautiously at first, under reflux for 20–30 minutes. Allow to cool, dilute with 30 ml. of water, and filter off the precipitated acid. Purify the crude acid by extraction with sodium carbonate solution, precipitation with dilute mineral acid, and recrystallization from hot water, benzene, etc.

3. **Nitration to a poly-nitro compound.** Aromatic mononitro compounds may sometimes be characterized by conversion into the corresponding dinitro or trinitro derivatives. It may be noted that many poly-nitro compounds form characteristic addition compounds with naphthalene.

The nitration of an aromatic compound, especially if its composition is unknown must be conducted with great care, preferably in the fume cupboard (hood), since many aromatic compounds react violently.

A. Add about 0·5 g. of the compound to 2·0 ml. of concentrated sulphuric acid. Introduce 2·0 ml. of concentrated nitric acid drop by drop, with shaking after each addition. Attach a small reflux condenser to the flask and heat in a beaker of water at 50° for 5 minutes. Pour the reaction mixture on to 15 g. of crushed ice and collect the precipitated solid by suction filtration. Recrystallize from dilute ethanol.

B. Proceed as in *A* but use 2·0 ml. of fuming nitric acid instead of the concentrated nitric acid, and warm the mixture on a boiling water bath for 5–10 minutes.

A number of selected nitro compounds, together with some derivatives, are collected in Table IX, 35 (Chapter IX). It will be noted that a few nitro aromatic esters have been included in the Table. These are given here because the nitro group may be the first functional group to be identified; aromatic nitro esters should be treated as other esters and hydrolysed for final identification.

IV, 36 Aliphatic Nitro Compounds

The following reactions will assist in the detection of aliphatic nitro compounds.

(i) **Action of alkali.** Add a few drops of the nitro compound to 1 ml. of 20 per cent sodium hydroxide solution; it dissolves to produce, in general, a yellow solution. Acidify with strong acetic acid at a low temperature; the nitro compound is regenerated.

(ii) **Reduction to the hydroxylamine.** This test gives a positive result {see *Aromatic Nitro Compounds*, Section **IV,35,**(ii)}.

(iii) **Sodium salt of the aci-form.** Dissolve 0·2 g. of sodium in 5 ml. of anhydrous methanol, and cool to room temperature. Add 0·5 ml. of the nitro compound, shake and cool. Both primary and secondary

$$\left(RCH=N\begin{smallmatrix}\nearrow O\\ -O^-\end{smallmatrix}\right)Na^+ \quad \text{and} \quad \left(R'R''C=N\begin{smallmatrix}\nearrow O\\ -O^-\end{smallmatrix}\right)Na^+$$

nitro compounds yield sodium derivatives which may be filtered off and washed with methanol to remove traces of sodium methoxide. They should be kept moist with methanol; the sodium derivatives, if allowed to dry, may become very explosive. Also, upon contact with a trace of water, they are liable to decompose with explosive violence. The sodium derivative may be dissolved by successively adding small quantities to cold water with continual stirring.

(iv) **Distinction between primary, secondary and tertiary aliphatic nitro compounds.** Dissolve a few drops of the nitro compound in concentrated sodium hydroxide solution, and add excess of sodium nitrite solution. Upon cautiously acidifying with dilute sulphuric acid, added a drop at a time, the following effects may be observed:

(a) Primary nitro compound: intense red colour, disappearing upon acidification. The coloration is that of the alkali salt of the nitrolic acid:

$$RCH_2NO_2 + HONO \rightarrow RCH(NO)NO_2 + H_2O$$

$$RCHNO_2\text{(NO)} + NaOH \rightarrow \left(RC(NO)=N\begin{smallmatrix}O\\O^-\end{smallmatrix}\right) Na^+ + H_2O$$

(b) Secondary nitro compound: dark blue or blue green colour due to nitroso derivatives. The coloured compound is soluble in chloroform, but insoluble in water and dilute alkali.

$$R'R''CHNO_2 + HONO \rightarrow R'R''C(NO)-NO_2 + H_2O$$

(c) Tertiary compound: no coloration.

CHARACTERIZATION

Reduction with tin and hydrochloric acid and characterization of the primary amine. Experimental details are given under *Aromatic Nitro Compounds*, in Section **IV,33,***1*. The amine is fairly volatile and cannot be diazotized (see under *Aliphatic Amines*, Section **IV,32**).

Most aliphatic nitro compounds are liquids: the physical properties (boiling point, density and refractive index) therefore provide valuable information for purposes of identification.

The physical properties of a number of aliphatic nitro compounds are listed in Table IX, 36 (Chapter IX).

IV, 37 Mercaptans and Thiophenols (Thiols)

Mercaptans RSH (also thioethers or sulphides R'SR" and disulphides R'SSR") are generally liquids and possess unpleasant odours.

Upon fusion with caustic alkali (for experimental details, see under *Aromatic Sulphonic Acids*, Section **IV,38,***1*) and acidification of the aqueous extract, hydrogen sulphide is evolved (detected by lead acetate paper). This test is given by all organic compounds of divalent sulphur (RSH, R'SR" and R'SSR").

Alkyl mercaptans are partly soluble in solutions of caustic alkalis, but their salts are hydrolysed in dilute aqueous solution back to the free mercaptans. Thiophenols are soluble in alkali hydroxide solutions. Upon treatment with sodium, hydrogen is evolved.

CRYSTALLINE DERIVATIVES OF THIOLS

Of the crystalline derivatives of thiols, those formed with 3,5-dinitrobenzoyl chloride are not very satisfactory since they have, in general lower melting points than those of the corresponding alcohols (compare *Aliphatic Alcohols*, Section **IV,5,***1*) and do not differ widely from ethyl to *n*-heptyl. The best results are obtained with 2,4-dinitrochlorobenzene.

1. **Alkyl (or Aryl) 2,4-dinitrophenyl-sulphides (or -thioethers) and the corresponding sulphones.** Mercaptans react with 2,4-dinitrochlorobenzene in alkaline solution to yield crystalline thioethers (2,4-dinitrophenyl-sulphides) (I):

$$RSNa + Cl-C_6H_3(NO_2)_2 \rightarrow RS-C_6H_3(NO_2)_2 \text{ (I)} + NaCl$$

The sulphides (I) can be readily oxidized in glacial acetic acid solution by potassium permanganate to the corresponding sulphones (II); the latter exhibit a wide range of melting points and are therefore particularly valuable for the characterization of mercaptans:

$$RS-C_6H_3(NO_2)_2 \text{ (I)} \xrightarrow{KMnO_4 \text{ [20]}} R-SO_2-C_6H_3(NO_2)_2 \text{ (II)}$$

Preparation of 2,4-*dinitrophenyl-sulphides*. Dissolve about 0·5 g. (or 0·005 mol) of the mercaptan in 10–15 ml. of rectified spirit (or in the minimum volume necessary for solution; warming is permissible) and add 2 ml. of 10 per cent sodium hydroxide solution. Mix the resulting sodium mercaptide solution with a solution of 1 g. of 2,4-dinitrochlorobenzene (*CAUTION:* see Section **IV,33,***6*) in 5 ml. of rectified spirit. Reaction may occur immediately with precipitation of the thioether. In any case reflux the mixture for 10 minutes on a water bath in order to ensure the completeness of the reaction. Filter the hot solution rapidly; allow the solution to cool when the sulphide will crystallize out. Recrystallize from ethanol.

Preparation of the sulphones. Dissolve the 2,4-dinitrophenylsulphide (0·005 mol) in the minimum volume of warm glacial acetic acid and add 3 per cent potassium permanganate solution with shaking as fast as decolorization occurs. Use a 50 per cent excess of potassium permanganate: if the sulphide tends to precipitate, add more acetic acid. Just decolorize the solution with sulphur dioxide (or with sodium bisulphite or ethanol) and add 2–3 volumes of crushed ice. Filter off the sulphone, dry, and recrystallize from ethanol.

2. 3,5-Dinitrothiobenzoates. Mercaptans react with 3,5-dinitrobenzoyl chloride in the presence of pyridine as a catalyst to yield 3,5-dinitrothiobenzoates:

$$O_2N\text{-}C_6H_3(NO_2)\text{-}COCl + RSH \xrightarrow{C_5H_5N} O_2N\text{-}C_6H_3(NO_2)\text{-}COSR + C_5H_5N, HCl$$

Mix 0·2 g. of 3,5-dinitrobenzoyl chloride, 6 drops of the mercaptan and 1–3 drops of pyridine in a test-tube, and heat the mixture in a beaker of boiling water until fumes of hydrogen chloride cease to appear (10–15 minutes). Add a few drops of water, followed by a drop or two of pyridine to eliminate the excess of the reagent. The product solidifies upon stirring with a glass rod. Add water, filter, and recrystallize from dilute ethanol or dilute acetic acid.

3. 3-Nitrothiophthalates. Mercaptans react with 3-nitrophthalic anhydride to yield 3-nitrothiophthalates (compare *Alcohols*, Section **IV,5,5**):

$$\text{3-NO}_2\text{-C}_6H_3(CO)_2O + RSH \rightarrow \text{3-NO}_2\text{-C}_6H_3(COOH)(COSR)$$

Mix 3-nitrophthalic anhydride (0·005 mol or 1·0 g.) and the mercaptan (0·0075 mol, or 1·0 g. if the molecular weight is not known) in a test-tube and heat gently over a free flame for about 30 seconds. Allow the mixture to cool, and add 0·5 ml. of $2N$ sodium hydroxide solution dropwise and with cooling in an ice bath. Then add about 0·3 ml. of $2N$ hydrochloric acid and shake the reaction mixture vigorously. Collect the solid which separates by suction filtration and dry it upon a porous tile. Recrystallize from dilute acetic acid or from aqueous acetone.

The melting points are determined using a bath preheated to about 100°. The compounds decompose slightly at the m.p. The neutralization equivalent may be evaluated by titration with standard alkali.

4. **Mercury mercaptides.** The ease of formation of insoluble mercury salts led to the name mercaptan (Latin *mercurium captans*, seizing mercury). Most mercaptans form characteristic mercury salts (mercaptides).

Add an excess of 10 per cent aqueous mercuric cyanide to a solution of the mercaptan (0·3 ml. or 6 drops) in ethanol (2 ml.), shake for a few minutes and cool in ice: the mercury salt separates. Filter off the mercuric mercaptide, dry it on a porous tile, and crystallize it from ethanol.

The melting points of the mercuric mercaptides of some typical thiols are: methyl, 175°; ethyl, 76°; *n*-propyl, 72°; isopropyl, 63°; *n*-butyl, 86°; isobutyl, 95°; *n*-amyl, 75°; isoamyl, 100°.

The melting points of the derivatives of the more commonly occurring thiols are collected in Table IX, 37 (Chapter IX).

IV, 38 Aromatic Sulphonic Acids and Their Salts

Sulphonic acids are frequently crystalline solids, readily soluble in water and often hygroscopic. Because of the difficulty of isolation of the free acids, they are usually encountered as the sodium, potassium, calcium and barium salts.

(i) **Fusion with caustic alkali.** When the preliminary tests for elements indicate the presence of sulphur (and frequently also of a metal), it is advisable to carry out a fusion with caustic alkali. In a nickel crucible of about 20 ml. capacity mix thoroughly 0·5–1 g. of the substance with 3 g. of potassium hydroxide pellets and 4–5 drops of water. Support the crucible in a circular hole in a sheet of asbestos or uralite board of such size that it fits tightly and only about one-third is below the board; this will ensure that the contents of the crucible are not contaminated by sulphur compounds from the gas flame. (Alternatively, place the nickel crucible in a larger iron crucible fitted with an asbestos ring so arranged that the nickel crucible is held about 5 mm. from the bottom of the iron crucible). Heat the crucible so that the mixture *just* melts and continue the fusion with occasional stirring with a small nickel spatula for 5–10 minutes. Allow to cool, add about 5 ml. of water and dissolve the mass by warming with a small flame. Pour the solution into a small test-tube; acidify by the cautious addition of 50 per cent sulphuric acid. Note whether there is any odour of sulphur dioxide: test for this gas either with filter paper moistened with acidified potassium dichromate solution, or better, by the highly sensitive **sulphur dioxide test reagent.** In the latter case it is best to use the semimicro technique for the identification of evolved gases.

$$ArSO_3K + 2KOH \rightarrow ArOK + K_2SO_3 + H_2O$$

The **sulphur dioxide test reagent is prepared** by mixing 50 ml. of $0 \cdot 1N$ hydrochloric acid, 15 ml. of N barium chloride solution and 5 ml. of $0 \cdot 1N$ potassium permanganate solution. Its use is based upon the transient formation of barium sulphite which is immediately oxidized by the permanganate to give a white precipitate of insoluble barium sulphate; the permanganate solution is simultaneously decolorized. The method is inapplicable in the presence of hydrogen sulphide, which gives the same visible result.

Extract the acidified solution with ether, remove the ether and identify the phenol in the usual manner (see *Phenols*, Section **IV,7**).* Add a few drops of bromine water or nitric acid to the aqueous layer and test for sulphate with barium chloride solution.

Once the presence of a sulphonate group has been established (and, if possible, the phenol isolated), the compound may be characterized by the preparation of a derivative. It must be remembered that both *sulphoxides* RSOR' and *sulphones* RSO_2R' yield sulphur dioxide on fusion with caustic alkali and acidification.

CRYSTALLINE DERIVATIVES

1. **Sulphonamides.** Mix together $1 \cdot 0$ g. of the dry acid or $1 \cdot 2$ g. of the anhydrous salt with $2 \cdot 5$ g. of phosphorus pentachloride† in a small

---

* The phenol cannot always be isolated in good yield, particularly if it contains substituent groups, owing to the destructive action of the alkali fusion upon the radical Ar. Potassium hydroxide or a mixture of sodium and potassium hydroxides gives a better yield of the phenol than sodium hydroxide alone.

† If preferred, the PCl_5 may be replaced by 4–5 ml. of $POCl_3$ and the mixture refluxed for 4 hours. The subsequent procedure is identical with that given in the text.

dry flask and heat under a reflux condenser in an oil bath at 150° for 30 minutes. Cool the mixture, add 20 ml. of dry benzene, warm on a steam bath and stir the solid mass well to extract the sulphonyl chloride: filter. Add the benzene solution slowly and with stirring to 10 ml. of concentrated ammonia solution. If the sulphonamide precipitates, separate it by filtration; if no solid is obtained, evaporate the benzene on a steam bath. Wash the sulphonamide with a little cold water, and recrystallize from water, aqueous ethanol or ethanol to constant m.p.

The procedure is not usually applicable to aminosulphonic acids owing to the interaction between the amino group and the phosphorus pentachloride. If, however, the chloroarylsulphonic acid is prepared by diazotization and treatment with a solution of cuprous chloride in hydrochloric acid, the crystalline chlorosulphonamide and chlorosulphonanilide may be obtained in the usual way. With some aminosulphonic acids, the amino group may be 'protected' by acetylation. Sulphonic acids derived from a phenol or a naphthol cannot be directly converted into the sulphonyl chloride by the phosphorus pentachloride method.

The **sulphonanilides** may be prepared by either of the following methods:—(i) Reflux the solution of the sulphonyl chloride in benzene obtained as above, with 2·5 g. of aniline for 1 hour. Concentrate the benzene solution to half its volume and cool in ice. Collect the solid which separates on a filter, wash with hot water, and recrystallize from ethanol or dilute ethanol.

(ii) Treat the crude sulphonyl chloride {isolated by evaporating the solvent after extraction with benzene (or ether or chloroform) as above} with 1 g. of *p*-toluidine and 30 ml. of *ca.* 2N sodium hydroxide solution. Shake for 10–15 minutes. Extract the alkaline solution with ether to remove excess of *p*-toluidine, acidify, filter, and recrystallize the residue as in (i).

$$ArSO_2ONa + PCl_5 \rightarrow ArSO_2Cl + POCl_3 + NaCl$$
$$ArSO_2Cl + 2NH_3 \rightarrow ArSO_2NH_2 + NH_4Cl$$
$$ArSO_2Cl + 2C_6H_5NH_2 \rightarrow ArSO_2NHC_6H_5 + C_6H_5NH_3^+Cl^-$$

2. *S*-**Benzylthiuronium sulphonates** (for a discussion of this reagent, see under *Aliphatic Carboxylic Acids*, Section **IV,20,4**). If the substance is the free sulphonic acid, dissolve 0·5 g. of it in 5–10 ml. of water, add a drop or two of phenolphthalein indicator and carefully neutralize with *ca. N* sodium hydroxide solution. Then add 2–3 drops of 0·1N

hydrochloric acid to ensure that the solution is almost neutral (*pale pink colour*): under alkaline conditions the reagent tends to decompose to produce the evil-smelling benzyl mercaptan. If the salt is available, this may be used directly.

To a solution of 0·5 g. of the salt in 5 ml. of water and 2–3 drops of 0·1 N hydrochloric acid (or to the solution of the acid treated as above), add a slight excess of a cold, 15 per cent aqueous solution of S-benzyl-thiuronium chloride (if the molecular weight of the compound is not known, use a solution of 1 g. of the reagent in 5 ml. of water), and cool in ice. Filter off the crystalline derivative and recrystallize it from 50 per cent alcohol.

$$\left\{ C_6H_5CH_2-S-C\begin{matrix}NH_2\\NH_2\end{matrix}\right\}^+ Cl^- + RSO_3^-Na^+ \rightarrow$$

$$\left\{ C_6H_5CH_2-S-C\begin{matrix}NH_2\\NH_2\end{matrix}\right\}^+ (RSO_3)^- + Na^+Cl^-$$

3. **Sulphonacetamides.** Sulphonacetamides are derivatives of sulphonamides (Section **IV**,39), but since the latter are readily prepared from the sulphonic acids or their salts, sulphonacetamides may also be employed for the characterization of sulphonic acids; for this reason they are included in this Section.

Sulphonamides upon heating with acetyl chloride are converted into the *N*-acetyl derivatives or sulphonacetamides:

$$ArSO_2NHR + CH_3COCl \rightarrow$$
$$ArSO_2NRCOCH_3 + HCl \; (R = H \text{ or alkyl})$$

The sulphonacetamides (R=H) are freely soluble in sodium bicarbonate solution thus rendering purification easy. Sulphonacetamides are moderately strong acids, and can generally be titrated in aqueous or aqueous-ethanolic solution with phenolphthalein as indicator. The acidic properties of sulphonacetamides may be used to effect a **separation of a sulphonamide from a *N*-alkylsulphonamide.** Acetylation of such a mixture gives a sulphonacetamide and a *N*-alkylsulphonacetamide, of which only the former is soluble in sodium bicarbonate solution. Both sulphonacetamides and *N*-alkylsulphonacetamides are readily hydrolysed by boiling with excess of 5 per cent potassium hydroxide solution for about 1 hour, followed by acidification with dilute hydrochloric acid, giving the corresponding sulphonamides and *N*-alkylsulphonamides respectively.

Reflux 1·0 g. of the sulphonamide with 2·5 ml. of acetyl chloride for 30 minutes; if solution is not complete within 5 minutes, add up to

2·5 ml. of glacial acetic acid. Remove the excess of acetyl chloride by distillation on a water bath, and pour the cold reaction mixture into water. Collect the product, wash with water and dissolve it in warm sodium bicarbonate solution. Acidify the filtered solution with glacial acetic acid; filter off the precipitated sulphonacetamide and recrystallize it from aqueous ethanol.

The melting points of a number of sulphonacetamides are: benzenesulphonic acid, 125°; *p*-toluenesulphonic acid, 137°; *p*-bromobenzenesulphonic acid, 203°; *m*-nitrobenzenesulphonic acid, 189°; *p*-nitrobenzenesulphonic acid, 192°; naphthalene-1-sulphonic acid, 185°; and naphthalene-2-sulphonic acid, 146°.

4. *p*-Toluidine salts of sulphonic acids. These are prepared by the interaction of the sulphonic acid or its sodium salt with *p*-toluidine hydrochloride in aqueous solution:

$$RSO_3^-Na^+ + H^+Cl^- + p\text{-}CH_3\text{---}C_6H_4\text{---}NH_2 \rightarrow$$
$$(p\text{-}CH_3\text{---}C_6H_4\text{---}NH_3)^+(RSO_3)^- + Na^+Cl^-$$

Method A. Dissolve 1·0 g. of the sulphonic acid or its sodium salt in the *minimum* volume of boiling water and add a saturated aqueous solution of 1 g. of *p*-toluidine hydrochloride. Cool, filter off the precipitate of the *p*-toluidine salt, and recrystallize it from hot water containing a drop of concentrated hydrochloric acid or from dilute ethanol.

Aniline salts of sulphonic acids are prepared similarly.

Method B. Dissolve 1·0 g. of the alkali metal salt of the sulphonic acid in the minimum volume of hot water and add 0·5 g. of *p*-toluidine and 2 ml. of concentrated hydrochloric acid. If a solid separates or the *p*-toluidine does not dissolve completely, add more hot water and a few drops of concentrated hydrochloric acid until a clear solution is obtained at the boiling point. Cool the solution; if crystallization does not occur immediately, 'scratch' the walls of the test-tube to induce crystallization. Collect the product by suction filtration, and recrystallize it as above.

The melting points of the derivatives of a number of selected sulphonic acids are collected in Table IX, 38 (Chapter IX); the melting points of the corresponding sulphonyl chlorides are included for purposes of reference; they may be isolated by evaporating the benzene solution obtained in 1 above and recrystallized from chloroform, light petroleum (b.p. 40–60°), or benzene-light petroleum (b.p. 40–60°). The acids do not possess sharp melting points; the

Elementary Practical Organic Chemistry [IV

sulphonic acids are therefore arranged in groups of related compounds.

In a subsidiary Table (IX, 38A), a number of sulphonic acids are arranged in the order of increasing melting points of the S-benzylthiuronium salts. This Table should prove useful to the student since these derivatives are easily and rapidly prepared either from the free acids or from the alkali metal salts.

IV, 39 Aromatic Sulphonamides

Sulphonamides are most readily identified by hydrolysis with concentrated hydrochloric acid or with 80 per cent sulphuric acid (for experimental details, see Section **V,12**):

$$ArSO_2NHR + HCl + H_2O \rightarrow ArSO_3H + RNH_3Cl$$
$$ArSO_2NRR' + HCl + H_2O \rightarrow ArSO_3H + RR'NH_2Cl$$

The amine is removed by the addition of alkali and characterized by a suitable derivative; the sulphonic acid may then be recovered as the sodium salt and converted into a crystalline derivative, *e.g.*, the S-benzylthiuronium sulphonate.

Primary sulphonamides RSO_2NH_2 may be most simply characterized by condensation with xanthydrol to yield the corresponding **N-xanthylsulphonamides**:

$$RSO_2NH_2 + \underset{\text{xanthydrol}}{\text{[structure]}} \rightarrow \underset{\text{N-xanthylsulphonamide}}{\text{[structure]}}$$

The experimental details are as follows. Dissolve 0·25 g. of xanthydrol and 0·25 g. of the primary sulphonamide in 10 ml. of glacial acetic acid. Shake for 2–3 minutes at the laboratory temperature and allow to stand for 60–90 minutes. Filter off the derivative, recrystallize it from dioxan-water (3:1), and dry at room temperature under water pump suction for 30 minutes. Unfortunately, only a few N-xanthylsulphonamides have been prepared, and some of these are listed in Table IX, 39A (Chapter IX). The melting points of sulphonamides, both aliphatic and aromatic, are collected in Table IX, 39B (Chapter IX).

Sulphonamides may also be characterized as **sulphonacetamides**; for experimental details, see Section **IV,38,3**.

IV, 40 Quinones

The number of quinones normally encountered in routine qualitative organic analysis is very limited; the following notes will be found useful for their detection and characterization.

(i) **General properties.** All quinones are coloured (generally yellow) crystalline solids. They are usually insoluble in water, soluble in ether, and sublime on heating. Frequently the vapour has a penetrating odour and attacks the eyes. The carbonyl groups of quinones often do not react in a normal manner with carbonyl group reagents, because of their oxidizing properties: thus benzoquinones are converted by sodium bisulphite to quinol sulphonic acids. Crystalline products are usually formed with one molecule of phenylhydrazine and of 2,4-dinitrophenylhydrazine, but these are not always of normal structure. Thus *p*-benzoquinone reacts with 2,4-dinitrophenylhydrazine hydrochloride in hot alcoholic solution to give 2,4-dinitro-4′-hydroxyazobenzene, m.p. 185–186°:

$$O_2N-C_6H_3(NO_2)-NHNH_2 + O{=}C_6H_4{=}O \rightarrow O_2N-C_6H_3(NO_2)-N{=}N-C_6H_4-OH + H_2O$$

Mono- and di-oximes are obtained by the action of hydroxylamine hydrochloride in aqueous-ethanolic solution.

(ii) **Sodium hydroxide solution.** Dark solutions are formed on warming owing to decomposition. Upon acidification, an amorphous solid may be precipitated.

(iii) **Hydriodic acid.** Compounds of the *p*-benzoquinone type liberate iodine from hydriodic acid.

Dissolve 0·1 g. of the quinone in a little rectified spirit. Add 10 ml. of 10 per cent aqueous potassium iodide solution to a mixture of 5 ml. of ethanol and 5 ml. of concentrated hydrochloric acid, and then introduce the quinone solution. Iodine is liberated immediately (brown coloration). This test is also given by other oxidizing agents.

(iv) **Reduction with zinc powder and acid.** Simple *p*-quinones are reduced to hydroquinones in the following manner. Dissolve or suspend 0·5 g. of the quinone in dilute hydrochloric acid (1 : 5) and add a little zinc powder. When the solution is colourless, filter, neutralize with sodium bicarbonate, extract the dihydric phenol with ether, remove the solvent, and identify (see under *Phenols*, Section **IV,7**).

Sulphurous acid produces a similar result, but some hydroquinone sulphonic acid is simultaneously produced.

(v) **Reduction with zinc powder and caustic alkali.** Compounds of the anthraquinone type are reduced to oxanthrols.

Treat 0·1 g. of the quinone with dilute sodium hydroxide solution and zinc powder. Upon boiling the mixture a red colour is produced: this disappears when the solution is shaken owing to aerial oxidation to the original quinone.

(vi) **Distillation with zinc powder.** Quinones derived from polycyclic hydrocarbons may be reduced to the parent hydrocarbon as follows. Grind 0·5 g. of the compound with 3–4 g. of zinc powder, pour the mixture into a Pyrex test-tube and cover it with an equal volume of zinc powder. Clamp the tube horizontally at the open end. Heat the zinc powder first, then the mixture of zinc powder and the compound to a dull red heat: the hydrocarbon sublimes into the cooler part of the tube. Remove the sublimate; determine the m.p. and identify it by the preparation of the picrate or sulphonamide (see under *Aromatic Hydrocarbons*, Section **IV,4**).

(vii) **Reaction with semicarbazide hydrochloride.** Many simple quinones yield crystalline mono-semicarbazones by the following procedure. Dissolve 0·2 g. of semicarbazide hydrochloride in a little water, add 0·2 g. of the quinone and warm. The mono-semicarbazone is immediately formed as a yellow precipitate. Filter and recrystallize from hot water; any di- (or bis-) semicarbazone will remain undissolved.

o-Phenylenediamine   Phenanthraquinone   Quinoxaline derivative

Ortho-quinones (and also aromatic α-diketones, *e.g.*, benzil) react with *o*-phenylenediamine to yield **quinoxalines** as follows. Dissolve the substance in alcohol or in glacial acetic acid, add an equivalent amount of *o*-phenylenediamine in alcoholic solution and warm for 15 minutes on a water bath. Cool, dilute with water, filter and recrystallize from dilute ethanol. The quinoxaline from phenanthraquinone has m.p. 217°; from benzil, 124°.

CHARACTERIZATION

1. **Reduction to hydroquinone.** Dissolve, or suspend, 0·5 g. of the quinone in 5 ml. of ether or benzene and shake vigorously with a solution of 1·0 g. of sodium dithionite ($Na_2S_2O_4$) in 10 ml. of N sodium hydroxide until the colour of the quinone has disappeared. Separate the alkaline solution of the hydroquinone, cool it in ice, and acidify with concentrated hydrochloric acid. Collect the product (extract with ether, if necessary) and recrystallize it from ethanol or water.

2. **Reductive acetylation.** Suspend 0·5 g. of the quinone in 2·5 ml. of pure acetic anhydride, and add 0·5 g. of zinc powder and 0·1 g. of powdered, anhydrous sodium acetate. Warm the mixture gently until the colour of the quinone has largely disappeared and then boil for 1 minute. Add 2 ml. of glacial acetic acid and boil again to dissolve the product and part of the precipitated zinc acetate. Decant the hot solution from the zinc acetate and zinc, and wash the residue with 3–4 ml. of hot glacial acetic acid. Combine the solutions, heat to boiling, carefully add sufficient water to hydrolyse the acetic anhydride and to produce a turbidity. Cool the mixture in ice, filter off the diacetate of the hydroquinone, and recrystallize it from dilute ethanol or from light petroleum.

3. **Thiele acetylation.** Quinones, when treated with acetic anhydride in the presence of perchloric acid or of concentrated sulphuric acid (strong acid catalyst), undergo simultaneous reductive acetylation and substitution to yield triacetoxy derivatives, *e.g.*, benzoquinone gives 1,2,4-triacetoxybenzene.

Add 0·1 ml. of concentrated sulphuric acid or of 72 per cent perchloric acid cautiously to a cold solution of 0·01 mol (or 1·0 g.) of the quinone in 3–5 ml. of acetic anhydride. Do not permit the temperature to rise above 50°. Allow to stand for 15–30 minutes and pour into 15 ml. of water. Collect the precipitated solid and recrystallize it from ethanol.

The properties of a number of quinones and their derivatives are summarized in Table IX, 40 (Chapter IX).

CHAPTER V

Class Reactions (Reactions for Functional Groups)

The preliminary analysis and the solubility behaviour of an unknown compound will serve to place it in one of the seven solubility groups (Table III, 3, 1). It is then necessary to ascertain to which of the classes of the particular solubility group the compound belongs, *i.e.*, to determine the functional group (or groups) present in the substance. Many of the functional groups are to be found in more than one of the solubility groups, consequently the ensuing discussion of the characteristic class reactions, will, in many instances, cover several solubility groups. Where an organic compound contains more than one functional group, the classification is generally based upon the one that is most readily detected and manipulated. Thus, benzoic acid, *p*-chlorobenzoic acid, *p*-methoxybenzoic acid (anisic acid), and *p*-nitrobenzoic acid will be classified as *acids* both by the solubility tests and the class reactions. The identification of, say, the nitrogen-containing acid *may* be completed by the preparation of derivatives of the carboxyl group without the absolute necessity of applying the class reactions that would discover the nitro group. However, if possible, it is always advisable to establish the nature of the subsidiary functional group (or groups) since this would provide extremely valuable additional evidence for the characterization of the unknown compound. It must also be remembered that in compounds containing two or more functional groups, the latter may influence one another so that the properties cannot easily be predicted: for example, in chlorobenzene the chlorine is not very reactive (say, towards ethanolic silver nitrate solution and to aniline), but in 1-chloro-2,4-dinitrobenzene the chlorine exhibits high reactivity to aniline (due to the presence of nitro groups in the *ortho* and *para* positions), but not to ethanolic silver nitrate.

V, 1 Unsaturated Hydrocarbons
Tests for Unsaturation

Unsaturated hydrocarbons are found in Solubility Group V. The two reagents employed for the detection of unsaturation, not only of unsaturated hydrocarbons but of all classes of unsaturated compounds (RR′C=CR″R‴), are:

(a) *a dilute solution (2–3 per cent) of bromine in carbon tetrachloride*, and

(b) *a dilute aqueous solution (2 per cent) of potassium permanganate*.

It is essential to apply *both* tests, since some symmetrically substituted ethylenic compounds (*e.g.*, stilbene $C_6H_5CH=CHC_6H_5$) react slowly under the conditions of the bromine test. With dilute permanganate solution the double bond is readily attacked, probably through the intermediate formation of *cis* diol; if the reaction mixture is heated, cleavage occurs and a carboxylic acid is ultimately produced:

$$C_6H_5CH=CHC_6H_5 \xrightarrow[H_2O]{[O]} C_6H_5\underset{OH}{CH}-\underset{OH}{CH}C_6H_5 \xrightarrow{[O]} 2C_6H_5COOH$$

Attention is directed to the fact that other classes of organic compounds, such as phenols, aromatic amines and enols which are found in other Solubility Groups, rapidly decolorize both the bromine and permanganate reagents, but there is a fundamental difference in the reaction with the former reagent. These compounds are *substituted* by bromine and an equivalent of hydrogen bromide is evolved during the reaction (white fumes when a glass stopper moistened with concentrated ammonia solution is held near the mouth of the test-tube).

The reaction with cold dilute potassium permanganate solution, sometimes known as *Baeyer's test* for unsaturation, is not specific for a double or triple bond: other easily oxidizable groups (*e.g.*, alcohols, aldehydes, phenols, arylamines, thiols, thio-ethers, sulphoxides) must be absent.

Bromine test. Dissolve 0·2 g. or 0·2 ml. of the compound in 2 ml. of carbon tetrachloride, and add a 2 per cent solution of bromine in carbon tetrachloride dropwise until the bromine colour persists for one minute. Blow across the mouth of the tube to detect any hydrogen bromide which may be evolved (compare Sections **IV,2** and **IV,3**).

Potassium permanganate test. Dissolve 0·2 g. or 0·2 ml. of the substance in 2 ml. of water or in 2 ml. of acetone (which gives a negative test with the reagent), and add 2 per cent potassium permanganate solution dropwise. The test is negative if no more than 3 drops of the reagent are decolorized.

V, 2 Saturated Hydrocarbons

Generally speaking the saturated aliphatic and cyclic hydrocarbons found in Solubility Group VI are inert to most simple chemical reagents. The aromatic hydrocarbons in this Solubility Group exhibit the usual reactivity associated with the presence of the aromatic nucleus (nitration, substitutive halogenation with chlorine or bromine in the presence of catalysts, sulphonation). The most satisfactory reagent for distinguishing between paraffin and aromatic hydrocarbons is *fuming sulphuric acid* (containing 20 per cent of free SO_3); only the latter react:

$$ArH + HOSO_2OH \rightarrow ArSO_2OH + H_2O$$
$$SO_3 + H_2O \rightarrow H_2SO_4$$

Fuming sulphuric acid test. Place 2 ml. of 20 per cent fuming sulphuric acid in a dry test-tube, add 0·5 ml. of the hydrocarbon and shake vigorously. Only aromatic hydrocarbons dissolve completely: heat is evolved, but excessive charring should be absent.

V, 3   Reactivities of Halogen Compounds

Halogen-containing compounds may be found in each of the seven Solubility Groups. Those in Group I are of low molecular weight and owe their solubility to the presence of such groups as OH, COOH, etc. Most halogen compounds in Solubility Group II are salts in which the halogen is present as an anion; these, with the exception of quaternary ammonium salts, are converted by dilute alkali into basic compounds of Solubility Group IV. Halogen compounds may also be present in Solubility Groups III and IV, but, like those in Groups I and II, they contain other functional groups which are more easily identified. The nature of the halogen in Solubility Groups V to VII is best determined with the aid of *a 2 per cent* solution of silver nitrate in absolute alcohol, the alcohol serving as a common solvent for the silver nitrate and the organic compound to be tested. For water-soluble compounds, aqueous silver nitrate solution should also be used after acidification with dilute nitric acid.

Organic compounds containing halogens react with silver nitrate in the following order of *decreasing* reactivity:

(i) Water-soluble compounds containing ionizable halogen or compounds such as acyl halides of low molecular weight which readily yield ionizable compounds with water, will react immediately, even with aqueous silver nitrate.

(ii) Acyl and sulphonyl halides, α-halogeno-ethers and alkyl iodides react instantly.

(iii) Alkyl chlorides and aromatic compounds containing halogen in the side chain do not usually react to any appreciable extent at room temperature, but react fairly rapidly on heating. For monohalogen-substituted compounds, the order of reactivity is

tertiary > secondary > primary, and I > Br > Cl > F

and, indeed, some tertiary halides may react in the cold.

(iv) Aromatic compounds in which the halogen is attached directly to the aromatic nucleus, polyhalogenated compounds with three or more halogens on the same carbon atom, and the α-halogenated ketones (*e.g.*, ω-chloroacetophenone or phenacyl chloride, $C_6H_5\text{-}COCH_2Cl$—a powerful lachrymator) do not react even on heating. The presence of nitro groups in the *ortho* and/or *para* positions may cause increased reactivity of the halogen.

Reaction with ethanolic silver nitrate. To carry out the test, treat 2 ml. of a 2 per cent solution of silver nitrate in ethanol with 1 or 2 drops (or 0·05 g.) of the compound. If no appreciable precipitate appears at the laboratory temperature, heat on a boiling water bath for several minutes. Some organic acids give insoluble silver salts, hence it is advisable to add 1 drop of *dilute* (5 *per cent*) nitric acid (1) at the conclusion of the test: most silver salts of organic acids are soluble in nitric acid.

Note
(1) If concentrated nitric acid is used, a dangerous explosion may result.

Another test, which indicates the reactivity of the halogen atom (chlorine and bromine), is based upon the fact that sodium chloride and sodium bromide are sparingly soluble in pure acetone:

$$RCl(Br) + NaI \rightarrow RI + NaCl(Br)$$

It consists in treating a solution of sodium iodide in pure acetone with the organic compound. The reaction is probably of the $S_N 2$ type involving a bimolecular attack of the iodide ion upon the carbon atom carrying the chlorine or bromine; the order of reactivities of halides is: primary > secondary > tertiary and Br > Cl.

Primary bromides give a precipitate of sodium bromide within 3 minutes at 25°; chlorides react only when heated at 50° for up to 6 minutes. Secondary and tertiary bromides must be heated at 50° for up to 6 minutes, but tertiary chlorides do not react within this time.

1,2-Dichloro- and dibromo-compounds give a precipitate with the reagent and also liberate free iodine:

$$RCHBr\text{—}CHBrR' + 2NaI \rightarrow RCHI\text{—}CHIR' + 2NaBr$$
$$\Updownarrow$$
$$RCH\text{=}CHR' + I_2$$

Polybromo compounds (bromoform, *s*-tetrabromoethane) react similarly at 50°, but simple polychloro compounds (chloroform, carbon tetrachloride and trichloroacetic acid) do not.

Sulphonyl chlorides give an immediate precipitate and also liberate iodine:

$$ArSO_2Cl + NaI \rightarrow ArSO_2I + NaCl \xrightarrow{NaI} ArSO_2Na + I_2$$

Acid chlorides and bromides, allyl halides, α-halo-ketones, -esters, -amides and -nitriles react at 25° within 3 minutes. Vinyl and aryl halides are inert.

Prepare the **reagent** by dissolving 7·5 g. of sodium iodide in 50 ml. of A.R. acetone. The colourless solution gradually acquires a yellow colour. Keep it in a dark bottle. When a red-brown colour develops, it should be discarded.

Apply the test to compounds which contain chlorine or bromine. If the compound is a solid, dissolve 0·1 g. in the minimum volume of pure, dry acetone. To 1 ml. of the sodium iodide-acetone reagent add 2 drops of the compound (if a liquid) or the acetone solution (if a solid). Shake and allow to stand at room temperature for 3 minutes. Note whether a precipitate is formed and also whether the solution acquires a reddish-brown colour (liberation of iodine). If no change takes place at room temperature, place the test-tube in a beaker of water at 50°. After 5 minutes, cool to room temperature, and observe whether a reaction has occurred.

V, 4 Aldehydes and Ketones

It is convenient to consider the indifferent or neutral oxygen derivatives of the hydrocarbons—(a) *aldehydes and ketones*, (b) *esters and anhydrides*, (c) *alcohols and ethers*—together. All of these, with the exception of the water-soluble members of low molecular weight, are soluble only in concentrated sulphuric acid, *i.e.*, fall into Solubility Group V. The above classes of compounds must be tested for in the order in which they are listed, otherwise erroneous conclusions may be drawn from the reactions for functional groups about to be described.

Both aldehydes and ketones contain the carbonyl group, hence a general test for carbonyl compounds will immediately characterize both classes of compounds. The preferred reagent is *2,4-dinitrophenylhydrazine*, which gives sparingly soluble dinitrophenylhydrazones with carbonyl compounds:

$$RC(H \text{ or } R')=O + H_2NHN-C_6H_3(NO_2)_2 \rightarrow RC(H \text{ or } R')=NHN-C_6H_3(NO_2)_2 + H_2O$$

Reaction with 2,4-dinitrophenylhydrazine. Add 2 drops (or 0·05–0·1 g.) of the substance to be tested to 3 ml. of the 2,4-dinitrophenylhydrazine reagent, and shake. If no precipitate forms immediately allow to stand for 5–10 minutes. A crystalline precipitate indicates the presence of a carbonyl compound. Occasionally the precipitate is oily at first, but this becomes crystalline upon standing.

2,4-Dinitrophenylhydrazine reagent may be **prepared** by either of the following methods.

Method 1. Suspend 2·0 g. of 2,4-dinitrophenylhydrazine in 100 ml. of methanol; add *cautiously* and slowly 4·0 ml. of concentrated sulphuric acid. The mixture becomes warm and the solid usually dissolves to produce a clear solution. Filter, if necessary.

Method 2. Dissolve 0·25 g. of 2,4-dinitrophenylhydrazine in a mixture of 42 ml. of concentrated hydrochloric acid and 50 ml. of water by warming on a water bath: dilute the cold solution to 250 ml. with distilled water. This reagent is more suitable for water-soluble aldehydes and ketones since alcohol is absent.

The above reagent is very dilute and is intended for qualitative reactions. It is hardly suitable for the preparation of crystalline derivatives except in very small quantities (compare *Aliphatic ketones*, Section **IV,18,***1*).

The **acetals** $RCH(OR')_2$ are so readily hydrolysed by acids that they may give a positive result in the above test:

$$RCH(OR')_2 + H_2O \xrightarrow{H^+} RCHO + 2R'OH$$

(For a more detailed discussion on *Acetals*, see Section **IV,16**.)

If an unknown compound gives a positive test with the 2,4-dinitrophenylhydrazine reagent, it then becomes necessary to decide whether it is an aldehyde or a ketone. Although the dimedone reagent (*Aliphatic Aldehydes*, Section **IV,15,***2*) reacts only with aldehydes, it is hardly satisfactory for routine use in class reactions.* It is much simpler to make use of three other reagents given below, the preparation and properties of which have already been described (Section **IV,15**).

Differentiation between aldehydes and ketones.

(i) **Schiff's reagent.** Aldehydes produce a red to violet-purple colour, while ketones are without effect. Use 2 drops (or 0·05 g.) of the compound and 2 ml. of Schiff's reagent and shake the mixture in the cold. Do not warm.

A number of aromatic aldehydes (*e.g.*, vanillin) give a negative result.

(ii) **Ammoniacal silver nitrate solution (Tollen's solution).** Aldehydes alone reduce Tollen's reagent and produce a silver mirror on the inside of the test-tube. Add 2–3 drops (or 0·05 g.) of the compound to 2–3 ml. of Tollen's solution contained in a *clean* test-tube (the latter is preferably cleaned with hot nitric acid). If no reaction appears to take place in the cold, warm to about 35° in a beaker of warm water.

---

* The dimedone reagent may, however, be used if it is desired to detect an aldehyde in the presence of a ketone.

CAUTION: After the test, pour the contents of the test-tube into the sink and wash the test-tube with dilute nitric acid. Any silver fulminate present, which is highly explosive when dry, will thus be destroyed.

(iii) **Fehling's solution.** Aldehydes alone reduce Fehling's solution to yellow or red cuprous oxide. Use 2 drops (or 0·05 g.) of the compound and 2–3 ml. of Fehling's solution: heat on a boiling water bath for 3–4 minutes. Benedict's solution is usually more trustworthy than Fehling's solution. The test is positive for aliphatic aldehydes but is usually indecisive for aromatic aldehydes.

If the tests for an aldehyde are negative, the unknown compound is a ketone. When once the compound has been established as an aldehyde or ketone, it is permissible to refer to tables of physical constants: information thus obtained may be of value in indicating other possible groups to be tested for, with due regard to possible complications caused by the presence of these groups.

V, 5   Esters and Anhydrides

When the compound for identification fails to respond to the 2,4-dinitrophenylhydrazine test given in Section **V,4** (aldehyde or ketone), the next class reactions to apply are the *hydroxamic acid test* and *saponification, i.e.,* hydrolysis in alkaline solution. These are the class reactions for **esters and anhydrides:** the rarely-encountered **lactones** react similarly.

Esters react with hydroxylamine to form an alcohol and a hydroxamic acid, RCONHOH. All hydroxamic acids react with ferric chloride, in acid solution, to form coloured (usually violet) complex salts:

$$RCOOR' + H_2NOH \rightarrow RCONHOH + R'OH$$
$$3RCONHOH + FeCl_3 \rightarrow (RCONHO)_3Fe + 3HCl$$

Lactones, which may be regarded as cyclic or inner esters, react similarly. Anhydrides of carboxylic acids also react with hydroxylamine to form hydroxamic acids:

$$RCOOCOR + NH_2OH \rightarrow RCONHOH + RCOOH$$

Acid chlorides also react with hydroxylamine to give a hydroxamic acid, but their presence will have been detected by the tests given in Section **V,3** and also by other tests.

$$RCOCl + H_2NOH \rightarrow RCONHOH + HCl$$

An ester is converted upon saponification into an alcohol and the salt of an acid, or the salts of both an acid and a phenol if it is an ester of a phenol. An anhydride upon hydrolysis yields *only* a salt of an acid.

RCOOR′ + NaOH → R′OH + RCOONa
Ester

RCOOAr + 2NaOH → ArONa + RCOONa + H$_2$O
Ester of a Phenol

(RCO)$_2$O + 2NaOH → 2RCOONa + H$_2$O
Anhydride

Anhydrides may often be hydrolysed in the cold with dilute alkali; they also react with primary amines (compare *Aliphatic Anhydrides*, Section **IV,23**). All anhydrides boil above 130°; thus acetic anhydride has b.p. 140°.

Some esters (oxalates, methyl and ethyl formates and acetates, etc.) are readily hydrolysed. In general, however, esters require heating with strong aqueous alkali. If the ester is sparingly soluble or insoluble in water, hydrolysis will usually be slow: saponification may then be carried out with ethyl alcoholic sodium or potassium hydroxide (compare *Aliphatic Esters*, Section **IV,25**), but difficulty will be experienced in obtaining a pure derivative of the resulting alcohol. This difficulty may be avoided by employing the inexpensive diethylene glycol ($\beta\beta'$-dihydroxyethyl ether), b.p. 244°, as the solvent: potassium hydroxide dissolves readily in this solvent, hydrolysis occurs rapidly at the elevated temperature, and all but high boiling point alcohols can be distilled from the reaction mixture in a fairly pure state (*e.g.*, benzyl alcohol, b.p. 205°, can be easily isolated). If the ester yields a glycol or polyhydric alcohol on saponification, the identification of the alcohol part is not possible although identification of the acid can still be made.

Aromatic aldehydes, and also aliphatic aldehydes containing no α-hydrogen atom, undergo the Cannizzaro reaction when treated with aqueous alkali, for example:

2C$_6$H$_5$CHO + H$_2$O $\xrightarrow[\text{aq.}]{\text{NaOH}}$ C$_6$H$_5$CH$_2$OH + C$_6$H$_5$COONa
Benzaldehyde　　　　　　　　　Benzyl alcohol　Sodium benzoate

The production of both an alcohol and the sodium salt of an acid might easily be confused with the hydrolysis products of an ester (in the above instance benzyl benzoate). Such an error would soon be discovered (*e.g.*, by reference to the b.p. and other physical properties), but it would lead to an unnecessary expenditure of time and energy. The above example, however, emphasizes the importance of conducting the class reactions of neutral oxygen-containing compounds in the proper order, *viz.*, (1) aldehydes and ketones, (2) esters and anhydrides, (3) alcohols, and (4) ethers.

Hydroxamic acid test for esters and anhydrides.

A. Carry out the following preliminary test. Dissolve a drop or a few small crystals of the compound in 1 ml. of rectified spirit (95 per cent ethanol) and add 1 ml. of *N* hydrochloric acid. Note the colour produced when 1 drop of 5 per cent ferric chloride solution is added to the solution. If a pronounced violet, blue, red or orange colour is produced, the hydroxamic acid test described below is not applicable and should not be used. It may be noted that the presence of acid prevents the development of coloured complexes of many phenols and many enols:

$$6ArOH + FeCl_3 \rightleftharpoons [Fe(OAr)_6]^{---} + 6H^+ + 3Cl^-$$

B. Mix 1 drop or several small crystals (*ca.* 0·05 g.) of the compound with 1 ml. of 0·5N hydroxylamine hydrochloride in 95 per cent ethanol and add 0·2 ml. of 6N aqueous sodium hydroxide. Heat the mixture to boiling and, after the solution has cooled slightly, add 2 ml. of N hydrochloric acid. If the solution is cloudy, add 2 ml. of 95 per cent ethyl alcohol. Observe the colour produced when 1 drop of 5 per cent ferric chloride solution is added. If the resulting colour does not persist, continue to add the reagent dropwise until the observed colour pervades the entire solution. Usually only 1 drop of the ferric chloride solution is necessary. Compare the colour with that produced in test *A*. A positive test will be a distinct burgundy or magenta colour as compared with the yellow colour observed when the original compound is tested with ferric chloride solution in the presence of acid.

Esters of carboxylic acids and also acid anhydrides give the test. Positive results are obtained with trihalo compounds ($CHCl_3$, $CHBr_3$, $C_6H_5CCl_3$ and $CCl_3CH(OH)_2$); formic and phthalic acids; primary or secondary aliphatic nitro compounds (because of the reaction of the ferric chloride with the *aci*-form produced by alkali); some imides (succinimide, phthalimide); and some, but not all, amides (formamide, phthalamide). A positive test is therefore only trustworthy for nitrogen-free esters. Some esters, mainly of carbonic, carbamic, sulphuric and other inorganic acids, give only a yellow colour.

Saponification of esters. *Aqueous sodium hydroxide method.* To hydrolyse **an ester of an alcohol,** reflux 5–6 g. with 25 ml. of 20 per cent sodium hydroxide solution for 1–2 hours* or until the ester layer disappears.† Distil the alkaline mixture and collect about 6 ml. of distillate. This will contain any volatile alcohol formed in the saponification. If the alcohol does not separate, *i.e.*, is water-soluble, saturate the distillate with solid potassium carbonate: an upper layer of

---

* The addition of about 0·2 g. of an emulsifying agent, such as sodium lauryl or oleyl sulphate, assists in reducing the time required for complete saponification: a large flask should be used since there is usually considerable foaming.

† A water-insoluble alcohol is sometimes formed and care should be taken that this is not confused with the original ester. It usually differs in physical properties (odour, b.p., etc.) from the original ester (see *Aliphatic Esters,* Section **IV,25).**

alcohol is then usually formed.* (The alcohol may be subsequently identified as the 3,5-dinitrobenzoate: see *Aliphatic Alcohols*, Section **IV,5,***1*). Cool the residual alkaline mixture, and acidify it with dilute sulphuric acid. If no crystalline acid is precipitated, the acid may frequently be isolated by ether extraction, or it may be distilled from the acidified solution and isolated from (or investigated in) the distillate. (The acid may be subsequently identified, *e.g.*, as the *S*-benzylthiuronium salt: see *Aliphatic Carboxylic Acids*, Section **IV,20,***5*.)

When dealing with esters of water-soluble, non steam-volatile, polyhydric alcohols (*e.g.*, ethylene glycol or glycerol), the distillate consists of water only (density 1·00). The water-soluble, non-volatile alcohol may be isolated by evaporation of the alkaline solution to a thick syrup on a water bath and extraction of the polyhydric alcohol from the salt with cold ethyl alcohol.

To hydrolyse **an ester of a phenol**† (*e.g.*, phenyl acetate), proceed as above but cool the alkaline reaction mixture and treat it with carbon dioxide until saturated (solid carbon dioxide may also be used). Whether a solid phenol separates or not, remove it by extraction with ether. Acidify the aqueous bicarbonate solution with dilute sulphuric acid and isolate the acid as detailed for the ester of an alcohol. An alternative method, which is not so time-consuming, may be employed. Cool the alkaline reaction mixture in ice water, and add dilute sulphuric acid with stirring until the solution is acidic to Congo Red paper and the acid, if aromatic or otherwise insoluble in the medium, commences to separate as a faint but permanent precipitate. Now add 5 per cent sodium carbonate solution with vigorous stirring until the solution is alkaline to litmus paper and the precipitate redissolves completely. Remove the phenol by extraction with ether. Acidify the

---

* The following alternative procedure is especially useful for the identification of alcohols isolated as dilute aqueous solutions. Mix the distillate (6 ml.) with an equal volume of A.R. acetone, and add anhydrous potassium carbonate in 1–2 g. portions with shaking and occasional cooling. When about 6 g. have been added, decant the liquid from the pasty solid to a small conical flask. Continue the addition of the potassium carbonate until the latter appears to have no action: about 10 g. of the desiccant may be required. Decant the liquid, add 0·5–1·0 g. of pure 3,5-dinitrobenzoyl chloride and heat on a boiling water bath (*CAUTION:* acetone) for 10–15 minutes: about half of the acetone will evaporate. Allow to cool, add 1–2 drops of water and stir with a glass rod. The 3,5-dinitrobenzoate of the alcohol separates within a few minutes, and can be recrystallized from light petroleum (b.p. 40–60°), ethanol or aqueous ethanol.

† Preliminary indication of the presence of a phenol ester may be obtained by heating the compound with soda-lime: esters of phenols and also aromatic hydroxy-acids usually give the phenol. (Likewise amides, imides, nitriles, substituted hydrazines, urethanes, etc. afford ammonia.)

residual aqueous solution and investigate the organic acid as above.

Diethylene glycol method. Place 0·5 g. of potassium hydroxide pellets, 3 ml. of diethylene glycol and 0·5 ml. of water in a 10 or 25 ml. distilling flask; heat the mixture gently until the alkali has dissolved and cool. Add 1–2 g. of the ester and mix well. Fit the flask with a thermometer and a small water-cooled condenser in the usual way. Heat the flask over a small flame whilst shaking gently to mix the contents. When only one liquid phase, or one liquid phase and one solid phase, remains in the flask, heat the mixture more strongly so that the alcohol distils. Identify the alcohol in the distillate by the preparation of the 3,5-dinitrobenzoate (*Aliphatic Alcohols*, Section **IV,5,***1*).

The residue in the flask is either a solution or a suspension of the potassium salt of the acid derived from the ester in diethylene glycol. Add 10 ml. of water and 10 ml. of ethyl alcohol to the residue and shake until thoroughly mixed. Then add a drop or two of phenolphthalein and dilute sulphuric acid, dropwise, until just acid. Allow the mixture to stand for about 5 minutes and then filter the potassium sulphate. Use the clear filtrate for the preparation of one or two crystalline derivatives of the acid (see *Aliphatic Carboxylic Acids*, Section **IV,20,***4*).

The determination of the saponification equivalent of an ester by the alcoholic potassium hydroxide method is described under *Aliphatic Esters* in Section **IV,25**: an alternative procedure using diethylene glycol is given below. This constant should be determined if possible in the preliminary examination, since a knowledge of its value together with the boiling point provides a basis for a fairly good approximation of the size of the ester molecule.

DETERMINATION OF THE SAPONIFICATION EQUIVALENT OF AN ESTER BY THE DIETHYLENE GLYCOL METHOD

The ethanolic potassium hydroxide method (*Aliphatic Esters*, Section **IV,25**) has the following undesirable features: (i) the reaction is often slow, necessitating long refluxing; (ii) possible transposition of the unknown ester (by ethoxide ions) to the corresponding ethyl ester and consequent possible loss because of increased volatility; and (iii) poor keeping quality of the standard solution. These disadvantages are largely overcome by using a solution of potassium hydroxide in diethylene glycol: the procedure is particularly valuable for esters which are insoluble in water.

The **reagent is prepared** by weighing about 6·0 g. of A.R. potassium hydroxide pellets into a 50 or 100 ml. flask, adding 30 ml. of diethylene glycol and heating to effect solution; it is essential to use a thermometer for stirring and to keep the temperature below 130°, otherwise a dark yellow colour will develop. As soon as the solid has dissolved, the warm solution is poured into 70 ml. of diethylene glycol in a glass-stoppered bottle. The solution is thoroughly mixed and allowed to cool. It is *ca.* 1·0N and is standardized by pipetting 10 ml. into a flask, adding 15 ml. of water, and titrating with standardized 0·25N or 0·5N hydrochloric acid using phenolphthalein as indicator. (Because of the high viscosity of the solution, it is advisable to open the tip of the pipette to an internal diameter of 2–3 mm. in order to facilitate drainage; the pipette should be recalibrated before use.)

To determine the saponification equivalent of an ester transfer 10 ml. of the reagent by means of a pipette into a 50 ml. glass-stoppered Pyrex conical flask. Place the sample of the ester in a weight burette or in a weighing bottle fitted with a cork carrying a small dropper pipette; transfer about 0·5 g. of the ester, accurately weighed, into the Erlenmeyer flask and insert the ground stopper. Mix the ester with the reagent by a rotary motion of the flask. Hold the stopper firmly in place and heat the mixture in an oil bath so that a temperature of 70–80° is reached within 2–3 minutes: agitate the liquid by a whirling motion during the heating. At this point remove the flask from the heating bath, shake the flask vigorously, allow to drain and loosen the stopper *carefully* to allow air to escape. Replace the stopper and heat again in an oil bath to 120–130°. (For esters of very high boiling point, the stopper may be removed and a thermometer inserted.) After 3 minutes at this temperature, cool the flask and its contents to 80–90°, remove the stopper and wash it with distilled water so that the rinsings drain into the flask. Add about 15 ml. of distilled water and a drop or two of phenolphthalein indicator, mix well and then titrate with standard 0·25N or 0·5N hydrochloric acid. Calculate the saponification equivalent from the expression:

$$\text{Saponification Equivalent} = \frac{\text{Weight of ester} \times 1000}{\text{Ml. of } N \text{ KOH used}}.$$

V, 6 Alcohols and Ethers

If the unknown neutral, oxygen-containing compound does not give the class reactions for aldehydes, ketones, esters and anhydrides, it is probably either an alcohol or an ether. Alcohols and ethers may be most simply distinguished by the use of two reagents—*metallic sodium and acetyl chloride*.

Metallic sodium reacts with alcohols with the evolution of hydrogen:

$$2ROH + 2Na \rightarrow 2Na^+(OR)^- + H_2$$

The most common interfering substance, especially with alcohols of low molecular weight, is water; this may result in an inaccurate interpretation of the test *if applied alone*. Most of the water may usually be removed by shaking with a little anhydrous calcium sulphate. Although dry ethers (and also the saturated aliphatic and the simple aromatic hydrocarbons) do not react with sodium, many other classes of organic compounds do. Thus:

(*a*) Aliphatic esters are converted (in solvents such as ether) into salts of acyloins:

$$2RCOR' + 4Na \rightarrow \underset{\substack{\| \\ RC-O^-Na^+}}{RC-O^-Na^+} + 2Na^+(OR')^-$$

Upon treatment with dilute sulphuric acid, the *acyloin* is produced:

$$\underset{\substack{\| \\ RC-O^-Na^+}}{RC-O^-Na^+} \xrightarrow{H_2O} \begin{bmatrix} RC-OH \\ \| \\ RC-OH \end{bmatrix} \rightarrow \underset{\substack{| \\ RCHOH}}{RC=O}$$

The term acyloin is commonly used as a class name for the symmetrical keto-alcohols RCOCH(OH)R, and the name of the individual compound is derived by adding the suffix *oin* to the stem name of the acid to which the acyloin corresponds, *e.g.*, acetoin, propionoin, butyroin, etc.

(*b*) Simple esters (*e.g.*, ethyl acetate) undergo the Claisen ester condensation. The effective condensing agent is sodium ethoxide, produced by the action of sodium upon traces of alcohol present in the ester:

$$2CH_3COOC_2H_5 + Na^+(OC_2H_5)^- \rightleftharpoons$$
$$Na^+[CH_3COCHCOOC_2H_5]^- + 2C_2H_5OH$$

(*c*) Ketones may react through their enolic forms (if they possess an α-hydrogen atom) or they may be partially reduced to a sodium pinacolate, the latter probably via the radical of the sodium ketyl $(RCH_2-\overset{\overset{O^-}{|}}{\underset{\bullet}{C}}R')$ produced by the donation of an electron by the sodium:

$$2RCH_2-\overset{O}{\overset{\|}{C}}R' + 2Na \rightarrow 2\begin{bmatrix} O^- \\ | \\ RCH=CR' \end{bmatrix}Na^+ + H_2$$

$$2RCH_2-\overset{O}{\overset{\|}{C}}R' + 2Na \rightarrow \begin{bmatrix} RCH_2-CR'-O^- \\ | \\ RCH_2-CR'-O^- \end{bmatrix}Na^+$$

This is another reason why aldehydes, ketones and esters must be tested for in the order already given, and why it is necessary to employ *both* the sodium and acetyl chloride tests.

Acetyl chloride reacts vigorously with primary and secondary alcohols to yield esters; it also reacts readily with any water present to form acetic acid:

$$CH_3COCl + ROH \rightarrow CH_3COOR + HCl$$
$$CH_3COCl + HOH \rightarrow CH_3COOH + HCl$$

The resulting esters differ sufficiently in odour and water solubility to be readily distinguished from the original alcohol. With tertiary alcohols the product is largely the alkyl chloride:

$$R_3COH + CH_3COCl \rightarrow R_3CCl + CH_3COOH$$

The differentiation between primary, secondary and tertiary alcohols with the aid of the Lucas reagent is described under *Aliphatic Alcohols* in Section **IV,5**,(vi); see also the chromic anhydride reagent (Section **IV,5**,(vii)) and the 'chromic acid' test (Section **IV,5**,(v)).

Benzoyl chloride may replace acetyl chloride as a class reagent: it possesses the advantage that it is only very slowly decomposed by cold water and consequently may be employed for detecting alcohols even in aqueous solution. The reaction is usually carried out in aqueous solution containing sufficient caustic alkali to decompose any excess of benzoyl chloride into the water-soluble alkali benzoate (Schotten-Baumann reaction). The benzoyl esters formed are insoluble in water:

$$C_6H_5COCl + ROH \rightarrow C_6H_5COOR + HCl$$

Ethers are unaffected by sodium and by acetyl (or benzoyl) chloride. Both the purely aliphatic ethers {*e.g.*, di-*n*-butyl ether (n-C_4H_9)$_2$O} and the mixed aliphatic-aromatic ethers (*e.g.*, anisole $C_6H_5OCH_3$) are encountered in Solubility Group V: the purely aromatic ethers {*e.g.*, diphenyl ether (C_6H_5)$_2$O} are generally insoluble in concentrated sulphuric acid and are found in Solubility Group VI. The purely aliphatic ethers are very inert and their final identification may, of necessity, depend upon their physical properties (b.p., density and/or refractive index). Ethers do, however, suffer fission when heated with excess of 57 per cent hydriodic acid, but the reaction is generally only of value for the characterization of symmetrical ethers ($R \equiv R'$):

$$R\text{—}O\text{—}R' + 2HI \rightarrow RI + R'I + H_2O$$

The mixed aliphatic-aromatic ethers are somewhat more reactive: in addition to cleavage by strong hydriodic acid and also by constant b.p. hydrobromic acid in acetic acid solution into phenols and alkyl halides, they may be brominated, nitrated and converted into sulphonamides (see under *Aromatic Ethers* in Section **IV,14**,*2*).

Sodium test. Treat 1·0 ml. of the compound with a *small* thin slice of freshly cut sodium (handle with the tongs or with a penknife) in a small, dry test-tube (75 × 10 mm. or 100 × 12 mm.). Observe whether hydrogen is evolved and the sodium reacts. (If the compound is suspected to contain water, dry it first with a little anhydrous calcium or magnesium sulphate.)

Acetyl chloride test. In a small dry test-tube treat 0·5 ml. of the compound with 0·3–0·4 ml. of redistilled acetyl chloride and note whether reaction occurs. Add 3 ml. of water and neutralize the aqueous layer with solid sodium bicarbonate. Look for a product different from the original alcohol.

Benzoyl chloride test. (This is an alternative to the acetyl chloride test.) Place 1·0 ml. of the compound, 0·5 ml. of redistilled benzoyl chloride (*CAUTION* in handling) and 2·5 ml. of 10 per cent aqueous sodium hydroxide in a small test-tube, cork the tube and shake vigorously until the odour of benzoyl chloride has disappeared. Observe the odour, density and other obvious properties of the product.

Fission of ethers with hydriodic acid. Reflux 1·0 ml. of the compound with 5 ml. of freshly distilled constant b.p. hydriodic acid (b.p. 126–128°) for 2–3 hours in a small flask fitted with a double surface condenser. Add 10 ml. of water, distil and collect about 7 ml. of liquid. Decolorize the distillate by the addition of a little sodium bisulphite and separate the two layers by means of a dropper pipette. If the original compound is suspected to be an aliphatic ether, determine the b.p. of the iodide by the Siwoloboff method: if the amount of product is insufficient, repeat the original experiment.

Acetals $RCH(OR')_2$ are stable in alkaline solution, but are readily hydrolysed by dilute acids to give aldehydes, which may be characterized as detailed in Section **V,4** (see *Acetals*, Section **IV,16**).

V, 7 The Iodoform Test

Neutral oxygen-containing compounds in Solubility Groups I, II and V which either contain the CH_3CO- group attached to H, alkyl, aryl, or the grouping $-CH_2COR'$ (*e.g.*, $CH_3\overset{H}{\underset{|}{C}}=O$ and $CH_3\overset{R}{\underset{|}{C}}=O$), or are oxidized to this structure under the conditions of the experiment (*e.g.*, $CH_3-\overset{H}{\underset{H}{\overset{|}{C}}}-OH$ and $CH_3-\overset{R}{\underset{H}{\overset{|}{C}}}-OH$), give iodoform with sodium hypoiodite solution. The reactions may be represented as:

$$RCH(OH)CH_3 + I_2 + 2NaOH \rightarrow RCOCH_3 + 2NaI + 2H_2O$$
$$RCOCH_3 + 3I_2 + 4NaOH \rightarrow RCOONa + HCI_3 + 3NaI + 3H_2O$$

If the compound to be tested is insoluble in water, it should be brought into solution by the addition of a little dioxan. Alcohols and some methyl ketones frequently react slowly: in such cases it is advisable to employ a large excess (4–5 fold) of the relatively unstable reagent (effectively a hypoiodite). Quinones and hydroquinones also give the iodoform reaction.

The iodoform test. Dissolve 0·1 g. or 4–5 drops of the compound in 2 ml. of water; if it is insoluble in water, add sufficient dioxan to produce a homogeneous solution. Add 2 ml. of 5 per cent sodium hydroxide solution and then introduce a potassium iodide-iodine reagent dropwise with shaking until a definite dark colour of iodine persists. Allow to stand for 2–3 minutes: if no iodoform separates at room temperature, warm the test-tube in a beaker of water at 60°. Add a few more drops of the iodine reagent if the faint iodine colour disappears: continue the addition of the reagent until the dark colour is not discharged after 2 minutes heating at 60°. Remove the excess of iodine by the addition of a few drops of dilute sodium hydroxide solution with shaking, dilute with an equal volume of water and allow to stand for 10–15 minutes. The test is positive if a yellow precipitate of iodoform is deposited. Filter off the yellow precipitate, dry upon pads of filter paper and determine the m.p.: iodoform melts at 120°.

The **potassium iodide–iodine reagent is prepared** by dissolving 20 g. of potassium iodide and 10 g. of iodine in 100 ml. of water.

V, 8 Polyhydric Alcohols and the Polyhydroxy Aldehydes and Ketones (Sugars)

The polyhydric alcohols of Solubility Group II are liquids of relatively high boiling point and may be detected *inter alia* by the reactions already described for *Alcohols* (see Section **V,6**). Compounds containing two hydroxyl groups attached to adjacent carbon atoms (1,2-glycols), α-hydroxy aldehydes and ketones, and 1,2-diketones may be identified by the periodic acid test, given in Section **V,9**.

The simple sugars or monosaccharides are essentially polyhydroxy aldehydes or ketones, and belong to Solubility Group II. They are termed tetroses, pentoses, hexoses, etc., according to the number of carbon atoms in the long chain constituting the molecule, and aldoses or ketoses if they are aldehydes or ketones. Most of the monosaccharides that occur in nature are pentoses and hexoses.

All carbohydrates (mono, di- and poly-saccharides) give the

Molisch colour test {for details, see under *Carbohydrates*, Section **IV,10,**(i)}.

Both aldoses and ketoses reduce Fehling's or Benedict's solution (for details, see Section **V,4**). This fact may appear surprising when it is remembered that Fehling's or Benedict's solution is one of the reagents for distinguishing between aldehydes and ketones (see Section **V,4**). The explanation lies in the fact that α-hydroxyketones are much more readily oxidized than simple ketones, perhaps because the hydroxy-ketone undergoes isomerization, in the presence of alkali, into an aldehyde. For example, fructose, a keto-hexose, might isomerize thus:

$$\begin{array}{ccc}
CH_2OH & CHOH & CHO \\
| & \| & | \\
C=O & C-OH & CHOH \\
| & \rightleftharpoons \quad | \quad \rightleftharpoons & | \\
(CHOH)_3 & (CHOH)_3 & (CHOH)_3 \\
| & | & | \\
CH_2OH & CH_2OH & CH_2OH \\
\text{Keto-hexose} & \text{Ene-diol} & \text{Aldo-hexose}
\end{array}$$

Positive results are given with aldoses and ketoses and with disaccharides containing potential aldehyde groups (*e.g.*, maltose). Disaccharides which do not contain potential aldehyde groups (*e.g.*, sucrose) and also polysaccharides (*e.g.*, starch and cellulose) do not reduce Fehling's or Benedict's solution. Non-reducing disaccharides and polysaccharides upon warming for a short time with 5 per cent hydrochloric acid or sulphuric acid are hydrolysed to monosaccharides: upon neutralization (to phenolphthalein) of the excess of acid with sodium hydroxide solution, a positive test is obtained with Fehling's or Benedict's solution.

Another reaction that is characteristic of α-hydroxy aldehydes or ketones, which has been found of value for the characterization of sugars, is the formation of **osazones** with phenylhydrazine. This reagent reacts with either an aldose or a ketose to yield a phenylhydrazone, which is then oxidized and converted into a bis-phenylhydrazone or osazone by more of the phenylhydrazine (see *Carbohydrates*, Section **IV,10,***1*). Certain osazones also possess characteristic appearances under the microscope (see Fig. *IV, 10*, 1).

Galactose and also carbohydrates which yield galactose upon hydrolysis (*e.g.*, lactose) are oxidized to the sparingly soluble mucic acid.

Oxidation of galactose (or a galactose-containing sugar) to mucic acid. Dissolve 1·0 g. of galactose or lactose in a mixture of 10 ml. of water and 5 ml. of concentrated nitric acid contained in a small evaporating dish, and evaporate the solution to dryness on a water bath. Stir the cold residue with 10 ml. of cold water, filter off the mucic acid, wash it with cold water, dry and determine the m.p. (212–213° with decomposition).

V, 9 The Periodic Acid Test

Periodic acid has a selective oxidizing action upon compounds having two hydroxyl groups or a hydroxyl and an amino group attached to adjacent carbon atoms and is characterized by the cleavage of the carbon-carbon bond (**Malaprade reaction**) (compare *Polyhydric Alcohols*, Section **IV,9**).

$$RCH(OH)CH(OH)R' + HIO_4 \rightarrow RCHO + R'CHO + HIO_3 + H_2O$$
$$RCH(OH)CH(NH_2)R' + HIO_4 \rightarrow RCHO + R'CHO + HIO_3 + NH_3$$

No oxidation occurs unless the hydroxyl groups or a hydroxyl and an amino group are attached to adjacent carbon atoms, hence the reaction may be employed for testing for the presence of contiguous hydroxyl groups (*e.g.*, 1,2-diols) and hydroxyl and amino groups. Carbonyl compounds in which the carbonyl group is contiguous to a hydroxyl group or a second carbonyl group are also oxidized, *e.g.*, α-hydroxy aldehydes or ketones, 1,2-diketones and α-hydroxy acids:

$$RCH(OH)COR' + HIO_4 \rightarrow RCHO + R'COOH + HIO_3$$
$$RCOCOR' + HIO_4 + H_2O \rightarrow RCOOH + R'COOH + HIO_3$$

The oxidation may proceed through the hydrated form of the carbonyl group $>CH(OH)_2$. The rate of oxidation is 1,2-glycols > α-hydroxy aldehydes > α-hydroxy ketones > α-hydroxy acids. Under the conditions enumerated below, α-hydroxy acids usually give a negative test.

In qualitative organic analysis, use is made of the fact that silver iodate is sparingly soluble in *dilute* nitric acid whereas silver periodate is very soluble. For water-insoluble compounds dioxan solutions may be employed.

The **periodic acid reagent is prepared** by dissolving 0·5 g. of paraperiodic acid H_5IO_6 in 100 ml. of distilled water.

Place 2 ml. of the periodic acid reagent in a small test-tube, add one drop (no more—otherwise the silver iodate, if formed, will fail to precipitate) of concentrated nitric acid, and shake well. Add one drop or a small crystal of the compound to be tested, shake the mixture for 15–20 seconds, and then add 1–2 drops of 5 per cent silver nitrate solution. The instantaneous formation of a *white* precipitate of silver iodate is a positive test. Failure to form a precipitate, or the appearance of a brown precipitate which redissolves on shaking, constitutes a negative test.

An alternative method for conducting the test (except for 1,2-diketones) is to detect the aldehyde produced by means of the fuchsin aldehyde reagent (Schiff's reagent). This modification is recommended for glycols, carbohydrates and compounds containing contiguous hydroxyl groups. A 2 per cent aqueous solution of paraperiodic acid is used.

Mix 2–3 ml. of 2 per cent paraperiodic acid solution in a test-tube with 1 drop of dilute sulphuric acid (*ca.* 2·5*N*) and add 20–30 mg. of the compound. Shake the mixture for 5 minutes, and then pass sulphur dioxide through the solution until it acquires a pale yellow colour (to remove the excess of periodic acid and also iodic acid formed in the reaction). Add 1–2 ml. of Schiff's reagent (Section **IV,15**,(iii)): the production of a red to violet-purple colour constitutes a positive test.

V, 10 Carboxylic Acids and Phenols

Most of the acidic compounds containing only the elements C, H and O are either carboxylic acids or phenols. They are found mainly in Solubility Group III, although the water-soluble members are in Solubility Groups I and II.

Carboxylic acids are:

(*a*) Soluble in 5 per cent sodium hydroxide solution *and* in 5 per cent sodium bicarbonate solution (the latter reaction is accompanied by the evolution of carbon dioxide).

(*b*) Non-reactive towards bromine water or a solution of bromine in carbon tetrachloride (unless an ethylenic or acetylenic or other unsaturated group is *also* present).

(*c*) Titratable with standard sodium hydroxide solution in aqueous or in ethanolic solution in the presence of phenolphthalein as indicator, thus enabling the equivalent weight to be determined.

Phenols (and enols), broadly speaking, give the following reactions:

(*a*) They are soluble in 5 per cent sodium hydroxide solution and *insoluble* in 5 per cent sodium bicarbonate solution; they are precipitated from their solutions in aqueous sodium hydroxide by carbon dioxide. [Exceptions: the presence of certain negative groups in phenols increases the acidity to such an extent that they may dissolve in sodium bicarbonate solution, for example, 2,4-dinitrophenol, picric acid and *s*-tribromophenol.]

(*b*) They react with a solution of bromine in carbon tetrachloride by *substitution* and an equivalent quantity of hydrogen bromide is evolved (compare *addition* with unsaturated compounds). When the test is conducted with bromine water and a dilute aqueous solution of a phenol, the sign of reaction is the separation of a sparingly soluble bromine substitution product.

(*c*) They yield intense colorations (blue, green, red or purple) when treated with a solution of ferric chloride. Some phenols (and enols) do not give this test in aqueous solution, but react readily in ethanolic solution. [The coloration is said to be due to a complex ion $[Fe(OAr)_6]^{---}$. Some phenolic acids, such as *m*- and *p*-hydroxybenzoic acids, do not give this test, but others, such as salicylic acid (which is the enolic form of a cyclo-β-keto acid), do.]

It must be borne in mind that there are many nitrogen-containing phenols and acids; of these the nitro and amino derivatives are the most common. The aromatic nitrocarboxylic acids may usually be identified through the reactions and derivatives of the carboxyl group without recourse to the reactions of the nitro group: examination for the latter will, however, provide additional confirmation. The influence of the nitro and other groups in the *o*- and *p*-positions upon the acidity of a phenol has already been noted: such groups tend to produce a marked deepening in the colour of alkaline solutions of the phenol. Amino substituents in water-insoluble phenols and acids cause these compounds to be soluble in both dilute acid and dilute alkali, *i.e.*, to be amphoteric. Frequently it is helpful to destroy the basic character of the nitrogen by conversion of the amino group into a neutral amide group by acetylation or benzoylation in aqueous alkaline solution: the resulting compound is not amphoteric and its equivalent may be determined.

An indication whether a water-insoluble compound is an acid or a phenol (or enol) will be obtained from the Solubility Tests: water-soluble acids will liberate carbon dioxide from 5 per cent sodium bicarbonate solution {see *Aliphatic Carboxylic Acids*, Section **IV,20**, (i)}.

Equivalent weight of an acid. Determine the equivalent weight of the acid (use about 0·2 g.) by titration with standard *ca.* $0.1N$ alkali with phenolphthalein as indicator; if the acid is sparingly soluble in water, add ethanol to increase the solubility.

The presence of simple water-insoluble phenols (or enols) will be indicated by the insolubility in 5 per cent sodium bicarbonate solution. Further evidence will be obtained by carrying out the following tests.

Bromine test (*cf.* Section **V,1**). Dissolve 0·2 g. or 0·2 ml. of the compound in 2 ml. of carbon tetrachloride and add a 2 per cent solution of bromine in carbon tetrachloride dropwise until the bromine colour persists for 1 minute. If no hydrogen bromide fumes are observed, blow gently across the mouth of the tube.

Dissolve 0·1 g. of the compound in 10–15 ml. of water and add bromine water until the colour of the latter persists. A white precipitate will form if a phenol is present.

Ferric chloride test. Dissolve 1 drop or 0·05 g. of the compound in 5 ml. of water and add 1 drop of ferric chloride solution: observe the colour produced. If the result is negative in aqueous solution, repeat the test in ethanolic solution.

V, 11 Amines (Basic Nitrogen Compounds)

Organic compounds that dissolve in dilute hydrochloric acid and are placed in Solubility Group IV contain nitrogen: the rarely encountered pyrones and anthocyanidin pigments are exceptions. Indeed, when solubility tests have placed a compound in Solubility Group IV but elementary analysis has failed to prove the presence of nitrogen, it is advisable to repeat the test for the elements. The most important basic nitrogen compounds are the **amines**—primary, secondary and tertiary amines. The only hydrazines commonly encountered in this Group are the **monoaryl hydrazines**: they are most conveniently detected by using benzaldehyde or some other suitable carbonyl compound as a reagent. The lower aliphatic amines and diamines are soluble in water and possess characteristic ammoniacal odours which distinguish them from the water-insoluble amines of Solubility Group IV. The reactions to be described below apply to both water-soluble and water-insoluble amines.

The following reagents may be conveniently employed for the detection of amines:

(1) Acetyl chloride or acetic anhydride.

Acetyl chloride reacts immediately and often violently with primary and secondary amines, but not with tertiary amines, for example:

$$2C_6H_5NH_2 + CH_3COCl \rightarrow C_6H_5NHCOCH_3 + C_6H_5NH_2,HCl$$
Aniline   Acetanilide

It will be observed that the reaction involves two equivalents of the amine and produces, in addition to the substituted amide, an equivalent quantity of the amine hydrochloride. Acetic anhydride, on the other hand, converts the amine quantitatively into the acyl derivative, for example:

$$C_6H_5NH_2 + (CH_3CO)_2O \rightarrow C_6H_5NHCOCH_3 + CH_3COOH$$

For this reason, acetic anhydride is generally preferred for the preparation of acetyl derivatives, but acetyl chloride, in view of its greater reactivity, is a better diagnostic reagent for primary and secondary amines.

(2) Benzoyl chloride.

This acid chloride is much less reactive than acetyl chloride and indeed it may be employed to benzoylate a primary or secondary amine in the presence of a dilute solution of sodium hydroxide (Schotten-Baumann reaction). The resulting benzoyl derivative is insoluble in the alkaline medium and can be separated by filtration or extraction. The slight excess of benzoyl chloride which is employed is decomposed by the alkali. The reactions which occur with a typical secondary amine, monoethylaniline, are:

$$C_6H_5NHC_2H_5 + C_6H_5COCl \rightarrow C_6H_5N(C_2H_5)COC_6H_5 + HCl$$
$$HCl + NaOH \rightarrow NaCl + H_2O$$
$$C_6H_5COCl + 2NaOH \rightarrow C_6H_5COONa + H_2O + NaCl$$

(3) Benzenesulphonyl chloride.

Benzenesulphonyl chloride reacts with primary and secondary, but not with tertiary, amines to yield substituted sulphonamides (for full discussion, see under *Aromatic Amines*, Section **IV,33,***3*). The substituted sulphonamide formed from a primary amine dissolves in the alkaline medium, whilst that produced from a secondary amine is insoluble in alkali; tertiary amines do not react. Upon acidifying the solution produced with a primary amine, the substituted sulphonamide is precipitated. The reactions form the basis of the Hinsberg procedure for the separation of amines {see Section **IV,33**,(vii) for details}. Feebly basic amines, such as *o*-nitroaniline, react slowly in the presence of alkali: in such cases it is best to carry out the reaction in pyridine solution (see Section **IV,33,***3*).

Some reference to the use of nitrous acid merits mention here. **Primary aromatic amines** yield diazonium compounds, which may be coupled with phenols to yield highly-coloured azo dyes (see Section **IV,33**,(ii)). **Secondary aromatic amines** afford nitroso compounds, which give Liebermann's nitroso reaction {see Section **IV,33**,(iv)}. **Tertiary aromatic amines** of the type of dimethylaniline, yield *p*-nitroso derivatives {see Section **IV,33**,(vi)}.

The carbylamine or isocyanide test for primary amines {Section **IV,33**,(i)} is so extremely delicate that it will detect traces of primary amines in secondary and tertiary amines: it must therefore be applied with due regard to this factor.

Acetyl chloride test (*for primary and secondary amines*). In a semi-micro test-tube (75 × 10 mm.) treat 0·5 ml. (or 0·5 g.) of the compound with acetyl chloride drop by drop. Note whether reaction occurs. If no solid separates, pour the contents of the tube into 3 ml. of water and neutralize the aqueous layer with solid sodium bicarbonate. Observe whether a product different from the original compound is produced.

Benzoyl chloride test (*for primary and secondary amines*). Place 0·5 ml. (or 0·5 g.) of the compound, 10 ml. of 5 per cent sodium hydroxide solution and 1 ml. of benzoyl chloride (*CAUTION*) in a test-tube, stopper the tube and shake until the odour of benzoyl chloride disappears. Examine the properties of the substance formed.

Benzenesulphonyl chloride test.* Proceed as in the benzoyl chloride test, but use 15–20 ml. of 5 per cent sodium hydroxide solution. Examine the product when the odour of the sulphonyl chloride has disappeared. (If no reaction has occurred, the substance is probably a tertiary amine.) If a precipitate appears in the alkaline solution, dilute with about 10 ml. of water and shake; if the precipitate does not dissolve, a secondary amine is indicated. If the solution is clear, acidify it cautiously to Congo Red with dilute hydrochloric acid: a precipitate is indicative of a primary amine.

---

* *p*-Toluenesulphonyl chloride is more convenient to handle and gives similar results.

V, 12 Acidic and Neutral Nitrogen Compounds

The imides, primary and secondary nitro compounds, oximes and sulphonamides of Solubility Group III are weakly acidic nitrogen compounds: they cannot be titrated satisfactorily with a standard alkali nor do they exhibit the reactions characteristic of phenols. The neutral nitrogen compounds of Solubility Group VII include: tertiary nitro compounds; amides (simple and substituted); derivatives of aldehydes and ketones (hydrazones, semicarbazones, etc.); nitriles; nitroso, azo, hydrazo and other intermediate reduction products of aromatic nitro compounds. All the above nitrogen compounds, and also the sulphonamides of Solubility Group VII, respond, with few exceptions, to the same classification reactions (*reduction and hydrolysis*) and hence will be considered together.

Nitro compounds and their reduction products. Tertiary nitro compounds (these are generally aromatic)* are reduced by zinc and ammonium chloride solution to the corresponding hydroxylamines, which may be detected by their reducing action upon an ammoniacal solution of silver nitrate or Tollen's reagent:

$$RNO_2 + 4H \xrightarrow[NH_4Cl\ aq.]{Zn\ and} RNHOH + H_2O$$

$$RNHOH + 2[Ag(NH_3)_2]OH \longrightarrow RNO + 2Ag + 4NH_3 + 2H_2O$$

It must be remembered, however, that nitroso, azoxy and azo compounds (which are usually more highly coloured than nitro compounds) may be reduced by zinc powder to the corresponding hydroxylamine, hydrazo and hydrazine compounds respectively, all of which reduce Tollen's reagent in the cold.

Nitro compounds are reduced in acid solution (for example, by tin and hydrochloric acid) to the corresponding primary amines, which may be detected as described in **V,11**:

$$RNO_2 + 6H \rightarrow RNH_2 + 2H_2O$$

Aromatic nitro compounds may be detected by the ferrous hydroxide test {see Section **IV,35**,(iii)}.

Nitrosamines are similarly reduced to secondary amines:

$$R_2N.NO + 6H \rightarrow R_2NH + NH_3 + H_2O$$

they (and some C-nitroso compounds that yield nitrous acid when treated with concentrated sulphuric acid) may be detected by Liebermann's reaction {see *Aromatic Amines*, Section **IV,33**,(iv)}.

* Nitro-paraffins may be primary, secondary or tertiary: $-CH_2.NO_2$, primary; $>CH.NO_2$, secondary; and $-\!\!>\!\!C.NO_2$, tertiary.

Azo compounds may be identified by examination of the amine(s) formed on reduction in acid solution:

$$RN=NR' + 4H \rightarrow RNH_2 + H_2NR'$$

They are always coloured but give colourless products upon reduction. **Hydrazo and azoxy compounds** are reduced in acid solution to the parent amine.

Amides. Simple (Primary) amides ($RCONH_2$) when warmed with dilute sodium hydroxide solution give ammonia readily, together with the salt of the corresponding acid:

$$RCONH_2 + HOH \rightarrow RCOOH + NH_3$$

Complete hydrolysis may be effected by boiling either with 10 per cent sodium hydroxide solution or with 10 per cent sulphuric acid for 1–3 hours. It is preferable to employ the non-volatile sulphuric acid for acid hydrolysis; this acid should also be used for acidification of the solution resulting from alkaline hydrolysis since any volatile organic acid (formic acid, acetic acid, etc.) may be distilled off.

Substituted amides suffer hydrolysis with greater difficulty. The choice of an acid or an alkaline medium will depend upon (a) the solubility of the compound in the medium and (b) the effect of the reagent upon the products of hydrolysis. Substituted amides of comparatively low molecular weight (e.g., acetanilide) may be hydrolysed by boiling either with 10 per cent sodium hydroxide solution or with 10 per cent sulphuric acid for 2–3 hours. Other substituted amides are so insoluble in water that little reaction occurs when they are refluxed with dilute acid or dilute alkali for several hours. These include such substances as benzanilide ($C_6H_5CONHC_6H_5$) and the benzoyl derivative of a naphthylamine ($C_6H_5CONHC_{10}H_7$) or a toluidine ($C_6H_5CONHC_7H_7$). For these substances satisfactory results may be obtained with 70 per cent sulphuric acid:* this hydrolysis medium is a much better solvent for the substituted amide than is water or more dilute acid; it also permits a higher reaction temperature (compare *Aromatic Amides*, Section **IV,29**):

$$RCONHR' + HOH \xrightarrow{H_2SO_4} RCOOH + R'NH_2, H_2SO_4$$

Simple amides and many substituted amides give the **hydroxamic acid test** but more drastic experimental conditions (use of a solvent of high boiling point, e.g., propylene glycol) than suffice for esters and anhydrides (compare Section **V,5**) are usually required:

$$R-\underset{O}{\overset{\parallel}{C}}-X + H_2NOH \rightarrow$$

$$R-\underset{O}{\overset{\parallel}{C}}-NHOH + HX \quad (X=NH_2, NHR', NR'R'')$$

---

* Prepared by adding 40 ml. of concentrated sulphuric acid cautiously and with stirring and cooling to 30 ml. of water.

Nitriles react with hydroxylamine under similar conditions to produce amido-oximes, which usually give red colours with ferric ions:

$$R\text{—}C\equiv N + NH_2OH \rightarrow \underset{NH}{R\text{—}\overset{\|}{C}\text{—}NHOH} \rightleftharpoons \underset{NH_2}{R\text{—}\overset{|}{C}=NOH}$$

$$3\ \underset{NH}{R\text{—}\overset{\|}{C}\text{—}NHOH} + FeCl_3 \rightarrow \left(\underset{NH}{R\text{—}\overset{\|}{C}\text{—}NHO} \right)_3 Fe + 3HCl$$

Nitriles. These are best hydrolysed by boiling either with 30–40 per cent sodium hydroxide solution or with 50–70 per cent sulphuric acid during several hours, but the reaction takes place less readily than with primary amides. Indeed the latter are intermediate products in the hydrolysis:

$$RCN + HOH \xrightarrow{NaOH} RCONH_2$$

$$RCONH_2 + HOH \xrightarrow{NaOH} RCOOH + NH_3$$

Nitriles and simple amides differ in physical properties: the former are liquids or low-melting solids, whilst the latter are generally solids. If the amide is a solid and insoluble in water, it may be readily prepared from the nitrile by dissolving in concentrated sulphuric acid and pouring the solution into water:

$$RC\equiv N \xrightarrow{HOSO_3H} \underset{OSO_3H}{RC=NH} \xrightarrow{HOH} \left[\underset{OH}{RC=NH} \right] \rightarrow RC\overset{\|}{\underset{O}{\text{—}}}NH_2$$

Oximes, hydrazones and semicarbazones. The hydrolysis products of these compounds, *i.e.*, aldehydes and ketones, may be sensitive to alkali (this is particularly so for aldehydes): it is best, therefore, to conduct the hydrolysis with strong mineral acid. After hydrolysis, the aldehyde or ketone may be isolated by distillation with steam, extraction with ether or, if a solid, by filtration, and then identified. The acid solution may be examined for hydroxylamine or hydrazine or semicarbazide: substituted hydrazines of the aromatic series are precipitated as oils or solids upon the addition of alkali.

$$RR'C=NOH + HOH \xrightarrow[H_2SO_4]{HCl\ or} RR'C=O + NH_2OH,HCl$$

Imides. Imides are generally water-soluble, consequently they are much more readily hydrolysed in an alkaline medium, *e.g.*, by refluxing with 10 per cent sodium hydroxide solution:

$$(RCO)_2NH + NaOH \rightarrow (RCO)_2NNa \xrightarrow[NaOH]{HOH} 2RCOONa + NH_3$$

Imides usually give a positive hydroxamic acid test under the mild experimental conditions specified for esters (compare Section **V,5**).

Sulphonamides. Sulphonamides are very resistant to the normal reagents for hydrolysis. Heating with 80 per cent sulphuric acid at 160–170° results in rapid hydrolysis:

$$ArSO_2NRR' + HOH \xrightarrow{H_2SO_4} ArSO_2OH + RR'NH \cdot H_2SO_4$$

The reaction product may then be examined for a sulphonic acid and an amine.

Reduction of a nitro compound to a hydroxylamine. Dissolve 0·5 g. of the compound in 10 ml. of 50 per cent ethanol, add 0·5 g. of solid ammonium chloride and about 0·5 g. of zinc powder. Heat to boiling and allow the ensuing chemical reaction to proceed for 5 minutes. Filter from the excess of zinc powder and test the filtrate with Tollen's reagent {see *Aliphatic Aldehydes*, Section **IV,15,**(i)}. An immediate black or grey precipitate or a silver mirror indicates the presence of a hydroxylamine formed by the reduction of the nitro compound. Alternatively, warm the filtrate with Fehling's solution: a hydroxylamine will precipitate red cuprous oxide. (A blank test should be performed with the original compound.)

Reduction of a nitro compound to a primary amine. In a 50 ml. round-bottomed or conical flask fitted with a reflux condenser, place 1·0 g. of the nitro compound and 2 g. of granulated tin. Measure out 10 ml. of concentrated hydrochloric acid and add it in three equal portions to the mixture. Shake thoroughly after each addition; if necessary, cool the flask to moderate the reaction. When the vigorous reaction subsides, heat under reflux on a water bath until the nitro compound has completely reacted (20–30 minutes). Shake the reaction mixture from time to time; if the nitro compound appears to be very insoluble, add 5 ml. of ethanol. Cool the reaction mixture, and add 20–40 per cent sodium hydroxide solution until the precipitate of tin hydroxide dissolves. Extract the resulting amine from the cooled solution with ether, and remove the ether by distillation. Examine the residue with regard to its solubility in 5 per cent hydrochloric acid and its reaction with acetyl chloride or benzenesulphonyl chloride.

Reduction of a nitrosamine to a secondary amine. Proceed as for a nitro compound. Determine the solubility of the residue after evaporation of the ether and also its behaviour towards benzenesulphonyl (or *p*-toluenesulphonyl) chloride.

Hydrolysis of simple (primary) amides in alkaline solution. Boil 0·5 g. of the compound with 5 ml. of 10 per cent sodium hydroxide solution and observe whether ammonia is evolved.

Hydrolysis of a substituted amide. *A. With 10 per cent sulphuric acid.* Reflux 1·0 g. of the compound (*e.g.*, acetanilide) with 20 ml. of 10 per cent sulphuric acid for 1–2 hours. Distil the reaction mixture and collect 10 ml. of distillate: this will contain any volatile organic acids which may be present. Cool the residue, render it alkaline with 20 per cent sodium hydroxide solution, cool, and extract with ether. Distil off the ether and examine the ether-soluble residue for an amine.

B. *With 70 per cent sulphuric acid.* Reflux 1·0 g. of the substance (*e.g.*, benzanilide) with 10–15 ml. of 70 per cent sulphuric acid (4:3 by volume) for 30 minutes. Allow to cool and wash down any acid which has sublimed into the condenser with hot water. Filter off the acid, wash it with water, and examine for solubility, etc. Render the filtrate alkaline with 10–20 per cent sodium hydroxide solution, cool, and extract with ether. Examine the residue, after evaporation of the ether, for an amine.

Hydrolysis of a nitrile to an acid. Reflux 1·0 g. of the nitrile with 5 ml. of 30–40 per cent sodium hydroxide solution until ammonia ceases to be evolved (2–3 hours). Dilute with 5 ml. of water and add, with cooling, 7 ml. of 50 per cent sulphuric acid. Isolate the acid by ether extraction, and examine its solubility and other properties.

Hydrolysis of a nitrile to an amide. Warm a solution of 1·0 g. of the nitrile (*e.g.*, benzyl cyanide) in 4 ml. of concentrated sulphuric acid to 80–90°, and allow the solution to stand for 5 minutes. Cool and pour the solution cautiously into 40 ml. of cold water. Filter off the precipitate; stir it with 20 ml. of cold 5 per cent sodium hydroxide solution and filter again. Recrystallize the amide from dilute ethanol, and determine its m.p. Examine the solubility behaviour and also the action of warm sodium hydroxide solution upon the amide.

Hydroxamic acid test for amides and for nitriles. First carry out the following preliminary experiment (*A*) (reaction with hydroxylamine in methanol) under the conditions of the hydroxamic acid test for esters, anhydrides and imides. If the latter groups are present, they will give a positive result under the more drastic conditions detailed below (*B*) and hence will interfere with the detection of amides and of nitriles.

A. To about 30 mg. or 1 drop of the compound in a test-tube, add 1 ml. of M hydroxylamine hydrochloride in methanol and 1 ml. of M potassium hydroxide in methanol. Heat the mixture gently at the boiling point for 2 minutes, cool, and add 0·5–1 ml. of 5 per cent ferric chloride hexahydrate in ethanol. Introduce sufficient $2M$ methanolic hydrochloric acid to dissolve any ferric hydroxide. A red or violet colour constitutes a positive test. [Alternatively, the procedure described in Section V,5 may be used.]

B. If test *A* is negative, proceed as follows. To 2 ml. of a *M* solution of hydroxylamine hydrochloride in propylene glycol contained in a test-tube, add 1 drop or 30 mg. of the compound and 1 ml. of *M* potassium hydroxide in propylene glycol. Heat the mixture to the boiling point for 2 minutes, cool to room temperature, and then add 0·5–1 ml. of 5 per cent ethanolic ferric chloride solution. A red to violet colour constitutes a positive test for an amide or for a nitrile. A yellow colour indicates a negative test; a brown colour or precipitate is indeterminate.

Hydrolysis of a sulphonamide. Mix 2·0 g. of the sulphonamide with 3·5 ml. of 80 per cent sulphuric acid* in a test-tube and place a thermometer in the mixture. Heat the test-tube, with frequent stirring by means of the thermometer, at 155–165° until the solid passes into solution (2–5 minutes). Allow the acid solution to cool and pour it into 25–30 ml. of water. Render the resulting solution alkaline with 20 per cent sodium hydroxide solution in order to liberate the free amine. Two methods may be used for isolating the base. If the amine is volatile in steam, distil the alkaline solution and collect about 20 ml. of distillate: extract the amine with ether, dry the ethereal solution with anhydrous potassium carbonate and distil off the solvent. If the amine is not appreciably steam-volatile, extract it from the alkaline solution with ether. The sulphonic acid (as sodium salt) in the residual solution may be identified as detailed in Section **V,13**.

V, 13 Sulphur Compounds

The following classes of sulphur compounds occur in Solubility Groups II, III and VI: sulphonic acids and derivatives, $ArSO_2OR$; sulphinic acids and derivatives, $ArSOOR$; mercaptans, RSH; thiophenols, $ArSH$; sulphides or thioethers, RSR'; disulphides, $RSSR'$; sulphoxides, $RR'SO$; sulphones, $RR'SO_2$; esters of sulphuric acid, $ROSO_2OR'$; salts of alkyl sulphuric acids, *e.g.*, $ROSO_2ONa$; bisulphite addition products of aldehydes, methyl ketones ($RCOCH_3$) and alicyclic ketones; isothiocyanates, $RN{=}C{=}S$; sulphates of amines; and sulphonamides. The sulphonamides have already been discussed in Section **V,12**. The sulphates of amines are converted by aqueous sodium hydroxide into the free bases; the sulphate anion can be detected in the resulting aqueous solution as barium sulphate in the usual manner.

Sulphonic acids. The aromatic sulphonic acids and their alkali-metal salts are soluble in water, but insoluble in ether (Solubility Group II).

---

* Prepared by cautiously mixing 3 volumes of concentrated sulphuric acid with 1 volume of water.

They are best characterized by conversion into crystalline S-benzyl-thiuronium salts (see *Aromatic Sulphonic Acids*, Section **IV,38,***1*), which possess characteristic melting points. A more time-consuming procedure is to treat the well-dried acid or its salt with phosphorus pentachloride or with phosphorus oxychloride, and to convert the resulting sulphonyl chloride (*a*) into a sulphonamide by pouring the reaction mixture into concentrated ammonia solution or (*b*) into a substituted sulphonamide by treating it with a primary amine in the presence of aqueous sodium hydroxide (compare *Aromatic Sulphonic Acids*, Section **IV,38,***1*):

$$ArSO_2ONa \xrightarrow{PCl_5 \text{ or } POCl_3} ArSO_2Cl \xrightarrow[RNH_2]{NH_3} \begin{array}{c} ArSO_2NH_2 \\ ArSO_2NHR \end{array}$$

Sulphinic acids. Aromatic sulphinic acids are found in Solubility Group II. They may be detected by dissolving in cold concentrated sulphuric acid and adding one drop of phenetole or anisole when a blue colour is produced (Smiles's test), due to the formation of a *para*-substituted aromatic sulphoxide. Thus the reaction with benzenesulphinic acid is:

$$C_6H_5SOOH + C_6H_5OC_2H_5 \rightarrow C_6H_5SOC_6H_4OC_2H_5 + H_2O$$

Aromatic sulphinic acids are oxidized by potassium permanganate to sulphonic acids and are reduced by zinc and hydrochloric acid to thiophenols.

Aromatic sulphinic acids are more stable than aliphatic and both are usually encountered as the relatively stable sodium and potassium salts. Useful derivatives are produced by alkylation; sulphones are generally formed:

$$ArSO_2Na + CH_3I = ArSO_2CH_3 + NaI$$

Salts of aliphatic sulphinic acids afford crystalline 1,2-dialkylsulphonylethanes with ethylene dibromide:

$$2RSO_2Na + BrCH_2CH_2Br \rightarrow \begin{array}{c} CH_2SO_2R \\ | \\ CH_2SO_2R \end{array} + 2NaBr$$

Mercaptans and thiophenols (thiols). The thiols are generally liquids with penetrating and disagreeable odours, which persist even at extremely low concentrations in the air. They are soluble in dilute sodium hydroxide solution. Thiols are best characterized as the crystalline 2,4-dinitrophenyl thioethers or as the corresponding sulphones (see under *Thiols*, Section **IV,37**).

Sulphides (thioethers). The organic sulphides are usually liquids with penetrating and disagreeable odours. In contrast to the oxygen analogues (ethers), they are readily oxidized; thus sulphoxides are produced with hydrogen peroxide, and sulphones with nitric acid or with potassium permanganate in glacial acetic acid solution:

$$\begin{array}{c}R\\R'\end{array}\!\!>\!\!S \xrightarrow{H_2O_2} \begin{array}{c}R\\R'\end{array}\!\!>\!\!S\!=\!O \xrightarrow{HNO_3} \begin{array}{c}R\\R'\end{array}\!\!>\!\!S\!\!<\!\!\begin{array}{c}O\\O\end{array}$$

Thioethers usually yield sulphonium salts when warmed with ethyl iodide and allowed to cool. The physical properties (b.p., density and refractive index) are useful for identification purposes.

Disulphides. Disulphides are liquids or low m.p. solids and have unpleasant odours, particularly if liquid. They are reduced by zinc and dilute acids to the mercaptans:

$$RSSR + 2H \rightarrow 2RSH$$

Sulphoxides. These are usually solids of low m.p. They may be oxidized in glacial acetic acid solution by potassium permanganate to the corresponding sulphones, and reduced to the sulphides by boiling with tin or zinc and hydrochloric acid.

Sulphones. Sulphones are usually crystalline solids, and are extremely stable to most oxidizing, reducing and hydrolytic reagents.

Sulphones, when fused with solid potassium hydroxide and the product acidified, yield sulphur dioxide (this test is also given by sulphoxides and sulphonates).

Esters of sulphuric acid. These compounds are generally water-insoluble liquids and are saponified by boiling with water or dilute alkali to the corresponding alcohols and sulphuric acid:

$$R_2SO_4 + 2H_2O \rightarrow 2ROH + H_2SO_4$$

They are usually poisonous and can be identified by using them to alkylate 2-naphthol.

The **alkyl esters of sulphonic acids** exhibit properties similar to those of the alkyl sulphates, and are hydrolysed, by boiling with aqueous alkalis, to the alcohols and sulphonates. Thus with ethyl p-toluene-sulphonate:

$$p\text{-}CH_3C_6H_4SO_2OC_2H_5 + HOH \rightarrow p\text{-}CH_3C_6H_4SO_2OH + C_2H_5OH$$

The **salts of monoalkyl sulphates** are frequently encountered as commercial detergents (for example, 'Dreft,' 'Gardinol' and 'Pentrone'): they are usually sodium salts, the alkyl components contain 12 or more carbon atoms, and give colloidal solutions. They are hydrolysed by boiling with dilute sodium hydroxide solution:

$$ROSO_2ONa + NaOH \rightarrow ROH + Na_2SO_4$$

Bisulphite compounds of aldehydes and ketones. These substances are decomposed by dilute acids into the corresponding aldehydes or ketones with the liberation of sulphur dioxide. The aldehyde or ketone may be isolated by steam distillation or by extraction with ether. Owing to the highly reactive character of aldehydes, the bisulphite addition compounds are best decomposed with saturated sodium bicarbonate solution: sodium carbonate solution is generally employed for the bisulphite compounds of ketones.

$$RCH(OH)SO_3Na + HCl \rightarrow RCHO + NaCl + SO_2 + H_2O$$

Isothiocyanates. These compounds, also known as **mustard oils**, are oils or low melting point solids, and usually possess irritating odours. Upon boiling with acids, for example with concentrated hydrochloric acid, they are hydrolysed to the primary amines and hydrogen sulphide is evolved:

$$RN{=}C{=}S + HCl + 2H_2O \rightarrow RNH_2, HCl + CO_2 + H_2S$$

They react with amines to form substituted thioureas:

$$RN{=}C{=}S + R'NH_2 \rightarrow RNHCSNHR'$$

this reaction is also employed for the characterization of amines (see under *Aliphatic Amines*, Section **IV,32,2**).

V, 14 Phosphorus Compounds

The presence of phosphorus may be revealed by a smell of phosphine during the sodium fusion test for the elements. It is usually advisable, if an organic phosphorus compound is suspected, to make a routine test for phosphorus as detailed in Section **II,3**.

Only esters of phosphoric and of phosphorous acid, both aliphatic and aromatic, need be considered. These esters may be identified by their physical properties (if liquids) and by the products of hydrolysis.

Hydrolysis, etc. Dissolve 5 g. of sodium hydroxide in 10 ml. of water, add 5 g. of the organic phosphorus compound, and reflux for 30–60 minutes or until the liquid becomes homogeneous. Distil and collect the first 3–5 ml. of distillate: test the distillate for an alcohol (Section **IV,5**) and, if present, prepare the 3,5-dinitrobenzoate.

If no alcohol is obtained, acidify the residual alkaline liquid with dilute sulphuric acid and extract the liberated phenol with ether. Dry the ethereal solution with anhydrous magnesium sulphate, distil off the ether and prepare a derivative (*e.g.*, the benzoate—see Section **IV,7**) of the phenol.

Use the acidic aqueous solution remaining after the removal of the alcohol or the phenol in testing for phosphate or phosphite. Apply the following tests to small portions:

(i) Add 1 ml. of concentrated nitric acid and 5 ml. of ammonium molybdate reagent, and warm the mixture gently. A yellow precipitate (ammonium phosphomolybdate) indicates the presence of a phosphate. (A phosphite may undergo oxidation when the mixture is heated and therefore gives a precipitate slowly.)

(ii) Render alkaline with ammonia solution and add magnesia mixture. A white crystalline precipitate (magnesium ammonium phosphate) indicates phosphate.

(iii) Add a few drops of potassium permanganate solution and warm gently. If the purple colour is discharged, a phosphite is indicated.

(iv) Add a little mercuric chloride solution and warm gently. A white precipitate of mercurous chloride indicates a phosphite.

V, 15 Summary of the More Important Class Reactions

It is convenient to summarize the more important class reactions given in this chapter.

Unsaturation:
(a) Bromine in carbon tetrachloride.
(b) Potassium permanganate solution.

Aromatic hydrocarbons:
Fuming sulphuric acid.

Halogens:
(a) Ethanolic silver nitrate solution.
(b) Sodium iodide in acetone.

Aldehydes and ketones:
2,4-Dinitrophenylhydrazine.

Aldehydes:
(a) Fuchsin aldehyde reagent (Schiff's reagent).
(b) Fehling's solution or Benedict's solution.
(c) Ammoniacal silver nitrate solution (Tollen's solution).

Esters and anhydrides:
(a) Hydroxamic acid test.
(b) Saponification; saponification equivalent.

Alcohols:
(a) Sodium, together with reaction (b).
(b) Acetyl chloride or benzoyl chloride.
(c) Hydrochloric acid-zinc chloride reagent.
(d) Chromium trioxide reagent.

(e) Oxidation ('chromic acid') test.
(f) Periodic acid (for polyhydric alcohols).

Ethers:
(a) Sodium.
(b) Acetyl chloride.
(c) Hydriodic acid.

Carboxylic acids:
(a) Sodium bicarbonate and sodium hydroxide solution.
(b) Neutralization equivalent.

Phenols:
(a) Sodium bicarbonate and sodium hydroxide solution.
(b) Bromine in carbon tetrachloride, and bromine water.
(c) Ferric chloride solution.
(d) Benzoyl chloride.

Amines:
(a) Acetyl, benzoyl or benzenesulphonyl chloride.
(b) Nitrous acid.

Nitro compounds:
(a) Zinc and ammonium chloride solution.
(b) Tin and hydrochloric acid.
(c) Ferrous hydroxide.

Amides:
(a) Dilute sodium hydroxide solution.
(b) Dilute sulphuric acid.
(c) Hydroxamic acid test (in propylene glycol).

Nitriles:
(a) Dilute sodium hydroxide solution.
(b) Dilute sulphuric acid.
(c) Hydroxamic acid test (in propylene glycol).

Sulphonic acids:
(a) Sulphur present.
(b) Sodium bicarbonate and sodium hydroxide solution.
(c) S-Benzylthiuronium chloride.
(d) Neutralization equivalent.

Sulphonamides:
(a) Sulphur and nitrogen present.
(b) Sodium hydroxide solution.
(c) Sulphuric acid (70–80 per cent).

CHAPTER VI

The Preparation of Derivatives

VI, 1 General Discussion

The steps so far taken in the identification of a compound, *viz.*, (i) determination of the physical constants and the establishment of the purity (Chapter I), (ii) qualitative analysis for the elements (Chapter II), (iii) study of the solubility behaviour towards selected solvents (Sections **III**,2 and **III**,3) and (iv) application of class reactions (Chapter V), will, in general, establish the class to which the compound belongs. The next step is to prove its identity with one of the members of the class. It is at this stage that the literature is consulted. In the first instance, the appropriate table or tables in Chapter IX (Physical Constants of Organic Compounds. Tables of Derivatives) are examined. Those compounds are selected which have melting points or boiling points within about 5° of the unknown: it is assumed, of course, that the latter was supplied or subsequently obtained in a state of purity. To distinguish between these, a suitable *derivative* is prepared and its physical properties determined; if these agree with those of the known derivative of one of the possibilities already considered, then the identity of the compounds may be assumed. If the list of possible compounds is long, the preparation of two derivatives may be desirable. It must, however, be pointed out that in eliminating compounds from the list of possibilities, due consideration must be paid to other sufficiently characteristic properties, such as density, refractive index, neutralization equivalent, molecular weight and optical rotation (where applicable), with adequate allowance for experimental error.

The **requirements of a satisfactory derivative include:**
(1) The derivative should be easily and quickly prepared in good yield by an unambiguous reaction, and be easily purified. In practice, this generally means that the derivative must be a solid, because of the greater ease of manipulation of small quantities of solids and the fact that melting points are more accurate and more easily determined than boiling points. The melting point should preferably be above 50°, but below 250°; compounds which melt below 50° are frequently difficult to crystallize. A melting point above 250° is undesirable because the

stem correction of the thermometer may amount to several degrees and also on account of the possible decomposition of the compound.

(2) The derivative should be prepared preferably by a general reaction, which under the same experimental conditions would yield a definite derivative with the other individual possibilities. Rearrangements and side reactions should be avoided.

(3) The properties (physical and chemical) of the derivatives should be markedly different from those of the original compound.

(4) The derivative selected in any particular instance should be one which clearly singles out one compound from among all the possibilities and thus enables an unequivocal choice to be made. The melting points of the derivatives to be compared should differ by at least 5–10°. Whenever possible, a derivative should be selected which has a neutralization equivalent as well as a melting point (*e.g.*, an aryloxyacetic acid derivative of a phenol, Section **IV,7,***4*, or a hydrogen 3-nitrophthalate of an alcohol, Section **IV,5,***5*).

The above considerations will assist the student in the selection of a derivative. It should also be borne in mind that when a compound has several functional groups, that functional group should be chosen for the preparation of a derivative which gives the least ambiguous reaction.

The methods of preparation of some of the more important derivatives of a number of classes of organic compounds are described largely in Chapter IV (Reactions and Characterization of Selected Classes of Organic Compounds): some are given in Chapter V {Class Reactions (Reactions for Functional Groups)}.

VI, 2 Summary of the More Useful Derivatives of Selected Classes of Organic Compounds

It is convenient to summarize some of the more useful derivatives: these should be considered first when a derivative is sought.

Aromatic hydrocarbons:
(*a*) Sulphonamides (Section **IV,4,***1*).
(*b*) Aroylbenzoic acids (Section **IV,4,***2*).
(*c*) Nitro derivatives (Section **IV,4,***3*).

Alcohols:
(*a*) 3,5-Dinitrobenzoates (Section **IV,5,***1*).
(*b*) Phenyl- and 1-naphthyl-urethanes (Section **IV,5,***4*).
(*c*) *p*-Nitrobenzoates (Section **IV,5,***2*).

Phenols:
(a) Acetates (Section **IV,7,***1*).
(b) Benzoates, *p*-nitrobenzoates (Section **IV,7,***2–3*).
(c) Aryloxyacetic acids (Section **IV,7,***4*).
(d) 1-Naphthylurethanes (Section **IV,7,***6*).
(e) 2,4-Dinitrophenyl ethers (Section **IV,7,***8*).
(f) Bromo derivatives (**IV,7,***9*).

Alkyl halides:
(a) Anilides, 1-naphthalides (Section **IV,11,***1*).
(b) Alkyl mercuric halides (Section **IV,11,***2*).
(c) *S*-Alkylthiuronium picrates (Section **IV,11,***3*).
(d) Picrates of alkyl 2-naphthyl ethers (Section **IV,11,***4*).

Halogenated aromatic hydrocarbons:
(a) Sulphonamides (with chlorosulphonic acid; aqueous ammonia) (Section **IV,12,***2*).
(b) Nitro derivatives (Section **IV,12,***1*).

Ethers (aliphatic):
(a) 3,5-Dinitrobenzoates (with 3,5-dinitrobenzoyl chloride) (Section **IV,13,***1*).

Ethers (aromatic):
(a) Sulphonamides (with chlorosulphonic acid; aqueous ammonia) (Section **IV,14,***2*).
(b) Bromo derivatives (Section **IV,14,***4*).
(c) Nitro derivatives (Section **IV,14,***5*).

Aldehydes and ketones:
(a) 2,4-Dinitrophenylhydrazones (Sections **IV,17,***7* and **IV,18,***1*).
(b) Phenylhydrazones (Section **IV,18,***5*).
(c) *p*-Nitrophenylhydrazones (Section **IV,18,***6*).
(d) Semicarbazones (Section **IV,18,***2*).
(e) Oximes (Section **IV,18,***3*).

Carboxylic acids:
(a) Amides, anilides, *p*-toluidides (Section **IV,20,***1*).
(b) *p*-Bromophenacyl esters (Section **IV,20,***2*).
(c) *p*-Nitrobenzyl esters (Section **IV,20,***3*).
(d) *S*-Benzylthiuronium salts (Section **IV,20,***5*).

Acid chlorides:
(a) Acids (Sections **IV,22** and **IV,24**).
(b) Amides, anilides, *p*-toluidides (Sections **IV,22** and **IV,24**).

Acid anhydrides:
(a) Acids (Section **IV,23**).
(b) Amides, anilides, *p*-toluidides (Section **IV,23**).

Nitriles:
(a) Acids (Section **IV,30**,(ii)).
(b) Acyl phloroglucinols: alkyl 2,4,6-trihydroxyphenyl ketones (Section **IV,30,***1*).
(c) Amines and derivatives thereof (Section **IV,30,***2*).

Amines (primary and secondary):
(a) Benzenesulphonamides (Section **IV,33,***3*).
(b) *p*-Toluenesulphonamides (Section **IV,33,***3*).
(c) Phenylthioureas (Section **IV,32,***2*).
(d) *N*-Substituted phthalimides (Section **IV,32,***4*).
(e) Acetamides (Section **IV,33,***1*).
(f) Benzamides (Section **IV,33,***2*).

Amines (tertiary):
Addition compounds with
(a) Methyl or ethyl iodide (Section **IV,33,***2'*).
(b) Methyl *p*-toluenesulphonate (Section **IV,33,***3'*).
(c) Picric acid (Section **IV,33,***1'*).

Amino acids:
(a) 2,4-Dinitrophenyl derivatives (Section **IV,34,***1*).
(b) *p*-Toluenesulphonates (Section **IV,34,***5*).

Mercaptans (thiols):
(a) 2,4-Dinitrophenyl-sulphides and the corresponding sulphones (Section **IV,37,***1*).
(b) 3,5-Dinitrothiobenzoates (Section **IV,37,***2*).

Aromatic sulphonic acids:
(a) Sulphonamides (Section **IV,38,***1*).
(b) Sulphonanilides (Section **IV,38,***1*).
(c) *S*-Benzylthiuronium salts (Section **IV,38,***2*).

Many classes of compounds can be hydrolysed to alcohols, aldehydes, carboxylic acids, amines, etc. and are often more easily identified by reference to such products. These include acetals, esters, acid anhydrides, acid chlorides, nitriles and amides. Nitro, azo, hydrazo and nitroso compounds may be reduced to the corresponding amines and identified by reference to such reduction products.

VI, 3 Reference Works for Qualitative Organic Chemical Analysis

It will be appreciated that the Tables given in Chapter IX (Physical Constants of Organic Compounds. Tables of Derivatives) are far from complete, but they do contain most of the common organic compounds which the student is likely to encounter in the course of his work in the laboratory. For compounds which are not listed in the Tables, reference should be made to larger treatises. These include:

N. D. Cheronis and J. B. Entrikin, *Identification of Organic Compounds, A Student's Text Using Semimicro Techniques*. Interscience Publishers, New York, 1963. (This book is included here because it contains useful literature references to procedures.)

N. D. Cheronis, J. B. Entrikin and E. M. Hodnett, *Semimicro Qualitative Organic Analysis. The Systematic Identification of Organic Compounds*. Third Edition. Interscience Publishers, New York, 1965.

R. L. Shriner, R. C. Fuson and D. Y. Curtin, *The Systematic Identification of Organic Compounds*. Fifth Edition. John Wiley, New York, 1964. (This book is included here because it contains useful literature references to procedures.)

M. Frankel and S. Patai, *Tables for the Identification of Organic Compounds*. Second Edition. Chemical Publishing Co., Cleveland, Ohio, 1964.

E. H. Huntress and S. P. Mulliken, *Identification of Organic Compounds, Order I* (*Compounds of carbon with hydrogen and with hydrogen and oxygen*). John Wiley, New York, 1941.

E. H. Huntress, *Organic Chlorine Compounds*. John Wiley, New York, 1948.

I. Heilbron. *Dictionary of Organic Compounds*. Fourth Edition, Edited by J. R. A. Pollock and R. Stevens. Five volumes, 1965. First Supplement, 1965. Eyre and Spottiswoode, London.

Elsevier's Encyclopaedia of Organic Chemistry. 19 volumes of Series III, 'Carboisocyclic Condensed Compounds' (Naphthalene derivatives, Tri- and Higher Cyclic Compounds, Steroids) have appeared during 1948–1965. Publication of this comprehensive work has unfortunately been largely discontinued but the published volumes are of considerable value.

Rodd's Chemistry of Carbon Compounds. Second Edition. Elsevier Publishing Co., Amsterdam, 1965– (incomplete).

Beilstein's Handbuch der organischen Chemie. Fourth Edition. Springer-Verlag, Berlin, 1918 to date. This is the most comprehensive reference work on organic compounds. The main series or *Hauptwerk* covers the literature to and including 1909 in 27 volumes. The method of classification of compounds is based on structure and, once one is familiar with this, it is usually possible to find the desired compound without reference to the index. Further details concerning the use of 'Beilstein' are to be found in the following books:

E. H. Huntress, *A Brief Introduction to the Use of Beilstein's Handbuch der organischen Chemie.* Second Edition. John Wiley, New York, 1938.

F. Richter and K. Ilberg, *Kurze Anleitung zur Orientierung in Beilstein's Handbuch der organischen Chemie.* J. Springer, Berlin, 1936.

Once a particular compound is located in the *Hauptwerk*, it is easily found in the supplements. The first supplement (*Erstes Ergänzungswerk*) covers the literature from 1910 to the end of 1919 in 27 volumes and has, as have all the later supplements, the same arrangement as in the *Hauptwerk*. Thus a compound found in Volume 2 of the *Hauptwerk* is in Volume 2 of the first supplement; also an auxiliary set of page numbers in the middle of each page of the supplements relates the material on that page to the corresponding page in the *Hauptwerk*. The second supplement (*Zweites Ergänzungswerk*) covers the material from 1920 to 1929 in 27 volumes. Volumes 28 and 29 are the collective subject and formulae indexes for the main work and the first supplement. The third supplement (*Drittes Ergänzungswerk*) covers the period 1930 to 1949: 5 volumes in 13 parts have been published to 1965 and publication continues at a rate of 1–2 volumes annually.

After 1927 the most trustworthy index for organic compounds is the Author and Subject Index to *Chemical Abstracts*. Decennial Indexes cover the years 1927–1936, 1937–1946 and 1947–1956; there is a further Collective Index covering the period 1957–1961 (Authors, Subjects, Formula). The Collective Formula Index to *Chemical Abstracts* for the years 1930–1946, although not complete, is very useful. The annual indexes to *Chemical Abstracts* must be consulted for later years (after 1961).

CHAPTER VII

Qualitative Analysis of Mixtures of Organic Compounds

VII, 1 General Discussion

The general method to be adopted for the analysis of mixtures of organic compounds is to separate them into their components and to identify each component as previously described. It is impossible, however, to give a set of procedures which will be applicable, without modification, to all of the great variety of combinations which may be encountered. The student will be expected to take advantage of any facts which have emerged in the preliminary examination and to adapt, if necessary, the general schemes given below to the mixture under examination. The preliminary examination is therefore of fundamental importance.

Broadly speaking, the separation of the components of mixtures may be divided into three main groups.

(1) **Separations based upon differences in the chemical properties of the components.** Thus a mixture of toluene and aniline may be separated by extraction with dilute hydrochloric acid: the aniline passes into the aqueous layer in the form of the salt, aniline hydrochloride, and may be recovered by neutralization. Whereas aniline is soluble in toluene and sparingly soluble in water, the salt (because of its polar nature) is soluble in water and insoluble in toluene. Similarly, a mixture of phenol and toluene may be separated by treatment with dilute sodium hydroxide. The phenol is converted into the salt, sodium phenoxide, which because of its highly polar character is soluble in water and insoluble in toluene. The above examples are, of course, simple applications of the fact that the various components may fall into different solubility groups (compare Section **III,2**). Another example is the separation of a mixture of di-*n*-butyl ether and chlorobenzene: concentrated sulphuric acid dissolves only the *n*-butyl ether and it may be recovered from solution by dilution with water. With some classes of compounds, *e.g.*, unsaturated compounds, concentrated sulphuric acid leads to polymerization, sulphonation, etc., so that the original component cannot be recovered unchanged: this

solvent, therefore, possesses limited application. Phenols may be separated from acids (for example, *o*-cresol from benzoic acid) by a dilute solution of sodium bicarbonate: the weakly acidic phenols (and also enols) are not converted into salts by this reagent and may be removed by ether extraction or by other means; the acids pass into solution as the sodium salts and may be recovered after acidification. (An equivalent result is obtained by dissolving the mixture of phenols and acids in dilute sodium hydroxide solution and saturating the solution with carbon dioxide by the addition of Dry Ice.) Aldehydes, *e.g.*, benzaldehyde, may be separated from liquid hydrocarbons (*e.g.*, benzene) and other neutral, water-insoluble liquid compounds by shaking with a solution of sodium bisulphite: the aldehyde forms a solid bisulphite compound (a typical salt), which may be filtered off and decomposed with dilute acid or with sodium bicarbonate solution in order to recover the aldehyde.

An interesting method for separating ketones from other neutral and water-insoluble compounds utilizes the **Girard-T reagent**, the hydrazide of carboxymethyltrimethylammonium chloride, prepared by reaction of ethyl chloroacetate with Trimethylamine, followed by reaction with hydrazine:

$$(CH_3)_3N + ClCH_2COOC_2H_5 + H_2NNH_2 \rightarrow$$

$$[(CH_3)_3\overset{+}{N}CH_2CONHNH_2]Cl^- + C_2H_5OH$$
Girard-T reagent

It reacts with the carbonyl compound to yield another quaternary ammonium salt:

$$RR'CO + [(CH_3)_3\overset{+}{N}CH_2CONHNH_2]Cl^- \rightarrow$$

$$[(CH_3)_3\overset{+}{N}CH_2CONHN=CRR']Cl^- + H_2O$$

The latter is a polar compound and is therefore soluble in water. Extraction with ether removes the water-insoluble compounds, leaving the salt in the aqueous layer. The ketone is easily regenerated by hydrolysis with dilute hydrochloric acid.

Attention is drawn to the fact that *o*-nitrophenol, salicylaldehyde, and many other *ortho*-disubstituted benzene derivatives are volatile in steam. The explanation of this apparently anomalous loss of polar character is that all these compounds can exist in cyclic forms (which tend to be non-polar) due to hydrogen bonding. It is a general rule that the presence in a molecule of two or more functional groups will render a compound non-volatile in steam.

In connexion with the above 'chemical' methods of separation, it is important to note that sufficient of the extracting reagent must be used to remove *completely* the component which it dissolves or with which it reacts.

(2) **Separations based upon differences in the volatilities of the components in aqueous solution.** This procedure is generally employed for the water-soluble compounds listed in Solubility Table III, 3, 1, and may also be applied to mixtures in which one of the components is slightly soluble in water. The water-soluble compounds include the lower members of the homologous series of alcohols, aldehydes, ketones, acids, esters, amines and nitriles; compounds containing two or more hydroxyl or amino groups; hydroxy-, amino-, di-, and poly-basic acids; sulphonic acids and salts. Compounds with one functional group are usually volatile in steam and distil with the water: compounds with two or more functional groups (*e.g.*, amino with hydroxyl or carboxyl) are not generally steam-volatile. The stable salts of steam-volatile bases and acids may be decomposed by a stronger non-volatile mineral acid (sulphuric acid or phosphoric acid) or base (sodium or potassium hydroxide), and the organic base or acid separated by steam distillation from the aqueous solution or suspension. The salts of weaker bases and acids (*e.g.*, the amine or ammonium salts of carboxylic acids and the alkali metal salts of some phenols) are sufficiently hydrolysed by boiling water to permit the basic or acidic compound to distil with the water. It should be noted that sulphonic acids and their salts are not volatile in steam. The only disadvantage of this procedure is that certain compounds may decompose or polymerize or otherwise undergo change under the influence of aqueous alkali or acid at 100°, and this fact must be borne in mind when the method is employed. Thus sugars are decomposed by alkali; these may sometimes be isolated by evaporation of the solvent at *p*H 7, preferably under diminished pressure.

The essential basis of the scheme for the separation of water-soluble compounds is, therefore, distillation of (*a*) an aqueous solution of the mixture, (*b*) an alkaline (with sodium hydroxide) solution of the mixture, and (*c*) an acidic (with sulphuric or phosphoric acid) solution of the mixture. The residue will contain the non-volatile components, which must be separated from inorganic salts and from each other by any suitable process.

The following are examples of the above procedure. A mixture of diethylamine and *n*-butyl alcohol may be separated by adding sufficient dilute sulphuric acid or phosphoric acid to neutralize the

Table VII, 1, 1.   Solubilities, Volatilities and Steam-Volatilities of Compounds

SOLUBILITY	TYPES OF COMPOUNDS	VOLATILITY	VOLATILITY IN STEAM
Soluble in water and ether.	Low molecular-weight alcohols, aldehydes, ketones, esters, amines, nitriles, acids and acid chlorides.	Distils readily. Many compounds boil below 100°.	Volatile in steam.
Soluble in water but insoluble in ether.	Polyhydroxy alcohols, carbohydrates, polybasic acids, diamines, amine salts; amino acids; hydroxy-aldehydes, -ketones, and -acids.	Low volatility. Generally cannot be distilled at normal pressure.	Not volatile in steam.
Insoluble in water but soluble in NaOH and NaHCO$_3$.	High molecular-weight acids; negatively substituted phenols.	Low volatility.	Generally not steam-volatile.
Insoluble in water and NaHCO$_3$ but soluble in NaOH.	Phenols, thiophenols, sulphonamides of primary amines, primary and secondary nitro compounds, imides.	High boiling points. Many cannot be distilled.	Usually not volatile in steam.
Insoluble in water but soluble in dilute HCl.	Hydrazines; amines containing not more than one aryl group attached to nitrogen.	High boiling points.	Many are volatile in steam.
Insoluble in water, dilute HCl and dilute NaOH but contain elements other than carbon, hydrogen and the halogens.	Negatively substituted amines, amides; sulphonamides of secondary amines; alkyl or aryl cyanides; sulphates; phosphates; azo and azoxy compounds.	High boiling points. Many cannot be distilled.	Some are volatile in steam.
Insoluble in water, dilute HCl and dilute NaOH, but soluble in conc. H$_2$SO$_4$.	Alcohols, aldehydes, ketones, esters and ethers of medium to high molecular weight; unsaturated compounds.	High boiling points.	Usually volatile in steam.
Insoluble in water, dilute HCl, dilute NaOH, and conc. H$_2$SO$_4$.	Aromatic, cyclic and aliphatic hydrocarbons, and their halogen derivatives.	Volatile.	Volatile in steam.

base: steam distillation will remove the alcohol. The amine can be recovered by adding sodium hydroxide to the residue and repeating the distillation. A mixture of diethyl ketone and acetic acid may be treated with sufficient dilute sodium hydroxide solution to transform the acid into sodium acetate and distilling the aqueous mixture. The ketone will pass over in the steam and the non-volatile, stable salt will remain in the flask. Acidification with dilute sulphuric acid liberates acetic acid, which can be isolated by steam distillation or by extraction.

(3) **Separations based upon differences in the physical properties of the components.** When procedures (1) or (2) are unsatisfactory for the separation of a mixture of organic compounds, purely physical methods may be employed. Thus a mixture of volatile liquids may be fractionally distilled: the degree of separation may be determined by the range of boiling points and/or the refractive indices and densities of the different fractions that are collected. A mixture of non-volatile solids may frequently be separated by making use of the differences in solubilities in inert solvents: the separation is usually controlled by m.p. determinations. Sometimes one of the components of the mixture is volatile and can be separated by sublimation.

It is convenient at this point to collect in a table the general properties of various compounds which may be useful in separations. These are given in Table VII, 1, 1.

VII, 2 Preliminary Examination of a Mixture

A. Liquid Mixtures

(i) **Physical properties.** Examine the mixture with regard to odour, viscosity and colour. If a solid is suspended in a liquid, remove the solid by filtration, and examine it separately.

(ii) **Solubility in water.** Transfer 1·0 ml. of the mixture by means of a calibrated dropper or a small pipette into a small graduated test-tube: add 1 ml. of water and shake. Observe whether there is complete or partial solution and if there is any sign of chemical reaction. If solution is not complete, add more water (in 1 ml. portions) and note (*a*) if the mixture dissolves completely, and (*b*) if a portion is insoluble and, if so, whether it is heavier or lighter than the aqueous layer. If an emulsion is formed, it may be assumed that at least one component of the mixture is insoluble in water and at least one component is soluble. Test the aqueous layer obtained with litmus and with phenolphthalein: if there is an acid reaction, test also with 5 per cent sodium bicarbonate solution.

(iii) **Presence or absence of water.** Determine the absence or presence of water in the solution by one or more of the following tests:

(a) Investigate its miscibility with ether or with benzene.

(b) Observe its action upon anhydrous copper sulphate.

(c) Distil a small portion and note the b.p. and properties of the distillate.

(d) Distil 3 ml. of the mixture with 3 ml. of dry toluene from a dry, 10 ml. distilling flask. Collect 2 ml. of the distillate and dilute it with 5 ml. of dry toluene; the formation of two layers or of distinct drops suspended in the toluene indicates the presence of water.

(iv) **Behaviour upon distillation.** If the original mixture is not an aqueous solution, place 5 ml. (or 10 ml.) of it in a 10 ml. (or 25 ml.) distilling flask, immerse the latter in a small beaker of cold water, and gradually heat to boiling. Observe the b.p. of any liquid which passes over and set it aside for subsequent examination. Determine the water solubility of any residue. If it dissolves in water, examine it by Table VII, 4, 1; if it is insoluble in water, apply Table VII, 3, 1.

(v) **Test for elements.** If the mixture is an aqueous solution, evaporate a small portion (*ca.* 1 ml.) to dryness upon platinum foil or in a small crucible. Use a portion of the residue to test for elements (Chapter II) and another portion for the *Ignition Test* (vi).

If no water is present in the mixture, use it directly in the tests for elements.

(vi) **Ignition test.** Place 0·1–0·2 g. of the mixture on a porcelain crucible cover: heat gently at first over a small flame and finally ignite strongly. Observe:

(a) The inflammability and nature of the flame (*e.g.*, smoky or otherwise).

(b) Odour of gases or vapours evolved (*CAUTION!*).

(c) Whether a residue is left after ignition; moisten with hydrochloric acid and test with a platinum wire.

(vii) **Miscellaneous solubility and other tests.** Determine the reaction of an aqueous solution or suspension to litmus and to phenolphthalein. If the mixture is distinctly acid, titrate 2·0 ml. with 0·1N sodium hydroxide solution in order to determine whether the acidity is due to traces of acids formed by hydrolysis of esters or whether substantial amounts of free acid are present. Perform the titration in an ice-cold solution and take the first pink colour of phenolphthalein as the end point.

Treat 1·0 ml. of the mixture with 5 per cent sodium hydroxide solution until strongly alkaline: note whether an oil or solid separates, whether any ammonia is evolved, and any colour changes which occur. Heat to boiling and cool: compare any odour with that of the original mixture (a change in odour may indicate the presence of esters). Add dilute hydrochloric acid and observe the result.

Treat 1·0 ml. of the mixture with dilute hydrochloric acid until strongly acid. Note any evolution of gas or the separation of a solid. Add dilute sodium hydroxide solution and observe the effect.

(viii) **Miscellaneous class reactions.** Determine the effect of the following class reagents upon small portions of the original mixture: (*a*) bromine in carbon tetrachloride solution, (*b*) potassium permanganate solution, (*c*) ethanolic silver nitrate solution, (*d*) 2,4-dinitrophenylhydrazine reagent, (*e*) Schiff's reagent, (*f*) acetyl chloride, (*g*) benzoyl chloride (in the presence of aqueous sodium hydroxide), (*h*) sodium (only if water is absent), (*i*) ferric chloride solution, and (*j*) bromine water.

B. SOLID MIXTURES

(i) **Physical properties.** Observe the colour, odour and crystalline form. Examine with a lens or a microscope, if available.

(ii) **Solubility in water.** Determine the solubility of 1·0 g. of the sample in water. If in doubt as to whether a portion of the mixture dissolves, remove the supernatant liquid with a dropper and evaporate to dryness on a water bath. Determine the reaction of the aqueous solution or suspension to litmus and to phenolphthalein.

(iii) **Test for elements.** See Chapter II.

(iv) **Ignition test.** Place 0·1–0·2 g. of the mixture upon a porcelain crucible cover or upon a piece of platinum foil; heat gently at first and finally ignite strongly. Note:

(*a*) Whether the mixture melts and if decomposition occurs.

(*b*) The inflammability and the nature of the flame (*e.g.*, if smoky or otherwise).

(*c*) Whether a residue is obtained after ignition (moisten with hydrochloric acid and test with a platinum wire).

(v) **Miscellaneous solubility and other tests.** Determine the reaction of an aqueous solution or suspension to litmus and to phenolphthalein.

Test the solubility behaviour of 0·5–1 g. of the mixture to 5 per cent sodium hydroxide solution, 5 per cent sodium bicarbonate solution and to 5 per cent hydrochloric acid (for details, see under *Liquid Mixtures*).

(vi) **Miscellaneous class reactions.** Determine the effect of the following class reagents upon small portions of the original mixture (for some of the tests an aqueous solution or suspension may be used): (a) bromine in carbon tetrachloride solution, (b) potassium permanganate solution, (c) ethanolic silver nitrate solution, (d) 2,4-dinitrophenylhydrazine reagent, (e) Schiff's reagent, (f) acetyl chloride, (g) benzoyl chloride (in the presence of aqueous sodium hydroxide), (h) ferric chloride solution and (i) bromine water.

A careful consideration of the results of the above tests will provide much useful information and will indicate which of the following general procedures should be applied and the modifications which are necessary. Thus if nitrogen is absent, it is doubtful whether the separation for bases is necessary.

VII, 3 Separation of a Mixture of Water-Insoluble Compounds

If the water-insoluble mixture is a liquid, evaporate a small sample (say, 4 ml.) in an evaporating dish on a water bath in order to determine the amount of volatile components, if any. If a liquid distils at the temperature of the boiling water bath, it is advisable to distil off this liquid on a water bath and to replace it by ether.

Place 10 ml. of the liquid mixture in a 25 ml. distilling flask arranged for distillation, and heat the flask on a boiling water bath until no more liquid passes over: redistil the distillate and if it is a single substance, identify it in the usual manner. Dissolve the residue (R) in ether and employ the same proportions as given for a solid mixture.

Step 1. Extraction and separation of any acidic components. Shake 4–5 g. of the solid mixture (or of the residue R obtained after the removal of the solvent on a water bath) with 25–30 ml. of pure ether.* If there is a residue (this probably belongs to Solubility Group II or it may be a polysaccharide), separate it by filtration, preferably through a sintered glass funnel, and wash it with a little ether. Shake the resulting ethereal solution in a small separatory funnel with 10 ml. portions of 5 per cent aqueous sodium hydroxide solution until *all* the acidic components have been removed. Two portions of alkali are usually sufficient. Wash the alkali extracted ether solution with 10 ml. of water and add the wash water to the aqueous alkaline extracts. Set aside the ethereal solution (E_1) for *Step* 2. Wash the

---

* Peroxide-free ether should be employed: for detection and removal of peroxides in diethyl ether, see Section **IV,13**.

combined sodium hydroxide extracts with 8–10 ml. of ether; place the ether in the *ETHER RESIDUES* bottle.

Render the entire alkaline extract acid to litmus with dilute sulphuric acid and then add excess of *solid* sodium bicarbonate. Alternatively, treat the sodium hydroxide extract with Dry Ice until no more is absorbed.

Separate any *phenolic or enolic compounds* which may be present by extracting the sodium bicarbonate solution with two 10 ml. portions of ether; remove the ether from the extract and examine any residue for phenols (or enols).

Cautiously acidify the residual sodium bicarbonate solution to Congo Red with dilute sulphuric acid. If a solid acid forms, filter. Extract the filtrate or the acidified solution with two 10 ml. portions of ether: keep the aqueous solution (A). Distil off the ether, and add the residual acid (if a solid) to the solid separated by filtration. Identify the acid.

Now distil the filtrate (A) and collect the distillate as long as it is acid to litmus. Should any solid separate out in the distilling flask during the distillation, add more water to dissolve it. Set aside the residue (B) in the flask. Identify the volatile acid in the distillate. A simple method is to just neutralize it with sodium hydroxide solution, evaporate to dryness and convert the residual sodium salt into the *S*-benzylthiuronium salt (*Aliphatic Carboxylic Acids*, Section **IV,20,5**).

The residue (B) in the distilling flask may still contain a water-soluble, non-volatile acid. Cool the acid solution, neutralize it with dilute sodium hydroxide solution to Congo Red, and evaporate to dryness on a water bath under reduced pressure (water pump). Heat a little of the residual salt (C) upon the tip of a nickel spatula in a Bunsen flame and observe whether any charring takes place. If charring occurs, thus indicating the presence of organic matter, extract the solid residue with 10 ml. portions of hot absolute ethyl alcohol. Evaporate the alcoholic extract and identify the material which remains. The residue (C) contains the sodium salt of a water-soluble, non-volatile acid which may be characterized as the *S*-benzylthiuronium salt.

Step 2. Extraction of any basic components. Extract the ethereal solution (E_1) with 10 ml. portions of 5 per cent hydrochloric acid until *all* the basic components have been removed: two extractions with acid are usually sufficient. Preserve the residual ethereal solution (E_2) for the separation of the neutral components. Wash the combined acid extracts with 10 ml. of ether: discard the ether extract as in

Table VII, 3, 1. General Scheme for Separation of a Mixture of Water-Insoluble Compounds

Treat the mixture with pure ether and filter, if necessary.

Residue. Examine for polysaccharides etc., according to nature of original mixture.	Filtrate or ether solution. Extract with 5 per cent NaOH solution and separate the ethereal layer.			
	Sodium hydroxide extract. This will contain the acids and phenols (or enols) present. *Either* acidify (litmus) with dilute sulphuric acid and add excess of solid sodium bicarbonate, *Or* add Dry Ice until no more is absorbed. Extract with ether.		**Ether solution.** (E_1). Extract with 5 per cent HCl. Separate the ether layer.	
	Ether solution. Contains phenolic (or enolic) compounds.	**Sodium bicarbonate solution.** Acidify with dilute H_2SO_4. (i) Filter or extract **acid** with ether. (ii) Distil aqueous solution (A) from (i) as long as distillate is acid to recover **water-soluble volatile acids.** (iii) Neutralize aqueous solution (B) from (ii), evaporate to dryness, and extract with absolute ethyl alcohol to recover **water-soluble, non-volatile compounds.** The residue may contain the sodium salt of a water-soluble, non-volatile acid.	**Hydrochloric acid extract.** This will contain any basic components present. Render alkaline with 10–20 per cent NaOH and extract with ether.	**Ether solution.** (E_2). This will contain any neutral compounds present. Dry with anhydrous magnesium sulphate, and distil off the ether. A residue indicates the presence of a **neutral component.** Determine the solubility of a portion in conc. H_2SO_4. Apply any other suitable tests.
			Ether solution. Contains water insoluble amines.	
			Aqueous solution. Will possess ammoniacal odour if water-soluble amines present. Distil as long as distillate is alkaline to recover **volatile water-soluble amines.**	

Step 1. Make the acid extract alkaline with 10–20 per cent sodium hydroxide solution: if any basic component separates, extract it with ether, evaporate the ether, and characterize the residue. If a water-soluble base is also present, it may be recognized by its characteristic ammoniacal odour: it may be isolated from the solution remaining after ether extraction of the insoluble base by distilling the aqueous solution as long as the distillate is alkaline to litmus. Identify the base with the aid of phenyl isothiocyanate or of benzenesulphonyl chloride (compare *Aromatic Amines*, Section **IV, 33**,*4*) or by other means (see *Aliphatic Amines*, Section **IV,32**).

Step 3. The neutral components. The ethereal solution (E_2) remaining after the acid extraction of *Step 2* should contain only the neutral compounds of Solubility Groups V, VI and VII (see Table III, 2, 1). Dry it with a little anhydrous magnesium sulphate and distil off the ether. If a residue is obtained, neutral compounds are present in the mixture. Test a portion of this with respect to its solubility in concentrated sulphuric acid; if it dissolves in the acid, pour the solution slowly and cautiously into ice water and note whether any compound is recovered. Examine the main residue for homogeneity and if it is a mixture, devise procedures, based for example upon differences in volatility, solubility in inert solvents, reaction with hydrolytic and other reagents, to separate the components.

The above procedure for water-insoluble mixtures is shown, in outline, in tabular form in Table VII, 3, 1. If the mixture is a liquid, any volatile solvent is assumed to have been removed.

VII, 4 Separation of a Mixture of Water-Soluble Compounds

A water-soluble mixture may be in the form of a mixture of water-soluble solids or in the form of a liquid. The liquid mixtures are frequently aqueous solutions. The preliminary examination of a liquid mixture (see Section **VII,2**) will indicate whether a volatile solvent (*i.e.*, removable on a boiling water bath) is present. If a volatile solvent is present, distil 10 g. of the mixture from a water bath until no more liquid passes over: set aside the volatile solvent for identification. Dissolve the residue (*R*) in water as detailed below for a mixture of solids.

Step 1. Distillation from acid solution and the separation of the volatile acidic and neutral compounds. Dissolve 4–5 g. of a solid mixture in 25–40 ml. of water: for a liquid mixture, use 4–5 g. of the residue (*R*) (non-volatile from a boiling water bath) and dilute with

25–40 ml. of water: for an aqueous solution use sufficient of it to contain 4–5 g. of the dissolved components and dilute, if necessary, to 25–40 ml. Acidify the solution with sufficient 20 per cent sulphuric acid to decompose the salts of all the acidic components and to ensure the presence of a slight excess of acid: many organic acids give an acid reaction with Congo Red, hence it is necessary to add the sulphuric acid somewhat beyond the point at which the mixture is acid to this indicator. If an insoluble acidic component separates, filter it off and identify it. Distil the acid solution so long as the distillate appears turbid, or is acid to litmus, or until 50–75 ml. are collected: in the last case, add more water to the contents of the distilling flask if the volume has been reduced below one-fourth of the original volume. Keep the residue (R_1) in the distilling flask for *Step 2*.

The distillate may contain volatile neutral compounds as well as volatile acids and phenols. Add a slight excess of 10–20 per cent sodium hydroxide solution to this distillate and distil until the liquid passes over clear or has the density of pure water. The presence of a volatile, water-soluble neutral compound is detected by a periodic determination of the density (see Section I,4); if the density is definitely less than unity, the presence of a neutral compound may be assumed. Keep this solution (S_1) for *Step 4*.

Cool the alkaline solution remaining from the distillation of the volatile neutral compounds, and *either* make it acid to litmus with dilute sulphuric acid, and add an excess of *solid* sodium bicarbonate *or* add Dry Ice until no more is absorbed. Extract this bicarbonate solution with two 20 ml. portions of ether; remove the ether from the combined ether extracts and identify the residual phenol (or enol). Then acidify the bicarbonate solution cautiously with dilute sulphuric acid; if an acidic compound separates, remove it by two extractions with 10 ml. portions of ether; if the acidified solution remains clear, distil and collect any water-soluble, volatile acid in the distillate. Characterize the acid as in Section VII,3.

Step 2. Distillation from alkaline solution. Treat the solution (R_1) remaining in the distilling flask after the volatile acidic and neutral compounds have been removed with 10–20 per cent sodium hydroxide solution until distinctly alkaline. If a solid separates, filter it off and identify it. Distil the alkaline solution until no more volatile bases pass over (distillate no longer turbid, or not basic to litmus: water-soluble bases also possess characteristic odours): add more water to the contents of the flask if the solution becomes too concentrated during this distillation. (Set aside the solution in the distilling

Table VII, 4, 1. General Scheme for Separation of a Mixture of Water-Soluble Compounds

Acidify the aqueous solution (25–40 ml.: prepared (a) from 4–5 g. of the solid mixture, (b) from 4–5 g. of the liquid residue (R) after distillation from a boiling water bath, or (c) from sufficient of the original aqueous solution to contain 4–5 g. of solute) with 20 per cent H_2SO_4 and distil.

Distillate. This will contain the steam-volatile acidic and neutral components present. Render alkaline with 10–20 per cent NaOH and distil.				**Aqueous acid solution (R_1).** Render alkaline with 10–20 per cent NaOH and distil.			
Distillate (S_1). This will contain the volatile neutral components present. Concentrate by distillation and saturate with solid K_2CO_3: the neutral component may separate.	**Aqueous alkaline solution.** This will contain any acids or phenols present. Cool. *Either* acidify (litmus) with dilute sulphuric acid and add excess of solid sodium bicarbonate, *Or* add Dry Ice until no more is absorbed. Extract with ether.			**Distillate.** Extract with ether.			**Aqueous alkaline solution (S_2).** Neutralize with dilute H_2SO_4 (Congo Red). Evaporate to dryness and extract with absolute ethyl alcohol. The alcoholic extract contains the water-soluble, non-volatile components.
	Ether solution. Contains phenolic compounds.	**Sodium bicarbonate solution** Acidify with dilute H_2SO_4. Extract with ether.		**Ether solution.** Contains volatile water-insoluble amines.*	**Aqueous solution.** Concentrate by distillation contains volatile water-soluble amines.*		
		Ether solution. Contains volatile water-insoluble acids.	**Aqueous solution.** Distil. The distillate may contain volatile water-soluble acids.				

* The separation of a mixture of amines by means of benzenesulphonyl chloride or *p*-toluenesulphonyl chloride (Hinsberg's procedure) is described under *Aromatic Amines* in Section **IV**,33,(vii).

flask (S_2) for *Step 3*.) If the volatile basic compounds are insoluble in water, remove them by extraction with two 20 ml. portions of ether, and identify the bases (compare *Amines*, Sections **IV,32** and **IV,33**) after evaporation on the ether. The water-soluble amines may be identified with phenyl isothiocyanate or with benzenesulphonyl chloride: it is best to concentrate the bases by redistilling and collecting the first half of the distillate separately.

Step 3. The non-steam-volatile compounds. The alkaline solution (S_2) remaining in the distilling flask from *Step 2* may contain water-soluble, non-volatile acidic, basic or neutral compounds. Add dilute sulphuric acid until the solution is just acid to Congo Red, evaporate to dryness, and extract the residual solid with boiling absolute ethyl alcohol: extraction is complete when the undissolved salt exhibits no sign of charring when heated on a metal spatula in the Bunsen flame. Evaporate the ethanolic solution to dryness and identify the residue.

Step 4. The steam-volatile neutral compounds. The solution (S_1) containing water-soluble neutral compounds obtained in *Step 1* is usually very dilute. It is advisable to concentrate it by distillation until about one-third to one-half of the original volume is collected as distillate; the process may be repeated if necessary and the progress of the concentration may be followed by determination of the densities of the distillates. It is frequently possible to salt out the neutral components from the concentrated distillate by saturating it with solid potassium carbonate. If a layer of neutral compound makes its appearance remove it. Treat this upper layer (which usually contains much water) with solid anhydrous potassium carbonate: if another aqueous layer forms, separate the upper organic layer and add more anhydrous potassium carbonate to it. Identify the neutral compound.

Notes

Some neutral compounds (*e.g.*, methyl alcohol) cannot be salted out with potassium carbonate: distillation of the saturated aqueous potassium carbonate solution frequently yields the organic compound in a comparatively pure state, or at least in sufficiently concentrated a form to enable certain derivatives to be prepared.

The above procedure for the separation of a water-soluble mixture is summarized in Table VII, 4, 1.

VII, 5 Other Methods for Separation of Mixtures of Compounds

A number of specialized methods of separation are available, the description of which is outside the scope of this volume. Nevertheless, some reference to their existence must be made and attention drawn to books where detailed information can be found. Some of the techniques can be applied to very small amounts of materials. The techniques include chromatography, vapour phase chromatography, ion exchange, electrophoresis, countercurrent distribution, zone refining, and molecular distillation. A few simple experiments are given in the author's *Elementary Practical Organic Chemistry.* Volume 1. *Small Scale Preparations,* Second Edition: these include experiments on adsorption chromatography, paper chromatography, thin layer chromatography, electrophoresis on filter paper, and ion exchange chromatography.

Chromatography

E. Lederer and M. Lederer, *Chromatography.* Second Edition. Elsevier Publishing Co., Amsterdam, 1957.

H. C. Cassidy, *Fundamentals of Chromatography* in A. Weissberger (Editor), *Technique of Organic Chemistry.* Volume X. Interscience Publishers, New York, 1957.

R. J. Block, E. L. Durrum and G. Zweig, *A Manual of Paper Chromatography and Paper Electrophoresis.* Second Edition. Academic Press, New York, 1958.

R. Stock and C. B. F. Rice, *Chromatographic Methods.* Chapman and Hall, London, 1963.

J. M. Bobbitt, *Thin Layer Chromatography.* Reinhold Publishing Corporation, New York, 1963.

K. Randerath, *Thin-Layer Chromatography.* Academic Press, New York, 1963.

E. Stahl, Editor, *Thin-Layer Chromatography. A Laboratory Handbook.* Springer Verlag, Berlin and Academic Press, New York and London, 1965.

Vapour-phase chromatography

D. Ambrose and B. A. Ambrose, *Gas Chromatography.* George Newnes, London, 1961.

S. Dal Nogare and R. S. Juvet, Jr., *Gas-Liquid Chromatography.* Interscience Publishers, New York, 1962.

A. B. Littlewood, *Gas Chromatography. Principles, Techniques and Applications.* Academic Press, New York, 1962.

H. Purnell, *Gas Chromatography.* John Wiley and Sons, New York, 1962.

Ion Exchange

C. Calmon and T. R. E. Kressman, *Ion Exchangers in Organic and Biochemistry.* Interscience Publishers, New York, 1957.

F. H. Helfferich, *Ion Exchange.* McGraw-Hill Book Co., New York, 1962.

R. Griessbach and G. Naumann, *Ionenaustauscher* in Houben-Weyl, *Methoden der Organische Chemie*, Volume 1. Fourth Edition. G. Thieme Verlag, Stuttgart, 1958.

Countercurrent Distribution

L. C. Craig and D. Craig, *Laboratory Extraction and Countercurrent Distribution* in A. Weissberger (Editor), *Technique of Organic Chemistry*, Volume III. Second Edition. Interscience Publishers, New York, 1956.

O. Jubermann, *Verteilung und Extrahieren* in Houben-Weyl, *Methoden der Organische Chemie*, Volume 1. Fourth Edition. G. Thieme Verlag, Stuttgart, 1958.

L. Alders, *Liquid–Liquid Extraction*. Second Edition. Elsevier Publishing Co., Amsterdam, 1959.

B. Keil, *Extraktion und Craig-Verteilung* in *Laboratoriumstechnik der Organischen Chemie*. Akademic-Verlag, Berlin, 1961.

R. E. Treybal, *Liquid Extraction*. Second Edition. McGraw-Hill Book Co., New York, 1963.

Electrophoresis

M. Lederer, *An Introduction to Paper Electrophoresis and Related Methods*. Second Edition. Elsevier Publishing Co., Amsterdam, 1962.

L. P. Ribeiro, E. Mitdieri and O. R. Affonso, *Paper Electrophoresis*. Elsevier Publishing Co., Amsterdam, 1961.

Zone Refining

W. G. Pfann, *Zone Melting*. Second Edition. John Wiley and Sons, New York, 1966.

E. F. G. Herrington, *Zone Melting of Organic Compounds*. W. Heffer and Sons, Cambridge, 1963.

Distillation (including Molecular Distillation)

A. Rose and E. Rose, *Distillation* in A. Weissberger (Editor) *Technique of Organic Chemistry*, Volume IV. Interscience Publishers, New York, 1951.

R. Jaekel, *Destillation und Sublimation im Fein- und Hochvakuum* in Houben-Wesyl, *Methoden der Organische Chemie*, Volume 1. Fourth Edition. G. Thieme, Verlag, Stuttgart, 1958.

K. Sigwart, *Destillatieren und Rektifizieren* in Houben-Weyl, *Methoden der Organischen Chemie*, Volume 1. Fourth Edition, 1958.

E. A. Coulson and E. F. G. Herrington, *Laboratory Distillation Practice*. George Newnes, London, 1958.

K. B. Wiberg, *Laboratory Technique in Organic Chemistry*. McGraw-Hill Book Co., New York, 1960.

CHAPTER VIII

The Use of Spectroscopic Methods in Qualitative Organic Analysis

The identification of organic compounds has been revolutionized by the availability of instruments which make it possible to measure rapidly and conveniently the ultraviolet, infrared, nuclear magnetic resonance and mass spectra of compounds with very small amounts of material. A brief discussion will be given in this Chapter of the use of ultraviolet, infrared, nuclear magnetic resonance and mass spectroscopy for the identification of functional groups: some reference will also be made to their use for the elucidation of the structure of organic compounds.

VIII, 1   The Electromagnetic Spectrum. Units

The wavelengths of electromagnetic waves of analytical interest vary from metres for short radio waves to about 10^{-8} cm. for X-rays. The electromagnetic spectrum can be conveniently divided into the regions shown in Table VIII, 1, 1.

Since ultraviolet and visible light, infrared radiation and radio waves differ greatly in wavelength, it is inconvenient to use the same units throughout to specify a position in a spectrum. A wave has associated with it both a wavelength λ and a frequency ν related by the equation

$$\nu\lambda = c$$

where c is the velocity of light (3×10^{10} cm. per second). The quantity $\bar{\nu} = 1/\lambda$ is termed the wave number, and the quantity $\nu = c/\lambda$ is the frequency expressed in reciprocal seconds (sec^{-1}). Some units of wavelength and frequency are tabulated below.

In the ultraviolet and visible regions, wavelengths are expressed in millimicrons or in Ångströms. In the infrared region, microns are employed. In radiofrequency spectra, absolute frequencies are generally used instead of wave numbers. A wavelength of 5 meters corresponds to a frequency c/λ of 6×10^7 cycles per second, which may be written 60 Mcps (megacycles per second) 1 Mc = 10^6 cycles); the corresponding wave number would be 2×10^{-3} cm^{-1}, which is

Table VIII, 1, 1. Regions of Electromagnetic Spectrum

SPECTRAL REGION	WAVELENGTH	FREQUENCY IN WAVE NUMBERS (cm^{-1})	SPECIAL PHENOMENA
Gamma rays	0·0001–0·01 mμ		Nuclear reactions
X-rays	0·01–2 mμ		Inner electron transitions
Vacuum ultraviolet	2–200 mμ	5,000,000–50,000	Ionization of atoms and molecules
Ultraviolet	200–400 mμ	50,000–25,000	Outer electron transitions
Visible	400–750 mμ	25,000–13,333	
Infrared	0·75–25 μ	13,333–400	(Stretching) Molecular vibrations (Bending)
Far infrared	25 μ–1 mm.	400–10	(Light molecules) Molecular rotation (Heavy molecules)
Microwave	1 mm.–30 cm.	10–0·033	Nuclear magnetic resonance Nuclear quadrupole resonance
Radio { Short wave	10–50 m.		
Medium wave	190–555 m.		
Long wave	1000–2000 m.		

The limitations on the extent of the various regions given above are, of course, arbitrary.

obviously a clumsy expression. In the infrared region, wave numbers are largely used, e.g., 2·50 μ = 4,000 cm^{-1}.

QUANTITY	UNIT	SYMBOL	DESCRIPTION
Wavelength	Ångström	Å	1 Å = 10^{-10} m. = 10^{-8} cm.
	Millimicron	mμ	1 mμ = 10^{-7} cm.
	Nanometer	nm	1 nm = 10^{-9} m.
	Micron	μ	1 μ = 10^{-4} cm. = 10^4 Å
Frequency	Cycles per second	cps	Vibrations per second
	Megacycles per second	Mcps	Vibrations per second × 10^{-6}
	Wave number	cm^{-1}	Reciprocal of wavelength stated in cm.

ULTRAVIOLET SPECTROSCOPY

VIII, 2 General Considerations

When a molecule absorbs ultraviolet or visible light of frequency ν or wavelength λ, an electron undergoes a transition from a lower to a higher energy level in the molecule. The energy level difference ΔE is given by the expression:

$$\Delta E = h\nu = hc/\lambda$$

where h is Planck's constant and c is the velocity of light.

By inserting the appropriate numerical values, one obtains

$$\Delta E = 286 \times 10^3/\lambda$$

ΔE being expressed in kcal/mole and λ in Ångström units. The absorption of ultraviolet and visible light corresponds to energy increments of about 30–200 kcal/mole and this coincides closely with the known range of electronic transitions; the spacings between electronic levels are relatively large. The spectra produced by electromagnetic radiations in the ultraviolet and visible region, due to the transfer (transition) of *electrons* from lower orbitals to higher orbitals, although usually called ultraviolet and visible spectra are also often described as **electronic spectra.** The spacings between the rotational and vibrational transitions of a polyatomic molecule are relatively small (about 0·1–10 kcal/mole), hence the rotational and vibrational structure is largely lost in the resulting broad absorption curve. The smaller the energy difference between the ground state and the excited state, the longer will be the wavelength of absorption.

In general, non-bonding lone-pair electrons of hetero atoms are the least strongly bound in a molecule, and in the bonding levels π-electrons have higher energy levels than the corresponding σ-electrons whilst in the antibonding levels the order is reversed (Fig. *VIII*, 2, 1).

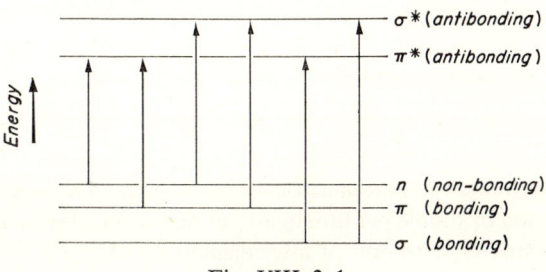

Fig. *VIII*, 2, 1.

The absorption of light energy by organic compounds in the ultraviolet and visible region involves promotion of electrons in σ, π and n orbitals (e.g., $\sigma \rightarrow \sigma^*$, $n \rightarrow \sigma^*$, $n \rightarrow \pi^*$ and $\pi \rightarrow \pi^*$). The most important transitions in organic compounds are:

(i) $\pi \rightarrow \pi^*$ in which a π (pi) electron is promoted to an antibonding π orbital (π^*, pi star). These are usually associated with multiple bonds of carbon with carbon, nitrogen, oxygen, sulphur, etc. and generally give rise to high intensity absorption.

(ii) $n \rightarrow \pi^*$ in which a non-bonding electron (lone pair) is promoted to an antibonding π orbital. These are usually associated with groups such as carbonyl, thiocarbonyl, nitroso, etc. and generally give rise to absorptions of relatively low intensity. In the spectra of simple molecules the bands due to $n \rightarrow \pi^*$ transitions lie at longer wavelengths than those arising from $\pi \rightarrow \pi^*$ excitations, whilst the $\sigma \rightarrow \sigma^*$ (sigma star) absorptions usually lie in the far ultraviolet.

VIII, 3 Law of Light Absorption. Nomenclature

The **Beer-Lambert law** states that the proportion of light absorbed by a transparent medium is independent of the intensity of the incident light and is proportional to the number of absorbing molecules in the light path:

$$\log_{10}(I_0/I) = E = acl$$

where I_0 = intensity of the incident light

I = intensity of the transmitted light

a = absorptivity

c = concentration of solute

l = cell (path) length (cm.)

E = extinction or absorbance or optical density

When c is expressed in moles per litre, the molar absorptivity or molecular extinction coefficient is denoted by ϵ, and

$$E = \epsilon cl \quad \text{or} \quad \epsilon = E/cl$$

It will be seen that ϵ is a measure of the absorbance of the solution at a concentration of 1 mole per litre in a 1 cm. cell. Beer's law is a limiting law and is strictly valid only at low concentrations.

When the molecular weight of the absorbing substance is unknown, the extinction of 1 per cent solution in a 1 cm. cell is generally used for comparison of the absorption intensities:

$$E_{1\,\text{cm.}}^{1\%} = E/cl$$

where c is in grams per 100 ml. and l is in cm. It is related to the molecular extinction coefficient by the expression

$$\epsilon = E_{1\,\text{cm.}}^{1\%} \times \text{M.W.}/10$$

Both ϵ and $E_{1\,\text{cm.}}^{1\%}$ are independent of concentration or cell length provided the Beer-Lambert law is obeyed; the latter constant does not involve the molecular weight and is therefore used for compounds of unknown or uncertain constitution.

The ultraviolet spectrum is a plot of the wavelength or frequency of absorption against the absorption intensity (optical density or absorbance $= \log_{10} I_0/I$, or of transmittance $= I/I_0$). Spectral data are also presented in which the absorption intensity is expressed as molecular extinction coefficient (or molar absorptivity) ϵ or $\log \epsilon$, i.e., a graphical plot of wavelength versus ϵ or $\log \epsilon$. The intensity of an absorption band in the ultraviolet spectrum is usually expressed as the molecular extinction coefficient ϵ or $\log \epsilon$ at maximum absorption. The smaller the difference between the ground state and the excited state, the longer will be the wavelength of absorption. The latter follows from the expression $\lambda = hc/\Delta E$. Thus absorption of light in the visible region, which is responsible for the colour of certain compounds, involves a lower energy transition as compared with absorption of light in the ultraviolet region.

VIII, 4 Solvents for Ultraviolet Spectroscopy

Organic compounds generally absorb too strongly to be used alone even in thin layers, and dilute solutions must be prepared with solvents that are transparent to ultraviolet light over the wavelength range of interest. Solvents in common use are n-hexane, n-heptane, cyclohexane, iso-octane, chloroform, water, methanol, ethanol, isopropanol, tetrahydrofuran and dioxan, all of which have transmission limits below about 2450 Å. In the far-ultraviolet, suitable solvents are n-hexane and n-heptane, which transmit sufficiently down to about 1750 Å. Certain solvents are available as 'spectroscopically pure' grade, although for some purposes analytical reagent grades are satisfactory if the cell length is small. The maximum extinction coefficient of an absorption band may be affected markedly by a change of solvent.

VIII, 5 General Discussion of Ultraviolet Spectra of Selected Organic Compounds

The use of ultraviolet spectroscopy for the identification of functional groups and of organic compounds is, unlike infrared spectroscopy, relatively limited. The information which is utilized includes a study of the shape of the absorption spectra curves; the absorbances at, and the position of, the maxima; the ratio of the absorbances at the maxima; and the changes that may occur after chemical and physical treatment.

The ultraviolet spectrum arises from electronic excitation of the molecule by the irradiating light. In general, only molecules containing multiple bonds have sufficiently stable excited states to give rise to absorption in the near ultraviolet; in consequence such spectra are diagnostic of unsaturation in the absorbing molecules. Thus saturated hydrocarbons, alcohols and ethers are transparent in this region.

Table VIII, 5, 1.   Ultraviolet absorption maxima of simple chromophoric groups

FUNCTIONAL GROUP	EXAMPLE	λ_{max}, mμ	ϵ	SOLVENT
—C≡C—	2-Octyne	223	160	Heptane
>C=C<	1-Octene	177	12,600	Heptane
>C=O	Acetaldehyde	290	17	Hexane
	Acetone	279	15	Hexane
—COOH	Acetic acid	208	32	Ethanol
—COCl	Acetyl chloride	220	100	Hexane
—CONH$_2$	Acetamide	220	63	Water
—COOR	Ethyl acetate	211	57	Ethanol
—NO$_2$	Nitromethane	274	17	Methanol
—ONO	Butyl nitrite	220	1,150	Hexane
—ONO$_2$	Butyl nitrate	270	17	Ethanol
—N=O	Nitrosobutane	300	100	Ether
>C=S	Diethyl thiocarbamate	330	205	Ethanol
>S=O	Cyclohexyl methyl sulphoxide	210	1,500	Ethanol

Monofunctional olefines, acetylenes, carboxylic acids, esters and amides have absorption spectra just outside the near ultraviolet region (at about 200 mμ) and usually show only end absorption. There is a third class of compounds, which includes aldehydes, ketones and aliphatic nitro compounds, which is characterized by absorption maxima in the near ultraviolet but they have such low intensities that they are rarely used for identification purposes. Acetone in *n*-hexane, for example, has a molecular extinction coefficient ϵ of 15 at its maximum of 279 mμ. By way of comparison, a moderately strong band will have ϵ of 1,000–10,000. Some data giving the positions of the absorption maxima and molecular extinction coefficients of some isolated (unconjugated) functional groups are collected in Table VIII, 5, 1.

Mention may be made of the **additivity principle** which states that the ultraviolet spectrum of a molecule containing two light absorbing units separated by one or more insulating units (*e.g.*, a —CH$_2$— group) is approximated closely by the addition of the spectra of the absorbing units. This principle has been helpful in structure determination.

Conjugated systems. If two or more chromophoric groups are present in a molecule and they are separated by two or more single bonds, the effect on the ultraviolet spectrum is usually additive; there is little electronic interaction between the isolated chromophoric groups.

However, if two such groups are separated by only one single bond (a conjugated system), a large effect on the spectrum results. When multiple bonds are separated by one single bond, the resulting electronic interaction may be designated π-π-conjugation. We may also have π-*p*-conjugation arising from the presence of such groups as —NR$_2$. Originally the term **chromophore** was used for unsaturated groups such as C=C, C=O, O←N=O and N=N (thought to be essential for colour) and the term **auxochrome** for groups such as —NR$_2$ and —OR (thought to play an auxiliary part in producing and modifying the colour). Nowadays the terms chromophore and auxochrome are employed to designate π-electron and *p*-electron groups respectively.

An auxochrome when attached to a chromophore alters both the wavelength and the intensity of the absorption spectrum. The following terms are frequently used:

bathochromic shift—the shift of absorption to a longer wavelength due to substituents or solvent effect;

hypsochromic shift—the shift of absorption to a shorter wavelength due to substituents or solvent effect;

hyperchromic effect—an increase in absorption intensity;

hypochromic effect—a decrease in absorption intensity.

Some typical results for two chromophores in conjugation are collected in Table VIII, 5, 2.

Table VIII, 5, 2.   Ultraviolet absorption due to two conjugated chromophores

SYSTEM	EXAMPLE	λ_{max}, mμ	ϵ	SOLVENT
C=C—C=C	Butadiene	217	21,000	Hexane
C=C—C≡C	Vinylacetylene	219	7,600	Hexane
C=C—C=O	Crotonaldehyde	217	16,000	Ethanol
		320	20	Ethanol
C≡C—C=O	1-Hexyne-3-one	214	4,500	Ethanol
		308	20	Ethanol
C=C—C=N	N-Butylcrotonaldimine	219	25,000	Hexane
C=C—C≡N	1-Cyanocyclohexene	211	11,000	Ethanol
O=C—C=O	Diacetyl	435	18	Hexane
C=C—NO$_2$	1-Nitro-1-propene	229	9,500	Ethanol
C=C—COOH	cis-Crotonic acid	206	13,500	Ethanol
		242	250	Ethanol
C≡C—COOH	n-Butylpropiolic acid	210	6,000	Ethanol

Table VIII, 5, 3.   Ultraviolet and visible absorption maxima for miscellaneous ring systems

COMPOUND	λ_{max}, mμ	ϵ	λ_{max}, mμ	ϵ
Benzene	255	230		
Pyridine	250	2,000		
Pyrimidine	243	3,000	275	300
Pyrazine	260	5,200	311	580
Naphthalene	276	5,600	312	250
Biphenyl	250	18,000		
Quinoline	275	4,500	311	6,300
Isoquinoline	262	3,700	318	3,600
Anthracene	252	200,000	375	8,000
Acridine	252	170,000	347	7,000
Phenazine	250	120,000	370	1,600
Phenanthrene	252	63,000	330	800
Phenanthridine	248	50,000	328	2,000

Aromatic systems. Benzene absorbs strongly at 184 mμ ($\epsilon = 47,000$) and at 200 mμ ($\epsilon = 8000$), and has a series of bands between 230 and 270 mμ of relatively low intensity of which that at 255 mμ ($\epsilon = 230$ in cyclohexane) is notable. Some data for miscellaneous ring systems are given in Table VIII, 5, 3.

A discussion of the influence of substituents upon the ultraviolet spectra of benzenoid compounds is outside the scope of this book but a few typical data are collected in Table VIII, 5, 4.

Table VIII, 5, 4.   Ultraviolet and visible absorption maxima of substituted benzenes

COMPOUND	λ_{max}, mμ	ϵ	λ_{max}, mμ	ϵ	SOLVENT
Benzene	200	8,000	255	230	Hexane
Chlorobenzene	210	7,500	280	1,000	Ethanol
Iodobenzene	226	13,000	256	800	Ethanol
Nitrobenzene	252	10,000	280	1,000	Hexane
Aniline	230	8,600	280	1,430	Water
Acetanilide	242	14,000	280	500	Ethanol
N-Methylaniline	245	11,600	295	1,800	Ethanol
NN-Dimethylaniline	251	14,000	298	1,900	Ethanol
Phenol	211	6,200	270	1,450	Water
Benzaldehyde	244	15,000	280	1,500	Ethanol
Acetophenone	240	13,000	278	1,100	Ethanol
Benzoic acid	230	10,000	270	800	Water
Cinnamic acid			273	20,000	Ethanol
Styrene	244	12,000	282	450	Ethanol
Phenylacetylene	236	12,500	278	650	Hexane

VIII, 6   Identification of Functional Groups from a Knowledge of Positions of Ultraviolet Absorption Maxima

Ultraviolet absorption spectra can provide information that can help in the identification of functional groups in an organic compound in two ways:

(i) by empirical correlations of absorption bands with known chromophores, and

(ii) by comparison with spectra of known or 'model' compounds. A few examples of interesting applications follow.

Quinoline reacts with cyanogen bromide and hydrogen cyanide to give two dicyanides of m.p. 100° and 135° respectively and which were believed to have the structures (I) and (II).

(I)

(II)

(III)

(IV)

No unambiguous degradative or synthetic method was available to decide which quinoline dicyanide was (I) and which was (II). A model

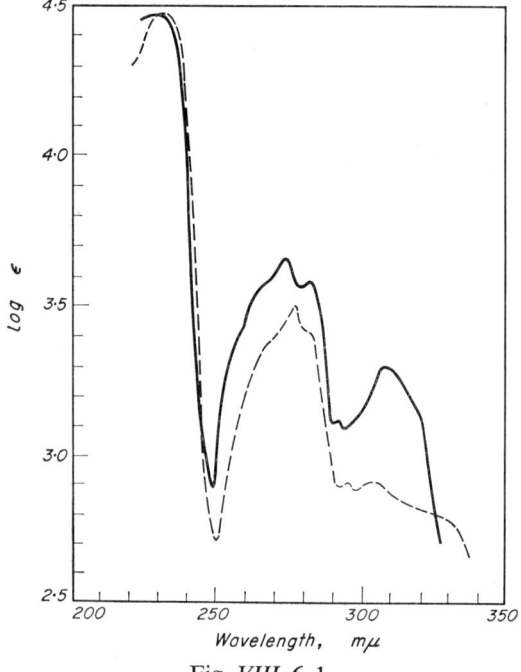

Fig. *VIII*, 6, 1.

substance for (I) was selected as phenylcyanamide (III) and N-methyl-o-styrylcyanamide (IV) was chosen as a model substance for (II). Comparison of the ultraviolet absorption spectra (Fig. *VIII*, 6, 1—the low m.p. isomer is the full line, (III) is the broken line; Fig. *VIII*, 6, 2—the high m.p. isomer is the full line, (IV) is the broken line) shows clearly that the low m.p. isomer is (I) and the high m.p. isomer is (II).

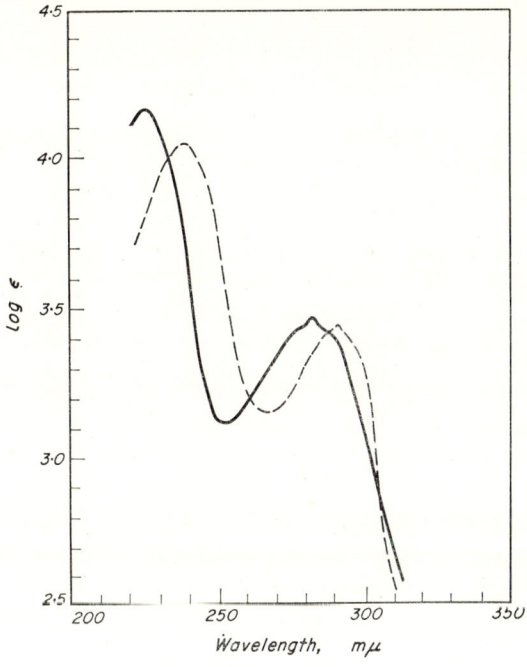

Fig. *VIII*, 6, 2.

The action of carbon disulphide upon acetaldehyde and ammonia gives the compound 'carbothialdine' to which the structures (V) and (VI) were assigned but it was not possible to decide by chemical means which of the two structures is correct.

The chief difference, spectroscopically, between the two structures is in the chromophores

$$HN-\overset{\displaystyle S}{\underset{\displaystyle \parallel}{C}}-S- \text{ in (V)} \quad \text{and} \quad N=\overset{\displaystyle S-}{\underset{\displaystyle |}{C}}-S- \text{ in (VI)}.$$

The model compounds (VII) and (VIII)

$$Me_2N-\overset{\displaystyle S}{\underset{\displaystyle \parallel}{C}}-SMe \text{ (VII)} \quad \text{and} \quad MeN=\overset{\displaystyle SMe}{\underset{\displaystyle |}{C}}-SMe \text{ (VIII)}$$

were prepared and their ultraviolet spectra examined. The results are tabulated below.

	λ_{max}, mμ	ϵ_{max}
'Carbothialdine'	288; 243	12,800; 5,000
(VII)	276; 246	10,000; 8,000
(VIII)	217	8,000

Hence units of type (VII) must be present and 'carbothialdine' has structure (V).

Of a pair of **geometrical isomers**, the *cis* form would be expected to be more sterically hindered than the *trans* form. Data obtained for *cis* and *trans* isomers show that the $\pi-\pi^*$ transition of the *trans* isomer occurs at longer wavelengths and has a larger extinction coefficient than the *cis* isomer, this qualitative relationship may be used to assign geometrical configuration to ethylenic systems. Some data are given in Table VIII, 6, 1.

Table VIII, 6, 1.   Ultraviolet absorption of *cis* and *trans* isomers

	Cis ISOMER		*Trans* ISOMER	
	λ_{max}, mμ	ϵ	λ_{max}, mμ	ϵ
Stilbene	276	10,000	301	28,500
Cinnamic acid	264	9,500	273	21,000
Phenyl styryl ketone	289	8,900	298	24,000
Azobenzene	281	5,260	320	21,300

In conjugated systems the intensities and positions of the absorption maxima depend upon the length of the conjugated systems; the longer such a system, the greater is λ_{max} and also ϵ. When the π-electron system is prevented from achieving coplanarity, the degree of overlap of the π-orbital system will be diminished and there is a marked effect on the ultraviolet spectrum. Hindered rotation in biphenyls may thus be studied. The π–π* transition of biphenyl, which readily achieves coplanarity, results in λ_{max} 251 mμ, $\epsilon = 16{,}300$; this is not the sum of the extinctions of two benzene rings. If large groups are present in the *ortho* positions, hindered rotation results, and attainment of coplanarity is rendered more difficult, and the length of the π-electron system is effectively diminished or, otherwise expressed, resonance interaction between the two rings is inhibited. Thus bimesityl (2,4,6,2',4',6'-hexamethylbiphenyl) shows λ_{max} 267 mμ, $\epsilon = 545$—an extinction coefficient only twice that of mesitylene itself (λ_{max} 267 mμ, $\epsilon = 260$).

An interesting application is to **tautomeric systems.** Tautomerism, *i.e.*, the existence of a substance as an equilibrium mixture of two or more readily interconvertible isomers, usually involves the migration of double bonds. The classical example is ethyl acetoacetate which can exist in the keto form (I) or the enol form (II); the former exhibits absorption typical of an isolated keto group whilst the latter

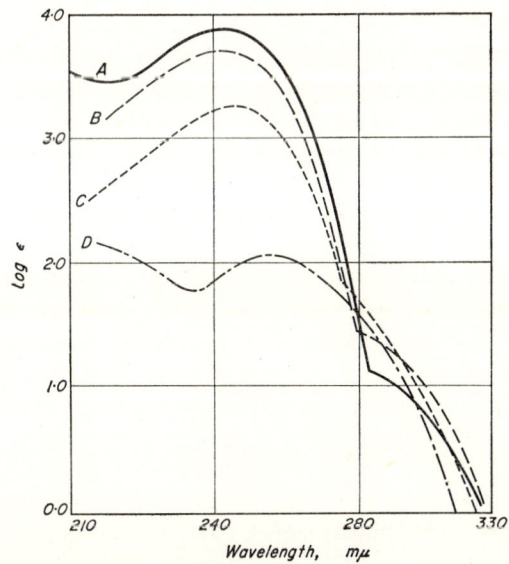

Fig. *VIII*, 6, 3.
(A = hexane, B = ether, C = ethanol, D = water.)

shows the high intensity associated with the conjugated system HO—C=C—COOEt.

$$\underset{\substack{\| \\ O \\ \lambda_{max}, 275\ m\mu,\ \epsilon = 16}}{\text{MeC—CH}_2\text{COOEt}} \quad (I) \qquad \underset{\substack{| \\ OH \\ \lambda_{max}, 244\ m\mu,\ \epsilon = 16{,}000}}{\text{MeC=CHCOOEt}} \quad (II)$$

The absorption curves of ethyl acetoacetate in various solvents are shown in Fig. *VIII, 6, 3*; the proportions of the two forms in these solvents are readily estimated from the curves.

VIII, 7 Instruments

The essential components of any spectrophotometer are a source of radiant energy, a monochromator, a cell or sample compartment, a detector and an amplifier for measuring the radiant energy; in the more expensive instruments a recorder is included. Most commercial apparatus used for ultraviolet spectrophotometry also cover the visible region and therefore generally use two light sources—a deuterium or hydrogen discharge lamp for the region 200 mμ to 370 mμ and a tungsten filament lamp for the region 325 mμ to 1000 mμ. A monochromator is a device to isolate monochromatic or narrow bands of radiant energy derived from the source; it incorporates a quartz or fused silica prism or a grating. Quartz or fused silica vary slightly in transparency at lower wavelengths and consequently the lowest wavelength at which monochromators of the prism type may be used varies from 180 to 220 mμ. The radiation that passes through the cell compartment falls on to the detector which may consist of photosensitive cells or a photomultiplier tube; the detector is followed by a suitable amplifying circuit. The cell compartment consists of a light-proof box and contains a platform carrying the cells or cell holders; the platform can be moved by means of an external control so that several cells are brought into the beam in turn. Cells for holding samples in the light beam are usually entirely of fused silica or quartz, or have end plates of this material. They are available in a variety of shapes and sizes ranging from 1 mm. to several cm. in length: a cell of 1 mm. path requires *ca.* 0·3 ml. of solution when full. Typical commercial manual ultraviolet and visible spectrophotometers include the Unicam SP-500, Beckman quartz Model DU and the Hilger Uvispek*. For routine work in qualitative

---

* A description of these instruments is given in the author's *Text-Book of Quantitative Inorganic Analysis including Elementary Instrumental Analysis*, Third Edition, Longmans, Green and Co. Ltd., 1961.

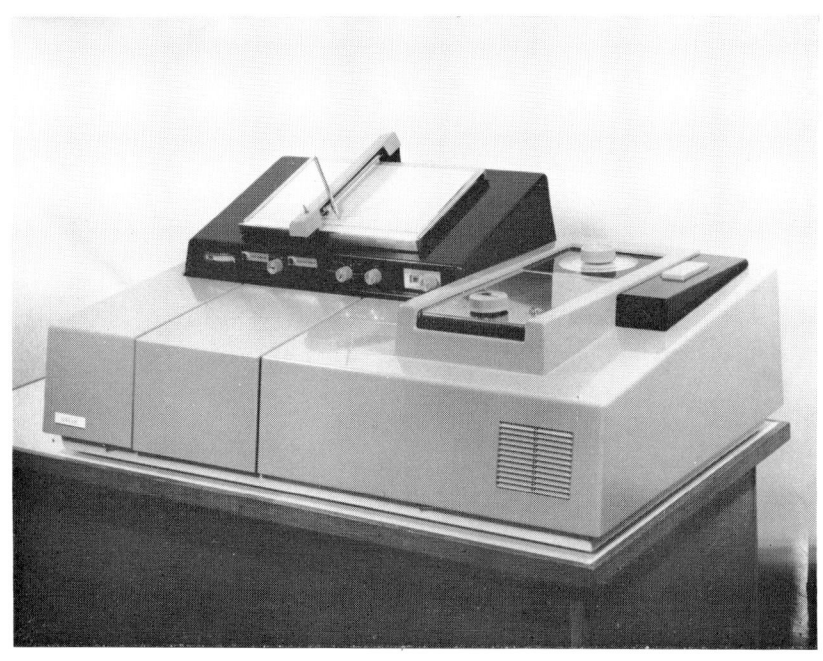

Fig. *VIII*, 7, 1. Unicam SP. 800 Ultraviolet and Visible Recording Spectrophotometer.

Ultraviolet Spectroscopy

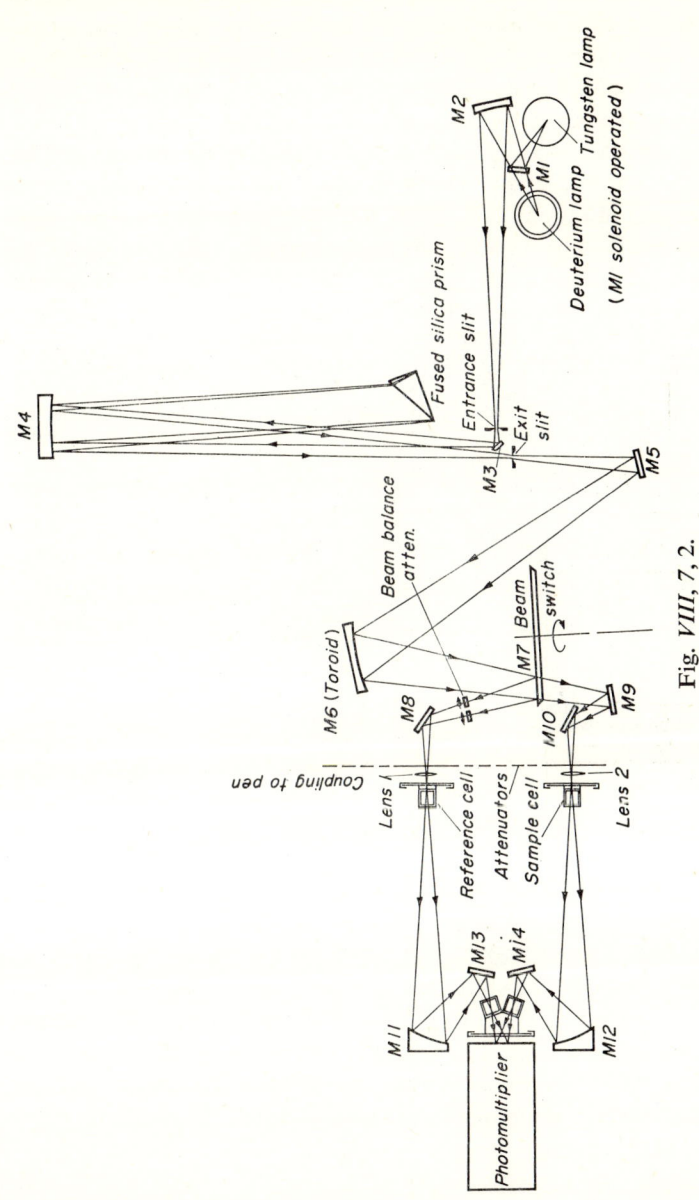

Fig. VIII, 7, 2.

organic analysis, a double beam spectrophotometer (which incorporates a recorder) is preferable. Here the cell compartment provides accommodation *inter alia* for two cells, the sample cell and the reference cell. The light beam is split into two equal parts that pass through the respective cells to separate detectors, or the light beam is directed alternately through the sample and reference cells and then to the same detector. The author has found the **Unicam SP.800 recording ultraviolet and visible recording spectrophotometer*** highly satisfactory. Fig. *VIII*, 7, 1 is a photograph of the instrument, Fig. *VIII*, 7, 2 presents the optics and Fig. *VIII*, 7, 3 is a block diagram showing the essential functional components. The instrument

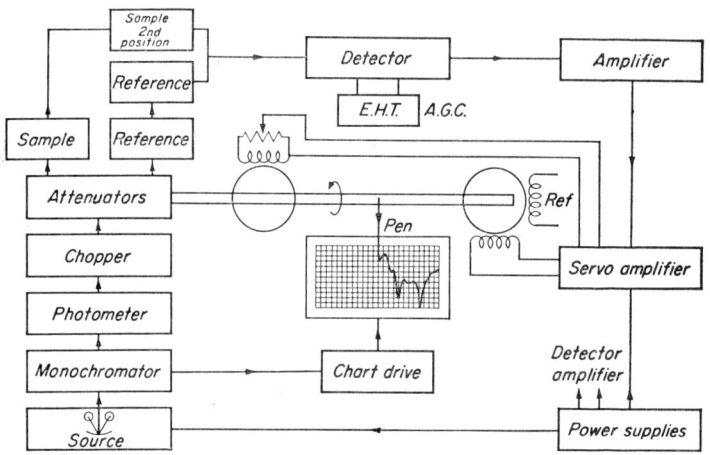

Fig. *VIII*, 7, 3.

automatically records absorbance against wavelength (No. SP 800A, 190–700 mμ; No. SP 800B; 190–850 mμ) or against wave number (SP 800C, 52,500–14,000 cm^{-1}; SP 800D, 52,500–11,500 cm^{-1}); the scales are linear. The ultraviolet source is an air-cooled high-energy deuterium arc; the second source is a tungsten filament lamp and automatic interchange takes place at 370 mμ. It incorporates a double beam null balance optical system. The 60° fused silica prism is thermostatted at 35°C to minimize calibration drift. The chart recorder is flat and the complete spectral range is scanned on two charts (foolscap size) with overlap between them; there are two scan speeds of 2 and 8

---

* Supplied by Unicam Instruments Ltd., York Street, Cambridge. Other satisfactory instruments include the Infracord 137UV (Perkin-Elmer Ltd., Beaconsfield, Bucks) and the Spectronic 505 (Bausch and Lomb, Rochester 2, New York).

minutes. In addition, a scale expansion device is available as well as various automatic accessories. Complete details are given in the Instruction Manual supplied with the instrument.

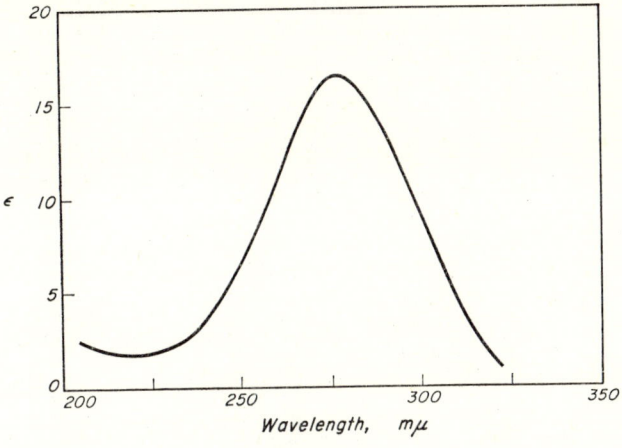

Fig. *VIII*, 7, 4.

Some typical ultraviolet spectra obtained with the Unicam SP 800 are shown in Figs. *VIII*, 7, 4 to *VIII*, 7, 7.

Fig. *VIII*, 7, 4 is ethyl methyl ketone in *n*-hexane. The band at 277 mμ is due to the excitation of an electron from one of the unshared electron pairs on oxygen, a $\pi \to \pi^*$ transition. The band for the

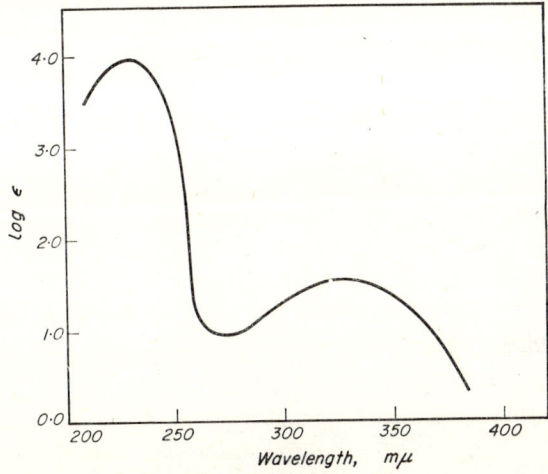

Fig. *VIII*, 7, 5.

carbonyl group is at about 185 mμ, which is outside the normal range of the spectrophotometer.

Fig. *VIII*, 7, 5 is mesityl oxide, $(CH_3)_2C{=}CHCOCH_3$, in *n*-hexane.

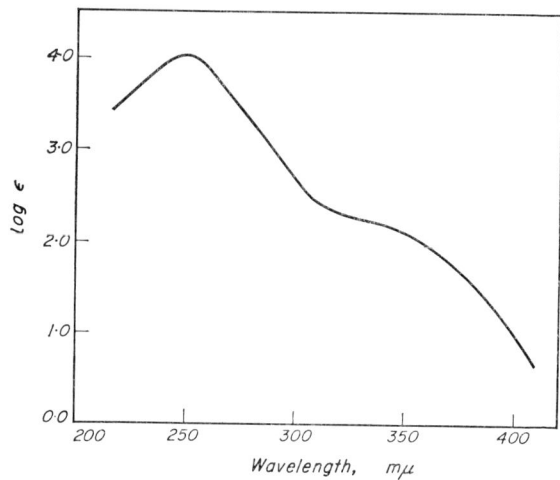

Fig. *VIII*, 7, 6.

The compound is a conjugated unsaturated ketone (*i.e.*, contains a carbon-carbon double bond in conjugation with a carbonyl group) and gives rise to a high intensity maximum at λ_{max} 227 mμ ($\epsilon = 10^4$) and a broad low intensity absorption band at about 330 mμ.

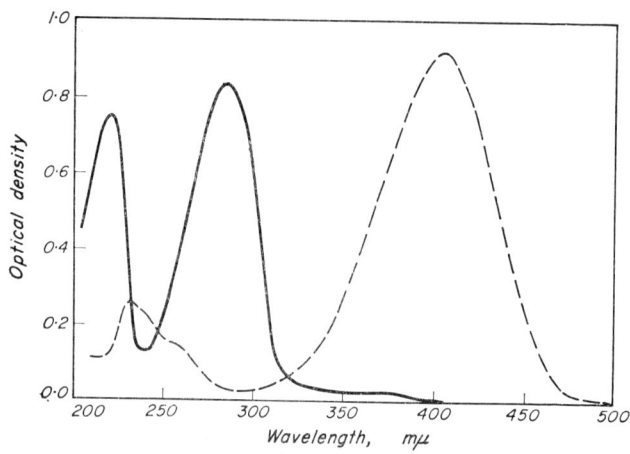

Fig. *VIII*, 7, 7.

Fig. *VIII*, 7, 6 is nitrobenzene in *n*-hexane, which shows a high intensity band at 251 mμ.

Fig. *VIII*, 7, 7 is *p*-nitrophenol in *n*-hexane. There is a high intensity band at 290 mμ; in alkaline solution (0·1 *N* sodium hydroxide) this band (dotted line) is shifted to the visible, 402 mμ, to give a yellow solution.

The above account is intended to serve as a brief introduction to the subject: further information will be found in the Selected Bibliography given below.

SELECTED BIBLIOGRAPHY

1. A. E. Gillam and E. S. Stern, *An Introduction to Electronic Absorption Spectroscopy in Organic Chemistry*. Second Edition. Edward Arnold, London, 1957.
2. E. A. Braude and F. Nachod (Editors), *Determination of Organic Structures by Physical Methods*. Chapter IV. *Ultraviolet and Visible Light Absorption* by E. A. Braude. Academic Press, New York, 1955.
3. G. H. Beaven, E. A. Johnson, H. A. Willis and R. G. J. Miller, *Molecular Spectroscopy. Methods and Applications in Chemistry*. Heywood and Company, London, 1961.
4. H. H. Jaffe and M. Orchin, *Theory and Applications of Ultraviolet Spectroscopy*. John Wiley, New York, 1962.
5. R. Baumann, *Absorption Spectroscopy*. John Wiley, New York, 1962.
6. C. R. N. Strouts, H. N. Wilson and R. T. Parry-Jones, *Chemical Analysis. The Working Tools*. Volume II. Chapter 24. *Ultraviolet Absorption Spectroscopy*. Clarendon Press, Oxford, 1962.
7. S. F. Mason, 'Molecular Electronic Absorption Spectra', *Quarterly Reviews*, 1961, 15, 287.

INFRARED SPECTROSCOPY

VIII, 8 Elementary Theory

Infrared radiation refers broadly to that of wavelength between 1 μ and 100 μ. The limited portion of infrared radiation between 2·5 μ and 15 μ (4000 cm^{-1} and 660 cm^{-1}) is of greatest practical use to the organic chemist: this range is obtained with the aid of a sodium chloride prism or a suitable grating.

Infrared radiation is absorbed and converted by an organic molecule into energy of molecular vibration. A single vibrational energy change is accompanied by a number of rotational energy changes and consequently vibrational spectra appear as bands rather than as lines. We are concerned largely with vibrational bands occurring between 2·5 μ and 15 μ. Band positions are presented either as wavelengths (microns, μ) or as wave numbers ($\bar{\nu}$, expressed as reciprocal centimetres, cm^{-1}): $\bar{\nu} = 10^4 \times 1/\lambda$. Band intensities are expressed either as transmittance T (the ratio of the radiant power transmitted by a sample to the radiant power incident on the sample) or the absorbance A {the logarithm to base 10 of the reciprocal of the transmittance, $A = \log_{10}(1/T)$}.

The positions of atoms in molecules may be regarded as mean equilibrium positions and the bonds between atoms may be considered as analogous to springs subject to stretching and bending. Each atom or group of atoms in a molecule oscillates about a point at which the attraction of nuclei for electrons balances the repulsion of nuclei by nuclei and electrons by electrons. These oscillations have natural periods which depend upon the masses of the atoms and the strengths of the bonds involved. The amplitude of the oscillations can be increased by supplying energy by means of electromagnetic radiation. Nuclei and electrons bear electric charges, the force required can be supplied by the oscillating electric vector of an electromagnetic wave of frequency and phase matching those of a particular molecular vibration. Transfer of energy in this way is possible if a change in amplitude of that vibration results in a change of molecular dipole moment (the dipole moment may be regarded as analogous to the coupling mechanism of a spring): radiant energy is then absorbed and the intensity of radiation at this particular wavelength is decreased on passing through the compound. The intensity of absorption bands depends upon the magnitude of the change in dipole moment of the bond during the transition and also is directly proportional to the number of bonds in the molecule responsible for the absorption band.

Thus hydrogen or carbon bonded to oxygen or nitrogen results in strong infrared absorption because of the polarity of the bonds. No absorption results from stretching vibrations if a homonuclear double or triple bond is symmetrically substituted. In addition to the bands resulting from fundamental modes of vibration, **overtones** may appear at wavelengths that are approximately a multiple of the fundamental frequency. These bands are usually very weak but the intensity may amount to as much as 10 per cent of that of the fundamental frequency; if the latter is a strong band, the overtone may be as strong as some of the weaker bands produced by fundamental vibrations. In addition, combinations of fundamental frequencies are observed.

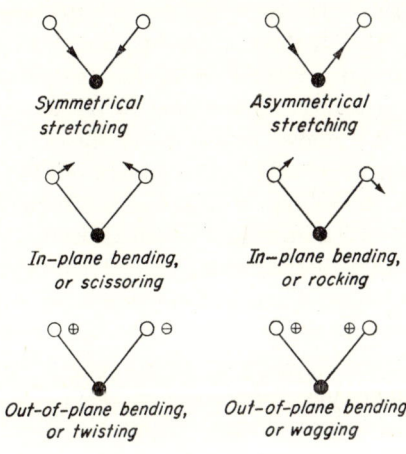

Fig. *VIII*, 8, 1.

There are two main types of molecular vibration: stretching and bending. A stretching vibration is a vibration along a bond axis such that the distance between the two atoms is decreased or increased. A bending vibration involves a change in bond angles. Only those motions which involve a change in the dipole moment of the molecule give rise to absorption in the infrared. It is the net change in charge distribution within the molecule, produced by stretching and bending, which renders possible interaction between the molecule and infrared radiation. The various stretching and bending modes for an $-AX_2$ or $>AX_2$ group, in which A is attached to other atoms or groups, are shown in Fig. *VIII*, 8, 1. Arrows indicate periodic oscillations in the directions shown. The $\oplus$ and $\ominus$ signs represent, respectively, relative movement at right angles to the surface of the page.

Stretching vibrations, as already pointed out, resemble the oscillations of two bodies connected by a spring. For a diatomic molecule A—B, the only vibration that can occur is a periodic stretching along the A—B bond. The two masses and their connecting bond may be treated, to a first approximation, as two masses joined by a spring and Hooke's law may be applied. This leads to the expression for the frequency of vibration $\bar{\nu}$ in wavenumbers (cm^{-1}):

$$\bar{\nu} = \frac{1}{2\pi c}\left(\frac{f}{m_A m_B/(m_A+m_B)}\right)^1$$

where c is the velocity of light (cm./sec.$^{-1}$), f is the force constant of the bond (in dynes/cm.) and m_A and m_B the masses (in g.) of the atoms A and B respectively*. The value of f is $ca.$ 5×10^5 dynes/cm. for single bonds and about two or three times this value for double and triple bonds respectively: it is a measure of the resistance of the bond to stretching and is roughly proportional to the energy of the bond. Application of the above equation to C—H stretching, using 19.8×10^{-24} g. and 1.64×10^{-24} g. as masses values for C and H respectively and accepted values of c and f, gives a frequency of 3040 cm^{-1} (3.29 mμ). The C—H stretching vibration associated with methyl and methylene groups are observed in the general region between 2975 and 2860 cm^{-1} (3.36–3.50 μ). The calculation is not precise because effects arising from the environment of the C—H within a molecule have been ignored.

A non-linear molecule of n atoms has $3n-6$ possible fundamental vibrations. The theoretical number of fundamental vibrations (absorption frequencies) will not always be observed for various reasons which need not be discussed here. Calculations have shown that specific absorption bands for particular bonds or groups within a molecule occur near the expected frequencies. Fairly constant shifts of band frequency have been correlated with certain structural or external environment. These results form the basis of qualitative work in organic chemistry.

Less energy is required to produce bending than stretching vibrations of the same bond; bending vibrations are therefore found at

---

* The expression is sometimes written in the form:

$$\bar{\nu} = \frac{1}{2\pi c}\left(\frac{f}{\mu}\right)^{1/2};$$

μ is the *reduced mass* of the system and is defined by

$$\mu = m_A m_B/(m_A+m_B)$$

where m_A and m_B are the individual masses (in g.) of A and B.

lower frequencies. Hydrogen bonding decreases stretching frequencies and increases bending frequencies.

VIII, 9 Uses of Infrared Spectroscopy

The main uses of interest in organic analysis are:

(1) *Identification of a compound.* The infrared spectrum of a compound is characteristic of that compound and may be used for identification provided the spectra of the known and unknown compounds are obtained under the same physical conditions, *e.g.*, in solution or in the solid state. It is advisable (i) to use equal concentrations of pure substances and compare spectra in two different media, *e.g.*, mull and solution or disc and solution and (ii) obtain spectra at concentrations high enough to permit comparison of minor peaks. The region 7·4–11·1 μ (1350–900 cm^{-1}) contains many absorptions caused by bending vibrations as well as absorptions caused by characteristic stretching vibrations (*e.g.*, C—C, C—O and C—N): the origin of all of these numerous bands is not easily determined but nevertheless they are characteristic of the compound and for this reason the zone 7·4–11·1 μ is often called the **fingerprint region.** Although similar molecules may give similar spectra in the region 2·5–7·0 μ (4000–1430 cm^{-1}), there will usually be discernible differences in the fingerprint region.

(2) *Identification of functional groups.* Many stretching and bending motions are virtually independent of changes of structure in other parts of the molecule. Thus the absorption maximum originating from the carbon–oxygen stretching of the C═O group in acetone is almost at the same frequency as for di-*n*-heptyl ketone. The characteristic frequencies of groups are affected slightly by electrical effects and by steric effects. Characteristic group frequencies are very useful when the spectrum of an unknown compound has been obtained. Thus if a spectrum contains a strong band at 1705–1720 cm^{-1}, the compound almost certainly contains a carbonyl group. The band by itself does not always provide information as to the exact nature of the group—whether an aldehyde, ketone, acid or an ester. The spectrum must be examined in detail for other diagnostic absorption bands and used in conjunction, where possible, with classical chemical reactions. Negative evidence is of great value: if the compound does not contain an absorption band of a certain group, the molecule does not contain that functional group. Many of the absorption bands in the infrared cannot be interpreted with confidence: details of characteristic

frequencies of typical functional groups are collected in Table VIII, 11, 1 and in Section **VIII,12**.

(3) *Determination of purity*. If the pure compound is available for a reference spectrum, direct comparison is possible. The presence of impurities will cause reduced sharpness of individual bands, a general blurring of the spectrum and the appearance of additional bands. The detection of impurities is limited by the relatively small extinction coefficients in the infrared and it is unusual for less than about 0·5 per cent of an impurity to be revealed by an infrared spectrum. An approximate curve for the impurities is produced by a subtraction procedure based upon the pure compound (reference beam) and the impure sample (sample beam of the instrument): this may allow identification of the impurities.

(4) *Determination of molecular structure*. Provided the molecular formula is known, it is frequently possible to interpret infrared spectra so as to provide a basis for the assignment of molecular structure, particularly of relatively simple compounds. Thus the lactam structure of 2- and 4-hydroxypyridines have been established by this means: also for 2- and 4-aminopyridines, only bands for the amino —NH_2 group are present and there is no evidence for the imino form.

VIII, 10 Instrumentation and Sample Handling

For routine work in the organic chemistry laboratory the **Unicam grating infrared spectrophotometer SP 200G*** is highly satisfactory. The instrument is depicted in Fig. *VIII, 10*, 1, its optical system in Fig. *VIII, 10*, 2, and a block diagram in Fig. *VIII, 10*, 3. This is a null-balance double beam instrument which produces a continuous record of the transmittance (energy transmitted by the sample/energy incident upon the sample) as a function of wavelength. The monochromator employs two gratings, used in their first order only. These are combined with a series of interference filters which automatically eliminate higher orders of radiation. The full coverage 4000–650cm^{-1} (2·5–15·4μ) is divided into two ranges: 4000–1300 cm^{-1} (2·5–7·7μ) and 2000–650 cm^{-1} (5·0–15·4μ), either of which is selected at the control panel switch and may be recorded on separate charts. Three scanning speeds, corresponding to 5, 10 and 30 minutes per range, can be selected by a second switch. The instrument is provided with a flat chart

---

* Manufactured by Unicam Instruments Ltd., York Street, Cambridge. The Perkin–Elmer Model 237 is a similar grating infrared spectrophotometer and is equally satisfactory for general use: it is supplied by Perkin–Elmer Ltd., Beaconsfield, Bucks.

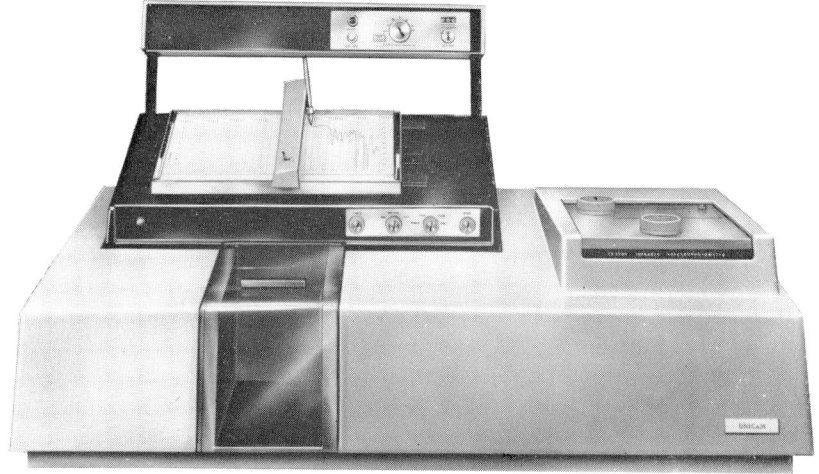

Fig. *VIII*, *10*, 1. Unicam SP. 200G Recording Infrared Spectrophotometer.

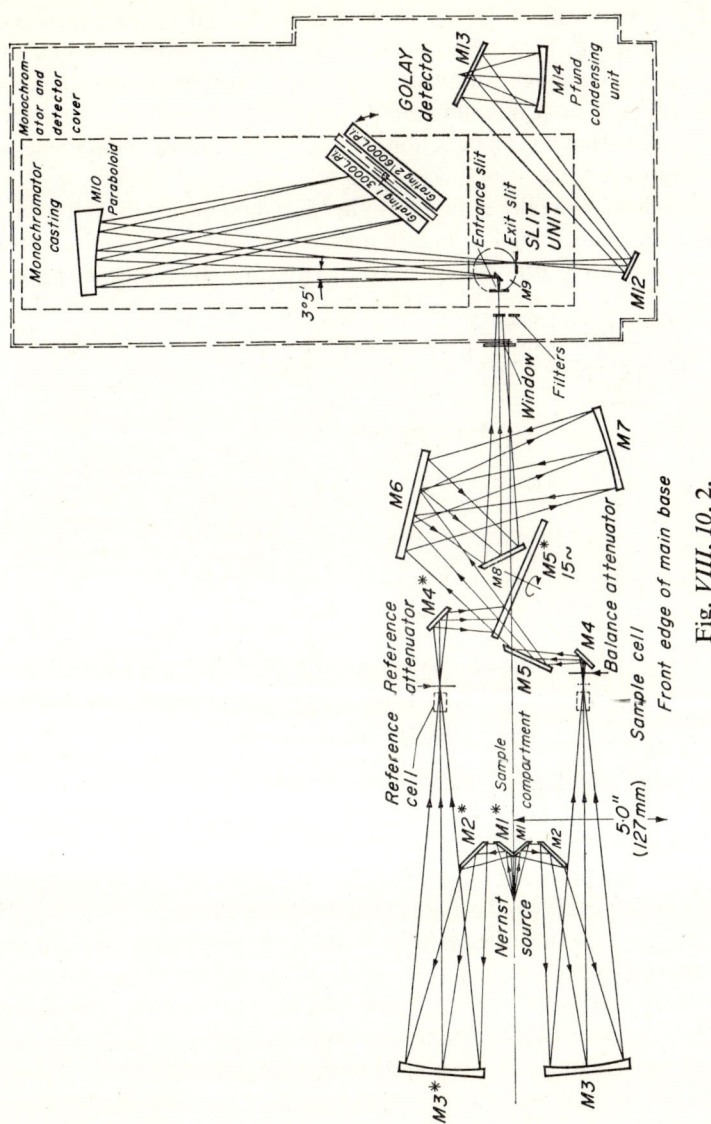

Fig. VIII, 10, 2.

recorder which, apart from obvious advantages of visibility at all times, etc., permits the simultaneous production of carbon copies.

No details will be given concerning the actual operation of the instrument and the various cells as these are fully described in the Instruction Manual supplied with the instrument. Some general remarks on sample handling are, however, desirable. It may be noted that the instrument can be calibrated with a thin film of polystyrene or with indene.

Solids are generally examined either as a mull or in an alkali halide disc. For *mulls*, Nujol (a high b.p. fraction from petroleum) is most commonly used, although when it is desired to study frequency ranges

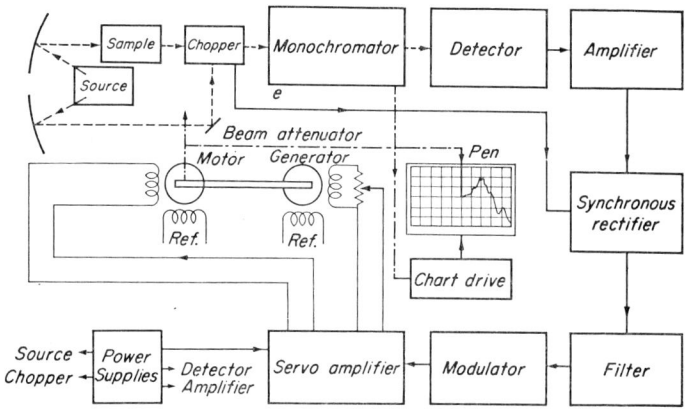

Fig. *VIII*, 10, 3.

in which Nujol absorption bands appear, Fluorolube (perfluorokerosene, a mixture of fluorinated hydrocarbons) or hexachlorobutadiene is employed.

Mulls are prepared by grinding about 2·5 mg. of the solid sample with one drop of Nujol using a clean dry pestle and mortar (preferably of agate): care must be taken that the larger aggregates of solid are continuously brought back to the centre of the mortar. The mull is transferred to a rock-salt plate by means of a fine spatula or a razor blade, then covered by a second plate which is pressed lightly to force the mull to spread as a thin film; the plates are then placed in the sample beam of the spectrophotometer, being retained there in a cell plate holder. Alkali halide plates are attacked by moisture; they should be stored in desiccators and handled appropriately: the breath, or moisture from the operator's fingers, can damage the plate surface. Cleaning after use is achieved by brief immersion of the plates in dry chloroform or other dry solvent and rapid drying with lens tissue or other dry, soft material (*e.g.*, 'Kleenex'). This operation is greatly facilitated by working near a suitable infrared heating lamp.

Pressed discs are made by intimately grinding together about 1 mg. of the sample and about 100 mg. of carefully dried potassium chloride or bromide. Pressing is usually carried out in a commercially available die-assembly under pressures of 20,000 to 50,000 lbs. per square inch. The resulting disc is mounted in a holder and held in the sample beam path. Dies must be scrupulously cleaned after use to remove all traces of alkali halide; the latter corrodes stainless steel.

Pure liquids may be examined between plates, with or without spacers (0·005–0·1 mm. thick). A small drop of the liquid is placed on a sodium chloride plate and spread as in the mull technique described above: the spectrum is then determined as a thin liquid film. Volatile liquids can be examined in sealed cells. The amount of material required is usually 1–10 mg.

Solutions of either solids or liquids are handled in cells of 0·1 mm. to 1 mm. thickness. Concentrations are generally between 0·05 per cent and 10 per cent; the amount of solid required is 1–15 mg. The solution is transferred to the cell by means of a small pipette or hypodermic syringe. Chloroform, carbon tetrachloride and carbon disulphide are the solvents most commonly employed. Solution cells (0·1 mm.–1 cm. thickness) are of two types: fully assembled sealed cells of fixed path length, and demountable or variable path cells, the separate components of which are assembled by the operator for each spectrum. Variable path cells are more easily cleaned and the plate surfaces may be polished prior to each spectrum. Fixed path cells are cleaned by repeated flushing with the solvent.* In practice it is found that most of the solution spectra may be obtained with the same path length (*ca.* 0·5 mm.). A set of four pairs with path lengths of 0·05, 0·1, 0·5 and 1·0 mm. will suffice for most purposes. Whenever solution cells are used, a compensation cell containing an equal thickness of solvent is necessary in the reference beam; the recorded spectrum is that of the solute except in those regions where the solvent absorbs strongly.

Some **typical infrared spectra**† are collected in Figs. *VIII, 10*, 4 to *VIII, 10*, 8: these incorporate selected functional groups. A few notes

* The excess of solvent is removed in a gentle stream of dry air whilst the cell is exposed to an infrared heating lamp.

† All, except Fig. *VIII, 10*, 4, *C*, were obtained with a Unicam SP 200G spectrophotometer: a Perkin–Elmer Infracord Model 137 was used for 1-hexyne. Unless otherwise stated, all compounds were examined as thin films.

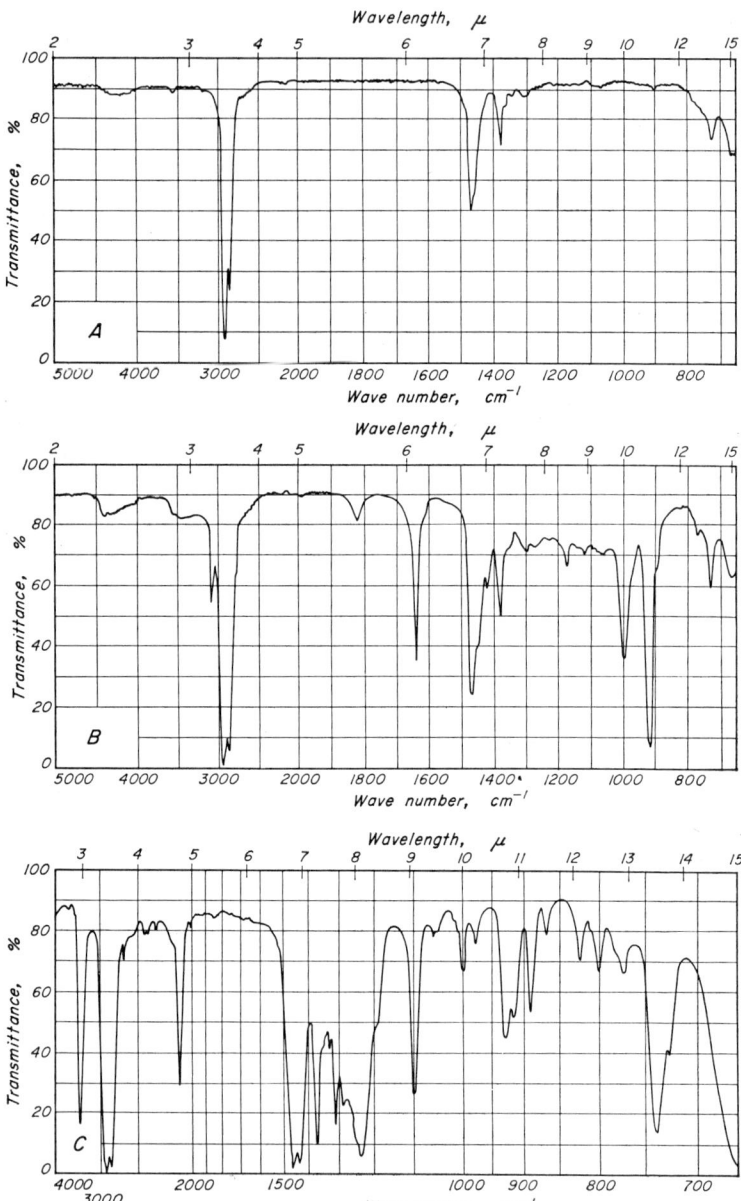

Fig. *VIII*, *10*, 4.
(*A*, *n*-Decane; *B*, 1-Octene; *C*, 1-Hexyne)

follow for each spectrum. The student should study each spectrum carefully and compare the wave numbers of the various peaks with those given in Sections **VIII,11** and **VIII,12** and, if possible, in standard reference works.

Fig. *VIII, 10*, 4. ***n*-Decane** (*A*)
2940 cm^{-1} C—H stretching frequency of a methyl group.
2850 cm^{-1} C—H stretching frequency of a methylene group.
1470 cm^{-1} Scissors-like bending of the CH_2 groups.
1380 cm^{-1} Symmetrical bending mode of the CH_3 groups.
720 cm^{-1} Arises from the rocking vibration of CH_2 groups in a straight chain of five carbon atoms or longer.

The fact that the C—H stretching frequencies all lie at lower wave numbers than 3000 cm^{-1} and the absence of characteristic skeletal frequencies between 1300 cm^{-1} and 750 cm^{-1} suggests that the compound is a saturated paraffin hydrocarbon.

1-Octene (*B*)
In addition to the paraffin C—H stretching frequencies as in *A*, the band at 3080 cm^{-1} shows hydrogen attached to an unsaturated centre.
1640 cm^{-1} Stretching frequency of C=C; olefine indicated.
998 cm^{-1} and 915 cm^{-1} C—H deformation frequencies of the vinyl group (—CH=CH_2); the latter is confirmed in the overtone at 1828 cm^{-1}.

1-Hexyne (*C*)
3300 cm^{-1} C—H stretching frequency of —C≡C—H group.
2110 cm^{-1} C≡C stretching vibration of —C≡C—H group.

Fig. *VIII, 10*, 5. ***n*-Propanol** (*A*)
Replacement of a hydrogen by a hydroxyl group at the end of an aliphatic chain introduces two new modes of vibration:
3350 cm^{-1} O—H stretching frequency.
1090 cm^{-1} and 1050 cm^{-1} C—OH stretching frequency.

Propionic acid (*B*)
3400 cm^{-1} to 2500 cm^{-1} Broad absorption band with minor peaks characteristic of carboxylic acid dimers (O—H stretching frequency).
2650 cm^{-1} O—H stretching frequency.
1710 cm^{-1} C=O stretching frequency.
1410 cm^{-1} CH_2 scissoring frequency, adjacent to COOH.
1230 cm^{-1} C—O stretching frequency.
920 cm^{-1} Broad band, O—H out-of-plane deformation in dimers.

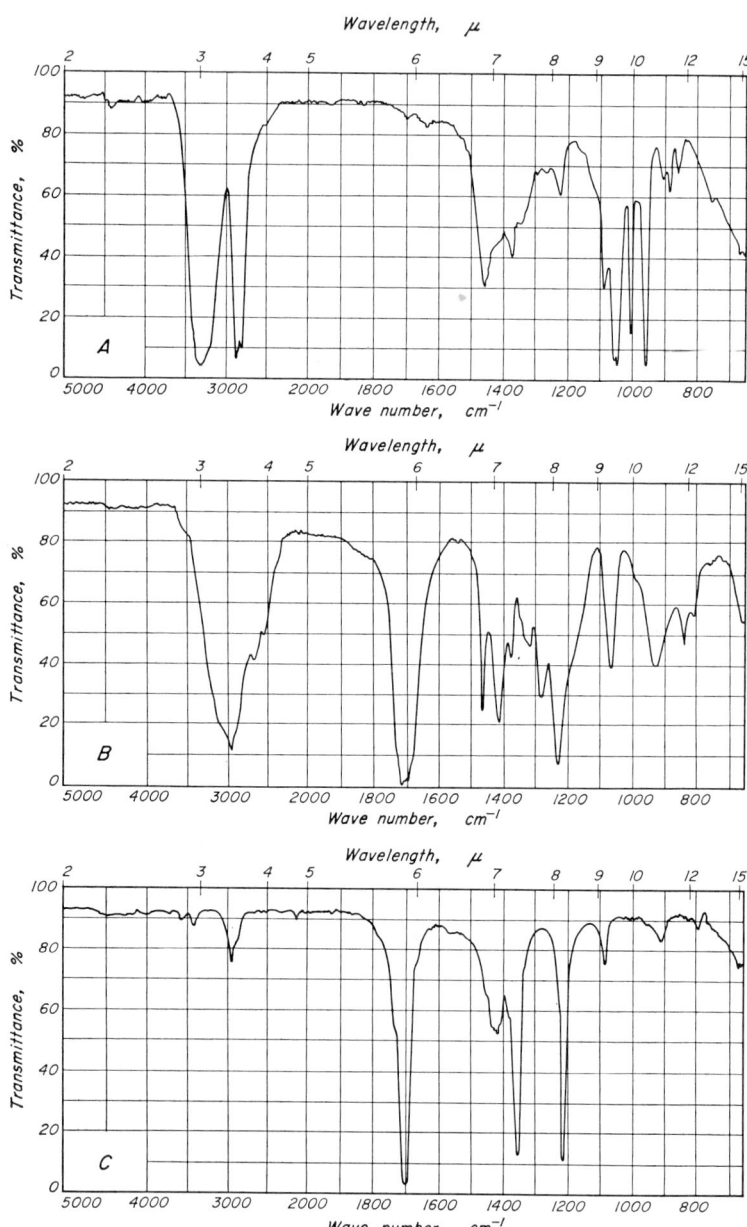

Fig. *VIII*, *10*, 5.
(*A*, *n*-Propanol; *B*, Propionic acid; *C*, Acetone)

Acetone (C)

2950 cm^{-1} — Absorption band below 3000 cm^{-1} only; this suggests saturated alkyl groups, no olefines nor aromatic compounds.

1705 cm^{-1} — C=O stretching frequency; could be ketone, aldehyde or ester but other bands typical of last two are absent.

Fig. VIII, 10, 6. **Di-n-butyl ether** (A)

3000 cm^{-1} region	C—H frequencies of alkyl groups.
2000 cm^{-1} to 1500 cm^{-1}	Absence of carbonyl group.
1470 cm^{-1} and 1380 cm^{-1}	Typical alkyl deformations.
1120 cm^{-1}	Intense band due to C—O—C stretching of a saturated ether.
740 cm^{-1}	Due to n-butyl chain.

n-Heptaldehyde (B)

2700 cm^{-1}	Sharp band due to C—H stretching frequency of the CHO group.
1720 cm^{-1}	Intense peak, C=O stretching frequency.
1470 cm^{-1}	CH$_3$, CH$_2$ deformation frequency.
1420 cm^{-1}	CH$_2$ adjacent to carbonyl.
730 cm^{-1}	Indicates methylene chain greater than C$_4$.

n-Butyl cyanide (C)

2930 cm^{-1}	Absorption band below 3000 cm^{-1}; saturated alkyl groups, no olefines nor aromatic compounds.
2240 cm^{-1}	C≡N stretching frequency.
740 cm^{-1}	Indicates polymethylene chain.

Fig. VIII, 10, 7. **n-Butylamine** (A)

3380 cm^{-1} and 3280 cm^{-1}	Doublet; N—H stretching frequency.
1600 cm^{-1}	N—H bending frequency.
1080 cm^{-1}	C—N stretching frequency.
900 cm^{-1} to 800 cm^{-1}	Broad band due to out-of-plane bending of —NH$_2$.

n-Caproamide (B)*

3360 cm^{-1} and 3180 cm^{-1}	Symmetric and anti-symmetric N—H stretching vibrations respectively of a primary amide.
1650 cm^{-1}	Carbonyl frequency of an amide (amide I band).
1630 cm^{-1}	N—H bending frequency (amide II band).
1430 cm^{-1}	Primary amide band.
705 cm^{-1}	Straight paraffin chain with number of adjacent CH$_2$ groups greater than four.

* This sample was measured in a potassium bromide disc.

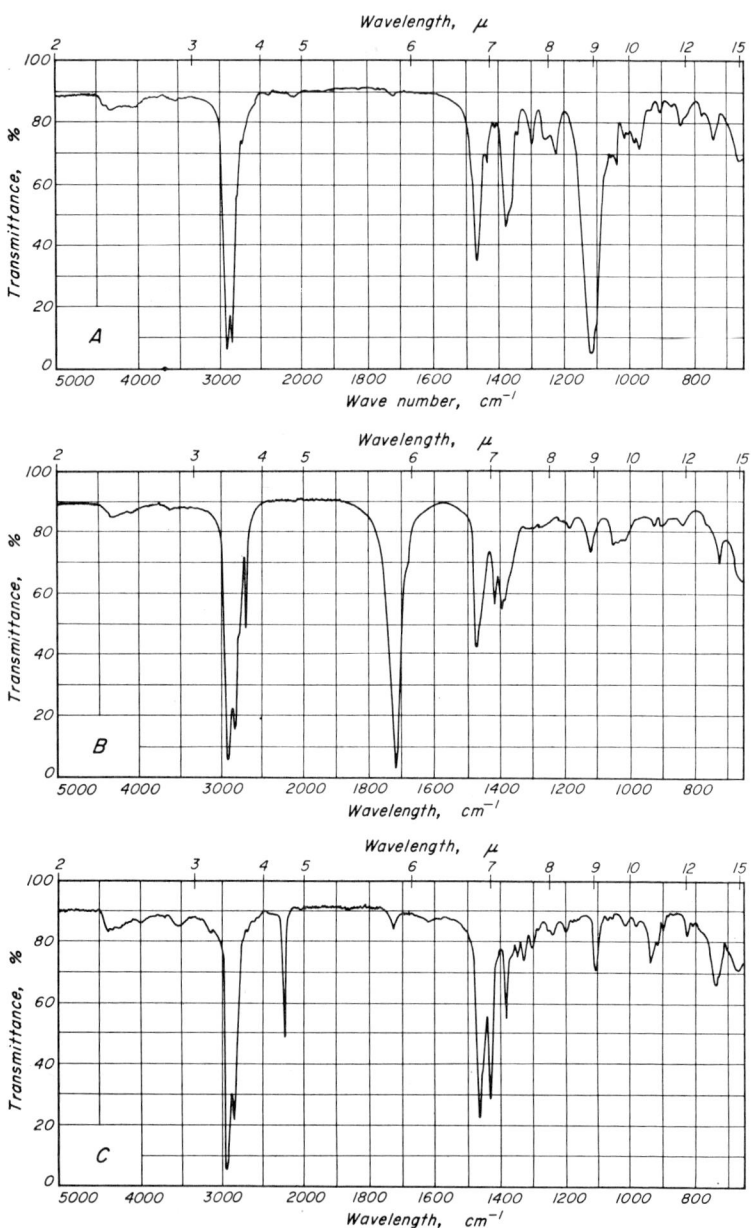

Fig. *VIII, 10,* 6.
(*A*, Di-*n*-butyl ether; *B*, *n*-Heptaldehyde; *C*, *n*-Butyl cyanide)

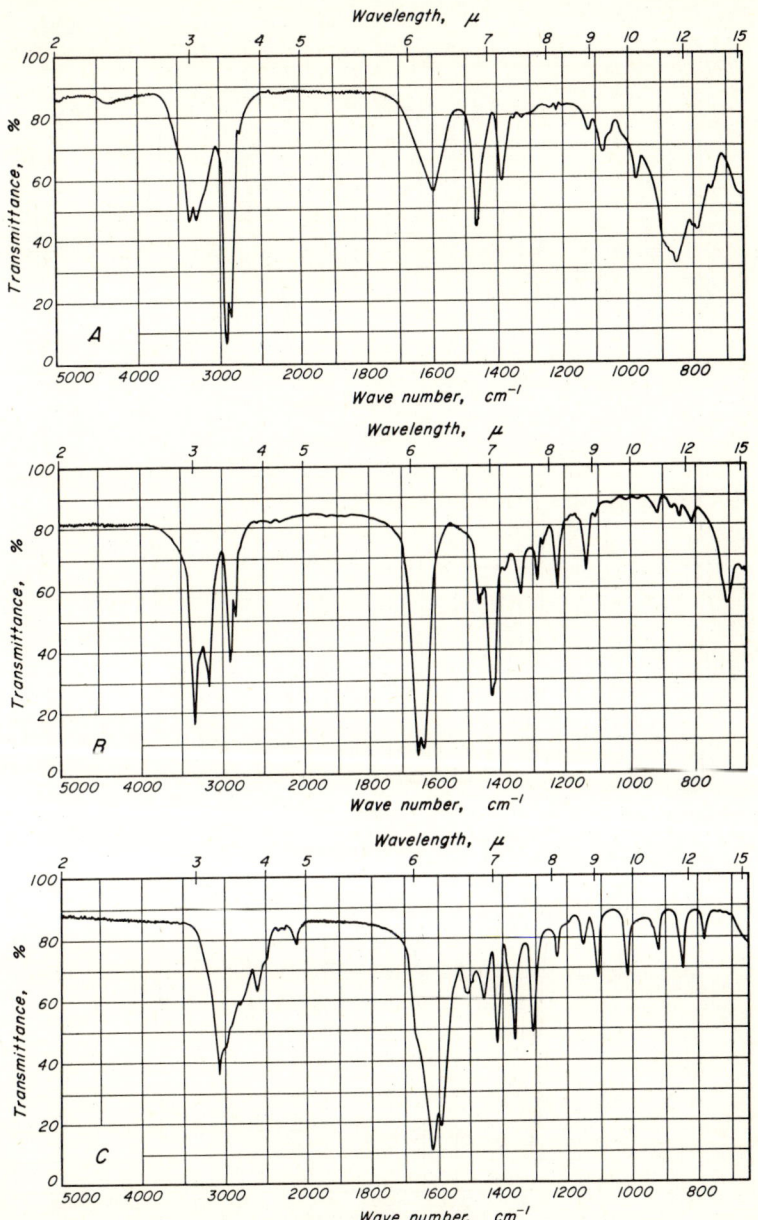

Fig. *VIII, 10*, 7.
(*A*, *n*-Butylamine; *B*, *n*-Caproamide; *C*, L-α-Alanine)

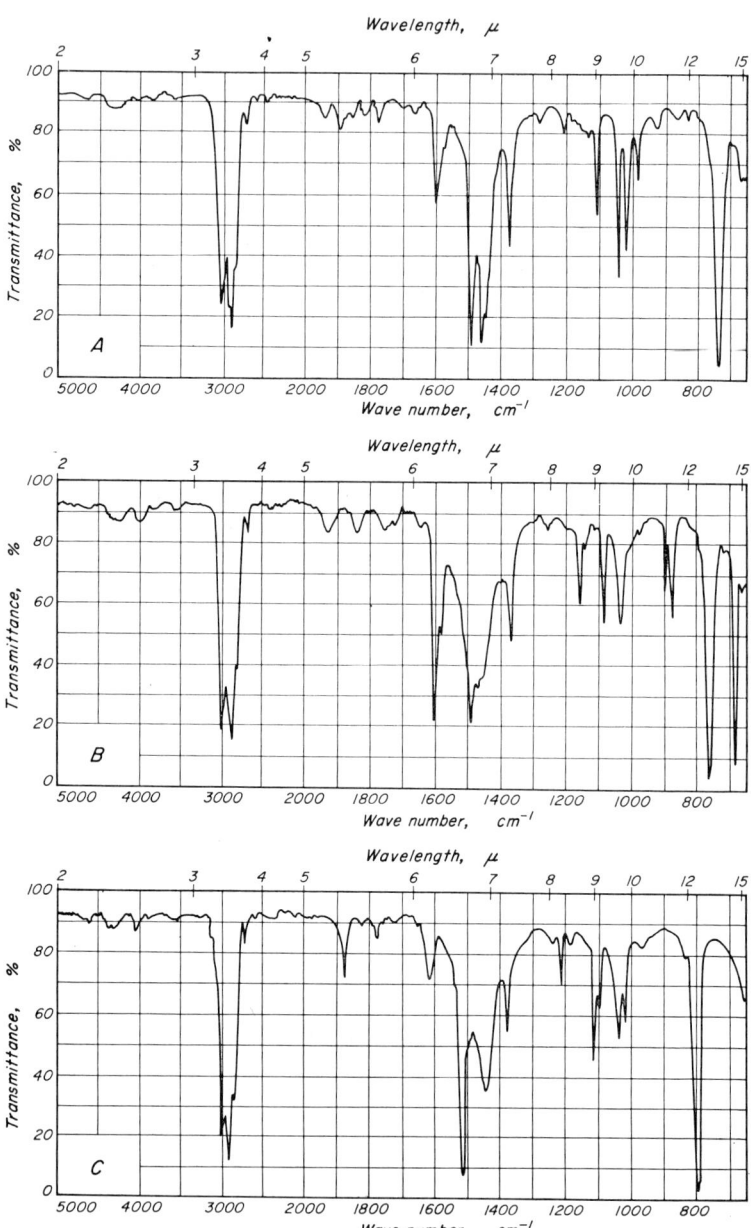

Fig. *VIII*, *10*, 8.
(*A*, *o*-Xylene, *B*, *m*-Xylene, *C*, *p*-Xylene)

L-α-Alanine (C)*

3100 cm^{-1} to 2000 cm^{-1}	Bands are typical of the NH_3^+ group in solid samples.
1620 cm^{-1}	Antisymmetric deformation of NH_3^+.
1590 cm^{-1}	Probably due to COO^- as is also band at 1415 cm^{-1}.
1360 cm^{-1}	Band due to CH_3—C group.
1305 cm^{-1}	Band characteristic of α-amino acids.

Fig. *VIII, 10*, 8. *o*-Xylene (A)

Bands at 3080 cm^{-1}, 1600 cm^{-1}, 1500 cm^{-1} and 1470 cm^{-1} indicate an aromatic compound.

It has been stated that the presence of a phenyl group is indicated by the two bands near 1600 cm^{-1} and 1500 cm^{-1} (stretching vibrations of the carbon-carbon bonds of the aromatic ring) and the sharp bands around 3000 cm^{-1} (aromatic C—H bonds).

This compound has four adjacent ring hydrogen atoms and exhibits an intense absorption band at about 740 cm^{-1}.

There are also characteristic absorption bands at 1020 cm^{-1}, 1050 cm^{-1} and 1110 cm^{-1}.

m-Xylene (B)

Bands at 3020 cm^{-1}, 1620 cm^{-1} and 1510 cm^{-1} indicate an aromatic compound.

This compound has three adjacent ring hydrogen atoms and a hydrogen atom with no adjacent partner. The three adjacent hydrogen atoms give rise to two bands near 770 cm^{-1} and 680 cm^{-1}; the single hydrogen atoms also yield a medium strength band at 880 cm^{-1}.

Other bands are at 1040 cm^{-1}, 1090 cm^{-1} and 1160 cm^{-1}.

p-Xylene (C)

The bands at 3020 cm^{-1}, 1620 cm^{-1} and 1510 cm^{-1} indicate an aromatic compound.

This compound has two adjacent hydrogen atoms and gives a high intensity band at about 800 cm^{-1}.

Other bands are at 1020 cm^{-1}, 1040 cm^{-1} and 1120 cm^{-1}.

VIII, 11 Group and Bond Frequencies

For a preliminary examination of infrared spectra Table VIII, 11, 1 (some infrared absorption bands of bonds and groups) may be employed: for detailed information, correlation charts and specialist monographs (see Bibliography) should be consulted. A limited amount of useful data on common functional groups is contained in Section **VIII, 12** and this should be used in conjunction with the table in this section.

Table VIII, 11, 1.   Some Bond and Group Frequencies

BOND OR GROUP	TYPE OF VIBRATION	WAVE NUMBER IN cm^{-1}	WAVELENGTH IN μ
O—H	Str.	3670–3230	2·73–3·10
N—H	Str.	3540–3300	2·83–3·03
≡C—H	Str.	3305–3270	3·03–3·06
C—H ar.	Str.	3100–3000	3·23–3·33
=CH$_2$	Str.	3095–3010	3·24–3·33
C—H al.	Str.	2975–2840	3·36–3·52
S—H	Str.	2590–2550	3·86–3·92
P—H	Str.	2440–2350	4·10–4·26
Si—H	Str.	2280–2080	4·39–4·81
N=C=O	Str.	2275–2240	4·40–4·46
—C≡N	Str.	2260–2120	4·43–4·72
C≡C	Str.	2260–2100	4·43–4·76
C=C=C	Str.	1970–1950	5·08–5·13
C=O	Str.	1870–1660	5·35–6·02
C=C	Str.	1690–1620	5·92–6·17
C=N	Str.	1690–1630	5·92–6·14
—O—N=O	Str.	1680–1610	5·95–6·21
N—H	Def.	1650–1580	6·06–6·33
—NO$_2$	Str.	1650–1500	6·06–6·67
N=N	Str.	1630–1575	6·14–6·35
C=C ar.	Str.	1625–1585	6·16–6·31
COO$^-$	Str.	1610–1550 / 1400–1300	6·21–6·45 / 7·15–7·70
COOH		1440–1395 / 1320–1210	6·94–7·17 / 7·58–8·26
C—N ar.	Str.	1360–1250	7·35–8·00
C—O	Str.	1300–1100	7·69–9·09
C—O—C	Str.	1250–1060	8·00–9·43
C=S	Str.	1235–1050	8·10–9·52
C—N al.	Str.	1220–1020	8·20–9·80
C—F	Str.	1110–1000	9·01–10·00
C—Cl	Str.	750–700	13·33–14·29
C—Br	Str.	ca. 650	ca. 15·4
C—I	Str.	ca. 500	ca. 20·0
—O—O—	Str.	890–830	11·24–12·05
S=O (sulphoxides)	Str.	1070–1030	9·35–9·71
S=O (sulphites)	Str.	1220–1170	8·20–8·55
SO$_2$ (sulphones)	Str.	1160–1120 / 1350–1300	8·62–8·93 / 7·41–7·69
SO$_2$ (sulphates)	Str.	1230–1150 / 1440–1350	8·13–8·70 / 6·94–7·41
P=O	Str.	1350–1175	7·41–8·51
P—O al.	Str.	1050–990	9·52–10·10
P—O ar.	Str.	1240–1180	8·07–8·48
Si—O—Si / S—O—C	Str.	1090–1020	9·17–9·80

VIII, 12 Some Characteristic Infrared Bands of Common Functional Groups

Some selected characteristic infrared bands of common functional groups are discussed below.

Alkanes. The C—H stretching vibration occurs at 2975–2860 cm^{-1} (3·36–3·50 μ). Deformation (bending) vibrations for the —CH$_2$— group are at 1480–1470 cm^{-1} (6·76–6·94 μ) and for a CH$_3$—C group at 1470–1435 cm^{-1} (6·80–6·97 μ) and at 1386–1370 cm^{-1} (7·22–7·30 μ).

Alkenes. The C=C band of non-conjugated olefines is usually found at 1680–1620 cm^{-1} (5·95–6·17 μ) and is weak. A C—H deformation vibration occurs at 995–985 cm^{-1} (10·05–10·15 μ). The olefinic C—H bending vibrations in RCH=CHR' are at: *cis* 730–665 cm^{-1} (13·70–15·04 μ); *trans* 980–960 cm^{-1} (10·20–10·42 μ). Conjugated dienes give two absorption bands, one near 1625 cm^{-1} (6·25 μ) and the other near 1650 cm^{-1} (6·06 μ).

Alkynes. The C—H stretching vibration for RC≡CH is at 3305–3270 cm^{-1} (3·03–3·06 μ); that for the C≡C stretching is at 2140–2100 cm^{-1} (4·67–4·76 μ).

Aromatic hydrocarbons. The C—H stretching band is at 3100–3000 cm^{-1} (3·23–3·33 μ). Stretching vibrations for C=C, ar bonds fall in the region 1625–1475 cm^{-1} (6·16–6·78 μ). Monosubstituted benzenes have a strong band at 770–730 cm^{-1} (12·99–13·70 μ) and at 710–690 cm^{-1} (14·08–14·99 μ). The bands for disubstituted benzenes are: 1,2—770–735 cm^{-1} (12·99–13·61 μ); 1,3—810–750 cm^{-1} (12·35–13·33 μ); 1,4—860–800 cm^{-1} (11·63–12·50 μ).

Ethers and peroxides. The C—O—C stretching vibration occurs at 1150–1060 cm^{-1} (8·70–9·43 μ) in aliphatic ethers, and at 1270–1230 cm^{-1} (7·87–8·13 μ) in aryl and vinyl ethers.

Aliphatic peroxides absorb in the region 890–830 cm^{-1} (11·24–12·50 μ) whilst acyl and aryl peroxides display frequencies arising from the carbonyl groups at 1820–1755 cm^{-1} (5·50–5·70 μ).

Alcohols and phenols. The most conspicuous bands result from the O—H stretching frequencies which occur in the region 3670–3580 cm^{-1} (2·73–2·79 μ) are only observed at high dilution in non-polar solvents. As the concentration of the solution increases, hydrogen-bonded molecules appear and additional bands occur at lower frequencies 3400–3230 cm^{-1} (2·94–3·10 μ) at the expense of the free hydroxyl band. The following assignments have been made for the C—O stretching frequency in alcohols and phenols observed as liquids: straight-chain primary alcohols 1075–1000 cm^{-1} (9·30–10·00 μ); secondary alcohols 1120–1105 cm^{-1} (8·93–9·05 μ); tertiary alcohols 1170–1100 cm^{-1} (8·55–9·09 μ); phenols 1230–1140 cm^{-1} (8·13–8·77 μ), but are said to have limited value for diagnostic purposes.

Ketones. Ketones, aldehydes, carboxylic acids, carboxylic esters, lactones, acid anhydrides and acid halides exhibit a strong C=O stretching absorption band at 1870–1540 cm^{-1} (5·35–6·50 μ) and its position is determined by the electrical and mass effects of neighbouring substituents, conjugation, ring strain, hydrogen bonding and the physical state. The stretching vibration of C=O in saturated aliphatic ketones and in six-membered or larger ring ketones in non-polar solvents lies between 1725 and 1700 cm^{-1} (5·80–5·87 μ). Conjugation with an ethylene group lowers the frequency to 1695–1660 cm^{-1} (5·90–6·02 μ), and with a benzene ring to 1700–1680 cm^{-1} (5·88–5·95 μ). Ring strain results in an increase in the C=O stretching frequency: cyclobutanone 1780–1760 cm^{-1} (5·62–5·68 μ); cyclopentanone 1750–1740 cm^{-1} (5·72–5·75 μ); and cycloheptanone 1715–1700 cm^{-1} (5·83–5·88 μ). In α-halogenated ketones, there is a shift to a higher frequency of about 20 cm^{-1} (0·07 μ to shorter wavelength). Aryl ketones absorb at 1700–1680 cm^{-1} (5·85–5·95 μ) and diaryl ketones at 1710–1670 cm^{-1} (5·99–6·02 μ). Methyl ketones display a C—H methyl bending frequency at 1360–1355 cm^{-1} (7·35–7·38 μ).

Aldehydes. Simple saturated aldehydes show a C=O absorption at 1740–1720 cm^{-1} (5·75–5·91μ). In $\alpha\beta$-unsaturated aldehydes the stretching frequency is reduced to 1705–1685 cm^{-1} (5·87–5·93 μ). For aryl aldehydes the value falls to 1715–1695 cm^{-1} (5·83–5·90 μ) and is affected by ring substitution. The C—H stretching vibration is at 2880–2650 cm^{-1} (3·47–3·77 μ) and this band, together with that of the carbonyl group, is good evidence for the presence of an aldehyde group.

Carboxylic acids. Strong hydrogen bonding affects the positions of both the O—H and C=O stretching frequencies, rendering them somewhat uncertain. The O—H stretching frequency is at 3300–2500 cm^{-1} (3·00–4·00 μ) but in the range 2700–2500 cm^{-1} (3·71–4·00 μ) the broad band is often composed of a continuous series of small bands. The C=O stretching vibration is at 1725–1700 cm^{-1} (5·80–5·88 μ) for saturated aliphatic acids and corresponds to that of a dimer. $\alpha\beta$-Unsaturated and aryl conjugated acids absorb at 1715–1680 cm^{-1} (5·83–5·95 μ). Intramolecular hydrogen bonding reduces the C=O frequency more than does intermolecular hydrogen bonding: thus fumaric acid absorbs at 1680 cm^{-1} (5·95 μ), maleic acid at 1705 cm^{-1} (5·87 μ), and salicylic acid at 1655 cm^{-1} (6·04 μ).

The carboxylate ion COO$^-$ gives rise to two stretching bands at 1610–1550 cm^{-1} (6·21–6·45 μ) and 1420–1300 cm^{-1} (7·15–7·70 μ).

Esters and lactones. The C=O stretching vibration of aliphatic esters (except formates) occurs at 1750–1735 cm^{-1} (5·71–5·76 μ); phenolic esters give bands at 1800–1770 cm^{-1} (5·56–5·65 μ). For formates, $\alpha\beta$-unsaturated and aryl esters, it is at 1730–1715 cm^{-1} (5·78–5·83 μ). α-Substitution of electron-withdrawing groups may lead to large shifts to higher frequencies, *e.g.*, ethyl trichloroacetate at 1770 cm^{-1} (5·65 μ) and ethyl cyanoacetate at 1750 cm^{-1} (5·71 μ). In β-keto esters, where enolization can occur, an additional band is observed at 1650 cm^{-1} (6·07 μ) which results from bonding between the C=O and the enolic O—H group.

Saturated γ-lactones (five-membered ring) absorb at shorter wavelengths than open-chain esters, *e.g.*, γ-valerolactone exhibits carbonyl absorption at 1780–1760 cm^{-1} (5·62–5·68 μ). Saturated δ-lactones (6-ring) absorb in the same region as esters, 1750–1735 cm^{-1} (5·71–5·76 μ). β-Lactones (4-ring) absorb in the 1840–1820 cm^{-1} (5·44–5·50 μ) range.

Acid anhydrides and acid halides. Acyclic anhydrides show two sharp C=O bands at 1840–1800 cm^{-1} (5·44–5·56 μ) and 1780–1740 cm^{-1} (5·62–5·75 μ). Conjugation results in a reduction of frequency of both bands by some 20 cm^{-1}. The frequency is enhanced when the C=O is part of a strained ring system: thus succinic anhydride absorbs at 1865 cm^{-1} (5·37 μ) and 1782 cm^{-1} (5·62 μ). There is also a characteristic C—O stretching vibration: for acyclic anhydrides at 1175–1045 cm^{-1} (8·51–9·57 μ) and for cyclic anhydrides at 1310–1210 cm^{-1} (7·63–8·26 μ).

Acid halides show a C=O absorption at 1815–1785 cm^{-1} (5·51–5·60 μ), and a reduction in frequency of *ca.* 15 cm^{-1} is exhibited by conjugated acid halides.

Amides. All amides give a C=O absorption band (amide I band) and its position is dependent upon the degree of hydrogen bonding. For primary amides in CCl$_4$ or CHCl$_3$ solution, this occurs at 1690–1650 cm^{-1} (5·92–6·06 μ). The N—H stretching frequency of primary amides is at 3540–3480 cm⁻¹ (2·83–2·88 μ) and also at 3420–3380 cm⁻¹ (2·92–2·96 μ) when free, and at 3360–3320 cm⁻¹ (2·98–3·01 μ) and at 3220–3180 cm⁻¹ (3·11–3·15 μ) when hydrogen-bonded. All primary and secondary amides display a band at 1650–1515 cm⁻¹ (6·06–6·60 μ) due to NH_2 or NH deformation. This is known as the amide II band and is not given by lactams. For primary amides the band is at 1650–1620 cm⁻¹ (6·06–6·17 μ) and for secondary amides it is at 1570–1510 cm⁻¹ (6·37–6·62 μ).

Amines. Primary amines show, in dilute solution, two N—H stretching bands at 3500–3300 cm⁻¹ (2·86–3·03 μ); secondary amines exhibit only one band in this region. The absorption due to N—H deformation occurs at 1650–1580 cm⁻¹ (6·06–6·33 μ) for primary amines and at 1650–1550 cm⁻¹ (6·06–6·45 μ) for secondary amines. The C—N stretching vibration for aliphatic amines is found at 1220–1020 cm⁻¹ (8·20–9·80 μ). For aromatic amines, strong C—N stretching vibrations occur as follows: primary, 1340–1250 cm⁻¹ (7·46–8·00 μ); secondary, 1350–1280 cm⁻¹ (7·41–7·81 μ); and tertiary, 1360–1310 cm⁻¹ (7·35–7·63 μ).

Nitriles. The C≡N stretching vibration is found at 2260–2240 cm⁻¹ (4·43–4·46 μ) for aliphatic nitriles, at 2260–2240 cm⁻¹ (4·43–4·46 μ) for aromatic nitriles, and at 2235–2215 cm⁻¹ (4·47–4·52 μ) for αβ-unsaturated and acyclic nitriles. Isonitriles give a band at 2185–2102 cm⁻¹ (4·58–4·72 μ).

Nitro compounds. Two bands are displayed at 1650–1500 cm⁻¹ (6·06–6·67 μ) and at 1350–1250 cm⁻¹ (7·42–8·00 μ). The exact positions of the bands depend upon unsaturation and substitution in the vicinity of the nitro group.

Nitrites. The nitrites R—O—N=O show strong N=O bands at 1680–1650 cm⁻¹ (5·95–6·06 μ) and 1625–1610 cm⁻¹ (6·16–6·21 μ), attributed to *cis* and *trans* forms. A pair of strong bands, due to N—O stretching, occurs at 815–750 cm⁻¹ (12·27–12·33 μ) and at 850–810 cm⁻¹ (11·76–12·35 μ).

Thiols. An S—H stretching vibration occurs as a weak band at 2590–2550 cm⁻¹ (3·86–3·92 μ).

Sulphoxides. Saturated and unsaturated sulphoxides display a strong S=O stretching vibration at 1070–1030 cm⁻¹ (9·35–9·71 μ).

Sulphones. Both saturated and unsaturated sulphones give two intense bands at 1160–1120 cm^{-1} (8·62–8·93 μ) and at 1350–1300 cm^{-1} (7·41–7·69 μ).

Sulphonamides. These display two strong bands at 1370–1300 cm^{-1} (7·30–7·69 μ) and at 1180–1140 cm^{-1} (8·48–8·77 μ).

Organo-halogen compounds. The bands arise from the stretching vibrations of carbon-halogen bonds and are influenced by neighbouring groups in the molecules. For monohalogenated compounds, the values given are: C—F, 1100–1000 cm^{-1} (9·01–10·00 μ); C—Cl, 750–700 cm^{-1} (13·33–14·29 μ); 700–550 cm^{-1} (14·29–18·18 μ); C—I, 600–500 cm^{-1} (16·67–20·00 μ).

SELECTED BIBLIOGRAPHY

1. L. J. Bellamy, *The Infra-red Spectra of Complex Molecules*. Second Edition. Methuen and Co., London, 1958.
2. R. P. Baumann, *Absorption Spectroscopy*. John Wiley, New York, 1962.
3. R. M. Silverstein and G. M. Bassler, *Spectrometric Identification of Organic Compounds*. John Wiley, 1963. (This book includes ultraviolet spectrometry, mass spectrometry and nuclear magnetic resonance spectrometry.)
4. K. Nakanashi, *Infrared Absorption Spectroscopy—Practical*. Holden-Day, San Francisco, 1962.
5. C. R. N. Strouts, H. N. Wilson and R. T. Parry-Jones, *Chemical Analysis. The Working Tools*. Volume II. Chapter 25. *Infra-red Absorption Spectrophotometry*. Clarendon Press, Oxford, 1962.
6. A. D. Cross, *Practical Infra-red Spectroscopy*. Second Edition. Butterworths, London, 1964.
7. J. R. Dyer, *Applications of Absorption Spectroscopy of Organic Compounds*. Prentice-Hall, Englewood Cliffs, N.J., 1965. (Includes sections on ultraviolet and n.m.r. spectroscopy.)
8. D. W. Mathieson (Editor), *Interpretation of Organic Spectra*. Academic Press, Inc., London, 1965. (Includes sections on n.m.r. and mass spectrometry.)
9. A. J. Baker and T. Cairns, *Spectroscopic Techniques in Organic Chemistry*. Heyden and Sons, London, 1965. (Includes sections on ultraviolet, n.m.r. and mass spectrometry.)

NUCLEAR MAGNETIC RESONANCE SPECTROSCOPY

VIII, 13   General Principles

Some atomic nuclei possess magnetic moments. If an external magnetic field is applied to a system of nuclei with magnetic moments, these nuclei will experience torques and will tend to be lined up parallel to the field. Under appropriate conditions it is possible for these magnets to absorb energy from a magnetic field oscillating with a frequency in the radiofrequency region: such absorption gives rise to what are called nuclear magnetic resonance spectra (often abbreviated to n.m.r. spectra). If a nucleus has no magnetic moment, no magnetic resonance spectrum will be obtained. By measuring n.m.r. spectra, we are using a nucleus essentially as a magnetic probe to investigate local magnetic effects inside a molecular system.

Nuclei of certain isotopes possess a mechanical spin or angular momentum. The total angular momentum depends upon the nuclear spin or spin number I, which may have values of $0, \frac{1}{2}, 1, \frac{3}{2}, \ldots$, depending upon the particular nucleus. Magnetic properties are found with nuclei of odd-numbered masses ^1H, ^{11}B, ^{13}C, ^{15}N, ^{17}O, ^{19}F, ^{31}P etc. and with nuclei of even mass but odd atomic number ^2H, ^{10}B, ^{14}N etc. Nuclei with even mass and even atomic numbers, like ^{12}C, ^{16}O, ^{24}Mg, ^{32}S, ^{28}Si, have no magnetic properties and do not give n.m.r. signals. Nuclei of interest to the organic chemist include ^1H, ^{11}B, ^{13}C, ^{19}F and ^{31}P. We shall be largely concerned with the n.m.r. spectrum of hydrogen (^1H); since the proton is involved, the spectrum is termed the *proton magnetic resonance spectrum* (p.m.r.). All these nuclei are classified as having spin I of $\frac{1}{2}$. This means that the component of their magnetic moments in any direction can have only two equal, but opposite, observable values that correspond to spin quantum numbers $+\frac{1}{2}$ and $-\frac{1}{2}$. Thus if the nuclei are introduced into a magnetic field H_0 in the z direction, they can only be regarded as lined up with the field ($I_z = +\frac{1}{2}$) or against the field ($I_z = -\frac{1}{2}$). As with compass needles in the earth's magnetic field, the slightly more favourable energy state is the one corresponding to alignment with the field. The difference in energy between the states ΔE will be expected to be proportional to the strength of the applied magnetic field H_0 at the nucleus and can be shown to be equal to $\gamma h H_0/2\pi$ where h is Planck's constant and γ is a proportionality constant, which depends upon the nature of the nucleus. Fig. *VIII, 13,* 1 is the energy level diagram for a magnetic nucleus of spin ½ in a magnetic field of strength H_0. The

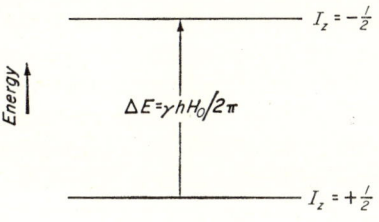

Fig. *VIII, 13,* 1.

quantity ΔE is related to the frequency ν by the equation $\Delta E = h\nu$, hence
$$\nu = \gamma H_0 / 2\pi \tag{1}$$

The basis of n.m.r. experiments is to induce transition between the energy levels by the absorption or emission of energy quanta. For a transition between neighbouring levels, the frequency of the radiation required can be found from the relationship:

$$h\nu = \mu H_0 / I \tag{2}$$

where μ is the magnetic moment. If the nucleus is the proton (with $\mu = 1\cdot4102 \times 10^{-23}$ erg/gauss), by substituting in equation (2) (with $h = 6\cdot624 \times 10^{-27}$ erg/sec.), we find that the appropriate frequency for $H_0 = 14,000$ gauss is 59·6 megacycles per second, which is conveniently produced by a radiofrequency (rf) oscillator.

To observe nuclear resonance absorption, we can maintain the frequency ν constant and vary the applied field H_0 until close to the point where $\nu = \gamma H_0 / 2\pi$. Energy is then absorbed by the nuclei, the current flow from the oscillator increases and can be observed by suitable means. Further increase of H_0 will eventually make ν very much less than $\gamma H_0 / 2\pi$ and the current will decrease to its original value. The form of the energy absorption curve as a function of H_0 will appear as shown in Fig. *VIII, 13,* 2 with the peak centred very near the point where $\gamma = \gamma H_0 / 2\pi$. N.m.r. frequencies are to a small but definite degree dependent on the molecular environment of the nucleus; the surrounding electrons shield the nucleus so that the effective magnetic field at the nucleus is not exactly the same as the applied magnetic field. Protons in different environments therefore give slightly different signals (resonance peaks) and herein lies the value of n.m.r. to the organic chemist.

Following the above elementary introduction, a somewhat more detailed treatment will be given which leads directly to the essential theory underlying the design of n.m.r. spectrometers. We will consider a bare nucleus, such as a proton, in a magnetic field of strength H_0 gauss. In the nucleus, the charge circulates or spins on the nuclear axis and this circulation of nuclear charge generates a magnetic dipole along the axis: the magnitude of this generated dipole is expressed in terms of a nuclear magnetic moment μ. A nucleus has two important properties associated with spin angular momentum: they are spin number I and magnetic moment μ. For a proton I is equal to $\frac{1}{2}$ and it can be compared with a very tiny bar magnet. Quantum mechanics enables us to state that the tiny proton magnet is restricted to only

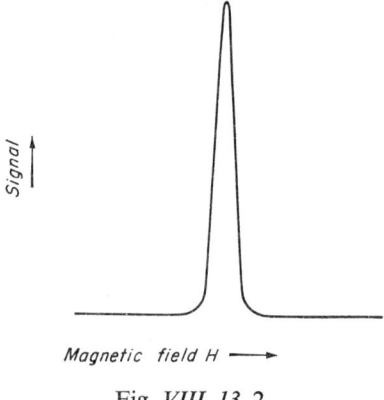

Fig. *VIII, 13*, 2.

two possible orientations $[(2I+1)=2]$ in an applied uniform magnetic field: these can be considered to be a low energy or parallel orientation in which the magnet is aligned with the field and a high energy or antiparallel orientation in which it is aligned against the field. The former is the low-energy (stable) state and the latter is the high-energy (unstable) state. These two orientations correspond to two energy states. It should be possible to induce transitions between them, and the frequency ν of the electromagnetic radiation which will effect such transitions is given by

$$\nu = \gamma H_0 / 2\pi$$

where γ is the magnetogyric ratio. The absorption or emission of the quantum of energy $h\nu$ causes the nuclear magnets to turn over or 'flip' from one orientation to the other. It has been shown above that for magnetic fields of the order of 14,000 gauss, the characteristic frequencies lie in the radiofrequency range of 60 mc/s.

The problem now is how to inject electromagnetic energy into protons aligned in a magnetic field so as to 'flip' the proton spin into a higher energy level and to measure the energy thus absorbed. For a very small magnet spinning in an external magnetic field, the axis of the magnet (proton) will precess about the axis of the external magnetic field similarly to the manner in which a spinning gyroscope precesses under the influence of gravity. The precessional angular velocity ω_0 is given by:

$$\omega_0 = \gamma H_0$$

and it therefore follows from the fundamental n.m.r. equation that

$$\omega_0 = 2\pi\nu$$

This means that if we can introduce the same frequency (γH_0, the energy required to 'flip' a proton), we shall be exactly attuned to the precessional angular velocity: otherwise expressed, the inserted frequency will be in resonance with the precessional frequency. The energy of the inserted frequency can thus be absorbed by the nucleus and, given the proper conditions, the nucleus can be caused to 'flip'.

We can now arrange the geometry for an n.m.r. experiment. When the protons are subjected to a powerful uniform magnetic field, they are aligned parallel with the field and are precessing about the axis of the applied magnetic field. Actually only a very small fraction of the total number of protons is properly aligned because of thermal distribution between the two energy levels, but this small number is sufficient. The electromagnetic frequency is applied in a manner that the magnetic component H_1 is at right angles to the main magnetic field H_0 and is rotating with the precessing proton. By using an oscillator coil whose axis is at right angles to the axis of the main magnetic field H_0, a linear oscillating magnetic field H_1 will be generated along the direction of the coil axis (Fig. *VIII, 13*, 3). A linear oscillating field can be resolved into two components rotating in opposite directions: one of these is rotating in the same direction as the precessional orbit of the nuclear magnetic dipole (the proton); the other component will have no effect on the nucleus. If H_0 is maintained constant and the oscillator frequency is increased, the angular velocity of the component of the rotating magnetic field H_1 will increase until it is equal to (and therefore in resonance with) the angular velocity ω_0 of the precessing proton. Energy is absorbed at this point, the nucleus 'flips' to its higher energy level and the recorder signals a peak. In actual practice, the oscillator frequency is constant, and H_0 is swept over a narrow range. It may be mentioned that since the individual nuclei in a system are not necessarily in the same environment, each may experience a slightly different local field due to neighbouring nuclei; consequently each type of nucleus will display its own resonance frequency (which is proportional to the sum of the main field H_0 and local fields). Finally, some mechanism to return the nucleus to its lower-energy state is required, otherwise all of the small excess

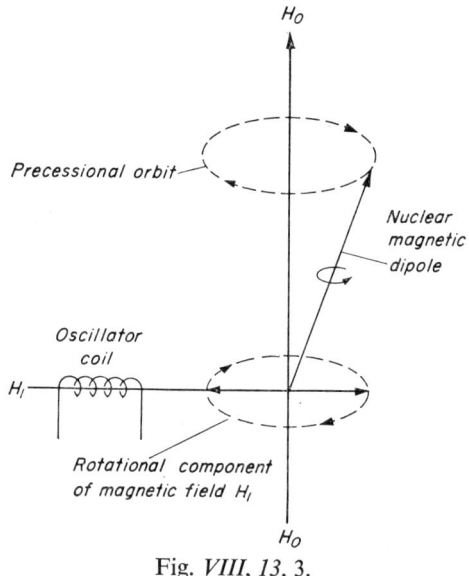

Fig. *VIII, 13,* 3.

population of nuclei in the lower-energy state will be raised to the higher-energy state and no further absorption of energy will occur. The nucleus in the higher-energy state can lose energy to its environment and thus return to its lower energy state by the so-called relaxation processes. The latter are of two kinds: spin-spin (or transverse) relaxation and spin-lattice (or longitudinal) relaxation. For further details, reference should be made to the books detailed in the Bibliography.

VIII, 14 Nuclear Magnetic Resonance Spectrometers

The apparatus consists essentially of the following components:
(i) A magnet capable of producing a very strong homogeneous field.

The magnet should possess a region between the pole faces in which the magnetic field is homogeneous to a high order (1 in 10^8), *i.e.*, the strength and direction of the field should not vary from point to point. Electromagnets or permanent magnets may be used: routine operation with the latter is somewhat simpler.

(ii) A radiofrequency oscillator.

This produces an electromagnetic field in a plane perpendicular to the direction of the applied magnetic field. By using a linearly oscillating field (which may be regarded as being the resultant of two components rotating in phase but in opposite directions), one component will be rotating in the same sense as the precessing nuclear magnet with which it will interact when the frequencies are the same. The frequency of the rf oscillator is usually fixed.

(iii) A means of continuously varying the magnetic field over a relatively small range.

The precessing magnetic nuclei can be brought into resonance with the rotating magnetic field by varying the applied static field: a direct current is applied to coils wound round the two pole pieces of the magnet by means of a sweep generator. The output of the sweep generator is synchronised with the trace along the X axis of an oscilloscope or is connected with a recorder.

(iv) A radiofrequency receiver.

This is the 'detector' or device which indicates when energy from the source is being absorbed by the sample.

(v) A recorder, calibrator, and integrator.

(vi) A sample holder, which positions the sample relative to the magnetic field, the oscillator and the receiver coil. The sample holder also spins the sample uniformly to increase the apparent homogeneity of the magnetic field and thereby improving the resolution.

A schematic diagram of an n.m.r. spectrometer is shown in Fig. *VIII*, *14*, 1. The sweep generator is, of course, suitably connected to the recorder.

Two commercial instruments are eminently suitable for routine work in organic chemistry: these are the Perkin–Elmer n.m.r. spectrometer Model R10* and the Varian n.m.r. spectrometer Model A-60†. Fig. *VIII*, *14*, 2 is a photograph of the Perkin–Elmer Model R10. It incorporates a thermostatted permanent magnet of field

---

* Supplied by Perkin–Elmer Ltd., Norwalk, Connecticut, U.S.A. and also Beaconsfield, Bucks, England.
† Supplied by Varian Associates Analytical Instruments, Palo Alto, California, U.S.A., and also Walton-on-Thames, Surrey, England.

strength 14,092 gauss, operates at 60 Mc/s, and has a power consumption of 750 watts. The Varian A-60 utilizes a 14,092 gauss electromagnet with a water-cooled solid-state power supply, and has a power consumption of 2,600 watts.

The solvents used for proton magnetic spectroscopy should be chemically inert, magnetically isotropic, and preferably devoid of hydrogen atoms. Carbon tetrachloride is the ideal solvent. Many compounds are insufficiently soluble in carbon tetrachloride and other solvents have to be used. These include carbon disulphide, acetylene tetrachloride, chloroform, dimethyl sulphoxide, deuterochloroform and deuterium oxide. The concentrations of the solutions are of the order 5–20 per cent. Organic liquids may be used directly without solvent provided they are not viscous. The sample is contained in a precision

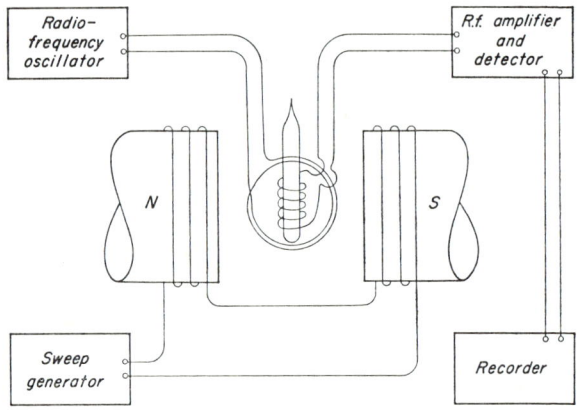

Fig. *VIII, 14, 1.*

tube of 5 mm. outside diameter and about 15 cm. high. About 0·4 ml. of the sample solution is required: a drop of tetramethylsilane (TMS) is added as internal standard when solubility conditions permit. The tube is placed between the pole faces of the magnet and the spectrum determined. The homogeneity of the magnetic field experienced by the sample is improved by spinning the sample about the vertical axis. On a 60 Mc instrument, the sweep generator periodically sweeps the main magnetic field in the immediate vicinity of 14,092 gauss: the range of sweep is of the order of 1,000 cps. Peak areas are measured by the integrator which superimposes a series of steps on the absorption peaks in the spectrum; the step heights are proportional to the number of protons under the respective peaks.

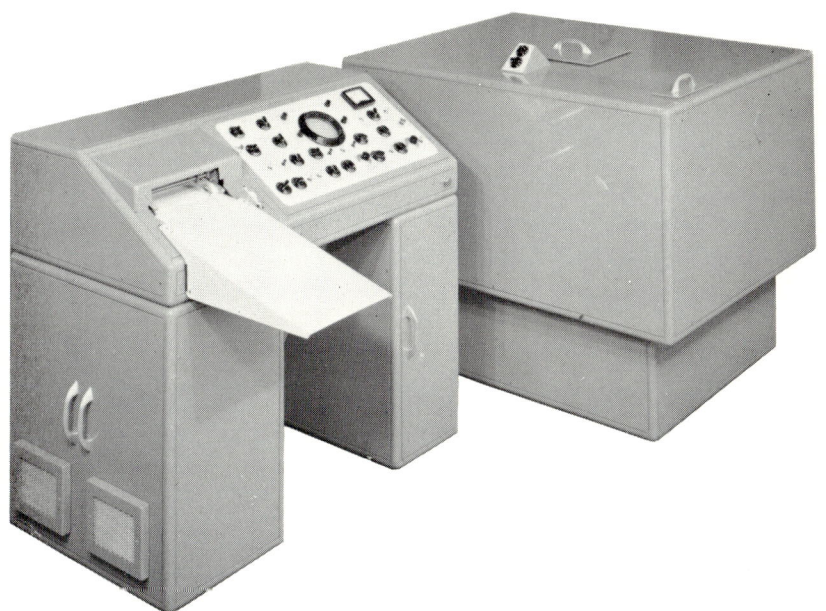

Fig. *VIII*, *14*, 2. Perkin-Elmer N.M.R. Spectrometer, Model R10.

VIII, 15 Chemical Shifts

The resonance line positions of nuclei in different structural environments occur at different field strengths and the differences relative to an arbitrarily chosen standard are called *chemical shifts*. Thus ethyl alcohol, CH_3—CH_2—OH, has three kinds of hydrogens: methyl (CH_3), methylene (CH_2) and hydroxyl (OH). In a magnetic field the protons (nuclei) of each type of hydrogen have slightly different magnetic environments due to the motions of their valence

Table VIII, 15, 1. Some Approximate Values of Chemical Shifts for the Protons of CH_3, CH_2 and CH Groups attached to Various Substituent Groups X*

X	CH_3X		$R'CH_2X$		$R''R'''CHX$	
	δ	τ	δ	τ	δ	τ
—R	0·9	9·1	1·2	8·8	1·5	8·5
—COOR	2·0	8·0	2·1	7·9		
—CN	2·0	8·0	2·5	7·5		
—$CONH_2$	2·0	8·0	2·1	7·9		
—COOH	2·1	7·9	2·3	7·7	2·6	7·4
—COR	2·1	7·9	2·4	7·6	2·5	7·5
—SII, —SR	2·1	7·9	2·4	7·6		
—NH_2, —NR_2	2·2	7·8	2·5	7·5	2·9	7·1
—I	2·2	7·8	3·2	6·8	4·2	5·8
—CHO	2·2	7·8	2·2	7·8	2·4	7·6
—C_6H_5	2·3	7·7	2·6	7·4	2·9	7·1
—Br	2·6	7·4	3·3	6·7	4·1	5·9
—NHCOR	2·9	7·1	3·3	6·7	3·5	6·5
—Cl	3·0	7·0	3·4	6·6	4·0	6·0
—OR	3·3	6·7	3·4	6·6	3·8	6·2
—OH	3·4	6·6	3·6	6·4	3·9	6·1
—OCOR	3·7	6·3	4·2	5·8	5·0	5·0
—OC_6H_5	3·7	6·3	3·9	6·1	4·0	6·0
—$OCOC_6H_5$	3·9	6·1	4·2	5·8	5·1	4·9
—F	4·3	5·7	4·4	5·6		
—NO_2	4·3	5·7	4·4	5·6	4·6	5·4

* R', R" and R''' are saturated hydrocarbon residues.

electrons and those of neighbouring atoms. The magnetic field strength at a particular nucleus is usually slightly less than the strength of the applied magnetic field because magnetic field due to the motions of the electrons results in a shielding effect (such as a diamagnetic shielding effect). These shielding effects will be different for each kind of hydrogen and hence the resonance signal produced will appear at different field strengths. A plot of resonance signal against

Table VIII, 15, 2. Some Approximate Values of Chemical Shifts of Miscellaneous Protons

	δ	τ
$RC\equiv CH$	1·8	8·2
$PhC\equiv CH$	3·1	6·9
$\diagup C=C \diagdown$ (H, H)	5·5	4·5
$H_\alpha, H_\gamma / C=C / H_\beta$	γ 5·9; α, β 5·0	4·1; 5·0
—CHO	9·9	0·1
—CO_2H	10–12	0 to −2
—SO_3H	11–12	−1 to −2
Ph—H	7·3	2·7
R—OH	1–6	9 to 4
Ph—OH	4–7	6 to 3
R—SH	1·4	8·6
Ph—SH	2·8–3·6	7·2 to 6·4
R—NH	0·5–5	9·5 to 5
Ph—NH	3–5	7 to 5
RCH_2NO_2	4·4	5·2
$\diagup O$ (ethers)	3·8	6·2
RCH_2Cl	3·6	6·4
RCH_2Br	3·4	6·6
RCH_2I	3·2	6·8
Ph—CH_2	2·3	7·7
RCH_2CN	2·6	7·4
RCH_2CONH_2	2·2	7·9
$(CH_3)_4Si$	0·0	10·0

field strength shows three principal groups of lines for ethanol with areas under each roughly in the ratio 1:2:3, *i.e.*, corresponding to OH, CH_2 and CH_3. The differences in field strength at which resonance signals are obtained for protons (or other nuclei of the same kind) located in different molecular environments are termed chemical shifts.

Chemical shifts are generally measured with reference to a standard.

The usual internal standard for protons in organic molecules is tetramethylsilane $(CH_3)_4Si$ (TMS); this substance is chemically inert, magnetically isotropic, volatile (b.p. 26°), miscible with organic solvents, and gives a single absorption line in a region where only a very few other kinds of protons absorb. The chemical shift is proportional to the field strength or to, what is equivalent, the rf oscillator frequency. It is obviously desirable to express resonance line positions in a form which is independent of the field strength and the frequency.

Table VIII, 15, 3. Chemical Shifts of Some Reference Standards Relative to TMS

SOLVENT	δ	τ
Trifluoroacetic acid	−9·83	0·17
Chloroform	−7·25	2·75
Benzene	−7·27	2·73
Methylene chloride	−5·30	4·70
Water	−5·1	4·9
Nitromethane	−4·33	5·67
Dioxan	−3·68	6·32
Dimethyl sulphoxide	−2·6	7·4
Acetone	−2·17	7·83
Acetonitrile	−2·00	8·00
Cyclohexane	−1·43	8·57
Tetramethyl silane	0·00	10·00

The chemical shift parameter is used and this is defined as

$$\delta = 10^6 \times (H_s - H_r)/H_r$$

where H_s and H_r are the field strengths corresponding to resonance for a particular nucleus in the sample and the reference respectively. Since spectra are usually calibrated in cycles per second (cps), we may rewrite the above equation as:

$$\delta = \frac{\Delta\nu \times 10^6}{\text{Oscillator frequency (cps)}}$$

where $\Delta\nu$ is the difference in absorption frequencies between sample and reference in cps. The oscillator frequency is characteristic of the instrument: a 60 Mc instrument has an oscillator frequency of 60×10^6 cps. The factor 10^6 is included for convenience: δ, which is dimensionless, is expressed in parts per million (ppm). If the signal for TMS is taken as the standard proton line, position δ will be negative for common organic protons. To obviate the inconvenience of using negative values, τ (tau) values have been introduced:

$$\tau = 10\cdot 00 - \delta$$

where τ is treated as a positive number.

Some typical proton chemical shifts in dilute chloroform solution relative to TMS are collected in Table VIII, 15, 1. Approximate values of the chemical shifts for a number of miscellaneous protons are given in Table VIII, 15, 2. The chemical shifts of some reference standards relative to tetramethyl silane are presented in Table VIII, 15, 3.

The correlation of the chemical shift with molecular structure, including the use of the so-called shielding constants, is outside the scope of this book: details will be found in some of the books listed in the Bibliography in Section **VIII,17**.

VIII, 16 Spin-spin Splitting

This effect is well illustrated by study of the n.m.r. spectrum of dry ethyl alcohol or of ethyl iodide under high resolution. It is found

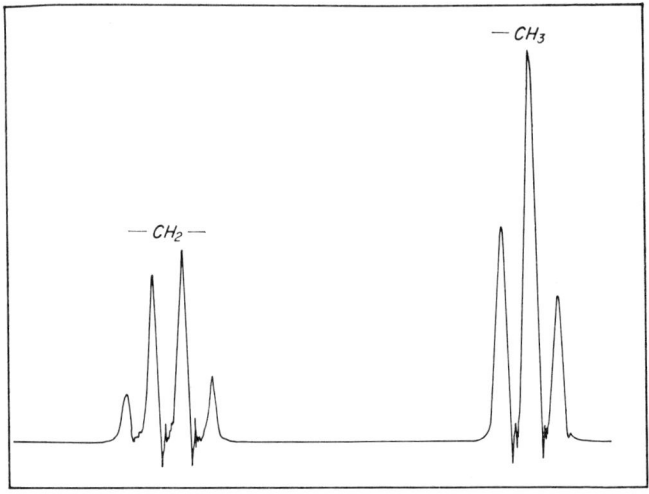

Fig. *VIII, 16*, 1.

(as shown schematically in Fig. *VIII, 16*, 1) that the principal resonance signals for protons of different chemical shifts are actually a group of lines that results from spin-spin splitting. The bands associated with the CH_2 and CH_3 groups appear as multiplets, the total areas of which are in the ratio 2:3. The methylene absorption is split into a quartet (relative areas 1:3:3:1) and the methyl absorption is split into a triplet (relative areas 1:2:1). These splitting patterns are explained qualitatively by assuming that the magnetic field experienced by the protons of one group is influenced by the magnetic field due to the spin arrangements of the protons in the adjacent group. For the two protons of the methylene group of CH_3CH_2X ($X=I$, etc.), there are three possible combinations of spin orientations that may affect the resonance frequencies of the protons of the adjacent methyl group (Fig. *VIII*, *16*, *2*: this shows schematically the possible spin orientations of an ethyl group; the methylene protons are on the left and the methyl protons on the right). If the effect of the instantaneous spin arrangements of the protons of the methylene group can be transmitted to the

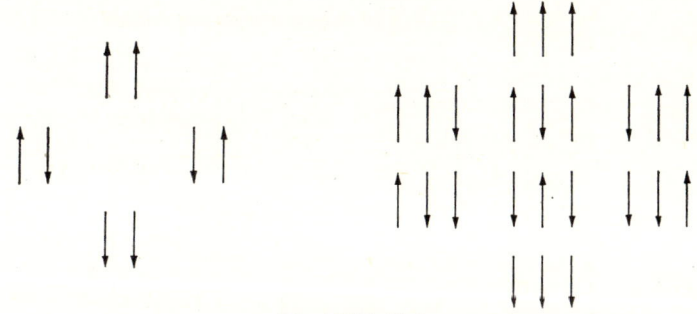

Fig. *VIII*, *16*, *2*.

protons of the adjacent methyl group, the protons of the methyl group would be split into three peaks (a triplet) having relative areas of 1:2:1. If the spin orientations of the methyl group (Fig. *VIII*, *16*, 2) have a similar effect on the protons of the methylene group, the protons of the latter would be split into four peaks (a quartet) having relative areas 1:3:3:1. That the spin-spin splitting arises from magnetic interaction of each group of protons with the other can be shown by isotopic substitution with deuterium D. Deuterons have much smaller magnetic moments than protons and substitution of one deuterium atom on the methyl of an ethyl group (XCH_2CH_2D) produces a triplet resonance for the methylene group: substitution of two deuterons (XCH_2CHD_2) produces a doublet resonance: with three deuterons (XCH_2CD_3), a one line XCH_2 spectrum is observed under moderate resolution. In general, coupling between hydrogens on adjacent atoms is large enough to lead to the kind of splitting described above, but if the protons are separated by three saturated carbon atoms the splitting is too small to be detected.

In addition to a knowledge of the number of peaks resulting from spin-spin coupling, the **spin-spin coupling constant** J, the parameter which is associated with the distances separating them, is of value. The coupling constant is unaltered by changes in field strength whereas the chemical shifts are directly proportional to such changes. The constant J is expressed in cycles per second. Some absolute values of coupling constants are presented in Table VIII, 16, 1 for protons attached to adjacent carbon atoms in molecules whose relative rigidity permits an estimate (in some cases) of the dihedral angle between protons. The constants are therefore of value for structural and stereochemical studies.

Table VIII, 16, 1. Spin-Spin Coupling Constants of Protons Attached to Adjacent Carbon Atoms

STRUCTURAL TYPE	J (CPS)	DIHEDRAL ANGLE
Olefinic hydrogens		
cis	5–14	0°
trans	11–19	180°
Aromatic hydrogens		
ortho	7–10	
meta	2–3	
para	0–1	
Cyclohexane derivatives		
H_{axial}–H_{axial}	8–12	180°
H_{axial}–$H_{equatorial}$	3–4.5	60°
—CH_2— (tetrahedral)	12–15	
$\rangle C{=}CH_2$	0–3.5	
$\rangle CH{-}C{\equiv}CH$	2–3	
$\rangle C{=}CH{-}CH{=}C\langle$	10–13	
$\rangle CH{-}\overset{\underset{\|}{O}}{C}{-}H$	1–3	

VIII, 17 Some Applications of N.M.R. Spectroscopy. Typical Spectra

An interesting application is to the solution of the classical problem of the structure of diketene in the liquid state. The production of formaldehyde and malonic acid by ozonolysis had suggested a β-lactone structure. Structures that merit consideration are:

```
O=C—CH        O=C—CH₂       H₃C—C=CH      H₂C=C—CH₂
 |  ||         |   |          |   |          |   |
H₂C—C—OH      H₂C—C=O        O—C=O          O—C=O
  (I)          (II)           (III)          (IV)
```

These should give n.m.r. spectra having: (I) three peaks in the ratio 2:1:1; (II) a single peak with an intensity equivalent to four protons; (III) two peaks with a 3:1 ratio; and (IV) two peaks of equal intensity corresponding to two protons each. Only two peaks of equal intensity are observed, thus confirming structure (IV).

N.m.r. spectra at various temperatures and under varying experimental conditions find application in the study of *rate processes*,

Fig. VIII, 17, 1.

which in turn may have valuable structural implications. Thus the n.m.r. spectrum of cyclohexane at room temperature confirms the rapid equilibrium between the two chair forms so that any proton experiences an averaged field intermediate between that of an axial and equatorial position. Upon lowering the temperature the absorption broadens, and at $-100°$ the proton spectrum appears as two partially resolved complex peaks, one associated with the axial and the other with the equatorial positions. With substituents on the cyclohexane ring, 'locking' of the molecule into a preferred conformation may occur at room temperature or above.

Another interesting example is the fluorine (^{19}F) resonance spectrum of 1,2-difluorotetrachloroethane. The molecule is most stable in the staggered rotational conformations (a)–(c) depicted in Fig. VIII, 17, 1: (a) and (b) will have identical n.m.r. spectra. The fluorines of (c) are in a different environment from those in (a) and (b) and should therefore have a different chemical shift from the fluorine atoms in (*a*) and (*b*). At room temperatures, rotation about the C—C bond occurs so rapidly that only a single fluorine resonance band is observed. As the temperature is lowered, the rate of rotation around the C—C bond is reduced, and at −120° the rate is so slow that one can observe the separate resonances of (*a*) and (*b*) and of (*c*) (chemical shift of about 1 ppm).

It will be seen from what has already been said that n.m.r. spectroscopy is an extremely valuable tool for the identification of groups and for the study of structures of organic molecules. This description will

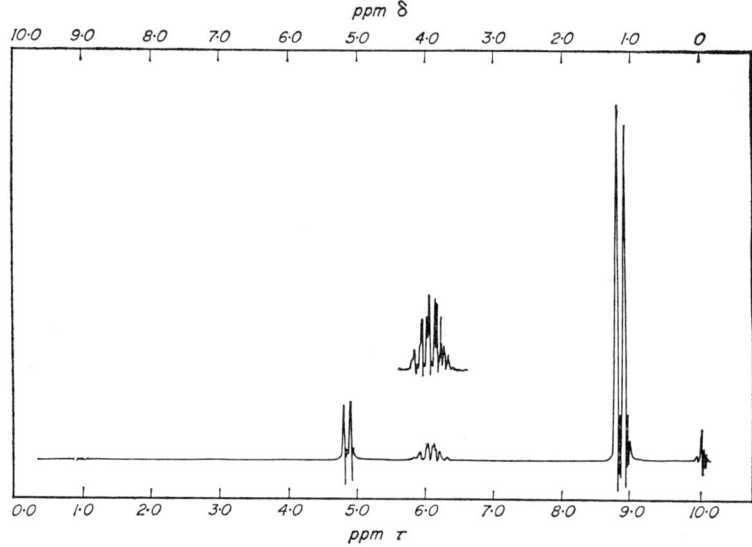

Fig. *VIII*, *17*, 2.

be concluded by showing some actual n.m.r. spectra obtained with the Perkin–Elmer n.m.r. spectrometer Model R-10, and drawing attention to certain important features. The spectra are presented in Figs. *VIII*, *17*, 2–4.

Isopropanol (Fig. *VIII*, *17*, 2). The methyl groups are revealed by the doublet at 8·85 τ, the isopropyl group single proton by the double septet at 6·05 τ (the septet is due to coupling with six equivalent methyl protons; the doublet is due to coupling to hydroxyl proton), and the hydroxyl group is shown as a doublet at 4·85 τ.

Acetylacetone (Fig. *VIII*, *17*, 3). The peaks observed are due to the two tautomeric species:

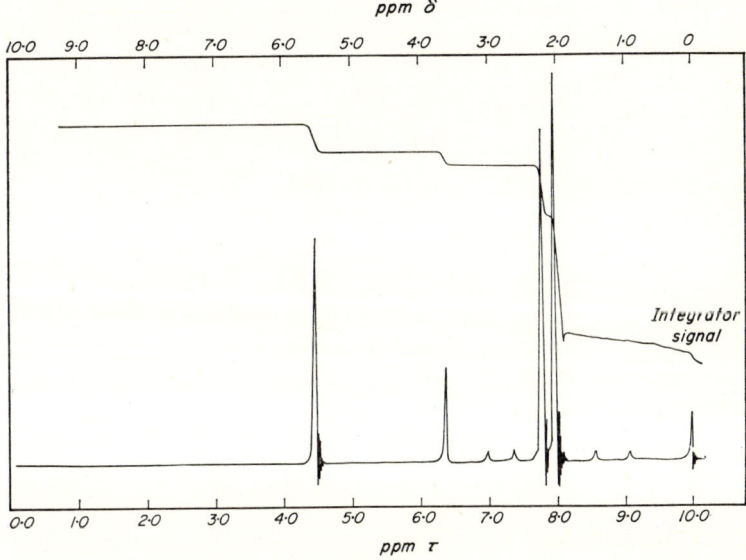

The following peaks (except that at $-3\cdot 8\ \tau$) are clearly discernible:

Hydroxyl proton, broad band at $-3\cdot 8\ \tau$ (peak broadened and moved to very low field compared with normal hydroxyl position by hydrogen bonding).

Enol-form olefinic proton at $4\cdot 45\ \tau$.
Keto-form methylene protons at $6\cdot 36\ \tau$.
Keto-form methyl groups at $7\cdot 82\ \tau$.
Enol-form methyl groups at $7\cdot 98\ \tau$.

Fig. *VIII, 17, 3*.

This spectrum illustrates how n.m.r. may be used to study tautomeric equilibria and hydrogen bonding: the integral shows that the ratio of enol to keto forms to be about 4:1.

Crotonaldehyde (Fig. *VIII, 17*, 4). The chief features are:
  Aldehyde proton, doublet at $0\cdot 60\ \tau$.
  Olefinic proton, multi-coupled peaks at $2\cdot 9$–$4\cdot 2\ \tau$.
  Methyl group, double doublet at $7\cdot 98\ \tau$.

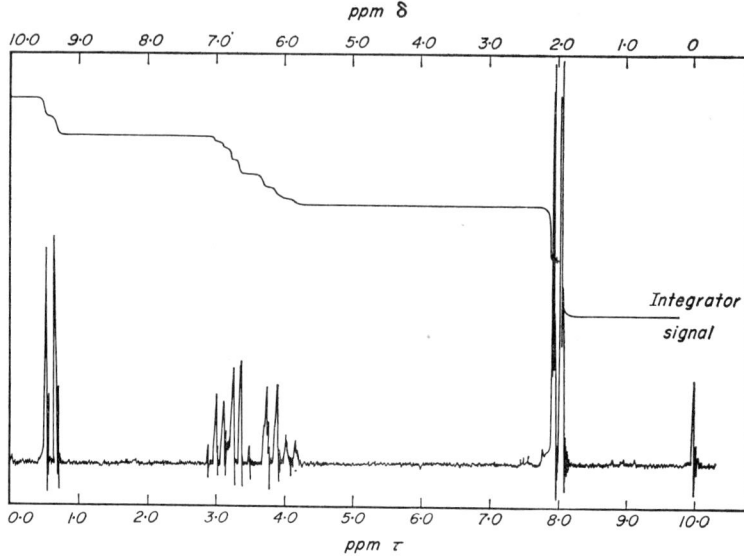

Fig. *VIII*, 17, 4.

It will be noted from the formula

$$\begin{array}{c}CH_3\\ \diagdown \\ H_x\end{array}\!\!\!C\!=\!C\!\begin{array}{c}\diagup H_y\\ \diagdown \\ H\end{array}\!\!\!C\!=\!O$$

that since the two protons, H_x and H_y, attached to the double bond are non-equivalent, they split each other as well as being coupled to the other protons present.

SELECTED BIBLIOGRAPHY

1. L. M. Jackman, *Applications of Nuclear Magnetic Resonance Spectroscopy in Organic Chemistry*. Pergamon Press, London, 1959.
2. J. D. Roberts, *Nuclear Magnetic Resonance. Applications to Organic Chemistry*. McGraw-Hill Book Company, New York, 1959.
3. J. A. Pople, W. G. Schneider and H. J. Bernstein, *High-resolution Nuclear Magnetic Resonance*. McGraw-Hill Book Company, New York, 1959.
4. H. S. Gutowsky, *Nuclear Magnetic Resonance* in A. Weissberger (Editor) *Physical Methods of Organic Chemistry*, Volume I, Part IV. Third Edition. Interscience Publishers, New York, 1959.

5. J. D. Roberts, *An Introduction to the Analysis of Spin-Spin Splitting in High Resolution Nuclear Magnetic Resonance Spectra*. W. A. Benjamin, New York, 1961.
6. K. B. Wiberg and B. J. Nist, *Interpretation of NMR Spectra*. W. A. Benjamin, New York, 1962.
7. W. D. Phillips, *High Resolution H^1 and F^{19} Magnetic Resonance Spectra of Organic Molecules* in F. Nachod and W. D. Phillips (Editors), *Determination of Organic Structures by Physical Methods*, Volume 2. Academic Press, New York, 1962.
8. R. J. Gillespie and R. F. M. White, *Nuclear Magnetic Resonance and Stereochemistry* in de la Mare and W. Klyne, *Progress in Stereochemistry*, Volume 3, Butterworths, London, 1962.
9. J. B. Stothers, *Applications of Nuclear Magnetic Resonance Spectroscopy* in A. Weissberger (Editor), *Technique of Organic Chemistry*, Volume XI. Interscience Publishers, New York, 1963.
10. H. H. Willard, L. J. Merritt and J. A. Dean, *Instrumental Methods of Analysis*. Fourth Edition. Van Nostrand, New Jersey, 1965. (This volume also contains accounts of ultraviolet, infrared and mass spectrometry.)

MASS SPECTROMETRY

VIII, 18 Elementary Principles and Apparatus

Let us imagine the vapour of a compound passing through a tube under a pressure sufficiently low for intermolecular collisions to be infrequent and that a beam of electrons, the energy of which can be varied, bombards the molecules of the compound in the tube. Collisions between electrons and molecules will then occur but no permanent changes in the molecules will result if the energy of the electrons is less than about 10 electron volts (e.v.). When the electron energy is increased to a critical value, the ionization potential of the parent compound, removal of electrons by the process

$$m + e^- \rightarrow m^+ + 2e^-$$

becomes possible so that the issuing vapour will contain positive ions as well as uncharged molecules. If the energy of the bombarding electrons is increased still further, these positive ions will have excess energy which may collect in a particular bond and may eventually be sufficient to break it, yielding a fragment ion plus an uncharged particle:

$$m^+ \rightarrow m_1^+ + m_2$$

In practice, an electron energy of 50–80 e.v. is generally used so that sufficient energy is available for practically any bond in the molecule to be broken. Indeed, the fragment ions may in turn break down further. Also, in addition to ions formed by bond cleavage, others occur in which atomic rearrangements accompany the fragmentation process. Bombardment of an organic molecule with high energy electrons may lead to a complex mixture of positive ions and uncharged species. The basic function of a mass spectrometer is to separate the various positive ions and to determine their relative abundance. Negative ions may also be formed but these are not normally investigated nor detected by routine instruments.

Mass spectrometry is basically a means of analysing mixtures of positive ions. In the magnetic analyser the ions, after their formation, are passed through a slit and then subjected to a potential of several thousand volts, yielding an essentially mono-energetic ion beam: beyond the slit they enter a semicircular magnetic field whereby separation occurs into individual beams of constant mass to charge ratio (m/e), the lighter ions being deflected more than the heavier ones. A particular ion beam may be separated through the exit slit where it falls on a collector plate. Measurement of the current that must flow in this plate to neutralize the ions striking it provides a measure of the relative number of ions of this particular m/e formed in the ion source. By continuously changing either the magnetic field or the accelerating voltage, the individual ion beams can be swept past the collector plate, the output of which will then indicate the relative abundances of the ions according to their m/e ratio. The **mass spectrum** is usually displayed from this output, after amplification, on an oscilloscope or chart recorder and is a recording of the relative abundance of charged particles against the mass number.

The radius of the semicircular path described by a particle of charge e depends upon the accelerating potential V and the strength of the magnetic field H. The potential energy eV of the particle will be equal to the kinetic energy after full acceleration:

$$eV = \tfrac{1}{2}mv^2 \tag{1}$$

where m is the mass of the ion and v is its velocity. In the magnetic field, the ion will experience a force Hev which is counterbalanced by the centrifugal force mv^2/r (r is the radius of the semicircular path described by the particle of charge e),

i.e., $\qquad\qquad\qquad Hev = mv^2/r$

or $\qquad\qquad\qquad r = mv/He \tag{2}$

Eliminating v from equations (1) and (2) gives:

$$m/e = H^2 r^2 / 2V \tag{3}$$

Various conclusions can be drawn from equation (3):

(a) At given values of H and V, not only ions of mass m arrive at the collector placed $2r$ from the source slit, but also those of mass $m'/2$ and $m''/3$ where $m' = 2m$ and $m'' = 3m$. Under the usual conditions for recording mass spectra of organic compounds, most of the ions formed are singly charged; double charged ions are encountered less frequently and ions of higher charge very rarely.

(b) The radius r corresponding to an ion of given mass to charge ratio can be changed by variation of V or H; it is obviously not feasible to move the collector and thus change r. Either H can be changed (magnetic scanning; V constant) or V can be varied (electric scanning; H constant). Both of these alternative procedures are in use.

Elementary Practical Organic Chemistry [VIII

A schematic diagram of the A.E.I. mass spectrometer MS9* is shown in Fig. *VIII*, *18*, 1, whilst Fig. *VIII*, *18*, 2 is a photograph of the actual instrument.

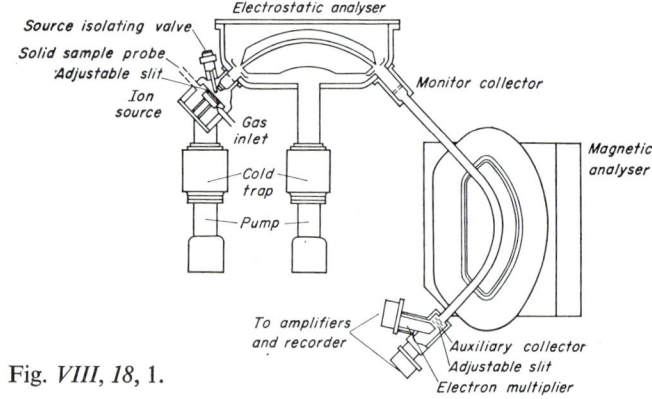

Fig. *VIII*, *18*, 1.

VIII, 19 The Ionization Process

An organic molecule is ionized when the electron energy applied exceeds the ionization potential (energy required to remove one electron) which is generally 9–15 electron volts. The usual ionizing beam, however, has an energy of about 70 e.v. and consequently the ion acquires a large excess of energy. As a result the ion undergoes immediate fragmentation into smaller ions and neutral free radicals. The following scheme includes some of the processes which may follow the impact of an electron of sufficient energy upon a hypothetical molecule $ABCD$:

$$ABCD + e^- \rightarrow ABCD^+ \text{ (parent ion)} + 2e^- \quad \text{(i)}$$

$$ABCD^+ \begin{cases} A^+ + BCD\cdot & \text{(ii)} \\ AB^+ + CD\cdot & \text{(iii)} \\ B^+ + A\cdot & \text{(iv)} \\ A^+ + B\cdot & \text{(v)} \\ CD^+ + AB\cdot & \text{(vi)} \\ AD^+ + BC\cdot & \text{(vii)} \end{cases}$$

* Manufactured by Associated Electrical Industries Ltd., Instrumental Division, Urmston, Manchester, England. Mass Spectrometers are also available *inter alia* from Consolidated Electrodynamics Corporation, Pasadena, California, from Hitachi Ltd., Tokio (distributed by Perkin–Elmer Corporation, Norwalk, Connecticut, U.S.A., and Beaconsfield, England), and from Mess und Analysen Technik GMBH., Bremen, Germany for MAT-Atlas instruments.

Fig. *VIII*, *18*, 2. A.E.I. Mass Spectrometer, Model MS9.

Equations (ii)–(vii) represent various possibilities for fragmentation leading to a positively charged fragment and a neutral one. The neutral fragment may be a free radical (as shown) or an uncharged molecule. Since only the positive ions are recorded on the mass spectrum, the steps in the various equations may give rise to different peaks in the spectrum. Any one of the positively charged fragments can, if it consists of more than one atom, decompose further into another positive ion and a neutral particle. A molecular ion or a positively charged fragment may become rearranged before it decomposes, and such processes lead to fragments or groups which were not present in this form in the original molecule. If the mechanism and also the structural requirements of the rearrangement are known, the presence of such rearranged fragments may be helpful for structure determination.

The above scheme explains why even simple molecules may give a relatively complex mass spectrum. The relative heights of the peaks are proportional to the relative numbers of different kinds of ions. Rearrangements and combinations of ions with neutral fragments can also occur. The intense peak with the highest mass number is of great importance: in the absence of any combination reactions of cracked fragments this corresponds to the parent molecule minus one electron M^+ (the parent molecular ion is sometimes written as $[P]^+$) and provides an accurate **method for determining molecular weights.** The 'cracking patterns' often serve as individual fingerprints of certain molecules and the relative abundances of various sized fragments have, in many instances, been correlated with molecular structure.

Owing to the presence of isotopes, the highest mass number is not necessarily the molecular weight of the compound, since even if an appreciable quantity of the original (parent) ions escape fragmentation small peaks with mass numbers one, two or three higher may be obtained depending upon the elements present. Mass numbers corresponding to the molecular weights must be even for carbon compounds containing hydrogen, oxygen, halogen or an even number of nitrogen atoms. All fragments formed by cleavage of single bonds have odd mass numbers unless they contain an odd number of nitrogen atoms.

Of the elements most frequently found in organic compounds, hydrogen, carbon, oxygen, nitrogen, sulphur, chlorine and bromine are mixtures of isotopes. The most abundant isotope is accompanied by isotopes of mass number one or two units higher. Table VIII, 19, 1 gives the amount of the isotopes of lower abundance present as per cent of the amount of the highest isotope.

Table VIII, 19, 1.   Per Cent of Isotope of Lower Abundance relative to Isotope of Highest Abundance

ISOTOPE	PER CENT	ISOTOPE	PER CENT
^{2}H	0·016	^{33}S	0·78
^{13}C	1·11	^{34}S	4·39
^{17}O	0·04	^{37}Cl	24·2
^{18}O	0·20	^{81}Br	49·48
^{15}N	0·37	^{29}Si	5·07
		^{30}Si	3·31

Since the ratio of the height of the peak for the most abundant element to the height of the $M+1$ or $M+2$ peak is the abundance ratio of the isotopes, the relative heights of these peaks can be used to establish the **empirical formula** of an ion. For ions of unit charge, the empirical formula is also the molecular formula: in such cases the relative heights of the peaks may be employed to determine the molecular weight. A simple example is provided by the mass spectrum of 1,2-benzanthracene (M.W. = 228) at low resolution, and is shown diagrammatically in Fig. *VIII, 19*, 1. It will be noted that beyond the large

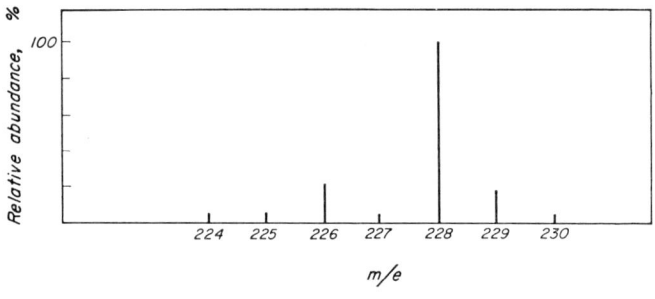

Fig. *VIII, 19,* 1.

m/e 228 peak, there are two additional peaks at 229 and 230. The m/e 229 peak indicates the number of benzanthracene molecules which contain one ^{13}C or deuterium atom ^{2}H in place of the normal ^{12}C or hydrogen atom ^{1}H, and the m/e 230 peak is due to molecules containing a combination of two such heavy atoms. The relative abundance of ^{13}C in naturally occurring carbon is 1·1 per cent and of deuterium in hydrogen 0·016 per cent. Benzanthracene with 18 carbon atoms should thus have $18 \times 1·1 = 19·8$ per cent containing one ^{13}C atom; similarly $12 \times 0·016 = 0·192$ per cent of its molecules should contain one deuterium atom ^2H. Thus in naturally occurring benzanthracene the abundance of molecules of molecular weight 229 vs. 228 should be nearly 20 per cent, which is close to that actually found. Similar calculations can be used for the expected m/e 230. Conversely, the relative abundance m/e 229/228 of 20 per cent indicates an empirical formula $C_{18}H_{12}$. Other possible empirical formulae for m/e 228, such as $C_{17}H_{24}$ and $C_{16}H_{20}O$, would give a 229/228 ratio of 19 per cent and 18 per cent respectively. Extensive tables are available listing the masses and isotope abundance ratios observed for various combinations of carbon, hydrogen, oxygen and nitrogen with masses up to 500: these may be used for obtaining empirical (or molecular) formulae from observed isotope abundance ratios. The presence of sulphur, chlorine and bromine is readily detected because of the high intensities of the $+2$ peaks.

VIII, 20 Mass Spectra of Some Classes of Organic Compounds. Functional Group Effects

Limitations of space will permit only a very abbreviated discussion and this will be confined to a few relatively simple compounds with selected functional groups.

Mono-olefines. These compounds tend to rupture at the carbon–carbon bond located beta to the double bond. Thus 1-heptene gives a base peak at m/e 41.

$$[H_2C\!\!=\!\!CH\!-\!CH_2\!-\!\!\vdots\!\!-\!C_4H_9]^+ \rightarrow H_2C\!\!=\!\!CH\!-\!CH_2^+ + C_4H_9\cdot$$
$$m/e = 41$$

Different fragmentation occurs when branched chains are present near the double bond.

Alkylbenzenes. Mono-alkylbenzenes $C_6H_5CH_2R$ give the highest peaks in their mass spectra by single cleavage (beta to the aromatic ring) and rearrangement thus:

$$[C_6H_5\!-\!CH_2\!-\!R]^+ \rightarrow R\cdot + C_6H_5\!-\!CH_2^+$$
$$m/e = 91$$

Elementary Practical Organic Chemistry [VIII

In the gas phase the benzyl ion is unstable and rearranges to the tropylium ion. With the three xylenes a methyl is easily lost and an intense peak at m/e 91 is obtained; it is possible that the xylene ion first rearranges to the methylcycloheptatriene or methyl tropylium ion and the latter loses methyl to yield the more stable tropylium ion.

Primary alcohols. Many primary alcohols give strong peaks at m/e 31, probably because the $^+CH_2OH$ ion is stabilized by resonance:

$$[R-CH_2OH]^+ \rightarrow R\cdot + [\overset{+}{C}H_2OH \leftrightarrow CH_2=\overset{+}{O}H]$$
$$m/e = 31$$

In ethanol, there is an additional less marked fragmentation leading to m/e 45:

$$CH_2=\overset{+}{O}H \leftarrow \left[CH_3 \overset{\cdot}{-} CH-OH \atop H\right]^+ \rightarrow CH_3-CH=\overset{+}{O}H$$
$$m/e = 31 \qquad\qquad\qquad\qquad\qquad\qquad m/e = 45$$

Secondary alcohols. Secondary alcohols give fragments which depend upon the location of the hydroxyl group. Thus 2-alkanols give a strong peak at m/e 45 and often a weaker one at m/e 59.

$$\left[\begin{array}{c}RCH-CH_3\\|\\OH\end{array}\right]^+ \rightarrow R\cdot + \left[\begin{array}{cc}\overset{+}{C}H-CH_3 & CH-CH_3\\| & \parallel\\OH & {}^+OH\end{array}\right]$$
$$m/e = 45$$

3-Alkanols give peaks at m/e 59 and also at 31, the latter due to the easy elimination of a molecule of ethylene:

$$\left[\begin{array}{c}RCHCH_2CH_3\\|\\OH\end{array}\right]^+ \rightarrow R\cdot + \left[\begin{array}{cc}\overset{+}{C}HCH_2CH_3 & CHCH_2CH_3\\| & \parallel\\OH & {}^+OH\end{array}\right]$$
$$m/e = 59$$

$$HO-\overset{+}{C}H \overset{CH_2}{\underset{H}{\overbrace{\quad}}} CH_2 \rightarrow HO\overset{+}{C}H_2 + CH_2=CH_2$$
$$m/e = 31$$

Tertiary alcohols. These (*e.g.*, 2-methyl-2-alkanols) give a strong peak at m/e 59, due to the marked stability of the tertiary carbonium ion:

$$\left[\begin{array}{c}CH_3\\|\\R-C-CH_3\\|\\OH\end{array}\right]^+ \rightarrow R\cdot + \begin{array}{c}CH_3\\|\\{}^+C-CH_3\\|\\OH\end{array}$$
$$m/e = 59$$

Ethers. Methyl ethers give a peak at m/e 29:
$$[CH_3-O-R]^+ \rightarrow CH_3O^+ + R\cdot$$
$$m/e = 31$$

Diethyl ether gives strong peaks at m/e 59 and m/e 31 (the latter is due to the loss of ethylene):

$$[CH_3CH_2OCH_2CH_3]^+ \rightarrow [CH_3CH_2\overset{+}{O}CH_2 \leftrightarrow CH_3CH_2\overset{+}{O}=CH_2] + \cdot CH_3$$
$$m/e = 59$$

$$CH_2=\overset{+}{O}\underset{H}{\overset{CH_2}{\diagup\diagdown}}CH_2 \rightarrow CH_2=\overset{+}{O}H + CH_2=CH_2$$
$$m/e = 31$$

With higher alkyl ethers alpha-cleavage occurs. Thus ethyl *sec*-butyl ethers gives two fragments, that of m/e 73 being much more abundant than that of m/e 87, *i.e.* the more highly substituted fragment is lost preferentially:

$$\underset{\underset{CH_3}{|}}{CH_3CH_2-CH}-\overset{+}{O}=CH_2 \quad \text{or} \quad CH_3CH_2-CH=\overset{+}{O}-CH_2CH_3 \quad + \cdot CH_3$$
$$m/e = 87 \qquad\qquad m/e = 87$$

$$\left[\underset{\underset{CH_3}{|}}{CH_3CH_2+CH}-O-CH_2+CH_3\right]^+$$

$$\underset{\underset{CH_3}{|}}{CH}=\overset{+}{O}-CH_2CH_3 + CH_3CH_2\cdot$$
$$m/e = 73$$

Further decomposition of these ions can occur with rearrangement and loss of a molecule of ethylene leading to m/e of 45 and 59. The latter probably arise as indicated below:

$$\underset{\underset{CH_3}{|}}{CH}=\overset{+}{O}-CH_2-CH_2\underset{H}{|} \rightarrow \underset{\underset{CH_3}{|}}{CH}=\overset{+}{O}H + CH_2=CH_2$$
$$m/e = 73 \qquad\qquad m/e = 45$$

$$CH_3CH_2CH=\overset{+}{O}-CH_2-CH_2\underset{H}{|} \rightarrow CH_3CH_2CH=\overset{+}{O}H + CH_2=CH_2$$
$$m/e = 87 \qquad\qquad m/e = 59$$

Aliphatic aldehydes. The molecule cleaves at either the alpha- or beta-bond:

$$\left[R\text{---}CH_2\text{---}CHO \right]^+$$

Alpha-cleavage predominates for low molecular weight aldehydes (up to C_3) leading to m/e 29 ($HC\overset{+}{=}O$). For higher molecular weight aldehydes, beta-cleavage predominates to yield an enol ion of m/e 44 $(CH_2=CHOH)^+$

$$\left[\begin{array}{c} HC\overset{O}{\diagup} \\ H_2C\diagdown_{C}\diagup CHR \\ H_2 \end{array} \right]^+ \rightarrow \left[\begin{array}{c} HC\diagup^{OH} \\ \| \\ CH_2 \end{array} \right]^+ + CH_2=CHR$$

$m/e = 44$

Aliphatic ketones. The major fragmentations are those resulting from cleavage at the carbon–carbon bonds adjacent to the carbonyl group:

$$R'\cdot + \begin{array}{c} R\text{---}\overset{+}{C} \\ \| \\ O \end{array} \leftarrow \left[\begin{array}{c} R\text{---}C\text{---}R' \\ \| \\ O \end{array} \right]^+ \rightarrow \begin{array}{c} \overset{+}{C}\text{---}R' \\ \| \\ O \end{array} + R\cdot$$

With methyl ketones m/e 43 (due to $CH_3\overset{+}{C}=O$) is common. For higher ketones m/e 57 (ethyl), 71 (n-propyl) and 87 (n-butyl) are common. The dominant cleavage with unsymmetrical ketones occurs in the longer chain.

Fission of the beta-bond with hydrogen transfer also occurs:

$$\left[\begin{array}{c} RC\overset{O}{\diagup} \\ H_2C\diagdown_{C}\diagup CHR' \\ H_2 \end{array} \right]^+ \rightarrow \left[\begin{array}{c} RC\diagup^{OH} \\ \| \\ CH_2 \end{array} \right]^+ + CH_2=CHR'$$

$m/e = 58, 72,$ etc.

Aliphatic carboxylic acids. Many normal carboxylic acids give a strong peak at m/e 60 probably arising from beta-cleavage with hydrogen rearrangement:

$$\begin{array}{c}\text{HO}\diagdown\diagup\text{O}^+\\ C\\ |\diagdown H\\ H_2C\diagup\\ \diagdown C\diagup CHR\\ H_2\end{array}\quad\rightarrow\quad\begin{array}{c}\text{HO}\diagdown\diagup\overset{+}{\text{O}}H\\ C\\ \parallel\\ CH_2\\ m/e=60\end{array}\quad+\ CH_2{=}CHR$$

Aliphatic carboxylic esters. Two types of cleavage are common:

$$\left[R{-}{\vdots}{-}\underset{\underset{O}{\parallel}}{C}{-}OR'\right]^+ \rightarrow R^+ + \cdot\underset{\underset{O}{\parallel}}{C}{-}OR'$$

$$\left[R{-}\underset{\underset{O}{\parallel}}{C}{-}{\vdots}{-}OR'\right]^+ \rightarrow R{-}\underset{\underset{O}{\parallel}}{C}^+ + \cdot OR'$$

Peaks at m/e 74 and 88 are found for methyl and ethyl esters respectively and arise from such cleavages as the following:

$$\left[\begin{array}{c}CH_3O\diagdown\diagup O\\ C\\ |\diagdown H\\ H_2C\diagup\\ \diagdown C\diagup CHR\\ H_2\end{array}\right]^+ \rightarrow \left[\begin{array}{c}CH_3O\diagdown\diagup OH\\ C\\ \parallel\\ CH_2\end{array}\right]^+ + CH_2{=}CHR$$

$$m/e = 74$$

$$\left[\begin{array}{c}C_2H_5O\diagdown\diagup O\\ C\\ |\diagdown H\\ H_2C\diagup\\ \diagdown C\diagup CH_2\\ H_2\end{array}\right]^+ \rightarrow \left[\begin{array}{c}C_2H_5O\diagdown\diagup OH\\ C\\ \parallel\\ CH_2\end{array}\right]^+ + CH_2{=}CH_2$$

$$m/e = 88$$

The fragmentation of the M^+ ion of ethyl n-butyrate is shown in some detail: it will be noted that it breaks down to give the enol form of ethyl acetate and ethylene. Support for this mechanism of fragmentation is provided by studies of the mass spectra of α-, β- and γ-deuterated ethyl n-butyrate.

Aliphatic amides. A common form of fragmentation for amides containing at least a three-carbon chain is the breaking of the beta-bond accompanied by transfer of a γ-hydrogen:

$$\left[\begin{array}{c} H_2N-C(=O)\cdots H \\ H_2C-C(H_2)-CHR \end{array}\right]^+ \rightarrow \left[\begin{array}{c} H_2N-C(OH) \\ \| \\ H_2C \end{array}\right]^+ + CH_2=CHR$$

$$m/e = 59$$

This is revealed by the peak at m/e 59.

For the lower amides (formamide, acetamide, propionamide and isobutyramide) alpha-fragmentation is the most important, resulting in the formation of ions of m/e 44:

$$[R-\underset{\underset{O}{\|}}{C}-NH_2]^+ \rightarrow R\cdot + \underset{\underset{O^+}{\|\|\|}}{C-NH_2} \leftrightarrow \underset{\underset{O}{\|}}{\overset{+}{C}=NH_2}$$

$$m/e = 44$$

Primary aliphatic amines. The so-called beta-fission occurs and the most abundant ion generally corresponds to the fragment containing nitrogen:

$$[R-CH_2-\!\!\mid\!\!-CH_2-NH_2]^+ \rightarrow R-CH_2\cdot + CH_2=\overset{+}{N}H_2$$

$$m/e = 30$$

Thus peaks occur at m/e 30, 44, etc.; a peak also sometimes occurs at m/e 14 corresponding to NH_4^+. In all cases, the largest alkyl group is lost preferentially.

Thiols and sulphides behave similarly to the corresponding oxygen compounds. If more than one hetero atom is present, the ion carrying the most electron-releasing element is the more stable. Thus 1,2-amino alcohols give a more intense peak for the nitrogen fragment because nitrogen is less electronegative than oxygen and can stabilize the positive charge more readily. With aminoethanol two peaks are obtained at m/e 30 and 31, but the peak at m/e 30 is about 10 times more intense than that m/e 31. The result will also be understood in terms of ionization potentials: that of ethylamine is 9·4–9·6 e.v. whilst that for ethanol is 10·7 e.v.

$$\begin{array}{c} \text{CH}_2 \quad \cdot\text{CH}_2 \\ \| \quad + \quad | \\ {}^+\text{OH} \quad \text{NH}_2 \end{array} \leftarrow \begin{bmatrix} \text{CH}_2-\text{CH}_2 \\ | \quad\quad | \\ \text{OH} \quad \text{NH}_2 \end{bmatrix}^+ \rightarrow \begin{array}{c} \cdot\text{CH}_2 \quad \text{CH}_2 \\ | \quad + \quad \| \\ \text{OH} \quad {}^+\text{NH}_2 \end{array}$$

$m/e = 31$ $\qquad\qquad\qquad\qquad\qquad\qquad\qquad\qquad m/e = 30$

Oxygen can compete better with the more electronegative sulphur, and in thioethanol the fragment of m/e 31 is more than half as intense as the fragment of m/e 47. Oxygen stabilizes the positive charge much better than does chlorine, as is borne out by the much more intense peak for ethylene chlorhydrin at m/e 31 as compared with that at m/e 49.

$$\begin{array}{cc} \text{CH}_2-\!\!-\text{CH}_2 \\ |\quad\quad\quad | \\ \text{SH}\quad\quad\text{OH} \end{array} \qquad\qquad \begin{array}{cc} \text{CH}_2-\!\!-\text{CH}_2 \\ |\quad\quad\quad | \\ \text{Cl}\quad\quad\text{OH} \end{array}$$

$m/e = 47 \quad m/e = 31 \qquad\qquad m/e = 49 \quad m/e = 31$

Sufficient has been said to indicate the value of mass spectrometry in the detection of functional groups and in structural studies of both simple and complex organic compounds. Further details will be found in the works listed in the Bibliography. The use of mass spectrometry in the solution of a simple problem—the structure of ketene dimer (compare Section **VIII,17**)—may be mentioned. Of the likely structures, only two need be considered (I) and (II):

$$\begin{array}{c} \text{H}_2\text{C}=\text{C}-\text{CH}_2 \\ |\quad\quad\quad | \\ \text{O}-\text{C}=\text{O} \end{array} \qquad\qquad \begin{array}{c} \text{H}_3\text{C}-\text{C}=\text{CH} \\ |\quad\quad\quad | \\ \text{O}-\text{C}=\text{O} \end{array}$$

$\qquad\qquad\qquad$ (I) $\qquad\qquad\qquad\qquad\qquad$ (II)

The mass spectrum is similar to that of a β-lactone: a prominent peak at m/e 14 (CH_2) suggests structure (I) in the vapour state.

VIII, 21 Some Mass Spectra

Two simple mass spectra (diagrammatic) are shown in Figs. *VIII, 21, 1* (ethyl *sec*-butyl ether) and Fig. *VIII, 21, 2* (*n*-butyraldehyde). In the mass spectrum for ethyl *sec*-butyl ether, the parent peak (P^+ or M^+) is at m/e 102. Alpha-cleavage gives rise to two ions with m/e 73 and m/e 87; the more highly substituted fragment is lost preferentially, *i.e.*, m/e 73 is more abundant than m/e 87. Further decomposition of these ions also occurs with rearrangement of a hydrogen atom and elimination of a neutral ethylene molecule leading to fragments of m/e 45 and m/e 29 respectively. The mode of

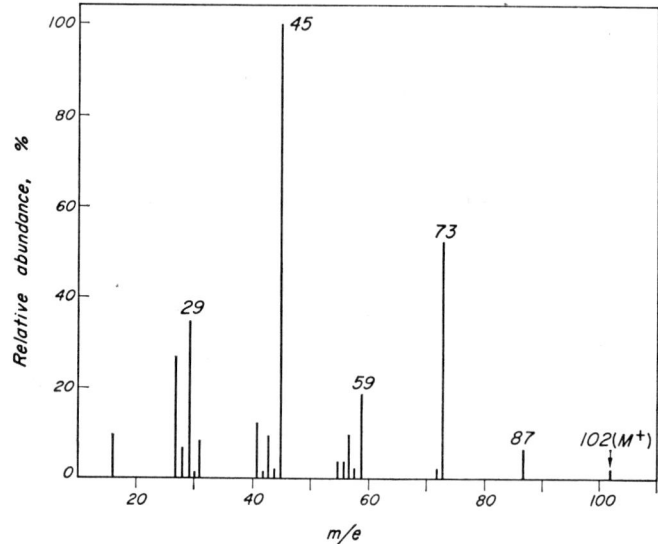

Fig. *VIII*, *21*, 1.

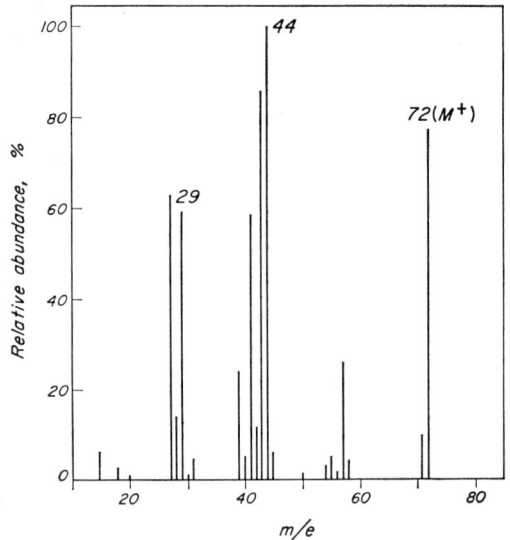

Fig. *VIII*, *21*, 2.

formation of these fragments is described in Section **VIII,20** under *Ethers*.

In the mass spectrum of *n*-butyraldehyde, the parent peak (M^+) is at m/e 72, and important peaks occur at m/e 44 and m/e 29 (see Section **VIII,20** under *Aldehydes*). There is a possibility that the peak at m/e 42 may be due to the olefine ion $C_3H_6^+$ and that at m/e 29 is partly due to the alkyl ion $C_2H_5^+$.

Fig. *VIII, 21*, 3 (kindly supplied by A.E.I. Ltd.) displays part of the mass spectrum of α-tetralone obtained with an MS9 spectrometer,

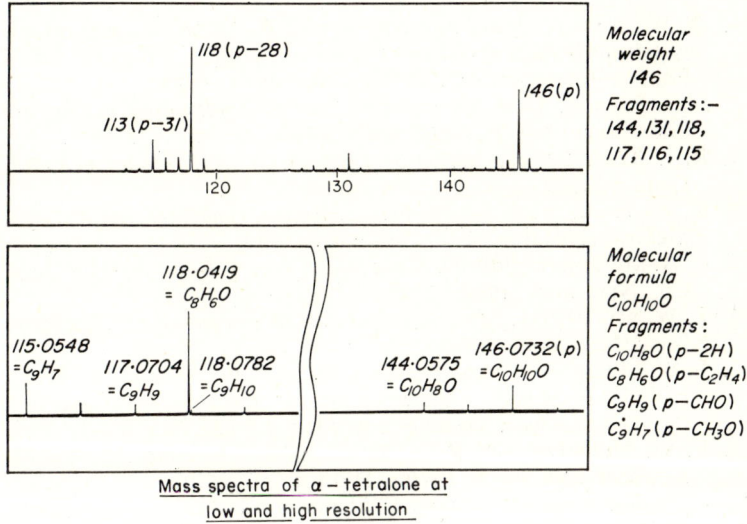

Fig. *VIII, 21, 3*.

one at low resolving power and the other at high resolving power: there is also a peak (not shown) at m/e 78 ($=P-68$) corresponding to the benzene cation $C_6H_6^+$. The parent ion (P^+ or p^+) is at m/e 146 which is the approximate molecular weight. It is evident that the peaks at m/e 131 and 128 correspond to ($P-CH_3$) and ($P-H_2O$) respectively. The peaks at m/e 118 and 117 are not easily and unambiguously interpreted from the low resolution spectrum. However, the high resolution spectrum provides valuable information. The molecular weight (P^+) is 146·0732 establishes the molecular formula as $C_{10}H_{10}O$. The 118 ($=P-28$) peak is revealed as a doublet and from the accurate masses it is found that the major peak leads to a mass of 118·0419 corresponding to C_8H_6O (or $P-C_2H_4$) and the minor peak gives a mass of 118·0782 corresponding to C_9H_{10} (or P-CO). The 117 peak (P-29) leads to a mass of 117·0704 corresponding to C_9H_9 (or P-CHO). These results provide evidence for the formula for α-tetralone as

SELECTED BIBLIOGRAPHY

1. D. W. Stewart, *Mass Spectrometry* in A. Weissberger (Editor), *Physical Methods of Organic Chemistry*, Volume I, Part IV. Third Edition. Interscience Publishers, New York, 1959.
2. J. H. Beynon, *Mass Spectrometry and its Applications in Organic Chemistry*. Elsevier, Amsterdam, 1960.
3. R. I. Reed, *Ion Production by Electron Impact*. Academic Press, London, 1962.
4. K. Biemann, *Mass Spectrometry: Organic Chemical Applications*. McGraw Hill Book Co., New York, 1962.
5. C. A. McDowell (Editor), *Mass Spectrometry*. McGraw-Hill Book Co., New York, 1962.
6. F. W. McLafferty, *Mass Spectrometry of Organic Ions*. Academic Press, New York, 1963.
7. F. W. McLafferty, *Mass Spectrometry* in F. W. Nachod and W. D. Phillips (Editors), *Determination of Organic Structures by Physical Methods*. Volume 2. Academic Press, New York, 1962.
8. F. W. Melpolder and R. A. Brown, *Mass Spectrometry* in I. M. Kolthoff and P. J. Elving (Editors), *Treatise on Analytical Chemistry*, Part I, Volume 4. Interscience Publishers, New York, 1963.
9. H. Budzikiewicz, C. Djerassi and D. H. Williams, *Identification of Mass Spectra of Organic Compounds*. Holden-Day, San Francisco, 1964.
10. F. W. McLafferty, *Mass Spectral Correlations*. American Chemical Society, Washington, D.C., 1965.

CHAPTER IX

Physical Constants of Organic Compounds.
Tables of Derivatives

IX, 1 Preface to Tables

The Tables in this Chapter contain lists of the more common members of the various classes of organic compounds arranged, as far as possible, in the order of increasing boiling points or melting points, together with the melting points of selected derivatives. Some of the Tables are subdivided: thus in Table IX, 7, **Phenols,** the additional sub-headings are *Halogeno-phenols* and *Nitro-phenols*. This subdivision renders the Tables less cumbersome and facilitates their use by students.

In describing compounds in the literature, the range of a certain number of degrees is usually recorded for the boiling point or the melting point; the highest point of the boiling point or melting point range is listed in the Tables and the value is given to the nearest whole degree. For those compounds which the author has purified or prepared, the actual observed boiling point or melting point is recorded. Densities are given for a temperature of 20° referred to water at 4° unless otherwise indicated. Refractive indices are recorded for the sodium D line at 20°. It must be remembered that the value obtained for a melting point depends somewhat upon the observer and upon the method which was used in the determination: this often accounts for the several slightly different values found in the literature for the same compound.

The numbering of the Tables has been arranged so that it corresponds to the Section numbers in Chapter IV (Reactions and Characterization of Selected Classes of Organic Compounds). Thus the Table for Section **IV,2, Saturated Aliphatic Hydrocarbons,** is numbered Table IX, 2. This numbering will simplify cross reference. Additional Tables corresponding to classes of compounds described in Chapter VI (The Preparation of Derivatives) follow and are numbered consecutively.

A complete Index to all the Tables in this Chapter follows.

Elementary Practical Organic Chemistry

Index to Tables

- IX, 2.   Saturated Aliphatic Hydrocarbons (Paraffins and Cycloparaffins).
- IX, 3.   Unsaturated Aliphatic Hydrocarbons.
- IX, 4.   Aromatic Hydrocarbons.
- IX, 5.   Aliphatic Alcohols.
- IX, 6.   Aromatic Alcohols.
- IX, 7.   Phenols.
- IX, 8.   Enols.
- IX, 9.   Polyhydric Alcohols.
- IX, 10.   Carbohydrates (Sugars).
- IX, 11.   Aliphatic Halogen Compounds.
- IX, 12.   Aromatic Halogen Compounds.
- IX, 13.   Aliphatic Ethers.
- IX, 14.   Aromatic Ethers.
- IX, 15.   Aliphatic Aldehydes.
- IX, 16.   Acetals.
- IX, 17.   Aromatic Aldehydes.
- IX, 18.   Aliphatic Ketones.
- IX, 19.   Aromatic Ketones.
- IX, 20.   Aliphatic Carboxylic Acids.
- IX, 21.   Aromatic Carboxylic Acids.
- IX, 22.   Acid Chlorides (Aliphatic).
- IX, 23.   Acid Anhydrides (Aliphatic).
- IX, 24.   Acid Chlorides and Acid Anhydrides of Aromatic Acids.
- IX, 25.   Aliphatic Esters.
- IX, 26.   Aromatic Esters.
- IX, 27.   Primary Aliphatic Amides.
- IX, 28.   Primary Aromatic Amides.
- IX, 29.   Substituted Aromatic Amides.
- IX, 30.   Aliphatic Nitriles (Cyanides).
- IX, 31.   Aromatic Nitriles.
- IX, 32.   Primary and Secondary Aliphatic Amines.
- IX, 33A.   Primary Aromatic Amines.
- IX, 33B.   Secondary Aromatic Amines.
- IX, 33C.   Tertiary Amines.
- IX, 34.   Amino Acids.
- IX, 35.   Aromatic Nitro Compounds.
- IX, 36.   Aliphatic Nitro Compounds.
- IX, 37.   Mercaptans (Thiols).

IX, 38. Sulphonic Acids.
IX, 39. Aromatic Sulphonamides.
IX, 40. Quinones.
IX, 41. Imides.
IX, 42. Nitroso, Azo, Azoxy and Hydrazo Compounds.
IX, 43. Miscellaneous Sulphur Compounds.
IX, 44. Miscellaneous Phosphorus Compounds.

Table IX, 2.   Saturated Aliphatic Hydrocarbons

PARAFFINS AND CYCLOPARAFFINS

HYDROCARBON	B.P.	$d_{4°}^{20°}$	$n_D^{20°}$
2-Methylbutane (isopentane)	28°	0·620	1·354
n-Pentane	36	0·627	1·358
n-Hexane	68·5	0·659	1·374
n-Heptane	98	0·683	1·388
n-Octane	125	0·703	1·397
n-Nonane	150·5	0·717	1·405
n-Decane	173	0·730	1·412
n-Undecane	196 (87°/20)	0·740	1·417
n-Dodecane	216 (94°/14)	0·750	1·422
n-Tridecane	92·5°/4·5	0·756	1·425
n-Tetradecane	252 (123°/12)	0·762	1·429
n-Pentadecane	270 (120°/4·5)	0·769	1·432
n-Hexadecane	143·5°/9 (m.p. 18°)	0·774	1·435
n-Octadecane	308 (m.p. 28°)	—	—
2-Methylpentane	60	0·653	1·372
2,2,4-Trimethylpentane	99	0·688	1·389
2,7-Dimethyl-n-octane (Di-isoamyl)	160	0·725	1·409
Cyclopentane	49	0·745	1·406
Cyclohexane	81	0·779	1·426
Methylcyclohexane	101	0·769	1·423
Cycloheptane	118	0·811	1·445
Ethylcyclohexane	130	0·784	1·432
Isopropylcyclohexane	154·5	0·802	1·441
n-Propylcyclohexane	155	0·790	1·436
n-Butylcyclohexane	177	0·800	1·440
Isoamylcyclohexane	193	0·802	1·442
n-Amylcyclohexane	200	0·804	1·444
Dicyclohexyl	237 (m.p. 3°)	0·889	1·480
trans-Decahydronaphthalene (Decalin)	185	0·870	1·470
cis-Decahydronaphthalene (Decalin)	194	0·895	1·481
1,2,3,4-Tetrahydronaphthalene (Tetralin)	207	0·971	1·540
trans-p-Menthane	161	0·792	1·439
cis-p-Menthane	169	0·816	1·451

Table IX, 3. Unsaturated Aliphatic Hydrocarbons

HYDROCARBON	B.P.	$d_{4°}^{20°}$	$n_{\text{D}}^{20°}$
1-Pentene	30°	0·641	1·371
2-Methyl-1-butene	31	0·650	1·378
2-Pentene	36	0·651	1·380
Trimethylethylene	38	0·662	1·388
1-Hexene	64	0·674	1·388
1-Heptene	93	0·697	1·400
1-Octene	121	0·716	1·409
1-Nonene	146	0·731	1·413
1-Decene	169	0·742	1·422
1-Undecene	193	0·779	1·444
1-Dodecene	213	0·760	1·430
1-Tetradecene	125°/15	0·773	1·437
1-Hexadecene	153°/14 (m.p. 15°)	0·782	1·441
1-Octadecene	180°/18 (m.p. 18°)	0·789	1·445
Isoprene (2-methyl-1,3-butadiene)	34	0·681	1·419
Piperylene (1,3-pentadiene)	42	0·680	1·431
1,5-Hexadiene (diallyl)	59	0·690	1·402
2,3-Dimethylbutadiene	69	0·726	1·439
Cyclopentene	45	0·772	1·420
Cyclohexene	83	0·810	1·445
1,3-Cyclopentadiene	42	0·803	1·443
Dicyclopentadiene	170 (m.p. 32°)	—	—
1,3-Cyclohexadiene	81	0·841	1·474
α-Pinene	156	0·860	1·456
Camphene	160 (m.p. 51°)	—	—
Dipentene (*dl*-limonene)	178	0·840	1·473
Sylvestrene	176	0·847	1·475
1-Pentyne (*n*-Propylacetylene)	39	0·695	1·385
2-Pentyne (Ethylmethylacetylene)	56	0·712	1·404
1-Hexyne (*n*-Butylacetylene)	71	0·715	1·399
1-Heptyne (*n*-Amylacetylene)	100	0·734	1·409
1-Octyne (*n*-Hexylacetylene)	126	0·746	1·416
1-Nonyne (*n*-Heptylacetylene)	151	0·758	1·423
Phenylacetylene	142	0·925	1·552
Furan	31	0·937	1·422
2,5-Dimethylfuran	94	0·888	1·436

For the melting points of some crystalline derivatives, see Section IV,3.

Table IX, 4. Aromatic Hydrocarbons

HYDROCARBON	B.P.	M.P.	$d_4^{20°}$	n_D^{20}	PICRATE	AROYL-BENZOIC ACID	COMPOUND WITH 1,3,5-TRINITRO-BENZENE	STYPHNATE	OTHER DERIVATIVES*
Benzene	80°	6°	0·879	1·501	—	128°	—	—	1,3-Dinitro, 90°
Toluene	111	—	0·867	1·497	—	138	—	—	2,4-Dinitro, 71
Ethylbenzene	135	—	0·868	1·496	97°	128	—	—	2,4,6-Trinitro, 37
p-Xylene	138	13	0·861	1·496	—	132	—	—	2,3,5-Trinitro, 139
m-Xylene	139	—	0·864	1·497	—	126	—	—	2,4,6-Trinitro, 182
o-Xylene	144	—	0·880	1·505	—	167	—	—	4,5-Dinitro, 71
Styrene (1)	146	—	0·909	1·546	—	—	—	—	—
Isopropylbenzene (2)	153	—	0·862	1·491	103	134	—	—	2,4,6-Trinitro, 109
n-Propylbenzene	159	—	0·864	1·493	97	126	—	—	—
Mesitylene (3)	164	—	0·865	1·499	97	212	—	—	2,4,6-Trinitro, 235
tert-Butylbenzene	169	—	0·867	1·493	—	—	—	—	2,4-Dinitro, 62
Pseudo-cumene (4)	169	—	—	1·504	97	149	—	—	3,5,6-Trinitro, 185
sec-Butylbenzene	172	—	0·861	1·490	—	—	—	—	$CrO_3 \to C_6H_5COCH_3$
p-Cymene (5)	177	—	0·857	1·490	—	124	—	—	2,6-Dinitro, 54
Hydrindene	177	—	0·965	1·538	—	—	—	—	—
m-Diethylbenzene	182	—	0·865	1·496	—	114	—	—	2,4,6-Trinitro, 62
Indene	182	—	0·992	1·576	98	—	102	—	—
n-Butylbenzene	182	—	0·861	1·490	—	—	—	—	—
Isodurene (6)	197	—	—	—	90	213	—	—	4,6-Dinitro, 157
Prehnitene (7)	204	—	0·901	1·523	—	—	—	—	5,6-Dinitro, 176; Dibromo, 208
n-Amylbenzene	204	—	0·859	1·488	—	—	—	—	Dibromo, 64
Tetralin (8)	207	—	0·971	1·540	—	154	—	—	5,7-Dinitro, 95
1,3,5-Triethylbenzene	218	—	0·863	1·497	—	—	—	—	2,4,6-Trinitro, 108
Cyclohexylbenzene	238	7	0·950	1·533	—	—	—	—	4-Nitro, 59
1-Methylnaphthalene	241	—	1·019	1·618	141	168	154	135	4-Nitro, 71
Diphenylmethane	262	25	—	—	—	—	—	—	2,2′,4,4′-Tetranitro, 172

Aromatic Hydrocarbons (continued)

HYDROCARBON	B.P.	M.P.	$d_4^{20°}$	$n_D^{20°}$	PICRATE	AROYL-BENZOIC ACID	COMPOUND WITH 1,3,5-TRINITRO-BENZENE	STYPHNATE	OTHER DERIVATIVES*
2-Methylnaphthalene	241°	34°	—	—	115°	190°	123°	130°	1-Nitro, 81°
Bibenzyl	284	52	—	—	—	—	102	—	4,4'-Dinitro, 180
Pentamethylbenzene	231	54	—	—	131	—	121	—	—
Biphenyl	255	70	—	—	—	220	—	—	4,4'-Dinitro, 234; 4,4'-Dibromo, 164
Durene (9)	193	79	—	—	—	264	—	—	3,6-Dinitro, 207
Naphthalene	218	80	—	—	150	173	156	168	1-Nitro, 61
Triphenylmethane	358	92	—	—	—	—	—	—	4,4′,4″-Trinitro, 212; Triphenylcarbinol, 162
Acenaphthene	278	95	—	—	162	200	168	154	5-Nitro, 101
Retene (10)	390	99	—	—	123	—	139	141	—
Phenanthrene	340	100	—	—	143	—	164	142	Phenanthraquinone, 202
Fluorene (11)	294	114	—	—	84	228	105	134	2-Nitro, 156; 2,7-Dibromo, 165
Stilbene (12)	306	124	—	—	—	—	120	142	—
Pyrene	—	149	—	—	227	—	245	191	—
1,1'-Binaphthyl	—	160	—	—	145	—	—	—	—
2,2'-Binaphthyl	—	188	—	—	184	—	—	—	—
Anthracene	340	216	—	—	138	214	164	180	Anthraquinone, 286
Chrysene (13)	448	254	—	—	273	—	186	—	—

(1) Phenylethylene.
(2) Cumene.
(3) 1,3,5-Trimethylbenzene.
(4) 1,2,4-Trimethylbenzene.
(5) 4-Isopropyl-1-methylbenzene.
(6) 1,2,3,5-Tetramethylbenzene.
(7) 1,2,3,4-Tetramethylbenzene.
(8) 1,2,3,4-Tetrahydronaphthalene.
(9) 1,2,4,5-Tetramethylbenzene.
(10) 7-Isopropyl-1-methylphenanthrene.
(11) Diphenylenemethane.
(12) *trans*-1,2-Diphenylethylene.
(13) 1,2-Benzphenanthrene.

* For melting points of Sulphonamides and Adducts with 3,4,7-Trinitro-9-fluorenone, see Sections IV,4,*l* and IV,4,5 respectively.

Table IX, 5.   **Aliphatic Alcohols**

ALCOHOL	B.P.	M.P.	3,5-DINITRO-BENZOATE	p-NITRO-BENZOATE	PHENYL-URETHANE	1-NAPHTHYL-URETHANE	HYDROGEN 3-NITRO-PHTHALATE	OTHER DERIVATIVES
Methyl	65°	—	109°	96°	47°	124°	153°	—
Ethyl	78	—	94	57	52	79	157	—
Isopropyl	82	—	122	110	86	106	153	—
tert-Butyl	83	25°	142	116	136	101	—	—
Allyl	97	—	50	29	70	109	124	—
n-Propyl	97	—	75	35	57	80	145	—
sec-Butyl	99	—	76	26	64	98	131	—
tert-Amyl	102	—	118	85	42	72	—	—
2-Methyl-3-butyn-2-ol	105	—	—	—	102	—	—	$d_4^{20°}$ 0·807, $n_D^{20°}$ 1·421
Isobutyl	108	—	88	68	86	104	179	—
Isopropylmethyl carbinol	113	—	76	—	69	109	—	—
Neopentyl (1)	113	52	—	—	144	100	—	$d_4^{20°}$ 0·948, $n_D^{20°}$ 1·432
2-Propyn-1-ol	114	—	100	17	63	95	121	—
3-Pentanol (2)	116	—	64	36	49	72	147	—
n-Butyl	118	—	62	17	61	76	103	—
2-Pentanol (3)	119	—	72	—	—	—	—	—
2-Methyl-2-pentanol	121	—	—	—	239	—	—	—
3-Methyl-3-pentanol	128	—	—	—	50	—	—	—
Active Amyl (4)	129	—	70	—	—	82	158	—
Isoamyl	132	—	62	21	57	68	166	—
3-Hexanol (5)	135	—	77	—	—	—	—	—
n-Amyl	138	—	46	11	46	68	136	—
Cyclopentanol	141	—	115	62	132	118	—	—
2-Ethyl-1-butyl	149	—	52	—	—	61	147	—
4-Heptanol (6)	156	—	64	35	—	80	—	—
n-Hexyl	156	—	61	5	42	59	124	—
2-Heptanol (7)	160	—	49	—	—	54	—	—
Cyclohexanol	161	25	113	50	82	129	160	—

ALCOHOL	B.P.	M.P.	3,5-DINITRO-BENZOATE	p-NITRO-BENZOATE	PHENYL-URETHANE	1-NAPHTHYL-URETHANE	HYDROGEN 3-NITRO-PHTHALATE	OTHER DERIVATIVES
2-Methylcyclohexanol	165°	—	115°	65°	103°	155°	—	—
Diacetone alcohol	166	—	55	48	—	—	—	2,4-Dinitrophenylhydrazone, 203°
Furfuryl	170	—	81	76	45	129	—	—
4-Methylcyclohexanol	174	—	134	—	125	160	—	—
3-Methylcyclohexanol	175	—	98	—	94	122	—	—
n-Heptyl	176	—	48	10	65	62	127°	—
Tetrahydrofurfuryl	177	—	34	47	61	90	—	—
2-Octanol	179	—	32	28	114	64	—	Diphenylcarbamate, 81
n-Octyl	194	—	62	12	74	66	128	—
l-Linalool	199	—	—	70	66	53	—	—
n-Nonyl	214	—	52	10	69	65	125	—
Isoborneol	216	35°	—	138	129	—	130	—
α-Terpineol	219	—	79	97	113	152	117	Diphenylcarbamate, 82
Geraniol	230	—	63	35	—	48	123	—
n-Decyl	231	6	57	30	60	71	123	—
n-Undecyl	243	16	55	29	62	73	124	—
n-Dodecyl (8)	259	24	60	45	74	80	123	—
n-Tetradecyl (9)	160°/10	39	67	51	74	82	—	—
l-Menthol	216	43	153	62	112	126	120	Benzoate, 54
n-Hexadecyl (10)	190°/15	50	66	52	73	82	—	—
2-Butyne-1,4-diol	145°/15	55	191	—	132	—	119	—
n-Octadecyl (11)	—	59	66	64	80	89	—	—
D-Borneol	212	205	154	153	138	127	—	—
Ethylene chlorohydrin	129	—	92	—	51	101	98	$d_4^{20°}$ 1·202, n_D^{20} 1·442
Trimethylene chlorohydrin	161d	—	77	—	—	76	—	$d_4^{20°}$ 1·131, n_D^{20} 1·447
Glycerol αγ-dichlorohydrin	176	—	129	—	73	115	—	$d_4^{20°}$ 1·353, n_D^{20} 1·480

Table IX, 5. Aliphatic Alcohols (*continued*)

ALCOHOL	B.P.	M.P.	3,5-DINITRO-BENZOATE	p-NITRO-BENZOATE	PHENYL-URETHANE	1-NAPHTHYL-URETHANE	HYDROGEN 3-NITRO-PHTHALATE	OTHER DERIVATIVES
Glycerol βγ-dichlorohydrin	183°	—	—	38°	73°	93°	—	—
Glycerol α-monochlorohydrin	213	—	—	108	—	—	—	—
1-Chloro-2-propanol	127	—	83°	—	—	—	—	—
2-Chloro-1-propanol	132	—	76	—	—	—	—	—
Trichloroethanol	151 (m.p. 19)	—	—	—	87	120	—	—
Ethylene bromohydrin	149	—	86	—	86	—	—	$d_4^{20°}$ 1·763, $n_D^{20°}$ 1·492
Glycerol αγ-dibromohydrin	219d	—	—	78	81	—	172°	$d_4^{25°}$ 2·120, $n_D^{25°}$ 1·550
Propylene glycol	187	—	—	127	153	176°	—	—
Ethylene glycol	198	—	169	141	157	164	—	Dibenzoate, 73°
Trimethylene glycol	215	—	178	119	137	198	—	Dibenzoate, 59
Tetramethylene glycol	230	19°	—	175	183	147	—	Dibenzoate, 82
Pentamethylene glycol	239	—	—	105	176	122	—	—
Diethylene glycol (12)	244	—	149	—	—	—	—	$d_4^{20°}$ 1·116, $n_D^{20°}$ 1·448
Hexamethylene glycol	250	42	—	—	—	192	—	—
Glycerol	290d	—	—	188	180	113	129	Tribenzoate, 72
Ethyleneglycol monomethyl ether (13)	124	—	—	50	—	—	118	$d_4^{20°}$ 0·966, $n_D^{20°}$ 1·402; 3,4,5-triiodobenzoate, 152
Ethyleneglycol monoethyl ether (14)	135	—	75	—	—	67	—	$d_4^{20°}$ 0·930, $n_D^{20°}$ 1·408; 3,4,5-triiodobenzoate, 128
Ethyleneglycol mono-isopropyl ether	142	—	—	—	—	—	—	$d_4^{20°}$ 0·903, $n_D^{20°}$ 1·410
Ethyleneglycol mono-n-propyl ether	151	—	—	—	—	—	—	$d_4^{20°}$ 0·911, $n_D^{20°}$ 1·413
Ethyleneglycol mono-n-butyl ether (15)	168	—	—	120	—	—	—	$d_4^{20°}$ 0·902, $n_D^{20°}$ 1·420; 3,4,5-triiodobenzoate, 85

Aliphatic Alcohols (continued)

ALCOHOL	B.P.	M.P.	3,5-DINITRO-BENZOATE	p-NITRO-BENZOATE	PHENYL-URETHANE	1-NAPHTHYL-URETHANE	HYDROGEN 3-NITRO-PHTHALATE	OTHER DERIVATIVES
Ethyleneglycol monophenyl ether (16)	245°	—	—	113°	—	—	—	$d_4^{20°}$ 1·104, $n_D^{20°}$ 1·534; 3,4,5-triiodobenzoate, 145; p-toluenesulphonate, 80
Diethyleneglycol monomethyl ether (17)	194	—	—	—	—	—	89°	$d_4^{20°}$ 1·036, $n_D^{20°}$ 1·424; 3,4,5-triiodobenzoate, 82°
Diethyleneglycol monoethyl ether (18)	202	—	—	—	—	—	—	$d_4^{20°}$ 1·024, $n_D^{20°}$ 1·430; 3,4,5-triiodobenzoate, 76
Diethyleneglycol mono-n-propyl ether	—	—	—	—	—	—	—	—
Diethyleneglycol mono-n-butyl ether (19)	232	—	—	—	—	—	—	$d_4^{20°}$ 0·958, $n_D^{20°}$ 1·434; 3,4,5-triiodobenzoate, 54
Monoethanolamine (20)	171	—	—	—	—	—	—	$d_4^{20°}$ 1·022, $n_D^{20°}$ 1·454 Picrate, 160
Diethanolamine (21)	270	28°	—	—	—	—	—	$d_4^{20°}$ 1·097, $n_D^{20°}$ 1·478; Picrate, 110
Triethanolamine (22)	360	—	—	—	—	—	—	$d_4^{20°}$ 1·124, $n_D^{20°}$ 1·485; Hydrochloride, 177

(1) tert-Butyl carbinol.
(2) Diethyl carbinol.
(3) Methyl n-propyl carbinol.
(4) sec-Butyl carbinol.
(5) Ethyl n-propyl carbinol.
(6) Di-n-propyl carbinol.
(7) Methyl n-amyl carbinol.
(8) Lauryl alcohol.
(9) Myristyl alcohol.
(10) Cetyl alcohol.
(11) Stearyl alcohol.
(12) 2,2'-Dihydroxydiethyl ether.
(13) 'Methyl cellosolve.'
(14) 'Ethyl cellosolve.'
(15) 'Butyl cellosolve.'
(16) 'Phenyl cellosolve.'
(17) 'Methyl carbitol.'
(18) 'Carbitol.'
(19) 'Butyl carbitol.'
(20) 2-Aminoethyl alcohol.
(21) 2,2'-Dihydroxydiethylamine.
(22) 2,2',2''-Trihydroxytriethylamine.

Table IX, 6. Aromatic Alcohols

ALCOHOL	B.P.	M.P.	3,5-DI-NITRO-BENZOATE	p-NITRO-BENZOATE	PHENYL-URETHANE	1-NAPH-THYL-URETHANE	HYDROGEN 3-NITRO-PHTHALATE	OTHER DERIVATIVES
1-Phenylethanol (1)	203°	20°	94°	43°	92°	106°	—	—
Benzyl	205	—	113	86	76	134	176°	—
α-Hydroxy-m-xylene (2)	217	—	111	89	—	116	—	—
1-Phenyl-1-propanol (3)	219	—	—	60	—	102	—	—
2-Phenylethanol (4)	220	—	108	63	80	119	123	—
1-Phenyl-1-butanol (5)	118°/18	16	—	58	—	99	—	—
1-Phenyl-1-pentanol (6)	137°/21	—	—	—	75	—	—	—
3-Phenyl-1-propanol (7)	237	—	92	46	48	—	117	—
o-Methoxybenzyl	249	—	—	—	—	136	—	Benzoyl, 59°
m-Methoxybenzyl	252	—	—	—	93	—	—	—
p-Methoxybenzyl (8)	259	25	—	94	91	—	—	Benzoyl, 38; anisic acid, 184
Cinnamyl	257	33	121	78	79	114	—	—
α-Hydroxy-o-xylene (9)	219	39	—	101	102	—	—	o-Toluic acid, 104
Piperonyl (10)	—	58	—	—	79	—	—	Benzoyl, 66
α-Hydroxy-p-xylene (11)	217	60	118	—	140	136	—	Acetyl, 42
Diphenylmethanol (12)	298	69	142	131	—	—	—	Acetyl, 84; diacetyl, 75
m-Hydroxybenzyl	—	73	—	—	—	—	—	Benzoyl, 51
o-Hydroxybenzyl (13)	—	87	—	—	—	—	—	—
p-Hydroxybenzyl	—	125	—	—	—	—	—	—
Benzoin	—	137	—	123	165	140	—	Acetyl, 83; benzoyl, 125; semicarbazone, 206d; 2,4-dinitrophenylhydrazone, 234
Triphenylcarbinol (14)	380	162	—	—	—	—	—	Acetyl, 88; triphenylmethane, 92

ALCOHOL	B.P.	M.P.	3,5-DI-NITRO-BENZOATE	p-NITRO-BENZOATE	PHENYL-URETHANE	1-NAPH-THYL-URETHANE	HYDROGEN 3-NITRO-PHTHALATE	OTHER DERIVATIVES
			HALOGENO-ALCOHOLS					
m-Chlorobenzyl	234°	—	—	—	—	—	—	—
m-Bromobenzyl	254	—	—	—	—	—	—	—
m-Iodobenzyl	165°/16	—	—	—	—	—	—	—
p-Iodobenzyl	—	72°	—	—	—	—	—	—
o-Chlorobenzyl	230	74	—	—	—	—	—	—
p-Chlorobenzyl	235	75	—	94°	—	—	—	—
p-Bromobenzyl	—	77	—	—	—	—	—	—
o-Bromobenzyl	—	80	—	—	—	—	—	Acetyl, 23°; o-Bromobenzoic acid, 150 ($KMnO_4$)
o-Iodobenzyl	—	90	—	—	—	—	—	—
			NITRO- AND AMINO-ALCOHOLS					
m-Nitrobenzyl	—	27°	—	—	—	—	—	Benzoyl, 72°
p-Aminobenzyl	—	65	—	—	—	—	—	Diacetyl, 188
o-Nitrobenzyl	270°	74	—	—	—	—	—	Benzoyl, 102
o-Aminobenzyl	—	82	—	—	—	—	—	N-Acetyl, 114; picrate, 110
p-Nitrobenzyl	—	93	—	—	—	—	—	Benzoyl, 95; acetyl, 78
m-Aminobenzyl	185°/12	97	—	—	—	—	—	N-Acetyl, 107; dibenzoyl, 114

(1) Methylphenylcarbinol.
(2) m-Tolylcarbinol.
(3) Ethylphenylcarbinol.
(4) Phenylethyl alcohol.
(5) Phenyl-n-propylcarbinol.
(6) n-Butylphenylcarbinol.
(7) Hydrocinnamyl alcohol.
(8) Anisyl alcohol.
(9) o-Tolylcarbinol.
(10) 3,4-Methylenedioxybenzyl alcohol.
(11) p-Tolylcarbinol.
(12) Diphenylcarbinol.
(13) Saligenin.
(14) Triphenylmethanol.

Table IX, 7.   **Phenols**

PHENOL	B.P.	M.P.	BROMO COMPOUND	ACETATE	BENZOATE	p-NITRO-BENZOATE	3,5-DI-NITRO-BENZOATE	ARYLOXY-ACETIC ACID	NN-DI-PHENYL-URETHANE	1-NAPH-THYL-URETHANE	p-TOLU-ENESUL-PHONATE	2,4-DINITRO-PHENYL ETHER
Salicylaldehyde (1)	197°	—	—	39°	—	128°	—	132°	—	—	64°	—
m-Cresol	202	12°	84°†	Liq.	55°	90	165°	103	101°	128°	56	74°
o-Ethylphenol	207	—	—	—	39	56	108	141	—	—	—	—
m-Ethylphenol	217	—	—	Liq.	52	68	—	75	—	—	—	—
Methyl salicylate	223	—	—	49	92	128	—	—	—	—	—	—
Ethyl salicylate	231	—	—	Liq.	80	108	—	—	—	—	—	—
Carvacrol	238	—	46	—	—	—	77	—	—	—	—	—
n-Propyl salicylate	239	—	—	Liq.	—	51	—	151	—	116	—	—
Isopropyl salicylate	241	—	—	—	—	—	—	—	—	—	—	—
m-Methoxyphenol (2)	244	—	104†	Liq.	70	81	131	114	—	129	—	115
Eugenol (3)	254	—	118‡	30	—	—	—	80	—	122	85	—
n-Butyl salicylate	260	—	—	—	—	—	—	—	—	—	—	—
Isoeugenol (4)	266	—	—	80	106	109	—	94	—	150	—	130
p-n-Butylphenol	248	22	—	—	127	68	—	81	—	—	—	—
o-Methoxyphenol (5)	205	28	116†	Liq.	58	93	142	119	118	118	85	97
2,4-Dimethylphenol (6)	211	28	179†	Liq.	38	105	164	142	—	135	—	—
o-Cresol	191	30	56*	Liq.	Liq.	94	138	152	73	142	55	90
p-Cresol	202	36	49*	Liq.	71	98	189	136	94	146	70	94
Phenol	182	42	95†	Liq.	69	126	146	99	105	133	96	69
Salol (7)	—	43	—	98	81	111	—	—	144	—	—	—
p-Ethylphenol	219	47	—	Liq.	60	81	132	97	—	128	—	—
2,6-Dimethylphenol (8)	203	49	79	—	—	—	159	140	—	—	—	—
Thymol (9)	233	51	55	Liq.	33	70	103	148	—	160	71	67
o-Cyclohexylphenol	—	55	—	—	—	—	—	—	—	—	—	—

Table IX, 7. **Phenols** (*continued*)

PHENOL	B.P.	M.P.	BROMO COMPOUND	ACETATE	BENZOATE	p-NITRO-BENZOATE	3,5-DI-NITRO-BENZOATE	ARYLOXY-ACETIC ACID	NN-DI-PHENYL-URETHANE	1-NAPH-THYL-URETHANE	p-TOLU-ENESUL-PHONATE	2,4-DINITRO-PHENYL ETHER
p-Methoxyphenol (10)	243°	56°	—	32°	87°	—	—	111°	—	—	—	—
o-Hydroxybiphenyl (11)	275	58	—	63	76	—	—	—	—	—	65°	—
Orcinol hydrate	289	58	104°†	25	88	214°	190°	217	154°	160	—	—
3,4-Dimethylphenol (12)	228	62	171†	—	58	—	181	163	—	142	—	—
3,5-Dimethylphenol (13)	219	68	166†	Liq.	24	109	195	86	—	—	—	—
2,4,6-Trimethylphenol (14)	220	69	158*	—	62	—	—	142	—	—	—	—
4-n-Hexylresorcinol	335	69	—	—	—	—	—	—	—	—	—	—
2,4,5-Trimethylphenol (15)	232	71	35	34	63	—	—	132	—	—	—	—
2,3-Dimethylphenol (16)	218	75	—	—	—	—	—	187	—	—	—	—
2,5-Dimethylphenol (17)	211	75	178†	Liq.	61	87	137	118	—	173	115	131°
Vanillin (18)	—	81	160	102	78	—	—	189	—	—	—	—
Saligen (19)	—	87	—	—	51	—	—	120	—	—	—	—
1-Naphthol	279	94	105*	49	56	143	217	192	—	152	88	128
2-Naphthyl salicylate	—	95	—	136	—	—	—	—	—	—	—	—
p-tert-Amylphenol	266	96	—	Liq.	61	—	—	—	—	—	54	—
2,3,5-Trimethylphenol	233	96	—	—	50	—	—	—	—	110	—	—
p-tert-Butylphenol	237	99	—	Liq.	82	—	—	86	—	175	—	—
Catechol	240	105	192‡	65	84	169	152	—	—	—	—	—
2,5-Dihydroxybiphenyl (20)	—	103	—	—	—	—	—	—	—	160	—	—
Orcinol (21)	289	108	104†	25	88	214	190	217	154	—	—	—
m-Hydroxybenzaldehyde	240	108	—	Liq.	38	—	—	148	—	—	—	—
1,2-Dihydroxynaphthalene (22)	—	108	—	106	—	—	—	—	—	—	—	—
2,2'-Dihydroxybiphenyl	—	109	—	95	101	—	—	—	—	—	190	—

327

Table IX, 7. Phenols (*continued*)

PHENOL	B.P.	M.P.	BROMO COMPOUND	ACETATE	BENZOATE	p-NITROBENZOATE	3,5-DINITROBENZOATE	ARYLOXYACETIC ACID	NN-DIPHENYLURETHANE	1-NAPHTHYLURETHANE	p-TOLUENESULPHONATE	2,4-DINITROPHENYL ETHER
Resorcinol	280°	110°	112°*	Liq.	117°	182°	201°	195°	130°	206°	81°	194°
Ethyl p-hydroxybenzoate	—	116	—	—	94	—	—	—	—	—	—	—
p-Hydroxybenzaldehyde	—	116	—	Liq.	90	—	—	198	—	—	—	—
2-Naphthol	285	123	84	72°	107	169	210	154	141	157	125	95
1,3-Dihydroxynaphthalene (23)	—	124	—	56	—	—	—	—	—	—	—	—
3,3'-Dihydroxybiphenyl	—	124	—	83	92	—	—	—	—	—	—	—
Methyl p-hydroxybenzoate	—	131	—	85	135	—	—	—	—	—	—	—
p-Cyclohexylphenol	—	132	—	—	118	137	168	—	—	—	—	—
Pyrogallol	309	133	158*	173	90	230	205	198	212	—	—	—
1,6-Dihydroxynaphthalene	—	138	—	73	104	—	—	—	—	—	—	—
Hydroxyhydroquinone (24)	—	140	—	97	120	—	—	—	—	—	—	118
1,8-Dihydroxynaphthalene	—	142	—	155	175	—	—	—	—	220	—	—
Salicylic acid (25)	—	159	—	135	132	205	—	191	—	—	177	—
p-Hydroxybiphenyl	306	165	—	88	151	—	—	—	—	—	159	—
Hydroquinone	286	170	186*	124	199	250	317	250	230	247	—	—
1,4-Dihydroxynaphthalene (26)	—	176	—	128	169	—	—	—	—	—	150	—
2,7-Dihydroxynaphthalene	—	190	—	136	139	—	—	149	176	—	—	—
m-Hydroxybenzoic acid	—	200	—	131	—	—	—	206	—	—	—	—
p-Hydroxybenzoic acid	—	214	—	187	—	—	—	278	—	—	—	—
Phloroglucinol	—	218	151†	104	174	283	162	—	—	—	—	—
1,5-Dihydroxynaphthalene	—	265	—	160	235	—	—	—	—	—	—	—
4,4'-Dihydroxybiphenyl	—	274	—	161	241	—	—	274	—	—	—	—

Table IX, 7. **Phenols** (*continued*)

PHENOL	B.P.	M.P.	BROMO COMPOUND	ACETATE	BENZOATE	p-NITRO-BENZOATE	3,5-DI-NITRO-BENZOATE	ARYLOXY-ACETIC ACID	N/N-DI-PHENYL-URETHANE	1-NAPH-THYL-URETHANE	p-TOLU-ENESUL-PHONATE	2,4-DINITRO-PHENYL ETHER
					HALOGENO-PHENOLS							
o-Chlorophenol	176°	9°	—	Liq.	Liq.	115°	143°	145°	—	120°	74°	99°
o-Bromophenol	195	5	95°†	Liq.	71°	—	—	143	—	129	78	89
m-Chlorophenol	214	33	—	Liq.	86	99	156	110	—	158	—	75
m-Bromophenol	236	33	—	Liq.	98	—	—	108	—	108	53	—
2,4-Dibromophenol	239	40	—	36°	98	184	—	153	—	—	120	135
m-Iodophenol	—	40	—	38	—	133	183	115	—	—	61	—
o-Iodophenol	—	43	—	—	34	—	—	135	—	—	—	95
p-Chlorophenol	217	43	—	Liq.	89	168	186	156	97°	166	71	126
2,4-Dichlorophenol	210	45	68	—	96	—	—	140	—	—	125	119
p-Bromophenol	235	64	95‡	21	102	180	191	159	99	169	94	141
2,4,5-Trichlorophenol	249	68	—	—	93	—	—	157	—	—	—	—
2,4,6-Trichlorophenol	246	69	—	—	75	106	136	182	143	188	—	136
2,4-Di-iodophenol	—	72	—	71	98	—	—	—	—	—	—	—
p-Iodophenol	—	94	—	32	119	—	—	156	127	—	99	156
2,4,6-Tribromophenol	—	95	120‡	87	81	153	174	200	153	153	113	135
Chlorohydroquinone	—	106	—	72	—	—	—	—	—	—	—	—
Bromohydroquinone	—	111	—	72	—	—	—	—	—	—	—	—
2,4,6-Tri-iodophenol	—	159	—	156	—	—	181	—	—	—	—	—
Pentachlorophenol	310d	191	—	150	164	—	—	196	—	—	145	—

Table IX, 7. Phenols (continued)

PHENOL	B.P.	M.P.	BROMO COMPOUND	ACETATE	BENZOATE	p-NITRO-BENZOATE	3,5-DI-NITRO-BENZOATE	ARYLOXY-ACETIC ACID	NN-DI-PHENYL URETHANE	1-NAPH-THYL-URETHANE	p-TOLU-ENESUL-PHONATE	2,4-DINITRO-PHENYL ETHER
					NITRO-PHENOLS							
o-Nitrophenol	216°	45°	117°*	41°	59°	141°	155°	158°	114°	113°	83°	142°
m-Nitrophenol	—	97	91*	56	95	174	159	156	—	167	113	138
2,4-Dinitrophenol	—	113	118	72	132	139	—	—	—	—	121	248
p-Nitrophenol	—	114	142*	83	142	159	186	187	112	151	97	120
Picric acid	—	122	—	76	—	—	—	—	—	—	—	—
Styphnic acid (27)	—	179	—	—	—	143	—	—	—	—	—	—

* Dibromo.   † Tribromo.   ‡ Tetrabromo.

(1) o-Hydroxybenzaldehyde.
(2) Resorcinol monomethyl ether.
(3) 4-Allyl-2-methoxy phenol.
(4) 2-Methoxy-4-propenylphenol (cis and trans).
(5) Guaiacol.
(6) 1,3,4-Xylenol; m-4-Xylenol.
(7) Phenyl salicylate.
(8) 1,3,2-Xylenol; m-2-Xylenol.
(9) 3-Hydroxy-4-isopropyltoluene.
(10) Hydroquinone monomethyl ether.
(11) o-Phenylphenol.
(12) 1,2,4-Xylenol; o-4-Xylenol.
(13) 1,3,5-Xylenol; m-5-Xylenol.
(14) Mesitol.
(15) Pseudo-cuminol.
(16) 1,2,3-Xylenol; o-3-Xylenol.
(17) 1,4,5-Xylenol; p-2-Xylenol.
(18) 4-Hydroxy-3-methoxybenzaldehyde.
(19) o-Hydroxybenzyl alcohol.
(20) Phenylhydroquinone.
(21) 4-Hydroxy-3-methoxybenzaldehyde.
(22) 1,2-Naphthohydroquinone.
(23) Naphthoresorcinol.
(24) 1,2,4-Trihydroxybenzene.
(25) o-Hydroxybenzoic acid.
(26) 1,4-Naphthohydroquinone.
(27) 2,4,6-Trinitroresorcinol.

Table IX, 8. Enols

COMPOUND	B.P.	M.P.	$d_4^{20°}$	$n_D^{20°}$	SEMICAR-BAZONE	PYRAZOLONE
Acetylacetone	139°	—	0·977	1·452	—	100°*
Methyl acetoacetate	170	—	1·077	1·419	152°	127
Methyl methylacetoacetate	177	—	1·030	1·418	138	120
Ethyl acetoacetate	180	—	1·028	1·419	129d	127
Ethyl methylacetoacetate	181	—	1·006	1·419	86	120
Methyl ethylacetoacetate	189	—	0·989	—	98	108
Acetonylacetone	194	—	0·974	1·428	220	92
Ethyl ethylacetoacetate	198	—	0·972	1·422	154d	108
Ethyl acetonedicarboxylate	250d	—	1·113	—	95	85
Ethyl benzoylacetate	265d	—	1·117	—	125	63
Ethyl oxalacetate	131°/24	—	1·131	1·454	162	—
Benzoylacetone	261	61°	—	—	—	63
Dibenzoylmethane	—	78	—	—	—	137

* 1-(*p*-Nitrophenyl)-3,5-dimethylpyrazole: with aqueous solution of *p*-nitrophenylhydrazine hydrochloride. Phenylhydrazine yields a liquid pyrazole, b.p. 273°.

Table IX, 9. Polyhydric Alcohols

ALCOHOL	B.P.	BENZOATE	p-NITRO-BENZOATE	3,5-DINITRO-BENZOATE	PHENYL-URETHANE	1-NAPHTHYL-URETHANE	OTHER DERIVATIVES
2,3-Butanediol (1)	182°	76°	—	—	201°	—	—
1,2-Propanediol (2)	189	—	127°	—	153	—	—
Ethylene glycol	198	73	141	169°	157	176°	—
1,3-Butanediol (3)	208	—	—	—	123	—	—
1,3-Propanediol (4)	215	59	119	178	137	164	—
1,4-Butanediol (5)	230	82	175	—	183	199	—
1,5-Pentanediol (6)	239	—	105	—	176	147	—
Diethylene glycol (7)	244	—	—	149	—	122	—
1,6-Hexanediol (8)	250*	—	—	—	108	—	—
Triethylene glycol (9)	285	—	—	—	131	—	—
2-Butyne-1,4-diol	145°/15**	—	—	190	180	192	—
Glycerol	190d	76	188	—	—	—	Acetate, 99°
Sorbitol	m.p. 110	129	—	—	—	—	Acetate, 121
Mannitol	m.p. 166	149	—	—	303	—	Acetate, 84
Pentaerythritol	m.p. 253	99	—	—	—	—	—

(1) 2,3-Dihydroxybutane. (2) 1,2-Dihydroxypropane. (3) 1,3-Dihydroxybutane.
(4) Trimethylene glycol. (5) Tetramethylene glycol. (6) Pentamethylene glycol.
(7) 2,2′-Dihydroxydiethyl ether. (8) Hexamethylene glycol. (9) Ethylene glycol di-(β-hydroxyethyl) ether.

* M.p. 42°. ** M.p. 55°.

Physical Constants of Organic Compounds

CARBOHYDRATE	M.P.*	$[\alpha]_D^{20°}$ IN WATER	OSAZONE M.P.	OSAZONE TIME OF FORMATION (MINUTES)	OTHER DERIVATIVES
†D-Glucose (hydrated)	146° 90° }	+52°	205°	4	Penta-acetate, α- 112°, β- 132; pentabenzoate, 179
D-Glucose (anhydrous)	95	—	166	—	—
D-Ribose	104	−21·5	205	—	—
D-Fructose	—	−92	—	2	Penta-acetate, α- 70, β- 109; pentabenzoate, 79
L-Rhamnose (hydrated)	125 105° }	+9	190	9	Penta-acetate, 99
L-Rhamnose (anhydrous)	106	+13·5	163	—	—
L-Lyxose	120	—	—	—	—
D-Galactose (hydrated)	170 132 }	+82	201	15–19	Penta-acetate, α- 95, β- 142; mucic acid, 213
D-Galactose (anhydrous)	145	+14·5	205	0·5	—
D-Mannose	160	+19	164	7	Penta-acetate, α- 74, β- 115
D-Xylose	161	+105	166	9	Penta-acetate, α- 59, β- 126
L-Arabinose	—	—	162	4	Penta-acetate, α- 94, β- 86
L-Sorbose	—	−43	—	—	—
Maltose (hydrated)	165 100 }	+130	206	—	Octa-acetate, α- 125, β- 160
Maltose (anhydrous)	185	+66·5	205	30	Octa-acetate, 69
Sucrose	190	+9·5	162	—	Octa-acetate, α- 189, β- 193
Gentiobiose	203	—	—	—	Octa-acetate, α- 152, β- 90; mucic acid, 213
Lactose (hydrated)	223 225 }	+52·5	200	—	—
Lactose (anhydrous)	—	—	—	—	—
Cellobiose	—	+35	198	—	Octa-acetate, α- 230, β- 192

* The melting points of carbohydrates (sugars) are not usually sharp and they are perhaps best expressed as decomposition points.
† The small capital letter prefix refers to configuration, related to D-glyceraldehyde, and not to the direction of optical rotation. The sign of optical rotation is expressed as (+) and (−) or as d and l or by the words *dextro* and *laevo*. Thus we have D-(−)-fructose and L-(+)-arabinose.

Table IX, 11. Aliphatic Halogen Compounds

Chlorides

Halide	B.P.	M.P.	d_4^{20}	n_D^{20}	Anilide	1-Naphtha-lide	Alkyl Mercuric Halide	S-Alkyl-thi-uronium Picrate	Picrate of Alkyl 2-Naphthyl Ether
Ethyl	12°	—	—	—	104°	126°	193°	188°	102°
Isopropyl	35	—	0·863	1·378	104	—	—	196	95
Allyl	45	—	0·940	1·416	114	121	140	154	99
n-Propyl	46	—	0·889	1·388	92	147	—	177	81
tert-Butyl	51	—	0·846	1·386	128	129	39	—	—
sec-Butyl	68	—	0·874	1·397	108	126	—	166	85
Isobutyl	69	—	0·881	1·398	110	112	128	—	84
n-Butyl	77	—	0·886	1·402	63	—	—	177	67
Neopentyl	85	—	0·879	—	126	138	—	—	—
tert-Amyl	85	—	0·865	1·405	92	—	—	—	—
3-Chloropentane	96	—	0·872	1·408	—	—	—	—	—
2-Chloropentane	97	—	0·873	1·408	—	111	—	173	94
Isoamyl	99	—	0·872	1·409	110	112	86	154	67
n-Amyl	106	—	0·882	1·412	96	—	110	—	—
Cyclopentyl	114	—	1·005	1·451	—	106	125	—	—
n-Hexyl	134	—	0·878	1·420	69	188	—	—	—
Cyclohexyl	142	—	0·989	1·462	146	95	119	—	—
n-Heptyl	159	—	0·877	1·426	57	91	151	—	—
n-Octyl	182	—	0·875	1·431	57	—	—	—	—
n-Nonyl	202	—	0·870	1·434	—	—	—	—	—
n-Decyl	223	—	0·868	1·437	—	—	—	—	—
n-Undecyl	241	—	0·868	1·440	—	—	—	—	—
n-Dodecyl	244	—	0·867	1·443	—	—	—	—	—
Benzyl	179°	—	1·100	1·539	117°	166°	—	188°	123°
1-Phenylethyl	195	—	1·063	1·530	133	—	—	—	—
2-Phenylethyl	198	—	1·073	—	97	—	—	—	84
Benzal	207	—	—	—	166	—	—	—	—
Benzotri-	218	—	—	—	—	—	—	—	—

Physical Constants of Organic Compounds

HALIDE	B.P.	M.P.	$d_4^{20°}$	$n_D^{20°}$	ANILIDE	1-NAPHTHA-LIDE	ALKYL MERCURIC HALIDE	s-ALKYL-THI-URONIUM PICRATE	PICRATE OF ALKYL 2-NAPHTHYL ETHER
BROMIDES									
Ethyl	38°	—	1·460	1·425	104°	126°	194°	188°	102°
Isopropyl	59	—	1·425	1·314	104	—	94	196	95
Allyl	70	—	1·432	1·470	114	121	—	154	99
n-Propyl	71	—	1·435	1·355	92	129	138	177	81
sec-Butyl	91	—	1·256	1·437	108	126	39	166	85
Isobutyl	91	—	1·253	1·435	110	112	56	167	84
n-Butyl	101	—	1·274	1·440	63	—	129	177	67
Neopentyl	109	—	1·225	—	126	—	—	—	—
2-Bromopentane	117	—	1·212	1·442	93	—	—	—	—
3-Bromopentane	118	—	1·211	1·443	124	111	80	173	94
Isoamyl	119	—	1·213	1·442	110	112	122	154	67
n-Amyl	129	—	1·219	1·445	96	—	—	—	—
Cyclopentyl	137	—	1·387	1·489	—	106	119	157	—
n-Hexyl	154	—	1·175	1·448	69	188	153	—	—
Cyclohexyl	164	—	1·336	1·495	146	95	115	142	—
n-Heptyl	178	—	1·140	1·451	57	91	109	134	—
n-Octyl	200	—	1·112	1·453	57	—	109	—	—
n-Nonyl	220	—	1·C90	1·454	—	—	—	—	—
n-Decyl	103°/6	—	1·C66	1·455	—	—	—	—	—
n-Undecyl	114°/5	—	1·054	1·457	—	—	108	—	—
n-Dodecyl	130°/6	—	1·038	1·458	—	—	—	—	—
n-Tetradecyl	179°/20	5°	1·017	1·460	—	—	—	137	—
n-Hexadecyl	201°/19	14	1·001	1·462	—	—	—	—	—
Benzyl	198°	—	1·438	—	117°	166°	119°	188°	123°
1-Phenylethyl	203	—	1·361	1·561	133	—	—	—	—
2-Phenylethyl	218	—	1·359	1·556	97	—	169	—	84

Table IX, 11. Aliphatic Halogen Compounds (*continued*)

HALIDE	B.P.	M.P.	$d_4^{20°}$	$n_D^{20°}$	ANILIDE	1-NAPHTHA-LIDE	ALKYL MERCURIC HALIDE	S-ALKYL-THI-URONIUM PICRATE	PICRATE OF ALKYL 2-NAPHTHYL ETHER
				IODIDES					
Methyl	42°	—	2·282	1·532	114°	160°	145°	224°	117°
Ethyl	73	—	1·940	1·514	104	126	182	188	102
Isopropyl	89	—	1·703	1·499	104	—	—	196	95
Allyl	100	—	1·777	1·578	114	121	112	154	99
n-Propyl	102	—	1·743	1·505	92	121	113	177	81
sec-Butyl	118	—	1·592	1·499	108	129	—	166	85
Isobutyl	119	—	1·602	1·496	110	126	72	167	84
tert-Amyl	128	—	1·479	—	92	138	—	—	—
n-Butyl	129	—	1·616	1·499	63	112	117	177	67
3-Iodopentane	142	—	1·511	1·497	—	—	—	—	—
2-Iodopentane	142	—	1·510	1·496	—	—	—	—	—
Isoamyl	147	—	1·503	1·493	110	111	122	173	94
n-Amyl	155	—	1·512	1·496	96	112	110	154	—
n-Hexyl	180	—	1·437	1·493	69	106	110	157	—
n-Heptyl	201	—	1·373	1·490	57	95	103	—	—
n-Octyl	221	—	1·330	1·489	—	—	—	—	—
Cyclopentyl	58°/22	—	1·709	1·547	—	—	—	—	—
Cyclohexyl	82°/20	—	1·624	1·547	—	—	—	—	—
Benzyl	93°/10	24°	—	—	116°	—	—	—	123°
2-Phenylethyl	116°/12	—	1·632	1·602	—	—	—	—	84

Table IX, 11. Aliphatic Halogen Compounds (*continued*)

HALIDE	B.P.	M.P.	$d_4^{20°}$	$n_D^{20°}$
			Chloro Compounds	
Methylene chloride	42°	—	1·336	1·425
Dichloroethylene (*trans*)	48	—	1·257	1·444
Ethylidene chloride	57	—	1·176	1·416
Dichloroethylene (*cis*)	60	—	1·282	1·446
Chloroform	61	—	1·489	1·446
2,2-Dichloropropane	70	—	1·092	1·412
Methyl chloroform	75	—	1·349	1·438
Carbon tetrachloride	77	—	1·594	1·461
Ethylene chloride	84	—	1·256	1·445
Trichloroethylene	87	—	1·465	1·478
Propylene chloride	96	—	1·155	1·439
Ethylene chlorobromide	107	—	1·689	1·491
1,1,2-Trichloroethane	114	—	1·443	1·471
Trimethylene chloride	120	—	1·183	1·449
Tetrachloroethylene	121	—	1·623	1·506
Trimethylene chlorobromide	143	—	1·593	1·471
sym-Tetrachloroethane	147	—	1·597	1·495
1,4-Dichlorobutane	153	—	1·139	1·455
1,2,3-Trichloropropane	157	—	1·334	1·486
Pentachloroethane	162	—	1·680	1·503
1,5-Dichloropentane	178d	—	1·100	1·457
1,6-Dichlorohexane	204d	—	1·069	1·457
Hexachloroethane	—	187° (sub.)	—	—

Table IX, 11.   **Aliphatic Halogen Compounds** (*continued*)

HALIDE	B.P.	M.P.	$d_4^{20°}$	$n_D^{20°}$
				BROMO COMPOUNDS
Methylene bromide	97°	—	2·496	1·541
Ethylidene bromide	113	—	2·055	1·513
Ethylene bromide	131	—	2·183	1·539
Propylene bromide	141	—	1·932	1·520
Bromoform	150	—	2·887	1·598
Isobutylene dibromide	150	—	1·783	1·512
2,3-Dibromobutane	157	—	1·792	1·515
1,3-Dibromopropane	165	—	1·982	1·523
1,2-Dibromobutane	166	—	1·820	—
1,4-Dibromobutane	198	—	1·826	1·519
1,2,3-Tribromopropane	220	—	2·402	1·582
1,5-Dibromopentane	221	—	1·702	1·513
1,6-Dibromohexane	240	—	1·603	1·506
sym-Tetrabromoethane	124°/19	—	2·967	1·638
Carbon tetrabromide	—	92°	—	—
				IODO COMPOUNDS
Methylene iodide	80°/25	—	3·324	1·741
Trimethylene iodide	90°/9	—	2·576	1·642
1,4-Di-iodobutane	110°/10	—	2·358	1·621
1,5-Di-iodopentane	132°/10	—	2·182	1·602
1,6-Di-iodohexane	140°/10	—	2·040	1·586
Ethylene iodide	—	81°	—	—
Iodoform	—	119	—	—

TABLE IX, 12.

Aromatic Halogen Compounds

COMPOUND	B.P.	M.P.	$d_4^{20°}$	$n_D^{20°}$	NITRATION PRODUCT POSITION	NITRATION PRODUCT M.P.	SULPHONAMIDE ($-SO_2NH_2$, 1) POSITION	SULPHONAMIDE ($-SO_2NH_2$, 1) M.P.	OTHER DERIVATIVES
m-Difluorobenzene	83°	—	1·153	1·439	—	—	—	—	—
Fluorobenzene	85	—	1·024	1·466	—	—	4, F	125°	Sulphone, 98°
p-Difluorobenzene	89	—	1·166	1·441	—	—	—	—	—
o-Difluorobenzene	93	—	1·157	1·443	—	—	—	—	—
o-Fluorotoluene	114	—	0·998	1·470	—	—	3, CH_3; 4, F	105	o-Fluorobenzoic acid, 127
m-Fluorotoluene	116	—	0·990	—	—	—	2, CH_3; 4, F	173	m-Fluorobenzoic acid, 124
p-Fluorotoluene	116	—	0·998	1·469	—	—	2, CH_3; 5, F	141	p-Fluorobenzoic acid, 186
Chlorobenzene	132	—	1·107	1·525	2,4	52°	4, Cl	143	—
Bromobenzene	156	—	1·494	1·560	2,4	75	4, Br	162	—
o-Chlorotoluene	159	—	1·082	1·527	3,5	64	3, CH_3; 4, Cl	126	o-Chlorobenzoic acid, 141
m-Chlorotoluene	162	—	1·072	1·522	4,6	91	2, CH_3; 4, Cl	185	m-Chlorobenzoic acid, 158
p-Chlorotoluene	162	7°	1·070	1·521	2	38	2, CH_3; 5, Cl	143	p-Chlorobenzoic acid, 242
m-Dichlorobenzene	173	—	1·288	1·546	4,6	103	2,4, diCl	180	—
Benzyl chloride	179	—	1·100	1·539	—	—	—	—	S-Benzylthiuronium picrate, 188
o-Dichlorobenzene	180	—	1·305	1·551	4,5	110	3,4, diCl	135	Sulphone, 176
o-Bromotoluene	181	—	1·425	—	3,5	82	3, CH_3; 4, Br	146	o-Bromobenzoic acid, 150
m-Bromotoluene	183	—	1·410	—	4,6	103	2, CH_3; 4, Br	168	m-Bromobenzoic acid, 155
p-Bromotoluene	185	26	1·390	—	2	47	2, CH_3; 5, Br	165	p-Bromobenzoic acid, 251
Iodobenzene	188	—	1·831	1·620	4	174	—	—	Sulphone, 202
o-Bromochlorobenzene	195	—	1·646	1·580	—	—	—	—	—
Benzyl bromide	198	—	1·438	—	—	—	—	—	—
2,4-Dichlorotoluene	199	—	1·249	1·549	3,5	104	2,4, diCl; 5, Me	176	2,4-Dichlorobenzoic acid, 164
2,6-Dichlorotoluene	199	—	1·269	1·551	3	53	2,4, diCl; 3, Me	204	2,6-Dichlorobenzoic acid, 139
m-Iodotoluene	204	—	1·698	—	—	—	—	—	m-Iodobenzoic acid, 186

Table IX, 12. Aromatic Halogen Compounds (*continued*)

COMPOUND	B.P.	M.P.	$d_4^{20°}$	$n_D^{20°}$	NITRATION PRODUCT POSITION	NITRATION PRODUCT M.P.	SULPHONAMIDE ($-SO_2NH_2$, 1) POSITION	SULPHONAMIDE ($-SO_2NH_2$, 1) M.P.	OTHER DERIVATIVES
Benzyl iodide	93°/10	24°	—	—	—	—	—	—	Benzaldehyde phenylhydrazone, 156°
Benzal chloride	205	—	1·250	1·550	—	—	—	—	—
o-Iodotoluene	207	—	1·698	—	6	103°	—	—	o-Iodobenzoic acid, 162
3,4-Dichlorotoluene	207	—	1·251	1·549	6	64	3,4, diCl; 6, Me	190°	3,4-Dichlorobenzoic acid, 208
Benzal bromide	156°/23	—	1·460	1·541	—	—	—	—	—
1,2,4-Trichlorobenzene	213	17	1·468	1·554	5	56	—	—	—
2-Fluoronaphthalene	212	61	—	—	—	—	—	—	Picrate, 101
1-Fluoronaphthalene	214	—	1·134	1·594	—	—	—	—	Picrate, 113
m-Dibromobenzene	219	—	1·952	1·606	—	—	—	—	—
Benzo-trichloride	220	—	1·173	—	4	62	2,4, diBr	189	Benzoic acid, 121
o-Dibromobenzene	224	7	1·956	1·609	4,5	114	3,4, diBr	176	Sulphone, 177
Bromomesitylene	225	−1	—	—	—	—	—	—	—
2-Bromocymene	234	—	1·267	—	—	—	—	—	—
2,5-Dibromotoluene	236	—	1·811	—	—	—	—	—	2,5-Dibromobenzoic acid, 157
3,4-Dibromotoluene	240	—	1·811	1·600	—	—	—	—	3,4-Dibromobenzoic acid, 235
m-Bromoiodobenzene	252	—	—	—	—	—	—	—	—
2-Chloronaphthalene	256	61	—	—	1,8	175	7, Cl	232	Picrate, 81
o-Bromoiodobenzene	257	—	2·262	1·665	—	—	—	—	—
1-Chloronaphthalene	259	—	1·192	1·633	4,5	180	4, Cl	186	Picrate, 137
1-Bromonaphthalene	281	—	1·484	1·658	4	85	4, Br	193	Picrate, 134
m-Di-iodobenzene	285	40	—	—	—	—	—	—	—
o-Di-iodobenzene	287	27	—	—	—	—	—	—	—
2-Bromobiphenyl	297	—	1·223	—	—	—	—	—	o-Bromobenzoic acid, 150 (CrO_3)
3-Bromobiphenyl	300	—	—	1·641	—	—	—	—	—

Table IX, 12. Aromatic Halogen Compounds *(continued)*

COMPOUND	B.P.	M.P.	$d_4^{20°}$	$n_D^{20°}$	NITRATION PRODUCT POSITION	NITRATION PRODUCT M.P.	SULPHONAMIDE ($-SO_2NH_2$, 1) POSITION	SULPHONAMIDE ($-SO_2NH_2$, 1) M.P.	OTHER DERIVATIVES
1-Iodonaphthalene	302°	—	1·729	—	—	—	—	—	Picrate, 127°
2-Iodobiphenyl	158°/6	—	1·609	1·662	—	—	—	—	
2-Chlorobiphenyl	273	32°	—	—	—	—	—	—	o-Chlorobenzoic acid, 141
p-Iodotoluene	211	35	—	—	—	—	—	—	p-Iodobenzoic acid, 269
1,2-Dichloronaphthalene	296	35	—	—	—	—	—	—	
m-Di-iodobenzene	285	40	—	—	—	—	—	—	
1,2,4-Tribromobenzene	275	44	—	—	—	—	—	—	
p-Dichlorobenzene	174	53	—	—	2	54°	2,5, diCl	180°	
1,2,3-Trichlorobenzene	218	53	—	—	4	56	2,3,4, triCl	230	
2-Iodonaphthalene	309	54	—	—	—	—	—	—	Picrate, 95
2-Bromonaphthalene	282	59	—	—	—	—	7, Br	208	Picrate, 86
2-Fluoronaphthalene	—	60	—	—	—	—	—	—	Picrate, 101
2,2′-Dichlorobiphenyl	256	61	—	—	—	—	—	—	
2-Chloronaphthalene	208	63	—	—	1,8	175	7, Cl	232	Picrate, 81
1,3,5-Trichlorobenzene	195	67	—	—	2	68	2,4,6, triCl	212	
p-Bromochlorobenzene	—	68	—	—	2	72	—	—	
1,2-Dibromonaphthalene	—	74	—	—	—	—	—	—	
4-Fluorobiphenyl	253	77	—	—	—	—	—	—	
4-Chlorobiphenyl	291	81	—	—	—	—	—	—	p-Chlorobenzoic acid, 242
2,2′-Dibromobiphenyl	—	81	—	—	—	—	—	—	
1,2,3-Tribromobenzene	—	88	—	—	—	—	—	—	

Table IX, 12. Aromatic Halogen Compounds (*continued*)

COMPOUND	B.P.	M.P.	$d_4^{20°}$	$n_D^{20°}$	NITRATION PRODUCT POSITION	NITRATION PRODUCT M.P.	SULPHONAMIDE ($-SO_2NH_2$, 1) POSITION	SULPHONAMIDE ($-SO_2NH_2$, 1) M.P.	OTHER DERIVATIVES
4-Bromobiphenyl	310°	89°	—	—	—	—	—	—	*p*-Bromobenzoic acid, 251° (CrO_3)
p-Dibromobenzene	219	89	—	—	2,5	84°	2,5, diBr	195°	—
p-Bromoiodobenzene	251	92	—	—	—	—	—	—	—
4,4′-Difluorobiphenyl	255	95	—	—	—	—	—	—	—
4-Iodobiphenyl	—	114	—	—	—	—	—	—	—
1,3,5-Tribromobenzene	271	120	—	—	—	—	2,4,6, triBr	222d	—
p-Di-iodobenzene	285	129	—	—	2,5	171	—	—	—
1,2,4,5-Tetrachlorobenzene	240	140	—	—	3	99	—	—	—
4,4′-Dichlorobiphenyl	—	149	—	—	—	—	—	—	*p*-Chlorobenzoic acid, 242 (CrO_3)
4,4′-Dibromobiphenyl	—	164	—	—	—	—	—	—	*p*-Bromobenzoic acid, 251 (CrO_3)
1,2,4,5-Tetrabromobenzene	—	181	—	—	3	168	—	—	—
Naphthalene tetrachloride (1,2,3,4)	—	183	—	—	—	—	—	—	—
Hexachlorobenzene	—	229	—	—	—	—	—	—	—

Table IX, 13. Aliphatic Ethers

ETHER	B.P.	$d_4^{20°}$	$n_D^{20°}$
Diethyl	34°	0·714	1·353
Ethyl vinyl	36	0·759	1·377
Allyl ethyl	67	0·765	1·388
Di-isopropyl	68	0·726	1·368
n-Butyl methyl	70	0·774	1·374
Di-n-propyl	90	0·749	1·381
n-Butyl ethyl	92	0·749	1·382
Diallyl	94	0·803	—
n-Amyl methyl	99	0·761	1·387
Cyclopentyl methyl	105	0·862	1·420
n-Amyl ethyl	118	0·762	1·393
Di-sec-butyl	121	0·764	1·396
Cyclopentyl ethyl	122	0·853	1·423
Di-isobutyl	123	0·756	—
n-Hexyl methyl	126	0·772	1·397
Cyclohexyl methyl	134	0·875	1·435
Di-n-butyl	141	0·770	1·399
Ethyl n-hexyl	142	0·772	1·401
Cyclohexyl ethyl	149	0·864	1·435
Di-isoamyl	171	0·778	1·409
Cineole	176	0·923	1·458
Di-n-amyl	188	0·785	1·412
Di-n-hexyl	229	0·793	1·420
Di-n-heptyl	259	0·801	1·427
Di-n-octyl	288	0·806	1·433
Di-n-decyl	185°/5 mm.	0·815	1·441
Chloromethyl methyl	59	1·070	1·397
1-Chloroethyl methyl	73	0·991	1·400
Chloromethyl ethyl	83d	1·026	1·404
2-Chloroethyl methyl	91	1·035	1·411
sym-Dichlorodimethyl	105	1·310	1·436
1,1′-Dichlorodiethyl	116	1·111	1·423
Epichlorohydrin	117	1·181	1·438
1,2-Dichlorodiethyl	140	1·177	1·444
2,2′-Dichlorodiethyl	118	1·210	1·457
Di-2-chloropropyl	188	1·109	1·447
Di-3-chloropropyl	215	1·139	1·452
Ethyleneglycol dimethyl	85	0·866	1·379
Ethyleneglycol diethyl	123	0·848	—
Diethyleneglycol diethyl	187	0·906	1·411
Tetraethyleneglycol dimethyl	266	1·009	1·432
Benzyl methyl	171	0·965	1·501
Benzyl ethyl	188	0·948	1·496
Dibenzyl	299d	1·042	—
Furan	32	0·937	1·422
Sylvan (2-methylfuran)	64	0·913	1·434
Tetrahydrofuran	65	0·889	1·407
Tetrahydrosylvan	79	0·855	1·407
Dihydropyran	86	0·923	1·440
Tetrahydropyran	88	0·881	1·421
Dioxan	102	1·034	1·422

Table IX, 14. Aromatic Ethers

ETHER	B.P.	M.P.	$d_4^{20°}$	$n_D^{20°}$	SULPHON-AMIDE	PICRATE	OTHER DERIVATIVES
Anisole	154°	—	0·996	1·518	111°	81°	Dinitro, 87°; 2,4-dibromo, 61°
Phenetole	170	—	0·965	1·507	150	92	p-Nitro, 58
Benzyl methyl ether	171	—	0·965	1·501	—	116	—
Methyl o-tolyl ether (1)	171	—	0·985	1·505	137	119	o-Methoxybenzoic acid, 101
Methyl p-tolyl ether	175	—	0·970	1·512	182	89	Anisic acid, 184
Methyl m-tolyl ether	177	—	0·972	1·513	130	114	m-Methoxybenzoic acid, 110
Ethyl o-tolyl ether	184	—	0·953	1·505	149	118	o-Ethoxybenzoic acid, 25
Benzyl ethyl ether	186	—	0·948	1·496	—	—	—
Phenyl n-propyl ether	188	—	0·949	1·510	—	—	—
Ethyl p-tolyl ether	190	—	0·949	1·505	138	111	p-Ethoxybenzoic acid, 196
Ethyl m-tolyl ether	191	—	0·949	1·506	111	115	m-Ethoxybenzoic acid, 137
Guaiacol (2)	205	28°	1·129	1·544	—	88	Tribromo, 116
Veratrole (3)	206	22	—	—	136	57	Dibromo, 93; nitro, 95
n-Butyl phenyl ethyl	208	—	0·934	1·497	—	112	—
Thymol methyl ether	212	—	—	—	—	—	Trinitro, 92
Resorcinol dimethyl ether	217	—	1·050	1·538	167	58	Dibromo, 140; trinitro, 124
Safrole (4)	232	11	1·100	—	—	105	Piperonylic acid, 228; pentabromo, 169
Anethole (5)	235	22	0·989	1·558	—	70	Anisic acid, 184; tribromo, 108
Resorcinol diethyl ether	235	12	—	—	184	109	—
Eugenol methyl ether (6)	244	—	1·050	1·532	—	—	Tribromo, 78; veratric acid, 179
Isosafrole (7)	248	7	1·122	1·578	—	75	Tribromo, 109; piperonylic acid, 228
Diphenyl ether	259	28	—	—	159	110	Dibromo, 55; dinitro, 144
Isoeugenol methyl ether (8)	264	—	1·053	1·569	—	—	—

344

ETHER	B.P.	M.P.	$d_4^{20°}$	$n_D^{20°}$	SULPHON-AMIDE	PICRATE	OTHER DERIVATIVES
Methyl 1-naphthyl ether	271°	—	1·092	1·696	157°	129°	Dibromo, 55°
Ethyl 1-naphthyl ether	280	5°	1·060	1·597	165	119	4-Bromo, 48
Dibenzyl ether	296	—	1·034	—	—	78	—
2-Methoxybiphenyl	274	29	—	—	—	—	Nitro, 95
Ethyl 2-naphthyl ether	282	37	—	—	163	100	1-Bromo, 66
Pyrogallol triethyl ether	—	39	—	—	—	—	—
Catechol diethyl ether	217	43	—	—	162	71	Trinitro, 122
Pyrogallol trimethyl ether	241	47	—	—	124	81	
Hydroquinone dimethyl ether	212	56	—	—	148	48	Nitro, 72; dibromo, 142
Methyl 2-naphthyl ether	274	72	—	—	151	117	Bromo, 63
Hydroquinone diethyl ether	—	72	—	—	155	—	Nitro, 49
Benzyl 1-naphthyl ether	—	77	—	—	—	—	—
4-Methoxybiphenyl	—	90	—	—	—	—	—
Benzyl 2-naphthyl ether	—	99	—	—	—	—	—

HALOGENO-ETHERS

ETHER	B.P.	M.P.	$d_4^{20°}$	$n_D^{20°}$	SULPHON-AMIDE	PICRATE	OTHER DERIVATIVES
m-Chloroanisole	194°	—	—	—	131°	—	—
o-Chloroanisole	195	—	1·191	1·545	151	—	Nitro, 95°
p-Chloroanisole	198	—	—	—	—	—	Nitro, 98
m-Chlorophenetole	205	—	1·171	—	133	—	—
o-Chlorophenetole	208	—	1·134	1·530	140	—	Nitro, 82
o-Bromoanisole	210	—	—	—	—	—	Nitro, 106
m-Bromoanisole	211	—	—	—	134	—	—
p-Chlorophenetole	212	21°	1·121	1·522	148	—	Nitro, 61
p-Bromoanisole	215	11	—	—	135	—	Nitro, 88
o-Bromophenetole	218	—	—	—	145	—	Nitro, 98
p-Bromophenetole	233	4	—	—		—	Nitro, 47

Table IX, 14. Aromatic Ethers (continued)

ETHER	B.P.	M.P.	$d_4^{20°}$	$n_D^{20°}$	SULPHON-AMIDE	PICRATE	OTHER DERIVATIVES
HALOGENO-ETHERS (continued)							
o-Iodoanisole	242°	—	—	—	—	—	—
m-Iodoanisole	244	—	—	—	—	—	—
o-Iodophenetole	246	—	—	—	—	—	—
m-Iodophenetole	134°/15	—	—	—	—	—	Nitro, 96°
p-Iodophenetole	252	29°	—	—	—	—	Nitro, 96
p-Bromodiphenyl ether	168°/15	—	—	—	131°	—	—
2,4,6-Trichlorophenetole	246	44	—	—	—	—	Dinitro, 100
p-Iodoanisole	240	52	—	—	—	—	—
2,4,6-Trichloroanisole	—	62	—	—	—	—	Dinitro, 95
2,4,6-Tribromophenetole	—	73	—	—	—	—	Nitro, 79
2,4,6-Tribromoanisole	—	88	—	—	—	—	—
NITRO-ETHERS							
o-Nitrophenetole	267°	—	—	—	—	—	o-Phenetidine, 228°
o-Nitroanisole	272	10°	1·254	1·562	—	—	o-Anisidine, 225
m-Nitrophenetole	284	34	—	—	—	—	m-Phenetidine, 248
m-Nitroanisole	258	39	—	—	—	—	m-Anisidine, 251
p-Nitroanisole	259	54	—	—	—	—	p-Anisidine, 246
p-Nitrophenetole	283	60	—	—	—	—	p-Phenetidine, 254
2,4,6-Trinitroanisole	—	68	—	—	—	—	—
2,4,6-Trinitrophenetole	—	78	—	—	—	—	—
2,4-Dinitrophenetole	—	87	—	—	—	—	—
2,4-Dinitroanisole	—	94	—	—	—	—	—

(1) o-Methoxytoluene.
(2) o-Methoxyphenol.
(3) Catechol dimethyl ether.
(5) p-Propenylanisole.
(6) 1-Allyl-3,4-dimethoxybenzene.
(7) 1,2-Methylenedioxy-4-propenylbenzene.

Table IX, 15.   **Aliphatic Aldehydes**

ALDEHYDE	B.P.	M.P.	ALKYLIDENE DIMEDONE	DIMEDONE 'ANHYDRIDE'	2,4-DINITRO-PHENYL-HYDRAZONE	SEMI-CARBAZONE	p-NITRO-PHENYL-HYDRAZONE	OTHER DERIVATIVES
Formaldehyde	−21°	—	189°	171°	166°	169°d	182°	Methylene di-2-naphthol, 190°
Acetaldehyde	20	—	141	174	168	163	129	Oxime, 47
Propionaldehyde	49	—	155	143	155	154 (89)	124	Oxime, 40
Glyoxal	50	—	186	224	328	270	311	Oxime, 178
Acrolein	52	—	192	163	165	171	151	—
Isobutyraldehyde	64	—	154	144	187	126	131	—
α-Methylacraldehyde	73	—	—	—	206	198	—	—
n-Butyraldehyde	75	—	142	141	123	106	87	—
Trimethylacetaldehyde	75	—	—	—	209	190	119	Oxime, 41
Isovaleraldehyde	92	—	155	173	123	132	110	Oxime, 48
Chloral	98	—	—	—	131	—	—	$d_4^{20°}$ 1·512, $n_D^{20°}$ 1·457
Crotonaldehyde	102	—	184	167	190	199	185	Phenylhydrazone, 56; oxime, 119
n-Valeraldehyde	104	—	105	113	107	—	—	Oxime, 52
Diethylacetaldehyde	117	—	102	—	130	99	—	—
4-Methylvaleraldehyde	121	—	—	133	99	127	—	—
Paraldehyde	124	—	—	—	—	—	—	$d_4^{20°}$ 0·994, $n_D^{20°}$ 1·420
n-Hexaldehyde	131	—	109	—	107	106	—	Oxime, 51
Tetrahydrofurfural	145	—	—	—	204	166	—	$d_4^{20°}$ 1·107, $n_D^{20°}$ 1·436
n-Heptaldehyde	155	—	103	112	108	109	73	Oxime, 57
Furfural	161	—	162	164	230 (213)	203	154	Phenylhydrazone, 98
Hexahydrobenzaldehyde	162	—	—	—	—	173	—	Oxime, 91
2-Ethylhexaldehyde	163	—	—	—	120	254d	—	—

Table IX, 15. Aliphatic Aldehydes (*continued*)

ALDEHYDE	B.P.	M.P.	ALKYLIDENE DIMEDONE	DIMEDONE 'ANHYDRIDE'	2,4-DINITRO-PHENYL-HYDRAZONE	SEMI-CARBAZONE	p-NITRO-PHENYL-HYDRAZONE	OTHER DERIVATIVES
n-Octaldehyde	170°	—	90°	101°	106°	101°	80°	Oxime, 60°
Bromal	174	—	—	—	—	—	—	—
n-Nonaldehyde	190	—	86	—	100	100	—	Oxime, 64
d-Citronellal	207	—	79	173	78	84	—	$d_4^{20°}$ 0·855, $n_D^{20°}$ 1·449
n-Decylaldehyde	208	—	92	—	104	102	—	Oxime, 69
Citral	229d	—	—	—	110	164	—	$d_4^{20°}$ 0·887, $n_D^{20°}$ 1·488
Aldol	83°/20	—	147	126	—	110	—	—
Choral hydrate	—	53°	56	—	131	—	—	Oxime, 56
Lauraldehyde	238	45	—	—	106	106	—	Oxime, 78
Myristaldehyde	155°/10	23	—	—	—	107	95	Oxime, 83
Palmitaldehyde	201°/29	34	—	—	108	109	97	Oxime, 88
Stearaldehyde	—	38	—	—	—	109	101	Oxime, 89
dl-Glyceraldehyde	—	142	—	—	170	160d	—	Oxime, 118

Table IX, 16. Acetals

NAME	FORMULA	B.P.	$d_{4°}^{20°}$	$n_D^{20°}$
Methylal	$CH_2(OCH_3)_2$	43°	0·859	1·353
Dimethylacetal	$CH_3CH(OCH_3)_2$	64	0·852	1·366
Ethylal	$CH_2(OC_2H_5)_2$	87	0·831	1·373
Acetal	$CH_3CH(OC_2H_5)_2$	103	0·826	1·381
1,3-Dioxan	$H_2C{<}^O_O{>}(CH_2)_3$	105	1·034	1·420
Isopropylal	$CH_2(OC_3H_7^\beta)_2$	122	0·818	1·384
Ethylpropylal	$CH_3CH_2CH(OC_2H_5)_2$	124	0·833	1·390
Acrolein acetal	$CH_2{=}CHCH(OC_2H_5)_2$	125	0·850	—
n-Propylal	$CH_2(OC_3H_7^\alpha)_2$	137	0·834	1·393
Ethylbutylal	$CH_3CH_2CH_2CH(OC_2H_5)_2$	143	0·921	1·402
n-Propylacetal	$CH_3CH(OC_3H_7^\alpha)_2$	147	0·830	1·397
Isobutylal	$CH_2(OC_4H_9^\beta)_2$	164	0·824	1·400
Isobutylacetal	$CH_3CH(OC_4H_9^\beta)_2$	176	0·821	1·403
n-Butylal	$CH_2(OC_4H_9^\alpha)_2$	181	0·835	1·406
n-Butylacetal	$CH_3CH(OC_4H_9^\alpha)_2$	187	0·833	1·409
n-Amylal	$CH_2(OC_5H_{11}^\alpha)_2$	219	0·838	1·416
n-Amylacetal	$CH_3CH(OC_5H_{11}^\alpha)_2$	222	0·839	1·418
n-Hexylal	$CH_2(OC_6H_{13}^\alpha)_2$	255	0·841	1·423
Benzaldehyde diethyl acetal	$C_6H_5CH(OC_2H_5)_2$	222	0·983	1·480

Table IX, 17.

Aromatic Aldehydes

ALDEHYDE	B.P.	M.P.	DIMEDONE	DIMEDONE ANHYDRIDE	2,4-DINITRO-PHENYL-HYDRAZONE	SEMI-CARBAZONE	OXIME	PHENYL-HYDRAZONE	p-NITRO-PHENYL-HYDRAZONE
Hexahydrobenzaldehyde	162°	—	—	—	—	173°	91°	—	—
Benzaldehyde	179	—	195°	200°	237°	224	35d	158°	192°
Phenylacetaldehyde	194	34°	165	126	121	156	99	63	151
Salicylaldehyde (1)	197	—	—	208	252	231	63	143	228
m-Tolualdehyde	199	—	172	206	194	223	60	91	157
o-Tolualdehyde	200	—	167	215	194	212	49	106	222
p-Tolualdehyde	204	—	—	—	233	234	80	112	201
Phenoxyacetaldehyde	215d	38	—	—	—	145	95	86	—
Hydrocinnamaldehyde	224	—	—	—	149	127	94	—	123
m-Methoxybenzaldehyde	230	—	—	—	—	—	40	—	171
Cuminaldehyde (2)	235	—	171	173	241	211	52	129	190
Anisaldehyde (3)	248	2	145	243	254	209	132 (65)	121	161
Cinnamaldehyde	252	—	213	175	255d	215	139	168	195
1-Naphthaldehyde	292	34	—	—	—	221	98	80	234
Piperonal (4)	263	37	178	220	265	234	110	106	200
o-Methoxybenzaldehyde	236	38	—	—	253	215	92	—	205
2,3-Dimethoxybenzaldehyde	—	54	—	—	—	231	99	138	—
Veratraldehyde (5)	285	58	—	—	264	177	95	121	—
2-Naphthaldehyde	—	61	—	—	270	245	156	206	230
2,4-Dimethoxybenzaldehyde	—	69	—	—	—	—	106	—	—
Vanillin (6)	—	81	197	228	269	239	117	105	228
m-Hydroxybenzaldehyde	240	108	—	—	259	198	90	130	222
p-Hydroxybenzaldehyde	—	116	189	246	280	224	72	178	266
Terephthaldialdehyde	246	116	—	—	—	—	200	278d	281
β-Resorcylaldehyde (7)	—	136	—	—	286	260	192	160	285
Protocatechuicaldehyde (8)	—	153	—	145	275	230	157	176	—

ALDEHYDE	B.P.	M.P.	DIMEDONE	DIMEDONE 'ANHYDRIDE'	2,4-DINITRO-PHENYL-HYDRAZONE	SEMI-CARBAZONE	OXIME	PHENYL-HYDRAZONE	p-NITRO-PHENYL-HYDRAZONE
HALOGENO-ALDEHYDES									
o-Chlorobenzaldehyde	213°	11°	205°	225°	209°	229° (146)	76d	86°	249°
m-Chlorobenzaldehyde	214	18	—	—	248	229	71d	134	216
o-Bromobenzaldehyde	230	22	—	—	—	214	102	—	240
m-Bromobenzaldehyde	234	—	—	—	—	205	72d	141	220
o-Iodobenzaldehyde	—	37	—	—	—	206	108	79	—
3,4-Dichlorobenzaldehyde	248	44	—	—	—	—	119	—	277
p-Chlorobenzaldehyde	214	47	—	—	265	232	107 (140)	127	220
m-Iodobenzaldehyde	—	57	—	—	—	226	62	155	212
p-Bromobenzaldehyde	—	67	—	—	—	228	111	113	208
2,6-Dichlorobenzaldehyde	—	71	—	—	—	—	150	—	—
2,4-Dichlorobenzaldehyde	—	72	—	—	—	—	—	—	—
p-Iodobenzaldehyde	—	78	—	—	—	224	—	121	201
NITRO- AND AMINO-ALDEHYDES									
o-Aminobenzaldehyde	—	40°	—	—	—	247°	135°	221°	220°
o-Nitrobenzaldehyde	—	44	—	—	265°	256	103	156	263
m-Nitrobenzaldehyde	—	58	—	—	292	246	122	121	247
p-Aminobenzaldehyde	—	72	—	—	—	173	124	156	—
p-Dimethylaminobenzaldehyde	—	74	—	—	325	222	185	148	182
p-Nitrobenzaldehyde	—	106	—	—	320	221	133	159	249
m-Aminobenzaldehyde	—	Amorphous	—	—	—	280d	195	162	226

(1) o-Hydroxybenzaldehyde.
(2) p-Isopropylbenzaldehyde.
(3) p-Methoxybenzaldehyde.
(4) 3,4-Methylenedioxybenzaldehyde.
(5) 3,4-Dimethoxybenzaldehyde.
(6) 4-Hydroxy-3-methoxybenzaldehyde.
(7) 2,4-Dihydroxybenzaldehyde.
(8) 3,4-Dihydroxybenzaldehyde.

Table IX, 18.   Aliphatic Ketones

KETONE	B.P.	M.P.	2,4-DINITRO-PHENYL-HYDRAZONE	SEMI-CARBAZONE	BENZAL DERIVATIVE	PHENYL-HYDRAZONE	p-NITRO-PHENYL-HYDRAZONE	OTHER DERIVATIVES
Acetone	56°	—	128°	190°	112°	42°	149°	Oxime, 59°
Ethyl methyl ketone	80	—	115	146	—	—	129	—
Methyl vinyl ketone	80	—	—	141	—	—	—	—
Biacetyl	88	—	315 (Di)	279 (Di)	53	243 (Di)	230	Dioxime, 234
Isopropyl methyl ketone	94	—	120	114	—	—	109	—
Methyl n-propyl ketone	102	—	144	112	—	—	117	Oxime, 58
Diethyl ketone	102	—	156	139	31	—	144	Oxime, 69
Pinacolone	106	—	125	158	41	—	—	Oxime, 78
Isobutyl methyl ketone	117	—	95	132	—	—	79	Oxime, 58
Di-isopropyl ketone	124	—	88	160	—	—	—	Oxime, 34
Ethyl n-propyl ketone	124	—	130	112	—	—	—	—
n-Butyl methyl ketone	128	—	107	125	—	—	88	Oxime, 49
Mesityl oxide	130	—	203	164	—	142	134	Oxime, 49
Cyclopentanone	131	—	146	210	190	55	154	Oxime, 57
Acetylacetone	139	—	209	—	—	—	—	Oxime, 149
2-Methylcyclopentanone	139	—	—	184	—	—	—	—
Di-n-propyl ketone	144	—	75	133	—	—	—	—
Acetoin (acetyl methyl carbinol)	145	—	318	185	—	—	—	—
Acetol (hydroxyacetone)	146	—	129	196	—	103	73	Oxime, 71
n-Amyl methyl ketone	151	—	89	127	—	207	147	—
Cyclohexanone	156	—	162	167	118	81	132	Oxime, 91
2-Methylcyclohexanone	165	—	137	197	—	—	209	Oxime, 43
Diacetone alcohol	166	—	203	—	—	—	—	Oxime, 58
Di-isobutyl ketone	168	—	92	122	—	—	—	—
Methyl acetoacetate	170	—	—	152	—	—	119	$d_4^{20°}$ 1·077, $n_D^{20°}$ 1·420
3-Methylcyclohexanone	170	—	155	191	122	94	128	Oxime, 39
4-Methylcyclohexanone	171	—	134	203	99	110	93	—
n-Hexyl methyl ketone	173	—	58	123	—	—	—	—

Table IX, 18. **Aliphatic Ketones** (*continued*)

KETONE	B.P.	M.P.	2,4-DINITRO-PHENYL-HYDRAZONE	SEMI-CARBAZONE	BENZAL DERIVATIVE	PHENYL-HYDRAZONE	p-NITRO-PHENYL-HYDRAZONE	OTHER DERIVATIVES
Cycloheptanone	180°	—	148°	162°	108°	—	—	—
Cyclohexyl methyl ketone	180	—	140	177	—	—	154°	Oxime, 60°
Ethyl acetoacetate	181	—	93	133	—	—	—	$d_4^{20°}$ 1·025, $n_D^{20°}$ 1·420
Di-n-butyl ketone	188	—	—	90	—	—	—	—
d-Fenchone	193	—	140	184	—	—	—	Oxime, 167
Acetonyl acetone	194	—	257 (Di)	220	—	120° (Di)	—	Dioxime, 137
Methyl laevulinate	196	—	142	143	—	96	—	$d_4^{20°}$ 1·050, $n_D^{20°}$ 1·423
Phorone	199	28°	118	221	—	—	—	Oxime, 48
β-Thujone	202	—	114	174	—	104	—	Oxime, 55
Ethyl laevulinate	206	—	102	148	—	53	—	$d_4^{20°}$ 1·011, $n_D^{20°}$ 1·423
l-Menthone	209	—	146	189	—	68	—	Oxime, 59
Isophorone	215	—	130	199	77	—	—	Oxime, 79
Pulegone	224	—	147	174	—	—	—	Oxime, 119
Di-n-amyl ketone	226	14	—	—	—	—	175	$d_4^{20°}$ 0·825, $n_D^{20°}$ 1·429
d-Carvone	230	—	191	163	—	110	97	Oxime, 73
Di-n-hexyl ketone	255	33	—	—	—	—	113	—
α-Ionone	130°/13	—	151	143 (108)	—	—	173	Oxime, 90
β-Ionone	139°/18	—	128	149	—	—	—	—
Furoin	—	135	217	—	—	81	199	Oxime, 161
Furil	—	165	215	—	—	184	217	Dioxime, 100
d-Camphor	209	179	177	238	98	233	—	Oxime, 119
Chloroacetone	119	—	125	150	—	—	—	—
1,1-Dichloroacetone	120	—	—	163	—	—	—	—
1,3-Dichloroacetone	173	45	133	120	—	—	—	—

Table IX, 19. Aromatic Ketones

KETONE	B.P.	M.P.	2,4-DINITRO-PHENYL-HYDRAZONE	SEMI-CARBAZONE	OXIME	PHENYL-HYDRAZONE	p-NITRO-PHENYL-HYDRAZONE	OTHER DERIVATIVES
Acetophenone	202°	20°	250° (237)	199°	59°	105°	185°	Benzal, 58°
2-Hydroxyacetophenone	215	—	—	210	117	110	—	—
2-Methylacetophenone (1)	216	—	159	203	61	—	145	—
Benzyl methyl ketone	216	27	156	198	69	87	—	—
Propiophenone (2)	218	19	191	174	53	147	—	—
3-Methylacetophenone (3)	220	—	207	198	55	—	—	—
Isobutyrophenone (4)	222	—	163	181	94	73	—	—
4-Methylacetophenone (5)	224	28	258	205	88	96	198	—
Benzyl ethyl ketone	226	—	—	136	—	—	—	—
n-Butyrophenone (6)	230	12	190	188	50	—	—	—
m-Methoxyacetophenone	240	—	—	196	—	—	—	—
n-Valerophenone (7)	242	—	166	166	52	162	—	—
o-Methoxyacetophenone	245	—	—	183	83	114	—	—
α-Tetralone	129°/12	—	257	217	89 (103)	84	231	Benzal, 105
β-Tetralone	138°/16	18	—	215	88	109	—	—
1-Acetylnaphthalene	302	34	—	229	139	149	—	Picrate, 116; benzal, 126
Phenyl o-tolyl ketone (8)	310	—	190	—	—	—	—	—
Phenyl m-tolyl ketone	314	—	221	—	101	—	—	—
Dibenzyl ketone	331	35	100	146	125	129	—	Benzal, 162
p-Methoxyacetophenone	258	39	220	198	87	142	—	—
α-Hydrindone	242	42	258	233	146	128	235	Benzal, 113
Benzalacetone	262	42	227	186	116	157	166	Benzal, 112
Benzophenone	306	49	238	165	144	137	155	—
2-Acetylnaphthalene	301	56	262	236	145	177	—	Picrate, 85
Benzalacetophenone (9)	347	58	245	168	115	119	—	Picrate, 97
Phenyl p-tolyl ketone	326	60	200	122	154	109	—	—
Deoxybenzoin (10)	320	60	206	148	98	116	163	Benzal, 102
p-Methoxybenzophenone	355	62	180	—	138	132	199	—

Table IX, 19. **Aromatic Ketones** (*continued*)

KETONE	B.P.	M.P.	2,4-DINI-TROPHENYL-HYDRAZONE	SEMI-CARBAZONE	OXIME	PHENYL-HYDRAZONE	p-NITRO-PHENYL-HYDRAZONE	OTHER DERIVATIVES
Fluorenone (11)	341°	83°	284°	—	195°	152°	269°	—
Phenacyl alcohol (12)	—	86	—	146°	70	112	—	Benzoyl, 118°; acetyl, 49°
Di-p-tolyl ketone	335	95	229	—	163	100	—	—
Benzil	347d	95	189	244 (Di)	237	235 (Di)	290	Quinoxaline, 126
m-Hydroxyacetophenone	—	96	—	195	—	—	—	—
p-Hydroxyacetophenone	—	109	261	199	145	151	173	—
Dibenzalacetone	—	112	180	189	143	153	—	Picrate, 114
p-Benzoquinone	—	116	186	243 (Di)	140	—	—	Picrate, 79
Acenaphthenone	—	121	—	—	175	90	—	Picrate, 113
1,4-Naphthaquinone	—	125	—	247	198	—	278	—
Benzoin	344	137	245	206	151 (99)	159	235	Benzoyl, 125; acetyl, 83
1,2-Naphthaquinone	—	146	—	184	162	138	—	—
Resacetophenone (13)	—	147	—	218	199	159	245	Dibenzoyl, 81; diacetyl, 38
9,10-Phenanthraquinone	—	207	313	—	158	165	—	—
Phloroacetophenone (14)	—	219	—	—	—	—	—	Tribenzoyl, 118; triacetyl, 103
Anthraquinone	—	285	—	—	224	183	—	—
HALOGENO-KETONES								
m-Chloroacetophenone	228°	—	—	232°	88°	—	176°	—
o-Chloroacetophenone	229	—	206°	160 (179)	113	—	215	—
p-Chloroacetophenone	236	20°	231	201	95	114°	239	—
o-Bromoacetophenone	112°/10	—	—	—	177	—	—	—
m-Bromoacetophenone	131°/16	8	—	238	—	—	—	—

Table IX, 19. Aromatic Ketones (continued)

KETONE	B.P.	M.P.	2,4-DINI-TROPHENYL-HYDRAZONE	SEMI-CARBAZONE	OXIME	PHENYL-HYDRAZONE	p-NITRO-PHENYL-HYDRAZONE	OTHER DERIVATIVES
\multicolumn{9}{c}{HALOGENO-KETONES (continued)}							
Phenacyl bromide (15)	—	51°	—	—	—	—	—	—
p-Bromoacetophenone	256°	51	230°	146°	89°	126°	—	—
p-Chlorobenzophenone	323	78	185	208	129	106	—	—
p-Bromobenzophenone	350	82	230	—	156 (95)	126	—	—
p-Iodoacetophenone	—	85	—	—	169	—	—	—
p-Bromophenacyl bromide	—	109	—	—	115	—	—	—
\multicolumn{9}{c}{NITRO- AND AMINO-KETONES}							
o-Nitroacetophenone	159°/16	—	—	—	—	—	—	—
o-Aminoacetophenone	251	20°	228°	290°	109°	108°	—	—
m-Nitroacetophenone	—	81	—	257	132	135	—	—
p-Nitroacetophenone	—	81	—	—	—	132	—	—
m-Aminoacetophenone	—	99	—	196	148	—	—	—
p-Aminoacetophenone	294	106	—	250	—	—	—	—

(1) Methyl o-tolyl ketone.
(2) Ethyl phenyl ketone.
(3) Methyl m-tolyl ketone.
(4) Isopropyl phenyl ketone.
(5) Methyl p-tolyl ketone.
(6) Phenyl n-propyl ketone.
(7) n-Butyl phenyl ketone.
(8) 2-Methylbenzophenone.
(9) Chalkone; Phenyl styryl ketone.
(10) Benzyl phenyl ketone.
(11) Diphenylene ketone.
(12) ω-Hydroxyacetophenone.
(13) 2,4-Dihydroxyacetophenone.
(14) 2,4,6-Trihydroxyacetophenone.
(15) ω-Bromoacetophenone.

Table IX, 20. Aliphatic Carboxylic Acids

ACID	B.P.	M.P.	ANILIDE	p-TOLUI-DIDE	AMIDE	p-BROMO-PHENACYL ESTER	p-NITRO-BENZYL ESTER	p-PHENYL-PHENACYL ESTER	s-BENZYL-THI-URONIUM SALT	p-BROMO-ANILIDE	HYDR-AZIDE*
Formic	101°	8°	50°	53°	3°	140°	31°	74°	151°	119°	54
Acetic	118	16	114	153	82	86	78	111	136	166	77
Acrylic	140	13	105	141	85	—	—	—	—	—	40
Propionic	141	—	106	126	79	63	31	102	152	148	—
Propiolic	144d	18	87	—	62	—	—	—	—	—	104
Isobutyric	154	—	105	109	129	77	—	89	149	151	44
n-Butyric	163	—	96	75	115	63	35	82	149	111	—
Pivalic (trimethylacetic)	164	35	133	120	154	76	—	—	—	—	—
Pyruvic	165d	13	104	130	125	—	—	—	—	—	68
Crotonic (*cis*)	165	15	102	—	102	—	—	—	—	—	—
Isovaleric	176	—	110	109	136	68	—	78	159	129	—
Methylethylacetic	177	—	112	93	112	55	—	63	—	—	—
n-Valeric	186	—	63	74	106	75	—	77	156	106	—
Diethylacetic	193	—	127	116	112	—	—	70	—	—	—
4-Methylpentanoic	199	—	112	63	121	77	—	—	—	—	—
Methoxyacetic	203	—	58	—	96	—	—	—	—	—	—
n-Hexoic (caproic)	205	—	—	74	100	72	—	70	159	105	—
Ethoxyacetic	207	—	95	80	82	104	—	62	—	95	—
n-Heptanoic (oenanthic)	223	—	71	—	96	72	—	54	—	—	105
2-Ethyl-n-hexanoic	228	—	—	—	103	—	—	—	—	—	—
Hexahydrobenzoic	233	31	144	70	186	67	—	67	157	102	—
n-Octanoic (caprylic)	239	16	57	70	107	84	61	71	—	—	111
Levulinic	246	33	102	109	108	69	—	—	—	100	—
n-Nonanoic (pelargonic)	254	12	57	84	99	67	—	—	149	102	—
n-Decoic (capric)	269	31	70	78	108	—	—	79	—	—	—
10-Undecenoic	275	25	67	68	87	68	—	145	153	—	—
n-Undecenoic	164°/15	29	71	80	103	113	43	86	141	—	—
dl-Lactic	122°/15	18	59	107	79	76	—	90	139	—	—
n-Dodecanoic (lauric)	225°/100	43	78	87	99	81	—	94	141	—	—
Myristic	250°/100	58	84	93	103	86	—	61	—	—	—
Palmitic	268°/100	63	91	98	106	45	—	—	—	—	—
Oleic	223°/10	16	41	43	76	—	—	97	—	—	—
Cyanoacetic	—	66	198	102	120	90	67	—	143	—	177
Stearic	291°/100	70	94	132	109	95	107	—	172	—	176
Crotonic (*trans*)	189	72	118	143	160	138	—	—	146	—	—
Glycollic	—	79	97	—	120	—	—	109	—	—	—
Citraconic	—	93	175	—	186	—	69	152	161	—	—
Glutaric	—	98	224	218	175	137	102	146	—	—	—
Citric (hydrated)	—	100	199	189	215	148	—	—	—	—	—

Table IX, 20. Aliphatic Carboxylic Acids (*continued*)

ACID	B.P.	M.P.	ANILIDE	p-TOLUI-DIDE	AMIDE	p-BROMO-PHENACYL ESTER	p-NITRO-BENZYL ESTER	p-PHENYL-PHENACYL ESTER	s-BENZYL-THI-URONIUM SALT	p-BROMO-ANILIDE	HYDR-AZIDE*
l-Malic (*dl*, m.p. 133°)	—	101°	197°	207°	157°	179°	124°	106°	124°	—	178°
Oxalic (dihydrate)	—	101	246	268	419d	242	204	165d	198	—	243
Pimelic	—	105	156	206	172	137	—	146d	—	—	182
Azelaic	—	106	187	202	209	131	44	141	155	—	—
Sebacic	—	133	202	201	—	147	73	140	—	—	—
Sorbic	—	134	153	—	—	129	—	—	—	—	80
Furoic (pyromucic)	—	134	124	108	142	139	134	86	211	—	—
Maleic	—	135	187	142	181	168	89	168	163	—	154
Malonic	—	135d	225	253	170	—	86	175	147	—	—
meso-Tartaric	—	140	—	—	190	—	93	—	—	—	—
2-Furylacrylic	—	141	187	219	169	144	85	151	—	—	171
Suberic	—	142	239	241	217	155	106	148	163	—	—
Adipic	—	152	190	—	220	117	90	—	—	—	—
Itaconic	—	165	264	—	192	216	163	204	154	—	168
D-Tartaric	—	170	230	255	196	211	88	208	—	—	—
Succinic	—	185	226	—	260	—	67	—	—	—	—
d-Camphoric	—	187	—	—	193	—	—	—	—	—	—
Aconitic (*trans*)	—	191	186	212	250	186	147	149	178	—	215
Mesaconic	—	204	—	—	176	—	—	—	—	—	—
dl-Tartaric	—	206	—	—	226	—	—	—	—	—	—
Mucic	—	214	—	150	128	—	—	—	195	—	—
Nicotinic	—	235	85	131	266	—	151	—	—	—	—
Fumaric	—	286	314	—	115	—	—	—	—	—	—
Thioacetic	93°	—	76	—	—	—	—	—	—	—	—

Halogeno-Acids

ACID	B.P.	M.P.	ANILIDE	p-TOLUI-DIDE	AMIDE	p-BROMO-PHENACYL ESTER	p-NITRO-BENZYL ESTER	p-PHENYL-PHENACYL ESTER	s-BENZYL-THI-URONIUM SALT	p-BROMO-ANILIDE	HYDR-AZIDE*
2-Chloropropionic	186°	—	92°	124°	80°	—	—	—	—	—	—
Dichloroacetic	194	10°	119	153	97	99°	—	—	178°	—	—
2-Bromopropionic	206	25	99	125	123	—	—	—	—	—	—
Monobromoacetic	208	50	130	91	91	—	—	—	—	—	—
Trichloroacetic	196	58	95	113	141	—	80°	—	148	—	—
Monochloroacetic	189	63	137	162	120	105	—	116°	160	—	—
Monoiodoacetic	—	84	144	—	95	—	—	—	—	—	—
Monofluoroacetic	167	35	—	—	108	—	—	—	—	—	—
Difluoroacetic	134	—	—	—	52	—	—	—	—	—	—
Trifluoroacetic	72	—	—	—	—	—	—	—	—	—	—

* See Section IV,25 for details of the preparation of hydrazides.

Table IX, 21. Aromatic Carboxylic Acids

ACID	M.P.	ANILIDE	p-TOLUI-DIDE	AMIDE	p-BROMO-PHENACYL ESTER	p-NITRO-BENZYL ESTER	p-PHENYL-PHENACYL ESTER	s-BENZYL-THI-URONIUM SALT	OTHER DERIVATIVES
o-Ethoxybenzoic	25°	—	—	132°	—	—	—	—	—
Hexahydrobenzoic (1)	31 (b.p. 233)	144°	—	185	—	—	—	—	—
Hydrocinnamic (2)	48	98	135°	105	104°	36°	95°	—	—
Phenylacetic	76	118	136	157	89	65	88	165°	—
Phenoxyacetic	99	101	—	101	148	—	—	—	—
o-Methoxybenzoic	101	131	—	129	—	113	131	146	Hydrazide, 124°
o-Toluic	105	125	144	143	57	91	95	140	—
m-Methoxybenzoic	110	—	—	—	—	—	—	166	Hydrazide, 97
m-Toluic	111	126	118	95	108	87	136	167	—
dl-Mandelic	120	152	172	134	—	123	—	183	Hydrazide, 112
Benzylmalonic	120d	217	—	225	—	120	—	—	—
Benzoic	121	162	158	129	119	89	167	144	—
o-Benzoylbenzoic	128	195	—	165	146	100	182	—	—
Cinnamic	133	153	168	147	—	117	—	—	—
1-Naphthylacetic	133	156	—	181	—	90	—	—	—
Acetylsalicylic	135	136	142	138	—	83	—	—	—
Phenylpropiolic	136	126	—	109	—	—	—	—	—
m-Ethoxybenzoic	137	—	—	139	—	—	111	—	—
2-Naphthylacetic	142	—	—	200	—	—	122	—	Acetyl, 98
Diphenylacetic	148	180	173	168	152	100	—	185	Acetyl, 153
Benzilic	150	175	190	155	—	147	—	—	—
p-Cresotic (3)	153	—	—	178	—	—	—	—	—

Table IX, 21. Aromatic Carboxylic Acids (*continued*)

ACID	M.P.	ANILIDE	p-TOLUI-DIDE	AMIDE	p-BROMO-PHENACYL ESTER	p-NITRO-BENZYL ESTER	p-PHENYL-PHENACYL ESTER	s-BENZYL-THI-URONIUM SALT	OTHER DERIVATIVES
Salicylic	158°	135°	156°	139°	140°	98°	148°	148°	Benzoyl, 132°; *p*-nitrobenzoyl, 205°
1-Naphthoic	162	163	—	202	—	—	—	—	—
o-Cresotic (4)	169	—	—	112	—	99	—	204	Acetyl, 113
m-Cresotic (5)	177	—	—	—	—	175	—	165	Acetyl, 139
p-Toluic	178	146	160	159	153	104	165	190	Hydrazide, 117
Anisic (6)	184	169	186	162	152	132	160	185	—
2-Naphthoic	185	170	191	192	—	—	—	—	—
p-Ethoxybenzoic	198	170	—	202	—	110	—	—	—
Protocatechuic (7)	199d	167	—	212	—	188	—	—	—
3-Hydroxybenzoic	201	157	163	167	176	108	167	—	Acetyl, 131
Phthalic	ca. 208d	251	—	219	153	155	—	158	—
Vanillic (8)	210	—	—	—	—	141	—	—	Acetyl, 146; benzoyl, 178
4-Hydroxybenzoic	213	197	204	162	191	192	240	145	Acetyl, 187
β-Resorcylic (9)	213	127	—	221	—	189	—	—	—
3-Hydroxy-2-naphthoic	223	244	222	218	—	—	—	—	—
1-Hydroxy-2-naphthoic	226	—	—	218	—	—	—	—	—
Diphenic	229	230	—	212	—	186	—	—	—
Piperonylic (10)	229	—	—	169	—	—	—	—	—
Gallic	ca. 240d	207	—	245	—	—	198d	—	Triacetyl, 172; tribenzoyl, 192
Isophthalic	347	—	—	280	179	203	280	216	Hydrazide, 220
Terephthalic	sub. >300	337	—	—	225	264	—	204	—
Trimesic (11)	380	—	—	365	197	—	—	—	Tri-Me-ester, 144; tri-Et-ester, 135

Table IX, 21. Aromatic Carboxylic Acids (*continued*)

ACID	M.P.	ANILIDE	p-TOLUI-DIDE	AMIDE	p-BROMO-PHENACYL ESTER	p-NITRO-BENZYL ESTER	p-PHENYL-PHENACYL ESTER	s-BENZYL-THI-URONIUM SALT	OTHER DERIVATIVES
				Halogeno-carboxylic acids					
m-Chlorophenoxyacetic	110°	—	—	—	—	—	—	—	—
m-Fluorobenzoic	124	—	—	130°	—	—	—	—	Hydrazide, 139°
o-Fluorobenzoic	127	—	—	116	—	—	—	—	Hydrazide, 73
o-Chlorobenzoic	141	118°	131°	141	107°	106°	123°	—	Hydrazide, 110
o-Chlorophenoxyacetic	146	121	—	150	102	110	98	171°	—
o-Bromobenzoic	150	141	—	155	126	105	155	168	—
m-Bromobenzoic	155	146	—	155	136	—	—	—	—
p-Chlorophenoxyacetic	157	125	—	133	117	107	154	—	—
m-Chlorobenzoic	158	124	—	134	110	111	143	155	Hydrazide, 158
o-Iodobenzoic	162	141	—	184	—	—	—	—	—
2,4-Dichlorobenzoic	164	—	—	194	—	—	—	—	Dinitro, 211
p-Fluorobenzoic	185	—	—	154	—	121	—	—	Hydrazide, 162
m-Iodobenzoic	187	—	—	186	128	—	—	—	—
3,4-Dichlorobenzoic	209	—	—	169	—	—	—	—	—
p-Chlorobenzoic	243	194	—	179	126	130	160	—	Hydrazide, 163
p-Bromobenzoic	252	197	—	189	134	141	160	—	Hydrazide, 164
p-Iodobenzoic	270	210	—	218	146	141	171	—	—

Table IX, 21. Aromatic Carboxylic Acids (*continued*)

ACID	M.P.	ANILIDE	*p*-TOLUI-DIDE	AMIDE	*p*-BROMO-PHENACYL ESTER	*p*-NITRO-BENZYL ESTER	*p*-PHENYL-PHENACYL ESTER	*s*-BENZYL-THI-URONIUM SALT	OTHER DERIVATIVES
				NITRO- AND AMINO-CARBOXYLIC ACIDS					
m-Nitrophenylacetic	120°	—	—	110°	—	—	—	—	—
m-Nitrobenzoic	141	154°	162°	142	132°	142°	153°	163°	—
o-Nitrophenylacetic	141	—	—	161	—	—	—	—	—
Anthranilic	146	131	151	109	—	205	—	149	*N*-Benzoyl, 81°; *N*-*p*-toluene-sulphonyl, 217°
o-Nitrobenzoic	147	155	—	175	107	112	140	159	—
p-Nitrophenylacetic	152	212	210	198	207	—	—	—	—
4-Nitrophthalic	165	—	—	200	—	—	120	—	—
m-Aminobenzoic	174	140	—	111	—	201	—	—	*N*-Acetyl, 248
2,4-Dinitrobenzoic	183	167	—	204	158	142	—	—	—
N-Acetylanthranilic	185	208	—	171	—	—	—	—	—
Hippuric (12)	187	—	—	183	151	136	163	—	Hydrazide, 162
p-Aminobenzoic	188	—	—	114	—	—	—	—	*N*-Acetyl, 250; *N*-benzoyl, 278
m-Nitrocinnamic	205	—	—	196	178	174	154	—	—
3,5-Dinitrobenzoic	207	234	—	183	159	157	149	—	—
3-Nitrophthalic	219	234	223	201	—	190	—	—	—
2,4,6-Trinitrobenzoic	228	—	—	264	—	—	—	—	—
p-Nitrobenzoic	239	211	203	201	136	169	182	182	—
o-Nitrocinnamic	240	—	—	185	142	132	146	—	—
β-Phenylalanine (13)	273	—	—	140	—	222	—	—	*N*-Benzoyl, 188
p-Nitrocinnamic	287	—	—	217	191	187	192	—	—

(1) Cyclohexanecarboxylic acid.
(2) 3-Phenylpropionic acid.
(3) 6-Hydroxy-*m*-toluic acid; 6-Hydroxy-3-methylbenzoic acid.
(6) *p*-Methoxybenzoic acid.
(7) 3,4-Dihydroxybenzoic acid.
(8) 4-Hydroxy-3-methoxybenzoic acid.
(9) 2,4-Dihydroxybenzoic acid.
(10) 3,4-Methylenedioxybenzoic acid.
(11) Benzene-1,3,5-tricarboxylic acid.
(12) Benzoylaminoacetic acid.
(13) 2-Amino-3-phenylpropionic acid.

Table IX, 22.   Acid Chlorides (Aliphatic)

ACYL CHLORIDE	B.P.	M.P.	$d_4^{20°}$	$n_D^{20°}$
Acetyl	52°	—	1·104	1·390
Propionyl	80	—	1·056	1·404
Isobutyryl	92	—	1·017	1·408
n-Butyryl	102	—	1·028	1·412
Chloroacetyl	105	—	1·420	1·454
Dichloroacetyl	108	—	—	—
Methoxyacetyl	113	—	1·187	1·419
Isovaleryl (3-methylbutanoyl)	115	—	0·987	1·416
Trichloroacetyl	118	—	1·620	1·470
Crotonyl	126	—	—	—
n-Valeryl	127	—	1·000	1·420
Isocaproyl (4-methylpentanoyl)	144	—	0·973	—
n-Caproyl (n-hexanoyl)	152	—	0·975	1·426
n-Heptanoyl (oenanthyl)	175	—	0·962	1·432
n-Octanoyl (caprylyl)	195	—	0·949	1·432
n-Nonanoyl (pelargonyl)	215	—	0·942	1·433
n Decanoyl (capryl)	232	—	—	—
Oxalyl	64	—	1·479	1·432
Succinyl	192	17°	1·375	1·468
Glutaryl	218	—	1·324	1·473
Adipyl	125°/11	—	—	—
Pimelyl	137°/15	—	—	—
Suberyl	150°/12	—	1·171	1·468
Azelayl	165°/13	—	—	—
Sebacyl	182°/16	—	1·212	1·468

Table IX, 23. Acid Anhydrides (Aliphatic)

ANHYDRIDE	B.P.	M.P.	$d_{4°}^{20°}$	$n_D^{20°}$
Acetic	140°	—	1·081	1·390
Propionic	168	—	1·022	1·404
Isobutyric	182	—	0·956	—
n-Butyric	198	—	0·968	1·413
Citraconic	213	7°	—	—
Isovaleric (β-Methyl-n-butyric) .	215	—	0·933	1·404
n-Valeric	218	—	0·925	—
Isocaproic (4-methylpentanoic) .	139°/19	—	—	—
n-Caproic (n-Hexanoic) . . .	245	—	0·920	1·430
Crotonic	248	—	1·040	1·474
n-Heptanoic (oenanthic) .	258	17	0·917	1·433
n-Octanoic (capric) . . .	285	—	0·910	1·434
Maleic	198	56	—	—
Glutaric	150°/10	56	—	—
Itaconic	139°/30	68	—	—
Succinic	261	120	—	—
d-Camphoric	270	221	—	—
Dichloroacetic	101°/16	—	—	—
Trichloroacetic	223	—	—	—
Monochloroacetic . . .	109°/11	46	—	—

Table IX, 24. Acid Chlorides and Acid Anhydrides of Aromatic Acids

ACID CHLORIDE	B.P.	M.P.
Benzoyl	197°	—
Phenylacetyl	210	—
o-Toluyl	212	—
m-Toluyl	219	—
p-Toluyl	227	—
m-Methoxybenzoyl	244	—
o-Methoxybenzoyl	254	—
s-Phthaloyl	281	16°
Anisoyl	145°/14 mm.	24
1-Naphthoyl	163°/10 mm.	24
Cinnamoyl	131°/11 mm.	36
2-Naphthoyl	305	53
Diphenylcarbamyl	—	86
p-Chlorobenzoyl	222	16
m-Chlorobenzoyl	225	—
o-Chlorobenzoyl	238	—
m-Bromobenzoyl	243	—
o-Bromobenzoyl	245	11
p-Bromobenzoyl	245	42
o-Nitrobenzoyl	148°/9 mm.	20
m-Nitrobenzoyl	278	35
2,4-Dinitrobenzoyl	—	46
3,5-Dinitrobenzoyl	196°/11 mm.	74
p-Nitrobenzoyl	—	75
3-Nitrophthaloyl	—	77

ANHYDRIDE	B.P.	M.P.
o-Toluic	—	39°
Benzoic	360°	42
m-Toluic	—	71
Phenylacetic	—	72
p-Toluic	—	95
Anisic	—	99
Phthalic	284	132
2-Naphthoic	—	135
Cinnamic	—	136
1-Naphthoic	—	146
1,2-Naphthalic	—	169
Diphenic	—	217
d-Camphoric	270	222
2,3-Naphthalic	—	246d
1,8-Naphthalic	—	274
o-Chlorobenzoic	—	79
m-Chlorobenzoic	—	95
p-Chlorobenzoic	—	194
Tetrachlorophthalic	—	255
Tetrabromophthalic	—	280
Tetra-iodophthalic	—	325
3,5-Dinitrobenzoic	—	109
4-Nitrophthalic	—	119
o-Nitrobenzoic	—	135
2,4-Dinitrobenzoic	—	160
m-Nitrobenzoic	—	163
3-Nitrophthalic	—	164
p-Nitrobenzoic	—	190

Table IX, 25. Aliphatic Esters

It is considered that the Table will be of greatest use to the student if the esters are subdivided under the various acids rather than arranged in order of increasing b.p. or m.p. irrespective of the nature of the carboxylic acid. The latter procedure leads to an unwieldy, heterogeneous Table which has relatively little pedagogic or, indeed, practical value.

ESTER	B.P.	$d_{4°}^{20°}$	$n_D^{20°}$
Methyl formate	32°	0·974	1·344
Ethyl formate	53	0·923	1·360
Isopropyl formate	71	0·873	1·368
n-Propyl formate	81	0·904	1·377
tert-Butyl formate	83	—	—
Allyl formate	84	0·946	—
sec-Butyl formate	97	0·884	1·384
Isobutyl formate	98	0·876	1·386
n-Butyl formate	106	0·892	1·389
Isoamyl formate	124	0·882	1·398
n-Amyl formate	131	0·885	1·400
Cyclopentyl formate	138	1·000	1·432
n-Hexyl formate	154	0·879	1·407
Cyclohexyl formate	161	0·994	1·443
Ethylene glycol diformate	177	1·229	—
Methyl acetate	56	0·939	1·362
Ethyl acetate	77	0·901	1·372
Isopropyl acetate	88	0·872	1·377
tert-Butyl acetate	97	0·867	1·386
n-Propyl acetate	101	0·887	1·384
Allyl acetate	104	0·928	1·404
sec-Butyl acetate	112	0·872	1·389
Isobutyl acetate	116	0·871	1·390
n-Butyl acetate	124	0·881	1·394
tert-Amyl acetate	124	0·873	1·392
Isoamyl acetate	141	0·872	1·400
n-Amyl acetate	148	0·875	1·402
Cyclopentyl acetate	153	0·975	1·432
n-Hexyl acetate	169	0·872	1·409
Cyclohexyl acetate	172	0·970	1·442
Furfuryl acetate	176	1·118	—
n-Heptyl acetate	192	0·865	1·414
Tetrahydrofurfuryl acetate	195	1·061	1·438
n-Octyl acetate	210	—	—
Methyl 'cellosolve' acetate	144	1·088	—
'Cellosolve' acetate	156	0·976	—
Ethylene glycol diacetate	190	1·104	1·415
Propylene glycol diacetate	191	1·059	1·417
Trimethylene glycol diacetate	210	1·069	—
'Carbitol' acetate	217	1·013	—
n-Butyl 'carbitol' acetate	246	0·983	—
α-Monoacetin (glycerol 1-acetate)	158°/15	1·206	1·416
Diacetin (mixture of αγ and αβ)	143°/12	1·180	—
Triacetin (glycerol triacetate)	153°/22	1·161	1·430

Table IX, 25. Aliphatic Esters (*continued*)

ESTER	B.P.	$d_4^{20°}$	$n_D^{20°}$
Methyl propionate	79°	0·915	1·377
Ethyl propionate	98	0·892	1·384
Isopropyl propionate	111	—	—
n-Propyl propionate	122	0·882	1·393
Allyl propionate	123	0·914	1·410
n-Butyl propionate	145	0·875	1·401
Isoamyl propionate	160	0·859	1·412
n-Amyl propionate	169	0·881	—
n-Hexyl propionate	190	0·870	1·419
Methyl n-butyrate	102	0·898	1·387
Ethyl n-butyrate	120	0·879	1·392
Isopropyl n-butyrate	128	—	—
n-Propyl n-butyrate	142	0·872	1·400
Allyl n-butyrate	142	0·902	1·416
n-Butyl n-butyrate	165	0·869	1·406
Isoamyl n-butyrate	179	0·864	1·411
n-Amyl n-butyrate	185	0·866	1·412
n-Hexyl n-butyrate	208	0·866	1·420
Methyl isobutyrate	91	0·888	1·383
Ethyl isobutyrate	110	0·869	1·387
Isopropyl isobutyrate	121	—	—
n-Propyl isobutyrate	134	0·864	1·396
n-Butyl isobutyrate	156	0·862	1·402
Methyl n-valerate	127	0·890	1·397
Ethyl n-valerate	144	0·874	1·400
Isopropyl n-valerate	154	0·858	1·401
n-Propyl n-valerate	164	0·870	1·407
n-Butyl n-valerate	184	0·868	1·412
Methyl isovalerate	116	0·881	1·393
Ethyl isovalerate	133	0·865	1·396
n-Propyl isovalerate	156	0·862	1·403
Isobutyl isovalerate	171	0·853	1·406
n-Butyl isovalerate	176	0·861	1·409
Methyl n-caproate (n-hexanoate)	149	0·885	1·405
Ethyl n-caproate	168	0·871	1·407
n-Propyl n-caproate	187	0·867	1·417
n-Butyl n-caproate	208	0·865	1·421
n-Amyl n-caproate	226	0·863	1·426
Methyl n-heptanoate (oenanthate)	171	0·882	1·412
Ethyl n-heptanoate	186	0·870	1·413
n-Propyl n-heptanoate	208	0·866	1·421
n-Butyl n-heptanoate	226	0·864	1·426

Table IX, 25.   Aliphatic Esters (*continued*)

ESTER	B.P.	$d_{4°}^{20°}$	$n_{\text{D}}^{20°}$
Methyl *n*-octanoate (*n*-caprylate)	192°	0·878	1·417
Ethyl *n*-octanoate	206	0·869	1·418
Methyl pelargonate (*n*-nonanoate)	214	—	—
Ethyl pelargonate	227	0·866	1·422
Methyl *n*-decanoate (caprate)	228	0·873	1·426
Ethyl *n*-decanoate	242	0·865	1·426
n-Propyl *n*-decanoate	115°/5	0·862	1·428
n-Butyl *n*-decanoate	123°/4	0·861	1·430
Methyl *n*-dodecanoate (laurate)	262	0·870	1·432
Ethyl *n*-dodecanoate	273	0·862	1·431
n-Propyl *n*-dodecanoate	140°/4	0·862	1·434
n-Butyl *n*-dodecanoate	154°/5	0·860	1·436
Methyl stearate	M.p. 39	—	—
Ethyl stearate	M.p. 33	—	—
Methyl chlorocarbonate (chloroformate)	73	1·223	1·387
Ethyl chlorocarbonate	94	1·136	1·397
n-Propyl chlorocarbonate	115	1·090	1·404
Isobutyl chlorocarbonate	129	1·040	1·406
n-Butyl chlorocarbonate	138	1·079	1·412
n-Amyl chlorocarbonate	61°/15	—	1·417
n-Hexyl chlorocarbonate	63°/10	—	—
Methyl chloroacetate	129	1·234	1·422
Ethyl chloroacetate	142	1·150	1·422
Methyl dichloroacetate	143	1·377	1·443
Ethyl dichloroacetate	156	1·283	1·438
Methyl trichloroacetate	152	1·488	1·457
Ethyl trichloroacetate	164	1·380	1·450
Methyl bromoacetate	144d	—	—
Ethyl bromoacetate	169	1·506	1·451
Methyl iodoacetate	170	—	—
Ethyl iodoacetate	180	1·818*	1·508*
Methyl methoxyacetate	130	1·051	1·396
Ethyl methoxyacetate	132	1·007	—
Methyl ethoxyacetate	148	1·006	—
Ethyl ethoxyacetate	158	0·970	1·403
Methyl acrylate	80	0·960	1·398
Ethyl acrylate	101	0·909	1·406

(13*)

Table IX, 25. Aliphatic Esters (*continued*)

ESTER	B.P.	$d_{4°}^{20°}$	$n_D^{20°}$
Methyl crotonate	119°	0·946	1·425
Ethyl crotonate	137	0·918	1·425
n-Propyl crotonate	157	0·908	1·428
n-Butyl crotonate	55°/4	0·899	1·432
Isoamyl crotonate	60°/4	0·891	1·434
n-Amyl crotonate	72°/5	0·894	1·436
Methyl lactate	145	1·089	1·414
Ethyl lactate	154	1·030	1·415
Methyl glycollate	151	1·166	—
Ethyl glycollate	160	1·082	—
Methyl pyruvate	138	—	—
Ethyl pyruvate	155	1·055	1·406
Methyl levulinate	196	1·049	1·423
Ethyl levulinate	206	1·011	1·423
Methyl furoate	181	1·180	1·486
Ethyl furoate	197 (m.p. 34)	1·117*	1·480*
Methyl orthoformate	105	0·968	1·379
Ethyl orthoformate	143	0·893	1·390
n-Propyl orthoformate	91°/17	0·879	1·407
n-Butyl orthoformate	127°/16	0·871	1·416
Methyl carbonate	90	1·071	1·369
Ethyl carbonate	126	0·976	1·384
n-Propyl carbonate	165	0·943	1·400
Isobutyl carbonate	188	0·914	1·407
n-Butyl carbonate	205	0·925	1·412
Methyl oxalate	M.p. 54	—	—
Ethyl oxalate	183	1·079	1·410
Isopropyl oxalate	191	0·995	1·413
n-Propyl oxalate	212	1·019	1·416
n-Butyl oxalate	241	0·987	1·423
Isoamyl oxalate	127°/7	0·961	1·427
n-Amyl oxalate	139°/9	0·966	1·429
Methyl malonate	179	1·119	1·420
Ethyl malonate	197	1·055	1·414
Allyl succinate	104	1·051	1·452
Methyl succinate	195	1·120	1·420

* Values at 21° with supercooled liquid.

Table IX, 25.   Aliphatic Esters (continued)

ESTER	B.P.	$d_{4°}^{20°}$	$n_D^{20°}$
Ethyl succinate	218°	1·042	1·420
Isopropyl succinate	82°/3	0·985	1·418
n-Propyl succinate	102°/3	1·006	1·425
Isobutyl succinate	116°/4	0·968	1·427
n-Butyl succinate	120°/3	0·977	1·430
Isoamyl succinate	130°/4	0·958	1·434
n-Amyl succinate	129°/2	0·960	1·434
Methyl glutarate	109°/21	1·087	1·424
Ethyl glutarate	118°/15	1·023	1·424
Methyl adipate	121°/17	1·063	1·428
Ethyl adipate	134°/17	1·009	1·428
Isopropyl adipate	120°/6	0·966	1·425
n-Propyl adipate	146°/9	0·981	1·431
n-Butyl adipate	159°/17	0·945	1·435
Isoamyl adipate	184°/13	0·945	1·437
n-Amyl adipate	186°/10	0·948	1·439
Methyl pimelate	128°/16	1·038	1·431
Ethyl pimelate	149°/18	0·993	1·430
Methyl suberate	120°/6	1·024	1·434
Ethyl suberate	131°/5	0·981	1·432
n-Propyl suberate	165°/8	0·962	1·435
n-Butyl suberate	176°/4	0·948	1·439
Methyl azelate	156°/20	1·007	1·436
Ethyl azelate	291	0·973	1·435

Table IX, 25. Aliphatic Esters (*continued*)

ESTER	B.P.	M.P.	$d_4^{20°}$	$n_D^{20°}$
Methyl sebacate . . .	293°	27°	—	—
Ethyl sebacate . . .	307	—	0·964	1·437
n-Propyl sebacate . . .	179°/5 mm.	—	0·950	1·439
Methyl maleate . . .	201	—	1·150	1·442
Ethyl maleate	220	—	1·066	1·440
n-Propyl maleate . . .	126°/12	—	1·025	1·443
n-Butyl maleate . . .	147°/12	—	0·994	1·445
Methyl fumarate . . .	193	102	—	—
Ethyl fumarate . . .	214	—	1·052	1·441
n-Propyl fumarate . .	110°/5	—	1·013	1·444
n-Butyl fumarate . . .	139°/5	—	0·987	1·447
Methyl itaconate . . .	208	38	—	—
Ethyl itaconate . . .	229	—	1·047	1·439
Methyl mesaconate . . .	205	—	1·120	1·454
Ethyl mesaconate . . .	225	—	1·043	1·448
Methyl citraconate . . .	210	—	1·112	1·448
Ethyl citraconate . . .	228	—	1·041	1·444
Methyl *d*-tartrate . . .	280	61	—	—
Ethyl *d*-tartrate . . .	280	18	1·203	1·447
n-Propyl *d*-tartrate . . .	297	—	1·139	—
n-Butyl *d*-tartrate . . .	200°/18	22	—	—
Methyl *dl*-tartrate . . .	282	90	—	—
Ethyl *dl*-tartrate . . .	280	18	1·203	1·447
n-Propyl *dl*-tartrate . .	286	25	—	—
n-Butyl *dl*-tartrate . . .	320	—	1·086	—
Methyl malate . . .	242	—	1·233	1·442
Ethyl malate . . .	253	—	1·129	1·436
Methyl mucate . . .	—	167	—	—
Ethyl mucate . . .	—	164	—	—
Methyl citrate . . .	—	76	—	—
Ethyl citrate . . .	294	—	1·137	1·466

Table IX, 25A.   Esters of Inorganic Acids

ESTER	B.P.	$d_4^{20°}$	$n_D^{20°}$
NITRITES			
Methyl nitrite	−12°	—	—
Ethyl nitrite	17	0·907 (10°)	1·331 (10°)
n-Propyl nitrite	48	0·886	1·360
Isopropyl nitrite	45	0·856	—
n-Butyl nitrite	76	0·882	1·377
Isobutyl nitrite	67	0·871	1·373
sec-Butyl nitrite	68	0·872	1·371
tert-Butyl nitrite	63	0·867	1·369
n-Amyl nitrite	104	0·882	1·389
Isoamyl nitrite	99	0·871	1·387
tert-Amyl nitrite	93	0·896	1·387
NITRATES			
Methyl nitrate	65°	1·208	1·375
Ethyl nitrate	88	1·108	1·385
n-Propyl nitrate	111	1·054	1·397
Isopropyl nitrate	102	1·035	1·391
n-Butyl nitrate	136	1·023	1·407
Isobutyl nitrate	124	1·015	1·403
sec-Butyl nitrate	124	1·026	1·402
n-Amyl nitrate	157	0·996	—
Isoamyl nitrate	148	0·998	1·413
SULPHITES			
Dimethyl sulphite	126°	1·213	1·409
Diethyl sulphite	157	1·083	1·414
Di-n-propyl sulphite	191	1·028	1·424
Di-isopropyl sulphite	170	1·006	1·415
Di-n-butyl sulphite	91°/5	0·996	1·431
Di-isobutyl sulphite	210	0·986	1·427
Di-n-amyl sulphite	111°/5	0·978	1·436
Di-isoamyl sulphite	98°/4	0·973	1·436
SULPHATES			
Dimethyl sulphate	188°	1·328	1·387
Diethyl sulphate	208	1·177	1·400
Di-n-propyl sulphate	94°/5	1·110	1·414
Di-n-butyl sulphate	116°/6	1·062	1·421
Di-isobutyl sulphate	133°/19	1·045	1·415
Di-n-amyl sulphate	117°/4	1·029	1·429

See Table IX, 44 for alkyl phosphates and alkyl phosphites.

Table IX, 26.   Aromatic Esters

It is considered that the Table will be of greatest use to the student if the esters are in the main subdivided under the various acids rather than be arranged in order of increasing b.p. or m.p. irrespective of the nature of the carboxylic acid. The latter procedure leads to an unwieldy, heterogeneous Table which has relatively little pedagogic or, indeed, practical value.

ESTER	B.P.	M.P.	$d_{4°}^{20°}$	$n_D^{20°}$
Methyl benzoate	199°	—	1·089	1·517
Ethyl benzoate	212	—	1·047	1·505
Isopropyl benzoate	218	—	1·015	1·491
n-Propyl benzoate	230	—	1·023	1·500
Allyl benzoate	230	—	1·052	—
Isobutyl benzoate	242	—	0·997	—
n-Butyl benzoate	248	—	1·005	1·497
Isoamyl benzoate	262	—	0·986	1·495
n-Amyl benzoate	137°/15	—	—	—
Ethylene glycol dibenzoate	—	73°	—	—
Methyl phenylacetate	215	—	1·068	1·507
Ethyl phenylacetate	228	—	1·033	1·497
n-Propyl phenylacetate	241	—	1·010	1·493
n-Butyl phenylacetate	256	—	0·994	1·489
Methyl o-toluate	213	—	1·068	—
Ethyl o-toluate	227	—	1·034	1·508
Methyl m-toluate	215	—	1·061	—
Ethyl m-toluate	227	—	1·028	1·506
Methyl p-toluate	217	34	—	—
Ethyl p-toluate	228	—	1·025	1·507
Methyl salicylate	223	—	1·184	1·537
Ethyl salicylate	234	—	1·125	1·522
n-Propyl salicylate	240	—	1·098	1·516
n-Butyl salicylate	260	—	1·073	1·512
Methyl m-hydroxybenzoate	—	70	—	—
Ethyl m-hydroxybenzoate	295	73	—	—
Ethyl p-hydroxybenzoate	297	116	—	—
Methyl p-hydroxybenzoate	—	131	—	—
Methyl o-methoxybenzoate	248	—	1·156	1·534
Ethyl o-methoxybenzoate	261	—	1·104	1·525
Methyl m-methoxybenzoate	237	—	1·131	1·522
Ethyl m-methoxybenzoate	251	—	1·100	1·515
Methyl anisate	255	49	—	—
Ethyl anisate	269	7	1·103	1·524
Methyl o-chlorobenzoate	234	—	—	1·536
Ethyl o-chlorobenzoate	243	—	1·190	1·522
Methyl m-chlorobenzoate	231	20	—	1·492
Ethyl m-chlorobenzoate	242	—	1·182	1·520
Ethyl p-chlorobenzoate	238	—	1·181	1·524
Methyl p-chlorobenzoate	—	44	—	—

Table IX, 26. Aromatic Esters (*continued*)

ESTER	B.P.	M.P.	$d_{4°}^{20°}$	$n_D^{20°}$
Methyl o-bromobenzoate	246°	—	—	—
Ethyl o-bromobenzoate	255	—	—	—
Ethyl m-bromobenzoate	259	—	—	—
Methyl m-bromobenzoate	—	32°	—	—
Ethyl p-bromobenzoate	263	—	—	—
Methyl p-bromobenzoate	—	81	—	—
Ethyl o-iodobenzoate	275	—	—	—
Methyl o-iodobenzoate	278	—	—	—
Ethyl m-iodobenzoate	150°/15	—	—	—
Methyl m-iodobenzoate	277	54	—	—
Ethyl p-iodobenzoate	153°/14	—	—	—
Methyl p-iodobenzoate	—	114	—	—
Ethyl o-nitrobenzoate	—	30	—	—
Methyl o-nitrobenzoate	275	—	1·286	—
Ethyl m-nitrobenzoate	297	47	—	—
Methyl m-nitrobenzoate	279	79	—	—
Ethyl p-nitrobenzoate	—	57	—	—
Methyl p-nitrobenzoate	—	96	—	—
Ethyl 3,5-dinitrobenzoate	—	94	—	—
Methyl 3,5-dinitrobenzoate	—	108	—	—
Ethyl 2,4-dinitrobenzoate	—	41	—	—
Methyl 2,4-dinitrobenzoate	—	70	—	—
Ethyl anthranilate	267	13	1·117	1·565
Methyl anthranilate	300	24	—	—
Ethyl m-aminobenzoate	294	—	—	—
Methyl m-aminobenzoate	—	38	—	—
Ethyl p-aminobenzoate	—	92	—	—
Methyl p-aminobenzoate	—	112	—	—
Ethyl cinnamate	273	—	1·049	1·560
n-Propyl cinnamate	284	—	1·028	1·551
n-Butyl cinnamate	162°/12	—	1·013	1·544
Methyl cinnamate	261	36	—	—
Methyl dihydrocinnamate	232	—	1·043	1·503
Ethyl dihydrocinnamate	248	—	1·016	1·495
n-Propyl dihydrocinnamate	262	—	0·998	1·491
n-Butyl dihydrocinnamate	123°/11	—	0·984	1·489
Ethyl o-nitrocinnamate	—	44	—	—
Methyl o-nitrocinnamate	—	73	—	—
Ethyl m-nitrocinnamate	—	79	—	—
Methyl m-nitrocinnamate	—	124	—	—
Ethyl p-nitrocinnamate	—	142	—	—
Methyl p-nitrocinnamate	—	161	—	—

Table IX, 26. **Aromatic Esters** (*continued*)

ESTER	B.P.	M.P.	$d_{4°}^{20°}$	$n_D^{20°}$
Methyl *o*-aminocinnamate	—	65°	—	—
Ethyl *o*-aminocinnamate	—	78	—	—
Ethyl *m*-aminocinnamate	—	64	—	—
Methyl *m*-aminocinnamate	—	84	—	—
Ethyl *p*-aminocinnamate	—	69	—	—
Methyl *p*-aminocinnamate	—	129	—	—
Methyl phenoxyacetate	245°	—	1·147	—
Ethyl phenoxyacetate	251	—	1·101	—
Ethyl *dl*-mandelate	255	37	—	—
Methyl *dl*-mandelate	—	58	—	—
Methyl *o*-benzoylbenzoate	352	52	—	—
Ethyl *o*-benzoylbenzoate	—	58	—	—
Ethyl diphenylacetate	—	58	—	—
Methyl diphenylacetate	—	60	—	—
Methyl phthalate	282	—	1·191	1·516
Ethyl phthalate	298	—	1·118	1·502
Propyl phthalate	130°/1	—	—	—
Isopropyl phthalate	154°/10	—	—	—
n-Butyl phthalate	205°/20	—	—	—
Ethyl isophthalate	285	11	1·121	1·507
Methyl isophthalate	—	68	—	—
Ethyl terephthalate	302	44	—	—
Methyl terephthalate	—	142	—	—
Ethyl 3-nitrophthalate	—	45	—	—
Methyl 3-nitrophthalate	—	69	—	—
Ethyl 4-nitrophthalate	—	34	—	—
Methyl 4-nitrophthalate	—	66	—	—
Methyl 1-naphthoate	116°/1	—	1·163	1·612
Ethyl 1-naphthoate	309	—	1·121	1·594
Ethyl 2-naphthoate	304	32	—	—
Methyl 2-naphthoate	290	77	—	—
Ethyl diphenate	—	42	—	—
Methyl diphenate	—	74	—	—
Methyl hexahydrobenzoate	183	—	0·990	1·451
Ethyl hexahydrobenzoate	196	—	0·962	1·448
Phenyl acetate	196	—	1·078	1·503
Phenyl propionate	211	20	1·050	—
Phenyl *n*-butyrate	228	—	1·023	—
Phenyl oxalate	190°/15	—	—	—
Phenyl salicylate (salol)	—	43	—	—

Table IX, 26.   **Aromatic Esters** (*continued*)

ESTER	B.P.	M.P.	$d_4^{20°}$	$n_D^{20°}$
Phenyl succinate	330°	121°	—	—
Phenyl benzoate	299	68	—	—
Phenyl cinnamate . . .	—	73	—	—
Phenyl carbonate	306	78	—	—
o-Cresyl acetate	208	—	1·045	—
p-Cresyl acetate	212	—	1·050	1·500
m-Cresyl acetate	212	12	1·043	1·498
Guaiacol acetate	240	—	1·133	1·512
Thymyl acetate	243	—	—	—
Carvacryl acetate	245	—	0·994	—
Resorcinol diacetate . . .	278	—	—	—
Eugenol acetate	282	30	—	—
1-Naphthyl acetate . . .	—	49	—	—
Catechol diacetate . . .	—	63	—	—
2-Naphthyl acetate . . .	—	70	—	—
Benzoin acetate	—	83	—	—
Phloroglucinol triacetate . .	—	104	—	—
Hydroquinone diacetate . .	—	124	—	—
Pyrogallol triacetate . . .	—	165	—	—
o-Cresyl benzoate . . .	307	—	—	—
Thymyl benzoate	—	33	—	—
m-Cresyl benzoate . . .	—	54	—	—
1-Naphthyl benzoate . . .	—	56	—	—
p-Cresyl benzoate . . .	316	72	—	—
Catechol dibenzoate . . .	—	84	—	—
Pyrogallol tribenzoate . . .	—	90	—	—
2-Naphthyl benzoate . . .	—	107	—	—
Resorcinol dibenzoate . . .	—	117	—	—
Phloroglucinol tribenzoate . .	—	185	—	—
Hydroquinone dibenzoate . .	—	199	—	—
o-Cresyl carbonate . . .	—	60	—	—
Phenyl carbonate	306	78	—	—
Guaiacol carbonate . . .	—	87	—	—
m-Cresyl carbonate . . .	—	111	—	—
p-Cresyl carbonate . . .	—	115	—	—
Benzyl formate	203	—	1·082	—
Benzyl acetate	214	—	1·057	1·523
Benzyl salicylate	186°/10	—	1·180	1·581
Benzyl benzoate	323	21	—	—
Benzyl succinate	—	45	—	—
1-Phenylethyl acetate . . .	222	—	—	—
2-Phenylethyl acetate . . .	224	—	1·059	1·512

Table IX, 27.   Primary Aliphatic Amides

AMIDE	M.P.	XANTHYLAMIDE
Formamide	2° (b.p. 193°d)	184°
Propionamide	79	214
Acetamide	82	245
Acrylamide	86	—
n-Heptamide	96	154
Dichloroacetamide	98	—
Lauramide	99	—
n-Caproamide	101	160
Myristamide	103	—
Palmitamide	106	142
n-Valeramide	106	167
n-Octamide	107	148
n-Decanoamide	108	—
Stearamide	109	141
n-Butyramide	115	187
Chloroacetamide	120	209
Cyanoacetamide	120	223
Isobutyramide	129	211
Isovaleramide	136	183
Trichloroacetamide	141	—
Furoamide	142	210
Trimethylacetamide	154	—
Allylurea	80	—
Methylurea	102	230
Urea	132	274
asym-Dimethylurea	182	250
Acetylurea	218	—
Thiourea	182	
Ethyl carbamate (urethane)	49	169
Methyl carbamate	54	193
n-Butyl carbamate	54	—
Isobutyl carbamate	55	—
n-Amyl carbamate	57	—
n-Propyl carbamate	61	—
Isoamyl carbamate	67	—
Isopropyl carbamate	92	—
Malonamide	170	270
Azelamide	172	—
Glutaramide	175	—
Maleamide	180	—
Sebacamide	209	—
Suberamide	217	—
Adipamide	220	—
dl-Tartaramide	226	—
Succinamide	260d	275
Oxamide	419d	—
Succinimide	126	246

Table IX, 28. Primary Aromatic Amides

AMIDE	M.P.	XANTHYLAMIDE
2-Phenylpropionamide	92°	158°
m-Toluamide	95	—
3-Phenylpropionamide	105	189
Hydrobenzamide	110	—
Benzamide	129	224
o-Methoxybenzamide	129	—
dl-Mandelamide	133	—
m-Chlorobenzamide	134	—
Salicylamide	139	—
o-Chlorobenzamide	141	—
m-Tolylurea	142	—
m-Nitrobenzamide	142	—
o-Toluamide	143	200
Phenylurea	147	225
Cinnamide	148	—
Benzylurea	149	—
o-Bromobenzamide	155	—
m-Bromobenzamide	155	—
Phenylacetamide	157	196
p-Toluamide	159	225
p-Hydroxybenzamide	162	—
Anisamide	162	—
Diphenylacetamide	167	—
m-Hydroxybenzamide	167	—
Piperonylamide	169	—
p-Phenetylurea (Dulcin)	173	—
o-Nitrobenzamide	175	—
p-Chlorobenzamide	179	—
p-Tolylurea	183	—
3,5-Dinitrobenzamide	183	—
o-Iodobenzamide	184	—
Hexahydrobenzamide	185	—
m-Iodobenzamide	186	—
asym-Diphenylurea	189	180
p-Bromobenzamide	189	—
o-Tolylurea	191	228
2-Naphthamide	192	—
p-Nitrobenzamide	201	232
1-Naphthamide	202	—
p-Ethoxybenzamide	202	—
p-Iodobenzamide	218	—
Phthalamide	219d	—
Phthalimide	235	177

Table IX, 29. Substituted Aromatic Amides

AMIDE	M.P.	AMIDE	M.P.
Formanilide	50°	o-Chloroacetanilide	88°
Pelargonanilide	57	m-Bromoacetanilide	88
Caprylanilide	57	o-Methoxyacetanilide	88
Lactanilide	59	m-Aminoacetanilide	88
n-Valeranilide	63	o-Nitroacetanilide	94
Caprianilide	70	o-Bromoacetanilide	99
Oenanthanilide	71	N-Methylacetanilide	103
Lauranilide	78	o-Iodoacetanilide	110
Myristanilide	84	Acetanilide	114
Acetoacetanilide	85	N-Ethyl-p-nitroacetanilide	118
Palmitanilide	91	Phenylacetanilide	118
Stearanilide	94	m-Iodoacetanilide	119
n-Caproanilide	95	p-Methoxyacetanilide	130
n-Butyranilide	96	o-Aminoacetanilide	132
Isobutyranilide	105	2,4-Dimethylacetanilide	133
Acrylanilide	105	2,5-Dimethylacetanilide	142
Propionanilide	106	4-Methyl-m-nitroacetanilide	148
Isovaleranilide	110	m-Hydroxyacetanilide	149
Acetanilide	114	N-Methyl-p-nitroacetanilide	153
Furoanilide	124	m-Nitroacetanilide	155
o-Toluanilide	125	p-Aminoacetanilide	163
m-Toluanilide	126	p-Bromoacetanilide	167
o-Methoxybenzanilide	131	p-Hydroxyacetanilide	168
Salicylanilide	135	p-Chloroacetanilide	179
p-Toluanilide	146	p-Iodoacetanilide	184
Cinnamanilide	153	2-Methyl-4-nitroacetanilide	196
m-Nitrobenzanilide	154	o-Hydroxyacetanilide	209
o-Nitrobenzanilide	155	p-Nitroacetanilide	216
Benzanilide	162	p-Hydroxy-N-methylacetanilide	240
1-Naphthanilide	163		
Anisanilide	169	Acetyl-m-toluidine	66
2-Naphthanilide	171	Acetyl-o-phenetidine	79
p-Nitrobenzanilide	211	Acetyl-m-anisidine	80
		Acetyl-o-anisidine	88
Pimelanilide	156	Acetyl-m-phenetidine	96
Suberanilide	187	Acetyl-o-toluidine	112
Maleic dianilide	187	Acetyl-p-anisidine	130
Azelaic dianilide	187	Acetyl-β-naphthylamine	134
Sebacanilide	202	Acetyl-p-phenetidine (phenacetin)	137
Glutaranilide	224	Acetyl-p-toluidine	154
Malonanilide	225	Acetyl-α-naphthylamine	160
Succinanilide	230		
Adipanilide	239		
Oxanilide	246	NN'-Diacetyl-o-phenylene-diamine	186
N-n-Propylacetanilide	50	NN'-Diacetyl-m-phenylene-diamine	191
N-Ethylacetanilide	54		
α-Chloroacetanilide	79	NN'-Diacetyl-p-phenylene-diamine	304
α-Methoxyacetanilide	80		

Table IX, 29.   Substituted Aromatic Amides (*continued*)

AMIDE	M.P.	AMIDE	M.P.
Benzoyl-*o*-anisidine . . .	60°	Benzoylpiperidine . . .	48°
Benzoyl-*m*-anisidine . . .	—	*N*-Phenylsuccinimide . . .	156
Benzoyl-*m*-phenetidine . .	103	*N*-Phenylphthalimide . .	205
Benzoyl-*o*-phenetidine . . .	104	Phthalimide	235
Benzoyl-*m*-toluidine . . .	125	Triphenylguanidine . . .	145
Benzoyl-*o*-toluidine . . .	144	Diphenylguanidine . . .	147
Benzoyl-*p*-anisidine . . .	154	Saccharin	220
Benzoyl-*p*-toluidine . . .	158		
Benzoyl-1-naphthylamine . .	161	*N*-Phenylurethane . . .	53
Benzoyl-2-naphthylamine . .	162	Ethyl oxanilate	67
Benzoyl-*p*-phenetidine . . .	173		
		s-Di-*m*-tolyurea	218
NN'-Dibenzoyl-*m*-phenylene-		*s*-Diphenylurea (carbanilide) .	238
diamine	240	*s*-Di-*o*-tolylurea	250
NN'-Dibenzoyl-*o*-phenylene-		*s*-Di-*p*-tolylurea	268
diamine	301	*s*-Di-1-naphthylurea . . .	287
NN'-Dibenzoyl-*p*-phenylene-		*s*-Di-2-naphthylurea . . .	310
diamine	>300		
Acetyl-*N*-methyl-2-naphthylamine.	51	Ethyl-*n*-butylbarbituric acid . .	125
Acetyl-*N*-methyl-*o*-toluidine .	56	Ethyl-*n*-hexylbarbituric acid . .	127
Acetyl-*N*-methyl-*m*-toluidine .	66	Ethyl-isoamylbarbituric acid .	154
Acetyl-*N*-methyl-*p*-toluidine .	83	Ethylphenylbarbituric acid . .	172
Acetyl-*N*-methyl-1-naphthylamine.	94	Diallylbarbituric acid . . .	172
		Diethylbarbituric acid . . .	198
		Ethyl-isopropylbarbituric acid .	201
		Barbituric acid	245
N-Formyldiphenylamine . .	74		
N-Acetyldiphenylamine . .	101	*n*-Butyl oxamate	88
N-Benzoyldiphenylamine . .	180	Ethyl oxamate	131

Table IX, 30.   Aliphatic Nitriles (Cyanides)

CYANIDE	NITRILE	B.P.	d_4^{20}	$n_D^{20°}$	ACYL PHLOROGLUCINOL	α-AMINO-ALKYL-MERCAPTOACETIC ACID HYDROCHLORIDE*
Vinyl	Acrylo-	78°	0·806	1·391	—	—
Methyl	Aceto-	82	0·784	1·344	218°	115°
Ethyl	Propio-	97	0·783	1·366	176	128
Isopropyl	Isobutyro-	108	—	—	—	137
n-Propyl	n-Butyro-	118	0·791	1·384	181	136
Allyl	Vinylaceto-	118	0·838	1·406	—	—
Chloromethyl	Chloroaceto-	127	1·193	—	—	—
Isobutyl	Isovalero-	131	0·788	—	—	—
n-Butyl	n-Valero-	141	0·799	1·397	149 (hydrate 88)	138
Isoamyl	Isocapro-	154	0·803	1·406	122 (hydrate 104)	128
n-Amyl	n-Capro-	162	0·805	1·407	121 (hydrate 96)	136
n-Hexyl	n-Heptano- (oenantho-)	183	0·810	1·414	—	—
n-Heptyl	n-Octano- (caprylo-)	199	0·817†	1·422†	—	—
n-Octyl	n-Nonano- (pelargono-)	224	0·822†	—	—	—
n-Nonyl	n-Decano- (caprino-)	244	0·829†	1·432†	—	—
n-Decyl	n-Undecano-	254	—	—	—	—
n-Undecyl	n-Dodecano- (lauro-)	275	0·827†	—	—	—
Methylene	Malono-	220 (1)	—	—	—	—
Ethylene	Succino-	267d (2)	—	—	—	—

Table IX, 30. Aliphatic Nitriles (Cyanides) (continued)

CYANIDE	NITRILE	B.P.	$d_4^{20°}$	$n_D^{20°}$	ACYL PHLOROGLUCINOL	α-AMINO-ALKYL-MERCAPTOACETIC ACID HYDROCHLORIDE*
Trimethylene	Glutaro-	286° (3)	0·988	1·429	—	—
Tetramethylene	Adipo-	295	0·962	1·439	—	—
Pentamethylene	Pimelo-	169°/15	0·945	1·441	—	—
Hexamethylene	Subero-	185°/15	0·933	1·445	—	—
Acetaldehyde cyanohydrin	2-Hydroxypropio-	183	0·988	—	—	—
Ethylene cyanohydrin	3-Hydroxypropio-	221	—	—	—	—
Trimethylene cyanohydrin	4-Hydroxybutyro-	240	1·079	—	—	—
Trimethylene chlorocyanide	4-Chlorobutyro-	197	1·101	—	—	—
Methyl cyanoacetate		200	1·063	—	—	—
Ethyl cyanoacetate		207	1·082	1·418	—	—
Furan-2-	Furo-	147		1·480	—	—
Phenyl	Benzo-	191°	1·006	1·528	—	—
Benzyl	Phenylaceto-	109°/15	1·016	1·523	—	146°
o-Tolyl	o-Tolu-	205	0·996	1·530	—	—
m-Tolyl	m-Tolu-	212	1·032	1·525	—	—

* Decomposition temperature. Sample placed in bath at 105–110°. † 15°.
(1) M.p. 31°. (2) M.p. 54°. (3) M.p. 9°.

Table IX, 31. Aromatic Nitriles

NITRILE	B.P.	M.P.
dl-Mandelonitrile	170°d	22°
Benzonitrile	191	—
o-Tolunitrile	205	—
m-Tolunitrile	212	—
2-Phenylpropionitrile	232	—
Phenylacetonitrile	234	—
3-Phenylpropionitrile	261	—
Cinnamonitrile	255	20
p-Tolunitrile	218	29
m-Bromobenzonitrile	225	38
1-Naphthonitrile	299	36
m-Chlorobenzonitrile	—	41
o-Chlorobenzonitrile	232	43
o-Bromobenzonitrile	252	53
o-Iodobenzonitrile	—	55
2-Naphthonitrile	306	66
p-Chlorobenzonitrile	223	96
o-Nitrobenzonitrile	—	111
p-Bromobenzonitrile	236	113
p-Nitrophenylacetonitrile	—	116
m-Nitrobenzonitrile	—	118
Phthalonitrile	—	141
p-Nitrobenzonitrile	—	149

Table IX, 32. Primary and Secondary Aliphatic Amines

AMINE	B.P.	$d_4^{20°}$	n_D^{20}	BENZENE-SULPHON-AMIDE	p-TOLUENE-SULPHON-AMIDE	PHENYL-THIOUREA	1-NAPH-THYL-THIOUREA	PICRATE	N-SUB-STITUTED PHTHAL-IMIDE	BENZ-AMIDE	ACET-AMIDE
Methylamine	−7°	—	—	30°	75°	113°	192°	215°	134°	80°	—
Ethylamine	17	—	—	58	63	106	121	165	78	71	—
Isopropylamine	35	0·689	1·374	26	51	101	143	150	86	100	—
tert-Butylamine	46	—	—	—	—	—	—	198	—	134	—
n-Propylamine	49	0·717	1·388	36	52	63	103	135	66	84	—
Allylamine	55	0·762	1·420	39	64	98	—	140	70	—	—
sec-Butylamine	63	0·725	1·393	70	55	101	—	140	—	76	—
Isobutylamine	68	0·735	1·397	53	78	82	137	151	93	57	—
n-Butylamine	77	0·741	1·401	—	—	65	109	151	34	42	—
Isoamylamine	97	0·749	1·408	—	65	102	97	138	—	—	—
n-Amylamine	105	0·754	1·411	—	—	69	103	139	—	—	—
n-Hexylamine	129	0·766	1·418	96	—	77	79	127	—	40	—
Cyclohexylamine	134	0·867	1·459	—	—	—	142	—	158	149	104°
n-Heptylamine	155	0·775	1·425	—	—	75	—	121	—	—	—
Ethanolamine	171	1·022	1·454	—	—	—	—	160	127	—	—
n-Octylamine	177	0·782	1·429	—	—	—	—	112	—	—	—
l-Menthylamine	212	0·854	—	—	—	135	—	—	—	157	145
Benzylamine	185	0·982	1·544	88	116	147	172	196	115	105	60
1-Phenylethylamine	187	—	—	—	—	—	—	189	—	120	57
2-Phenylethylamine	198	0·854	—	69	66	135	—	174	130	116	114
Ethylenediamine	117 (1)	0·898	1·457	168	160	102	—	233	—	244	172
Propylenediamine	120	0·874	—	—	—	—	—	137	—	193	139
Trimethylenediamine	136	0·889	1·460	—	—	—	—	250	—	148	101

Table IX, 32. Primary and Secondary Aliphatic Amines (*continued*)

AMINE	B.P.	$d_4^{20°}$	$n_D^{20°}$	BENZENE-SULPHON-AMIDE	p-TOLUENE-SULPHON-AMIDE	PHENYL-THIOUREA	1-NAPH-THYL-THIOUREA	PICRATE	N-SUB-STITUTED PHTHAL-IMIDE	BENZ-AMIDE	ACET-AMIDE
Tetramethylenediamine	159° (2)	—	—	—	224°	168°	—	255°d	—	177°	137°
Pentamethylenediamine	180	—	—	119°	—	148	—	—	—	135	—
Hexamethylenediamine	205 (3)	—	—	154	—	—	—	220	—	158	—
Dimethylamine	7	—	—	47	79	135	168°	158	—	41	—
Diethylamine	56	0·707	1·386	42	60	34	108	155	—	42	—
Di-isopropylamine	84	0·717	1·392	94	—	—	—	140	—	—	—
Di-*n*-propylamine	110	0·738	1·405	51	—	—	161	75	—	—	—
Diallylamine	111	—	—	—	—	—	—	—	—	—	—
Di-*sec*-butylamine	135	0·753	1·411	—	—	—	—	—	—	—	—
Di-isobutylamine	137	0·746	1·409	—	—	—	—	59	—	—	—
Di-*n*-butylamine	159	0·760	1·418	—	—	86	123	—	—	—	—
Di-isoamylamine	186	0·771	1·423	—	—	—	118	—	—	—	—
Di-*n*-amylamine	205	0·777	1·427	—	—	—	—	—	—	—	—
Dicyclohexylamine	255d (4)	—	—	—	119	—	—	173	153°	—	103
Diethanolamine	270d (5)	1·097	1·478	130	99	—	—	110	—	—	—
Pyrrolidine	89	0·854	1·424	—	123	—	—	112	—	—	—
Piperidine	106	0·861	1·453	94	96	—	—	152	—	48	—
2-Methylpiperidine	118	—	—	—	55	—	—	135	—	45	—
3-Methylpiperidine	126	—	—	—	—	—	—	138	—	—	—
4-Methylpiperidine	128	—	—	—	—	—	—	—	—	—	—
Morpholine	130	1·000	1·455	119	147	136	—	148	—	75	—
Pyrrole	131	0·969	1·505	—	—	—	—	69d	—	—	—
Piperazine	140 (6)	—	—	292 (di)	173 (mono)	—	—	280	—	196 (di)	144 (di)

Table IX, 32. Primary and Secondary Aliphatic Amines (*continued*)

Ester-Amides (Derivatives of Aminoformic Acid, NH_2COOH)

AMINE	B.P.	M.P.	$d_4^{20°}$	$n_D^{20°}$	DERIVATIVES
Methyl carbamate (NH_2COOCH_3)	177°	54°	—	—	*N-p*-Nitrobenzoyl, 152°; Benzal, 179°
Ethyl carbamate (urethane)	184	50	—	—	
n-Propyl carbamate	195	61	—	—	—
n-Butyl carbamate	204d	54	—	—	—
n-Amyl carbamate	—	57	—	—	—
Isoamyl carbamate	—	67	—	—	—
N-Methylurethane (Ethyl *N*-methyl carbamate)	170	—	—	—	—
N-Ethylurethane (Ethyl *N*-ethyl carbamate)	170	—	0·981	1·422	—
N-n-Propylurethane	192	—	—	—	—
N-n-Butylurethane	202	—	—	—	—
N-sec-Butylurethane	194	—	—	—	—
N-Phenylurethane (Ethyl *N*-phenyl carbamate)	237	53	—	—	*N*-Acetyl, 59; *N*-Benzoyl, 161; *N*-Nitroso, 62
Ethyl oxanilate ($C_6H_5NHCOCOOC_2H_5$)	—	67	—	—	*N*-Acetyl, 65

Note.—Esters of carbamic acid upon boiling with aniline yield carbanilide (m.p. 238°), ammonia and the corresponding alcohol.
(1) M.p. 8°.   (3) M.p. 42°.   (5) M.p. 28°.
(2) M.p. 28°.   (4) M.p. 20°.   (6) M.p. 104°; Hydrate, $6H_2O$, m.p. 44°.

AMINE	B.P.	M.P.	ACET-AMIDE	BENZ-AMIDE	BENZENE-SULPHON-AMIDE	p-TOLU-ENESUL-PHON-AMIDE	BENZAL DERIV-ATIVE	PICRATE	3-NITRO-PHTHAL-IMIDE	2,4-DINITRO-PHENYL DERIV-ATIVE	FORMYL DERIV-ATIVE	PHENYL THIO-UREA
Aniline	183°	—	114°	163°	112°	103°	54°	—	138°	156°	47°	154°
Benzylamine	185	—	60	105	88	116	—	199°	143	—	—	156
1-Phenylethylamine	187	—	57	120	—	—	—	167	—	—	—	—
2-Phenylethylamine	198	—	51	116	69	110	—	213	—	—	—	135
o-Toluidine	200	—	112	144	124	114	—	200	150	126	59	136
m-Toluidine	203	—	66	125	95	232	—	—	130	161	—	104
p-Xylidine (1)	214	15°	142	140	—	—	—	—	—	150	—	—
p-Ethylaniline	215	—	94	151	—	—	—	—	—	—	—	—
m-2-Xylidine (2)	215	11	177	168	—	212	—	180	—	—	176	148
o-Ethylaniline	216	—	112	147	—	—	—	—	—	—	—	—
m-4-Xylidine (3)	216	—	130	192	130	181	—	209	—	156	114	152
m-5-Xylidine (4)	220	10	144	136	—	—	—	209	—	—	77	153
o-Anisidine (5)	225	5	88	60	89	127	—	200	—	—	83	136
3,4-Dimethylaniline	226	49	99	—	118	154	—	—	185	151	—	—
unsym-Methylphenyl-hydrazine	227	—	92	153	132	—	—	—	—	—	—	—
o-Phenetidine (6)	229	—	79	104	102	164	—	—	164	164	62	137
Mesidine (7)	232	—	216	206	—	167	—	193	—	—	—	193
Phenylhydrazine	242	23	128	168	—	—	—	—	—	—	145	172
m-Phenetidine	248	—	96	103	—	157	—	158	158	138	52	138
m-Anisidine	251	—	80	—	—	68	—	169	—	—	57	—
o-Aminoacetophenone	251d	20	77	98	—	148	—	—	—	—	—	—
p-Phenetidine	254	—	135	173	—	107	76	69	173	118	76	148
Methyl anthranilate	255	24	101	100	143	—	—	106	—	—	58	—
p-Aminodiethylaniline	261	—	104	172	—	112	—	—	—	—	—	—

Table IX, 33A.   Primary Aromatic Amines (*continued*)

AMINE	B.P.	M.P.	ACET-AMIDE	BENZ-AMIDE	BENZENE-SULPHON-AMIDE	p-TOLU-ENESULPHON-AMIDE	BENZAL DERIV-ATIVE	PICRATE	3-NITRO-PHTHAL-IMIDE	2,4-DINITRO-PHENYL DERIV-ATIVE	FORMYL DERIV-ATIVE	PHENYL THIO-UREA
Ethyl anthranilate	266°d	13°	61°	98°	93°	112°	—	—	—	—	57°	—
Ethyl m-aminobenzoate	294	—	—	114	—	—	—	—	—	—	—	—
p-Aminodimethylaniline	262	41	132	228	—	—	98°	188°	—	168°	108	—
p-Toluidine	200	45	154	158	120	118	—	181	156°	137	53	141°
o-Aminobiphenyl (8)	299	50	121	102	—	—	—	—	—	—	75	—
1-Naphthylamine	300	50	160	161	169	157	73	163	223	190	139	165
p-Aminobiphenyl (9)	302	51	171	230	—	255	—	—	—	—	172	—
p-Anisidine	246	57	130	154	96	114	62	—	—	—	81	144
2-Aminopyridine	204	58	71	87	—	216	—	221	197	141	—	—
2,5-Diaminotoluene (10)	273	64	220	307	—	—	—	—	—	—	—	—
3-Aminopyridine	252	64	133	119	—	—	—	—	—	—	—	—
p-Tolylhydrazine	244d	65	130	146	—	—	—	—	—	—	—	—
m-Phenylenediamine	283	64	191	240	194	172	105	184	171	172	155	—
o-Nitroaniline	—	71	94	98	104	110	—	73	—	—	122	—
4-Amino-2-nitrotoluene	—	78	145	172	160	163	—	—	—	—	—	—
m-Aminoacetanilide	—	88	191	—	—	241	—	—	—	—	—	—
3,4-Diaminotoluene (11)	265	90	210	264	179	—	—	131	—	—	—	—
Ethyl p-aminobenzoate (12)	—	92	110	148	—	—	—	—	—	—	—	—
6-Nitro-2-aminotoluene	—	92	158	168	—	—	—	—	—	—	—	—
3-Nitro-2-aminotoluene	—	97	158	—	—	—	—	—	—	—	—	—
m-Aminoacetophenone	—	99	129	—	—	130	175	—	—	—	177	—
2,4-Diaminotoluene (13)	292	99	224	224	191	192	106	208	—	184	170	—
o-Phenylenediamine	257	102	186	301	186	202	—	—	—	—	—	—
p-Aminoacetophenone	294	106	167	205	128	203	—	—	—	—	179	—
2-Amino-4-nitrotoluene	—	107	151	186	172	—	116	—	—	—	179	—
2-Naphthylamine	294	113	134	162	102	133	—	195	212	179	129	129

Primary Aromatic Amines (continued)

AMINE	B.P.	M.P.	ACET-AMIDE	BENZ-AMIDE	BENZENE-SULPHON-AMIDE	p-TOLU-ENESUL-PHON-AMIDE	BENZAL DERIV-ATIVE	PICRATE	3-NITRO-PHTHAL-IMIDE	2,4-DINITRO-PHENYL DERIV-ATIVE	FORMYL DERIV-ATIVE	PHENYL THIO-UREA
m-Nitroaniline	—	114°	155°	157°	136°	139°	73°	143°	219°	—	134°	160°
4-Amino-3-nitrotoluene	—	117	96	148	102	146	78	—	—	—	—	—
5-Nitro-1-naphthylamine	—	119	220	—	183	160	—	—	—	—	199	—
1-Nitro-2-naphthylamine	—	126	123	168	156	—	130	—	—	—	162	—
p-Aminoazobenzene	—	126	145	211	—	—	238	—	—	—	—	—
Benzidine	—	126	317	352	235	243	—	185	—	—	254	—
o-Tolidine (14)	—	129	314	265	—	—	152	—	—	—	—	—
2-Amino-5-nitrotoluene	—	129	202	174	159	174	—	—	—	—	—	—
o-Aminoacetanilide	—	132	—	—	—	—	—	—	—	—	—	—
2,6-Dinitroaniline	—	138	197	—	—	—	—	—	—	—	—	—
p-Phenylenediamine	267°	141	304	>300	247	266	140	—	—	177°	206	—
2-Nitro-1-naphthylamine	—	144	199	175	—	—	—	—	—	—	—	—
Anthranilic acid	—	146	185	181	214	217	127	—	255	—	168	—
p-Nitroaniline	—	148	216	199	139	191	115	—	—	—	194	—
p-Nitrophenylhydrazine	—	157d	205	193	—	—	—	—	—	—	—	—
4-Aminopyridine	—	158	150	202	—	—	—	100	—	—	—	—
p-Aminoacetanilide	—	163	304	—	—	—	—	120	—	—	—	—
Sulphanilamide (15)	—	166	219	284	211	—	—	216	—	—	225	—
m-Aminobenzoic acid	—	174	250	—	—	—	119	—	—	—	—	—
2,4-Dinitroaniline	—	180	121	220	212	219	—	—	—	—	—	—
p-Aminobenzoic acid	—	187	251	278	211	—	193	—	—	—	268	—
Picramide (16)	—	190	230	196	212	—	—	—	—	—	—	—
4-Nitro-1-naphthylamine	—	195	190	224	173	185	—	—	—	—	—	—
2,4-Dinitrophenylhydrazine	—	198d	198	207	—	—	—	—	—	—	—	—
2-Aminoanthraquinone	—	302	257	228	271	304	—	—	—	—	—	—

Table IX, 33A. Primary Aromatic Amines (*continued*)

AMINE	B.P.	M.P.	ACET-AMIDE	BENZ-AMIDE	BENZENE-SULPHON-AMIDE	p-TOLU-ENESULPHON-AMIDE	BENZAL DERIV-ATIVE	PICRATE	3-NITRO-PHTHAL-IMIDE	2,4-DINITRO-PHENYL DERIV-ATIVE	FORMYL DERIV-ATIVE	PHENYL THIO-UREA
C-HALOGENO-AMINES													
o-Chloroaniline	209°	—	88°	99°	130°	105°	34°	134°	136°	150°	77°	156°
2-Amino-3-chlorotoluene	215	—	120	—	110	—	—	—	—	—	—	—
4-Amino-3-chlorotoluene	223	7°	113	137	121	138	—	177	172	184	58	124
m-Chloroaniline	230	—	79	122	—	—	—	—	—	—	—	—
2-Amino-4-chlorotoluene	237	22	140	149	—	—	—	—	—	—	—	—
4-Amino-3-bromotoluene	240	26	117	142	125	—	—	—	—	—	—	—
2-Amino-5-chlorotoluene	241	29	140	173	—	—	—	—	—	—	—	—
2-Amino-6-chlorotoluene	245	—	159	120	—	—	—	—	—	—	—	—
m-Bromoaniline	251	18	88	151	—	—	—	180	187	—	—	143
m-Iodoaniline	—	25	119	—	—	128	—	—	—	—	—	—
2-Amino-4-bromotoluene	255	32	165	116	—	90	—	129	—	161	—	146
o-Bromoaniline	229	32	99	120	—	—	—	—	—	—	—	166
2,5-Dichloroaniline	255	50	132	115	—	—	—	—	—	—	—	—
2-Amino-5-bromotoluene	240	59	157	139	—	—	—	—	—	—	—	—
o-Iodoaniline	—	60	110	117	—	—	—	112	—	116	—	—
2,4-Dichloroaniline	245	63	146	222	128	—	86	106	—	—	109	153
p-Iodoaniline	—	63	184	204	—	—	67	180	202	158	102	148
p-Bromoaniline	—	66	167	193	134	101 (141)	62	178	199	167	180	152
p-Chloroaniline	232	71	179	174	122	96 (121)	—	83	—	—	146	171
2,4,6-Trichloroaniline	263	78	206	134	—	—	—	124	—	—	—	—
2,4-Dibromoaniline	—	79	146	—	—	—	—	124	—	—	—	—
2,6-Dibromoaniline	—	84	210	178	—	215	—	—	—	—	—	—
2,4-Diaminochlorobenzene	—	88	243	161	—	164	—	—	—	—	—	—
2-Chloro-4-nitroaniline	—	108	139	—	—	110	—	—	—	—	—	—
4-Chloro-2-nitroaniline	—	116	104	232	108	—	95	—	—	—	222	—

AMINO-PHENOLS

AMINE	B.P.	M.P.	ACET-AMIDE	BENZ-AMIDE	BENZENE-SULPHON-AMIDE	p-TOLU-ENESULPHON-AMIDE	BENZAL DERIV-ATIVE	PICRATE	3-NITRO-PHTHAL-IMIDE	2,4-DINITRO-PHENYL DERIV-ATIVE	FORMYL DERIV-ATIVE	PHENYL THIO-UREA
p-Dimethylaminophenol*	—	76°	78°	158°	130°	—	—	—	—	—	—	—
2,4-Diaminophenol (17)	—	79d	222 (di)	231	—	—	—	—	—	—	—	—
p-Methylaminophenol(18)†	—	86	43	174	—	135°	—	—	—	—	—	—
o-Methylaminophenol†	—	96	(mono) 64 (di)	(mono) 160	—	(mono)	—	—	—	—	—	—
m-Aminophenol	—	123	101 (di)	153 (di)	—	—	—	—	—	—	—	—
Picramic acid (19)	—	169	201 (N)	229 (N)	—	191 (N)	—	—	—	—	—	—
5-Amino-2-hydroxytoluene	—	173	103 (di)	194	—	110	—	—	—	—	—	—
o-Aminophenol	—	174	124 (di)	184 (di)	141	139	89°	—	—	199°	129°	156°
p-Aminophenol	—	186d	150 (di)	234 (di)	125	253	182	—	—	190	140	—
8-Amino-2-naphthol	—	207	165	208	—	—	—	—	—	—	—	146
1-Amino-2-naphthol	—	dec.	206	235	—	—	—	—	—	—	—	150

* See also Table IX, 33C. † See also Table IX, 33B.

(1) 2,5-Dimethylaniline or 2-amino-p-xylene.
(2) 2,6-Dimethylaniline or 2-amino-m-xylene.
(3) 2,4-Dimethylaniline or 4-amino-m-xylene.
(4) 3,5-Dimethylaniline or 5-amino-m-xylene.
(5) o-Methoxyaniline.
(6) o-Ethoxyaniline.
(7) 2,4,6-Trimethylaniline.
(8) o-Xenylamine.
(9) p-Xenylamine.
(10) 2,5-Tolylenediamine.
(11) 3,4-Tolylenediamine.
(12) Benzocaine.
(13) 2,4-Tolylenediamine.
(14) 4,4′-Diamino-3,3′-dimethylbiphenyl.
(15) p-Aminobenzenesulphonamide.
(16) 2,4,6-Trinitroaniline.
(17) Hydrochloride = *Amidol*.
(18) Sulphate = *Metol*.
(19) 2-Amino-4,6-dinitrophenol.

Table IX, 33B. Secondary Aromatic Amines

AMIDE	B.P.	M.P.	ACET-AMIDE	BENZ-AMIDE	BENZENE-SULPHON-AMIDE	p-TOLU-ENESUL-PHON-AMIDE	PICRATE	FORMYL DERIV-ATIVE	OTHER DERIVATIVES
N-Methylbenzylamine	181°	—	—	—	—	95°	—	—	—
Methylaniline	194	—	103°	63°	79°	95	145°	—	Phthalamic acid, 194°
N-Ethylbenzylamine	199	—	—	—	—	50	118	—	Urea (with PhNCO), 81
Ethylaniline	205	—	55	60	—	88	138	—	Phthalamic acid, 204
N-Methyl-m-toluidine	206	—	66	66	—	—	—	—	—
N-Methyl-o-toluidine	208	—	56	53	—	120	90	—	—
N-Methyl-p-toluidine	210	—	83	72	—	60	131	—	N-Nitroso, 52
N-Ethyl-o-toluidine	214	—	—	39	—	75	—	—	—
N-Ethyl-p-toluidine	217	—	—	72	—	71	—	—	—
N-Ethyl-m-toluidine	221	—	47	56	54	—	—	—	Phthalamic acid, 225
n-Propylaniline	222	—	—	—	—	56	—	—	Phthalamic acid, 204
n-Butylaniline	240	—	94	—	—	164	—	—	—
N-Methyl-1-naphthylamine	294	—	—	112	68	—	—	52°	—
Dibenzylamine	300d	—	51	84	—	78	145	—	N-Nitroso, 88
N-Methyl-2-naphthylamine	317	—	49	—	—	—	—	—	—
N-Ethyl-2-naphthylamine	315	—	68	—	—	—	—	—	—
N-Ethyl-1-naphthylamine	325	—	70	—	—	—	—	—	—
o-Nitro-N-methylaniline	—	37°	58	107	119	140	—	48	N-Nitroso, 36
Benzylaniline	306	38	103	180	123	142	182	74	N-Nitroso, 58
Diphenylamine	302	54	89	—	—	—	—	—	N-Nitroso, 67
m-Nitro-N-ethylaniline	—	60	115	152	—	—	—	—	—
N-Phenyl-1-naphthylamine	—	62	95	155	83	—	—	—	N-Nitroso, 76
m-Nitro-N-methylaniline	—	68	88	125	—	—	—	—	N-Nitroso, 101
Di-p-tolylamine	330	79	43	174	—	135	—	—	N-Nitroso, 136
p-Hydroxy-N-methylaniline	—	86	(mono) 64 (di)	(mono) 160	—	(mono)	—	—	—
o-Hydroxy-N-methylaniline	—	96	—	(mono)	—	—	—	—	N-Nitroso, 130

Table IX, 33B. **Secondary Aromatic Amines** (*continued*)

AMINE	B.P.	M.P.	ACET-AMIDE	BENZ-AMIDE	BENZENE-SULPHON-AMIDE	p-TOLU-ENESUL-PHON-AMIDE	PICRATE	FORMYL DERIV-ATIVE	OTHER DERIVATIVES
p-Nitro-N-ethylaniline	—	96°	119°	—	—	—	—	—	N-Nitroso, 120°
N-Phenyl-2-naphthylamine	—	108	93	136°	—	—	—	119°	—
p-Nitro-N-methylaniline	—	152	152	111	120°	—	—	—	N-Nitroso, 104
Pyrrolidine	89°	—	—	—	—	123°	—	—	—
Piperidine	106	—	—	48	94	96	152°	—	—
2-Methylpiperidine	117	—	—	45	—	55	134	—	—
3-Methylpiperidine	125	—	—	—	—	—	137	—	—
4-Methylpiperidine	128	—	—	—	—	—	—	—	—
Tetrahydro-isoquinoline	232	—	46	129	154	—	195	—	—
Tetrahydroquinoline	250	20	—	76	67	—	—	—	—
Indole	254	52	—	68	—	—	187	52	N-Nitroso, 171
Piperazine	140	104*	—	196	282	—	280	—	N,N-Dinitroso, 158
Carbazole	355	246	69	98	—	137	185	—	—

* Hydrate, 6H$_2$O, m.p. 44°.

Table IX, 33C.   **Tertiary Amines**

AMINE	B.P.	M.P.	METHIODIDE	PICRATE	METHYL p-TOLUENE-SULPHONATE	OTHER DERIVATIVES
Trimethylamine	3°	—	230°	216°	—	d_4^{20} 0·728; n_D^{20} 1·401
Triethylamine	89	—	—	173	—	—
Triallylamine	155	—	—	—	—	—
Tri-n-propylamine	156	—	208	117	—	Ethiodide, 238°; d_4^{20} 0·756; n_D^{20} 1·417
Tri-n-butylamine	212	—	186	106	—	Benzyl chloride, 185°; d_4^{20} 0·778; n_D^{20} 1·430
Tri-isoamylamine	245	—	—	125	—	d_4^{20} 0·785; n_D^{20} 1·433
Tri-n-amylamine	257	—	—	—	80°d	d_4^{20} 0·791; n_D^{20} 1·437
Dimethylbenzylamine	184	—	179	93	—	—
Dimethyl-o-toluidine	185	—	210	122	—	—
Dimethylaniline	193	—	228	164	—	p-Nitroso, 87; ethiodide, 136
Methylethylaniline	201	—	125	134	161	Ethiodide, 102; p-nitroso, 66
Diethyl-o-toluidine	210	—	224	180	—	—
Dimethyl-p-toluidine	211	—	220	130	—	Benzyl chloride, 171
Dimethyl-m-toluidine	212	—	177	131	85	—
Diethylaniline	218	—	102	142	—	p-Nitroso, 84; benzyl chloride, 104
Diethyl-p-toluidine	229	—	184	110	—	—
Diethyl-m-toluidine	231	—	—	97	—	—
Di-n-propylaniline	245	—	156	—	—	—
Di-n-butylaniline	271	—	—	125	180	—
Dimethyl-1-naphthylamine	273	—	—	145	—	—
Benzylmethylaniline	306	—	164	127	—	—
Benzylethylaniline	186°/22	—	161	121	—	—
Dimethyl-2-naphthylamine	305	47°	—	206	—	—
p-Bromodimethylaniline	264	55	—	—	—	—
Dibenzylaniline	300	70	135	132	—	—
p-Hydroxydimethylaniline	—	76	201	—	—	p-Nitroso, 91
p-Nitrosodimethylaniline	—	87	—	140	—	o-Acetyl, 79

Table IX, 33C.

Tertiary Amines (*continued*)

AMINE	B.P.	M.P.	METHIODIDE	PICRATE	METHYL p-TOLUENE-SULPHONATE	OTHER DERIVATIVES
Tribenzylamine	380°	92°	184°	190°	—	Ethiodide, 190°
Triphenylamine	365	127	—	—	—	—
p-Nitrodimethylaniline	—	163	—	—	—	—
Pyridine	115	—	118	167	139°	Ethiodide, 90
α-Picoline (1)	129	—	227	169	150	Ethiodide, 123; picolinic acid, 136
2,6-Lutidine (2)	142	—	238	163	—	Dipicolinic acid, 226
γ-Picoline	143	—	152	167	—	Isonicotinic acid, 308
β-Picoline	144	—	92	150	—	Nicotinic acid, 228
2,4-Lutidine	159	—	113	183	—	—
2,5-Lutidine	160	—	—	169	—	—
2,3-Lutidine	164	—	—	188	—	—
2,4,6-Trimethylpyridine (3)	172	—	—	156	—	—
5-Ethyl-2-methylpyridine	178	—	—	166	—	—
3-Ethyl-4-methylpyridine	196	—	—	150	—	—
Ethyl nicotinate	223	—	—	—	—	—
Nicotine	246	—	—	218	—	Nicotinic acid, 228
Methyl nicotinate	204	38	—	—	—	—
2,2'-Bipyridyl	273	70	—	158	—	—
Quinoline	238	—	72* (133)†	203	126	Ethiodide, 158
Isoquinoline	242	24	159	223	163	Ethiodide, 148
Quinaldine (4)	247	—	195	195	161	Ethiodide, 234
8-Methylquinoline	248	—	—	200	—	—
6-Methylquinoline	258	—	219	229	154	Benzyl chloride, 239
Lepidine (5)	262	—	174	211	—	—

* Monohydrate. † Anhydrous.

Table IX, 33C.   Tertiary Amines (*continued*)

AMINE	B.P.	M.P.	METHIODIDE	PICRATE	METHYL p-TOLUENE-SULPHONATE	OTHER DERIVATIVES
2,4-Dimethylquinoline	264°	—	264°	194°	—	Ethiodide, 214°
6-Methoxyquinoline	284	26°	236	237	—	—
7-Methylquinoline	252	39	160	143	—	—
8-Methoxyquinoline	283	50	237	191	175°	—
2,6-Dimethylquinoline	267	60	143	204	—	Ethiodide, 227
8-Hydroxyquinoline	267	76	—	—	—	—
8-Nitroquinoline	—	92	—	—	—	—
6-Nitroquinoline	—	154	245	—	—	—
6-Hydroxyquinoline	—	193	—	236	—	—
3-Chloropyridine	149	—	—	135	156	—
3-Bromopyridine	170	—	165	—	120	—
2-Chloropyridine	170	—	—	—	127	—
2-Bromopyridine	194	—	—	—	219	—
3,5-Dibromopyridine	222	112	274	—	—	—
2,6-Dibromopyridine	249	119	—	—	—	—
6-Bromoquinoline	278	19	278	217	—	—
2-Chloroquinoline	267	38	—	122	—	—
6-Chloroquinoline	262	41	248	—	143	Ethiodide, 169
2-Bromoquinoline	—	49	210	—	—	—
Acridine	—	111	224	208	—	Trinitrobenzene, 115
Hexamethylenetetramine	—	280 Sub.	190	179	205	—

(1) 2-Methylpyridine.
(2) 2,6-Dimethylpyridine.
(3) γ-Collidine.
(4) 2-Methylquinoline.
(5) 4-Methylquinoline.

Table IX, 34.   Amino Acids

AMINO ACID	M.P.*	BENZOATE	3,5-DINITRO-BENZOATE	PHENYL-UREIDO ACID	p-TOLUENE-SULPHONATE	2,4-DICHLORO-PHENOXY-ACETATE	1-NAPH-THYL-UREIDO ACID	PHTHALYL DERIVATIVE	2,4-DINITRO-PHENYL DERIVATIVE
N-Phenylglycine	126°	63°	—	195°	—	—	—	—	—
Anthranilic acid	145	182	278°	181	217°	—	—	—	—
m-Aminobenzoic acid	174	248	270	270	—	—	—	—	—
dl-β-Amino-isobutyric acid	177	—	—	—	—	—	—	—	—
p-Aminobenzoic acid	186	278	290	300	223	—	—	—	146°
β-Alanine	196	165	202	174	117	—	236°	159°	—
D- or L-Glutamic acid	198	138	217	—	—	—	236	—	—
p-Aminophenylacetic acid	200	206	—	—	—	—	—	—	—
dl-Proline	203	—	—	170	—	145°	—	—	181
Sarcosine	210	103	217	170	102	106	—	—	138
D- or L-Proline	222	150	153	184	133	87	199	—	171
D- or L-Lysine	224	189	169	164	175	—	199	—	181
D- or L-Asparagine	227	156	196	—	213	192	—	—	149
dl-Glutamic acid	227	—	—	—	—	—	—	—	174
L-Serine	228	187	179	163	150	235	191	192	204
Glycine	232	148	—	—	—	139	—	103	178
dl-Threonine	235	230	—	—	—	—	—	—	—
dl-Arginine	238	171	183	169	213	195	191	—	201
dl-Serine	246	148	180	160	205	216	—	—	145
D- or L-Threonine	253	181	—	162	140	202	115	193	109
D- or L-Cystine	260	185	—	—	105	145	—	—	187
D- or L-Aspartic acid	272	151	93	182	135	180	—	175	117
dl-Methionine	272	188	240	—	176	148	—	—	186
dl-Phenylalanine	274	188	—	—	—	—	—	—	—
dl-Tryptophane	275	—	—	—	—	—	—	—	—

Table IX, 34. Amino Acids (continued)

AMINO ACID	M.P.*	BENZOATE	3,5-DINITRO-BENZOATE	PHENYL-UREIDO ACID	p-TOLUENE-SULPHONATE	2,4-DICHLORO-PHENOXY-ACETATE	1-NAPH-THYL-UREIDO ACID	PHTHALYL DERIVATIVE	2,4-DINITRO-PHENYL DERIVATIVE
D- or L-Histidine	277°	249°	189°	—	204°	—	—	296°	233°
α-Amino-isobutyric acid	Sub. 280	202d	—	—	—	—	198°	—	—
dl-Aspartic acid	280	165	—	—	—	217°	—	221	196
D- or L-Methionine	283	150	95	—	—	134	186	—	—
D- or L-Isoleucine	284	117	—	120°	132	—	178	121	113
D- or L-Tryptophane	289	104	233	166	176	—	158	—	221
dl-Isoleucine	292	118	—	—	141	143	—	—	175
dl-α-Alanine	295	166	177	174	139	213	198	161	—
D- or L-α-Alanine	297	151	—	190	139	199	202	—	—
dl-Valine	298	132	—	164	110	159	204	102	184
dl-Norvaline	303	—	182	—	—	—	—	—	—
dl-α-Amino-n-butyric acid	307	147	—	170	—	—	194	96	143
D- or L-Valine	315	127	181	147	149	—	—	115	132
dl-Tyrosine	318	197	254	—	—	—	—	268	—
D- or L-Phenylalanine	320	146	93	181	165	155	—	112	189
dl-Norleucine	327	—	—	—	124	—	—	141	—
dl-Leucine	332	141	—	165	—	138	—	116	—
D- or L-Leucine	337	107	187	115	124	150	163	—	94
D- or L-Tyrosine	344	166	—	104	119	—	205	—	180
dl-Asparagine	>300	—	—	—	—	—	—	—	—
dl-Histidine	—	—	—	—	—	129	—	—	—
dl-Lysine	—	249	—	196	—	176	—	171	—

* These melting points are probably better described as decomposition points and their values will depend somewhat upon the rate of heating. Many of the naturally-occurring amino acids are *l*-rotatory.

Table IX, 35. Aromatic Nitro Compounds

NITRO COMPOUND	B.P.	M.P.	NITRO COMPOUND	B.P.	M.P.
Nitrobenzene (1)	211°	6°	m-Nitrochlorobenzene	236°	46°
o-Nitrotoluene (2)	222	—	m-Nitrobenzyl chloride	—	46
2-Nitro-m-xylene	226	—	o-Nitrobenzyl bromide	—	47
m-Nitrotoluene (3)	229	16	o-Nitrobenzyl chloride	—	49
2-Nitro-p-xylene	237	—	2,4-Dinitrochlorobenzene	315	51
3-Nitro-o-xylene	240	15	o-Nitroiodobenzene	—	54
4-Nitro-m-xylene	244	—	m-Nitrobromobenzene	256	56
2-Nitro-p-cymene (4)	264	—	2,5-Dichloronitrobenzene	267	56
o-Nitroanisole	265	10	m-Nitrobenzyl bromide	—	59
m-Nitrophenetole	267	2	p-Nitrobenzyl chloride	—	71
m-Nitrobenzyl alcohol	—	27	o-Nitrobenzyl iodide	—	75
4-Nitro-o-xylene	254	30	2,4-Dinitrobromobenzene	—	75
m-Nitrophenetole	284	34	Picryl chloride	—	83
2-Nitrobiphenyl	320	37	p-Nitrochlorobenzene	242	83
m-Nitroanisole	258	39	2-Nitro-p-dibromobenzene	—	84
Nitromesitylene	255	44	m-Nitrobenzyl iodide	—	86
p-Nitrotoluene	238	54	2,4-Dinitroiodobenzene	—	88
p-Nitroanisole	259	54	p-Nitrobenzyl bromide	—	100
ω-Nitrostyrene	260d	58	p-Nitrobromobenzene	256	127
p-Nitrophenetole	283	60	p-Nitrobenzyl iodide	—	127
1-Nitronaphthalene	304	61	p-Nitroiodobenzene	—	174
m-Nitrobenzyl cyanide	—	62			
2,4,6-Trinitroanisole	—	68	Methyl o-nitrobenzoate	275	—
2,4-Dinitrotoluene	—	71	Ethyl o-nitrobenzoate	—	30
o-Nitrobenzyl alcohol	270	74	Diethyl 4-nitrophthalate	—	34
5-Nitro-m-xylene	273	74	Ethyl o-nitrocinnamate	—	44
2,4,6-Trinitrophenetole	—	79	Diethyl 3-nitrophthalate	—	46
2-Nitronaphthalene	—	79	Ethyl m-nitrobenzoate	297	47
2,4,6-Trinitrotoluene	—	82	Ethyl p-nitrobenzoate	—	57
o-Nitrobenzyl cyanide	—	84	Dimethyl 4-nitrophthalate	—	66
2,4-Dinitrophenetole	—	87	Dimethyl 3-nitrophthalate	—	69
m-Dinitrobenzene	—	90	Methyl o-nitrocinnamate	—	73
p-Nitrobenzyl alcohol	—	93	Methyl m-nitrobenzoate	—	78
2,4-Dinitroanisole	—	95	Ethyl m-nitrocinnamate	—	79
4-Nitrobiphenyl	—	114	Ethyl 3,5-dinitrobenzoate	—	94
p-Nitrobenzyl cyanide	—	117	Methyl p-nitrobenzoate	—	96
o-Dinitrobenzene	—	118	Ethyl 3,5-dinitrosalicylate	—	99
1,3,5-Trinitrobenzene	—	122	Ethyl 5-nitrosalicylate	—	102
2,2′-Dinitrobiphenyl	—	124	Methyl 3,5-dinitrobenzoate	—	112
1,8-Dinitronaphthalene	—	173	Ethyl 3-nitrosalicylate	—	118
p-Dinitrobenzene	—	173	Methyl 5-nitrosalicylate	—	119
1,5-Dinitronaphthalene	—	217	Methyl m-nitrocinnamate	—	124
4,4′-Dinitrobiphenyl	—	236	Methyl 3,5-dinitrosalicylate	—	127
			Methyl 3-nitrosalicylate	—	132
o-Nitrochlorobenzene	245	33	Ethyl p-nitrocinnamate	—	142
m-Nitroiodobenzene	—	38	Methyl p-nitrocinnamate	—	161
o-Nitrobromobenzene	261	42			
3,4-Dichloronitrobenzene	255	43	Phenylnitromethane	227	—

(1) $d_{4°}^{20°}$ 1·204; $n_D^{20°}$ 1·553.
(2) $d_{4°}^{20°}$ 1·168; $n_D^{20°}$ 1·546.
(3) $d_{4°}^{20°}$ 1·157; $n_D^{20°}$ 1·547.
(4) $d_{4°}^{20°}$ 1·074; $n_D^{20°}$ 1·531.

Table IX, 36. **Aliphatic Nitro Compounds**

NITRO COMPOUND	B.P.	$d_{4°}^{20°}$	$n_D^{20°}$
Nitromethane	101°	1·137	1·381
Nitroethane	114	1·050	1·392
2-Nitropropane	120	0·988	1·394
1-Nitropropane	131	1·001	1·401
1-Nitro-*n*-butane	152	0·971	1·410
1-Nitro-*n*-pentane	66°/16 mm.	0·953	1·418
1-Nitro-*n*-hexane	82°/15	0·940	1·423
Phenylnitromethane	227	1·160	1·532

Table IX, 37.   Mercaptans (Thiols)

MERCAPTAN (THIOL)	B.P.	M.P.	2,4-DINITRO-PHENYL-THIOETHER	2,4-DINITRO-PHENYL-SULPHONE	3,5-DINITRO-THIO-BENZOATE	HYDROGEN 3-NITRO-THIO-PHTHALATE
Methyl	6°	—	128°	190°	—	—
Ethyl	36	—	115	160	62°	149°
Isopropyl	58	—	95	141	84	145
n-Propyl	67	—	81	128	52	137
Isobutyl	88	—	76	106	64	136
Allyl	90	—	72	105	—	—
n-Butyl	97	—	66	92	49	144
Isoamyl	117	—	59	95	43	145
n-Amyl	126	—	80	83	40	132
n-Hexyl	151	—	74	97	—	—
Cyclohexyl	159	—	148	172	—	—
n-Heptyl	176	—	82	101	53	132
n-Octyl	199	—	78	98	—	—
n-Nonyl	220	—	86	92	—	—
n-Decyl	114°/13	—	85	93	—	—
n-Dodecyl (lauryl)	154°/24	—	89	101	—	—
n-Hexadecyl (cetyl)	—	51°	91	105	—	—
1,2-Ethane dithiol	146	—	248	—	—	—
1,3-Propane dithiol	173	—	194	—	—	—
1,4-Butane dithiol	196	—	—	—	—	—
1,5-Pentane dithiol	217	—	170	—	—	—
1,6-Hexane dithiol	237	—	218	—	—	—
Phenyl (thiophenol)	169	—	121	161	149	130
Benzyl	194	—	130	183	120	137
o-Thiocresol	194	15	101	155	—	—
m-Thiocresol	195	—	91	145	—	—
p-Thiocresol	195	44	103	190	—	—
α-Phenylethyl	199	—	90	133	—	—
β-Phenylethyl	105°/23	—	—	—	—	—
α-Thionaphthol	161°/20	—	176	—	—	—
β-Thionaphthol	162°/20	81	145	—	—	—
Mercaptobiphenyl	—	111	146	170	—	—
Furfuryl	84°/65	—	130	—	—	—
Thienyl	166	—	119	143	—	—

For the melting points of some mercury derivatives, see Section IV,37.

Table IX, 38. Sulphonic Acids

Note. Aromatic sulphonic acids are usually hygroscopic solids and do not generally [have] sharp melting points: they are frequently supplied in the form of their sodium (or other me[tal]) salts. It is therefore not possible to classify them in order of increasing melting points. In T[able] IX, 38, related compounds are grouped together. For the convenience of the student a subsid[iary] Table (IX, 38A) is given in which sulphonic acids are listed in the order of increasing me[lting] points of the *S*-benzylthiuronium salts; these derivatives are easily prepared either from the acid or from the salt.

ACID	SULPHON-AMIDE $ArSO_2NH_2$	S-BENZYL-THI-URONIUM SALT	SULPHON-ANILIDE $ArSO_2NHPh$	p-TOLUI-DINE SALT	SULPHO[NYL] CHLOR[IDE] $ArSO_2$[Cl]
Benzenesulphonic	153°	150°	110°	205°	—
o-Toluenesulphonic	156	170	136	204	68
m-Toluenesulphonic	108	—	96	—	12
p-Toluenesulphonic	137	182	103	198	71
o-Chlorobenzenesulphonic	188	—	—	—	28
m-Chlorobenzenesulphonic	148	—	—	—	—
p-Chlorobenzenesulphonic	144	175	104	209	53
o-Bromobenzenesulphonic	186	—	—	—	51
m-Bromobenzenesulphonic	154	—	—	—	—
p-Bromobenzenesulphonic	166	170	119	216	75
o-Nitrobenzenesulphonic	193	—	115	—	69
m-Nitrobenzenesulphonic	168	146	126	222	64
p-Nitrobenzenesulphonic	179	—	136	—	80
Sulphanilic	164	187	200	—	—
Orthanilic	153	132	—	—	—
Metanilic	142	148	—	—	—
o-Sulphobenzoic (salt)	—	206	—	200	79
m-Sulphobenzoic	170	163	—	—	20
p-Sulphobenzoic	236	213	—	—	57
Phenol-p-sulphonic	177	169	—	202	—
Thymolsulphonic	—	213	—	—	—
o-Xylene-4-sulphonic	144	208	—	—	52
m-Xylene-4-sulphonic	138	146	110	—	3[4]
p-Xylenesulphonic	148	184	—	—	2[.]
Naphthalene-1-sulphonic	150	137	112	181	68
Naphthalene-2-sulphonic	217	191	132	221	7[9]
Anthraquinone-1-sulphonic	—	191	216	—	21[7]
Anthraquinone-2-sulphonic	261	211	193	—	19[7]
1-Naphthylamine-4-sulphonic	206	195	—	—	—
1-Naphthylamine-5-sulphonic	260	180	—	—	—
1-Naphthylamine-6-sulphonic	219	191	—	—	—
1-Naphthylamine-7-sulphonic	181	—	—	—	—
1-Naphthylamine-8-sulphonic	—	300	140	—	—
2-Naphthylamine-1-sulphonic	—	139	—	—	—
2-Naphthylamine-6-sulphonic	—	184	—	—	—
1-Naphthol-2-sulphonic	—	170	—	—	—
1-Naphthol-4-sulphonic	—	104	200	196	—

Sulphonic Acids (*continued*)

ACID	SULPHON-AMIDE ArSO$_2$NH$_2$	S-BENZYL-THI-URONIUM SALT	SULPHON-ANILIDE ArSO$_2$NHPh	p-TOLUI-DINE SALT	SULPHONYL CHLORIDE, ArSO$_2$Cl
aphthol-5-sulphonic	—	—	201°	—	—
Naphthol-1-sulphonic	—	136°	—	162°	124°
Naphthol-6-sulphonic	238°	217	—	248	—
Naphthol-8-sulphonic	—	218	195	232	—
nzene-*o*-disulphonic	254	206	241	—	143
nzene-*m*-disulphonic	229	214	144	—	63
nzene-*p*-disulphonic	288	—	—	—	131
phthalene-1,4-disulphonic	273	—	179	—	—
phthalene-1,5-disulphonic	310	257	249	332	183
phthalene-1,6-disulphonic	298	235	—	315	129
phthalene-2,6-disulphonic	305	256	—	360	225
phthalene-2,7-disulphonic	243	211	—	300	159
Naphthylamine-4,8-disulphonic	—	210	—	—	—
Naphthylamine-5,8-disulphonic	—	276	—	—	—
Naphthylamine-6,7-disulphonic	—	—	—	—	—
Naphthylamine-3,6-disulphonic	—	—	—	—	—
Naphthylamine-3,8-disulphonic	—	—	—	—	—
Naphthol-3,6-disulphonic	—	217	—	—	—
Naphthol-4,8-disulphonic	—	205	—	—	—
Naphthol-3,6-disulphonic	—	233	202	—	—
Naphthol-6,8-disulphonic	—	228	195	—	162
amphorsulphonic	132	210	—	—	88

ALIPHATIC SULPHONIC ACIDS

SULPHONIC ACID	B.P.	SULPHONYL CHLORIDE, B.P.	SULPHON-AMIDE, M.P.	S-BENZYL-THI-URONIUM SALT, M.P.	SULPHON-ANILIDE M.P.
thane	167°/10	163°	90°	—	99°
ane	—	177	59	115°	58
ropane	—	79°/18	60	—	84
ropane	—	78°/13	52	—	—
utane	—	75°/10	45	—	—

Elementary Practical Organic Chemistry [IX

Table IX, 38A.   Sulphonic Acids

(Arranged in the order of increasing melting points of the S-benzylthiuronium salts.)

SULPHONIC ACID	M.P.	SULPHONIC ACID	M.P.
1-Naphthol-4-	104°	1-Naphthylamine-6-	191°
Ethane-	115	1-Naphthylamine-4-	195
Orthanilic acid	132	1-Naphthol-4,8-di	205
2-Naphthol-1-	136	Benzene-*o*-di-	206
Naphthalene-1-	137	*o*-Sulphobenzoic acid	206
2-Naphthylamine-1-	139	*o*-Xylene-4-	208
m-Nitrobenzene-	146	*d*-Camphor-	210
m-Xylene-4-	146	2-Naphthylamine-4,8-di-	210
Metanilic acid	148	Naphthalene-2,7-di-	211
Benzene-	150	Anthraquinone-2-	211
m-Sulphobenzoic acid	163	*p*-Sulphobenzoic acid	213
Phenol-*p*-	169	Thymol-	213
p-Bromobenzene-	170	Benzene-*m*-di-	214
1-Naphthol-2-	170	2-Naphthol-6-	217
o-Toluene-	170	1-Naphthol-3,6-di-	217
p-Chlorobenzene-	175	2-Naphthol-8-	218
1-Naphthylamine-5-	180	2-Naphthol-6,8-di-	228
p-Toluene-	182	2-Naphthol-3,6-di-	233
2-Naphthylamine-6-	184	Naphthalene-1,6-di-	235
p-Xylene-	184	Naphthalene-2,6-di-	256
Sulphanilic acid	187	Naphthalene-1,5-di-	257
Naphthalene-2-	191	2-Naphthylamine-5,8-di-	276
Anthraquinone-1-	191	1-Naphthylamine-8-	300

Table IX, 39A.   Aromatic Sulphonamides

SULPHONAMIDE	M.P.	*N*-XANTHYL-SULPHONAMIDE
p-Ethylbenzene-	109°	196°
2,4-Dimethylbenzene-	137	188
Toluene-*p*-	137	197
2,4,6-Trimethylbenzene- (mesityl-)	142	203
2,5-Dimethylbenzene-	147	176
Benzene-	153	200
Toluene-*o*-	156	183
p-Aminobenzene- (sulphanilamide)	165	208
Saccharin	226d	198
Benzene-1,3-di-	229	170

Table IX, 39B. Sulphonamides, RSO_2NH_2

SULPHONAMIDE	M.P.	SULPHONAMIDE	M.P.
1-Butane-	45°	2-Naphthalene-	217°
1-Propane-	52	o-Sulphobenzimide	
Ethane-	59	(saccharin)	226d
2-Propane-	60	1,3-Benzenedi-	229
m-Ethylbenzene-	86	2,7-Naphthalenedi-	242
Methane-	90	1,2-Benzenedi-	254
2,6-Dimethylbenzene-	96	2-Anthraquinone-	261
o-Ethylbenzene-	100	1,4-Naphthalenedi-	273
Benzyl-	105	p-Sulphamidobenzoic acid	280
m-Toluene-	108	1,4-Benzenedi-	288
p-Ethylbenzene-	109	1,6-Naphthalenedi-	298
p-Methoxybenzene-	111	1,5-Naphthalenedi-	310
3,5-Dimethylbenzene-	135	1,3,5-Benzenetri-	312
d-Camphor-8-	137	1,8-Anthraquinonedi-	340
2,4-Dimethylbenzene-	137		
p-Toluene-	137	*Halogeno-sulphonamides*	
2,4,6-Trimethylbenzene-			
(mesityl-)	142		
m-Aminobenzene-	142		
3,4-Dimethylbenzene-	144	p-Fluorobenzene-	125°
2,5-Dimethylbenzene-	147	3,4-Dichlorobenzene-	135
p-Ethoxybenzene-	150	p-Chlorobenzene-	144
1-Naphthalene-	150	m-Chlorobenzene-	148
Benzene-	153	m-Bromobenzene-	154
o-Aminobenzene-	153	p-Bromobenzene-	166
o-Toluene-	156	3,4-Dibromobenzene-	175
m-Nitrobenzyl-	159	2,4-Dichlorobenzene-	180
p-Aminobenzene-		2,5-Dichlorobenzene-	181
(sulphanilamide)	165	o-Bromobenzene-	186
2,3-Dimethylbenzene-	167	p-Bromobenzyl-	188
m-Nitrobenzene-	168	o-Chlorobenzene-	188
p-Nitrobenzene-	179	2,4-Dibromobenzene-	190
2,4,5-Trimethylbenzene-	181	2,5-Dibromobenzene-	194
o-Nitrobenzene-	193	p-Iodobenzyl-	206
p-Nitrobenzyl-	204	2,4,6-Trichlorobenzene-	212d
1-Nitro-2-naphthalene-	214	2,3,4-Trichlorobenzene-	230d

Table IX, 40. Quinones

QUINONE	M.P.	SEMI-CARBAZONE	OXIME	HYDRO-QUINONE	DIACETATE OF HYDRO-QUINONE	THIELE ACETYLATION PRODUCT	OTHER DERIVATIVES
Thymoquinone	45°	204°	162°	143°	74°	—	—
2-Methyl-1,4-benzoquinone	69	179	135	124	52	114°	—
2-Methyl-1,4-naphthoquinone	106	247	167	—	—	113	—
Duroquinone (1)	112	—	—	239	207	—	—
p-Benzoquinone	116	243d	240d	171	123	97	Picrate, 179°
1,4-Naphthoquinone	125	247	198	176	128	135	—
1,2-Naphthoquinone	116–120	184	162	103	105	135	—
1-Methylanthraquinone	172	—	—	—	—	—	—
2-Methylanthraquinone	177	—	—	—	217	—	—
3-Methyl-1,2-benzoquinone	195	—	140	—	—	—	—
Camphorquinone	199	236	170	—	—	—	Quinoxaline, 78
Quinizarin (2)	201	—	—	—	—	207	—
9,10-Phenanthraquinone	206	220d	162	148	202	—	Quinoxaline, 220
Acenaphthenequinone	261	192	222 Di	—	—	—	Quinoxaline, 241
Anthraquinone	286	—	224	—	—	—	—
Chloranil (3)	290*	—	—	180	260	—	—
Alizarin	290	—	—	232	251	—	—
					182		

* Sealed tube.

(1) 2,3,5,6-Tetramethyl-1,4-benzoquinone. (2) 1,4-Dihydroxyanthraquinone. (3) 2,3,5,6-Tetrachloro-1,4-benzoquinone.

Table IX, 41. Imides

COMPOUND	M.P.
N-2-Bromoethylphthalimide	82°
N-Phenylmaleimide	91
Maleimide	93
Allyl-(1-methylbutyl)-barbituric acid	100
Succinimide	125
Ethyl-n-hexyl-barbituric acid (*Ortal*)	126
Ethyl-n-butyl-bartituric acid (*Neonal*)	128
N-2-Hydroxyethylphthalimide	128
Ethyl-(1-methylbutyl)-barbituric acid (*Pentobarbital*)	130
Allyl-isopropyl-barbituric acid (*Alurate*)	137
Ethyl-isoamyl-barbituric acid (*Amytal*)	155
N-Phenylsuccinimide	156
Alloxan ($4H_2O$)	170d
Ethyl-phenyl-barbituric acid (*Phenobarbital*)	172
Diallylbarbituric acid (*Dial*)	173
Diethylbarbituric acid (*Veronal*)	190
Ethyl-isopropyl-barbituric acid (*Ipral*)	201
N-Phenylphthalimide	205
3-Nitrophthalimide	216
o-Sulphobenzimide (saccharin)	226d
Phthalimide	233
Barbituric acid	245d
Naphthalimide	300

Table IX, 42. Nitroso, Azo, Azoxy and Hydrazo Compounds

COMPOUND	M.P.
Nitroso Compounds:	
Methylphenylnitrosoamine . . . B.P. 120°/13	—
Ethylphenylnitrosoamine . . . B.P. 134°/16	—
p-Nitrosotoluene	48°
m-Nitrosotoluene	53
N-Nitrosodiphenylamine	66
Nitrosobenzene	68
o-Nitrosotoluene	72
p-Nitroso-*N*-ethylaniline	78
p-Nitroso-*NN*-diethylaniline	84
p-Nitroso-*NN*-dimethylaniline	87
1-Nitrosonaphthalene	98
1-Nitroso-2-naphthol	109
p-Nitroso-*N*-methylaniline	118
p-Nitrosophenol	125d
p-Nitrosodiphenylamine	144
2-Nitroso-1-naphthol	152d
4-Nitroso-1-naphthol	198
Azo Compounds:	
2,2'-Dimethylazobenzene	55°
3,3'-Dimethylazobenzene	55
Azobenzene	68
4-Anilinoazobenzene	82
3,3'-Diethoxyazobenzene	91
3,3'-Dichloroazobenzene	101
1-Benzeneazo-2-naphthylamine	104
p-Dimethylaminoazobenzene	117
4-Benzeneazo-1-naphthylamine	123
p-Aminoazobenzene	126
4-Hydroxy-3-methylazobenzene	128
2,2'-Diethoxyazobenzene	131
1-Benzeneazo-2-naphthol	134
2,2'-Dichloroazobenzene	137
2-Benzeneazo-1-naphthol	138
4,4'-Dimethylazobenzene	144
o-Azobiphenyl	145
p-Hydroxyazobenzene	152
4,4'-Diethoxyazobenzene	160
4,4'-Dichloroazobenzene	188
1,1'-Azonaphthalene	190
4-Benzeneazo-1-naphthol	206d
2,2'-Azonaphthalene	208
p-Azobiphenyl	250

Table IX, 42. Nitroso, Azo, Azoxy and Hydrazo Compounds (*continued*)

COMPOUND	M.P.
Azoxy Compounds:	
Azoxybenzene	36°
3,3'-Dimethylazoxybenzene	39
3,3'-Diethoxyazoxybenzene	50
3,3'-Dimethoxyazoxybenzene	52°
2,2'-Dichloroazoxybenzene	56
2,2'-Dimethylazoxybenzene	60
4,4'-Dimethylazoxybenzene	70
2,2'-Dimethoxyazoxybenzene	81
3,3'-Dichloroazoxybenzene	97
2,2'-Diethoxyazoxybenzene	102
4,4'-Dimethoxyazoxybenzene	119
1,1'-Azoxynaphthalene	127
4,4'-Diethoxyazobenzene	138
4,4'-Dichloroazoxybenzene	158
o-Azoxybiphenyl	158
2,2'-Azoxynaphthalene	168
p-Azoxybiphenyl	212
Hydrazo Compounds:	
3,3'-Dimethylhydrazobenzene	38°
4,4'-Diethoxyhydrazobenzene	86
2,2'-Diethoxyhydrazobenzene	89
2,2'-Dimethoxyhydrazobenzene	102
3,3'-Diethoxyhydrazobenzene	119
Hydrazobenzene	127
4,4'-Dimethylhydrazobenzene	134
2,2'-Hydrazonaphthalene	141
2,2'-Hydrazodiphenol	148
1,1'-Hydrazonaphthalene	153
2,2'-Dimethylhydrazobenzene	165
4,4'-Hydrazodibiphenyl	169
2,2'-Hydrazodibiphenyl	182

Table IX, 43. Miscellaneous Sulphur Compounds

COMPOUND	B.P.	M.P.	$d_{4°}^{20°}$	$n_D^{20°}$
Dimethyl sulphide	38°	—	0·849	1·436
Ethyl methyl sulphide	66	—	0·846	1·440
Diethyl sulphide	92	—	0·837	1·442
Di-isopropyl sulphide	119	—	0·817	1·440
Di-allyl sulphide	140	—	—	—
Di-*n*-propyl sulphide	142	—	0·839	1·449
Di-isobutyl sulphide	169	—	0·826	1·447
Di-*sec*-butyl sulphide	165	—	0·835	1·451
Di-*n*-butyl sulphide	187	—	0·840	1·453
Di-isoamyl sulphide	86°/5	—	0·834	1·453
Di-*n*-amyl sulphide	85°/4	—	0·841	1·456
Di-*n*-hexyl sulphide	114°/4	—	0·841	1·459
Di-*n*-heptyl sulphide	142°/4	—	0·842	1·461
Di-*n*-octyl sulphide	162°/4	—	0·845	1·469
Diphenyl sulphide	145°/8	—	1·114	1·633
Dibenzyl sulphide	—	50°	—	—
Di-*p*-tolyl sulphide	—	57	—	—
Dimethyl disulphide	109	—	1·065	1·526
Diethyl disulphide	153	—	0·992	1·507
Di-isopropyl disulphide	176	—	0·944	1·492
Di-*n*-propyl disulphide	194	—	0·960	1·498
Di-allyl disulphide	100°/48	—	—	—
Di-isobutyl disulphide	215	—	0·928	1·487
Di-*tert*-butyl disulphide	65°/5	—	0·923	1·490
Di-*n*-butyl disulphide	231	—	0·938	1·493
Di-*n*-amyl disulphide	119°/7	—	0·922	1·489
Di-isoamyl disulphide	115°/9	—	0·919	1·486
Di-*p*-tolyl disulphide	—	48	—	—
Diphenyl disulphide	—	60	—	—
Dibenzyl disulphide	—	73	—	—
Diphenyl sulphoxide	—	70	—	—
Di-*p*-tolyl sulphoxide	—	95	—	—
Dibenzyl sulphoxide	—	134	—	—
Di-*n*-propyl sulphone	—	29	—	—
Di-*n*-butyl sulphone	—	44	—	—
Diethyl sulphone	248	74	—	—
Trional	—	76	—	—
Dimethyl sulphone	238	109	—	—
Sulphonal	—	126	—	—
Diphenyl sulphone	—	128	—	—
Dibenzyl sulphone	—	150	—	—
Di-*p*-tolyl sulphone	—	159	—	—

Table IX, 43.   Miscellaneous Sulphur Compounds (*continued*)

COMPOUND	B.P.	M.P.	$d_4^{20°}$	$n_D^{20°}$
Methyl thiocyanate	131°	—	1·082	—
Ethyl thiocyanate	147	—	1·024	1·465
Isopropyl thiocyanate	151	—	—	—
n-Propyl thiocyanate	165	—	0·981	1·463
n-Butyl thiocyanate	184	—	0·961	1·464
Benzyl thiocyanate	—	38°	—	—
Allyl isothiocyanate	152	—	1·010	1·524
Phenyl isothiocyanate	221	—	1·134	1·651
Thiophene	84	—	1·062	1·525
Methyl *p*-toluenesulphonate	—	28	—	—
Ethyl *p*-toluenesulphonate	173°/15	33	—	—
n-Propyl *p*-toluenesulphonate	165°/10	—	—	—
n-Butyl *p*-toluenesulphonate	175°/10	—	—	—
Phenyl *p*-toluenesulphonate	—	96	—	—
Allyl thiourea	—	78	—	—
sym-Di-*m*-tolyl thiourea	—	112	—	—
Phenyl thiourea	—	154	—	—
sym-Diphenylthiourea (thiocarbanilide)	—	154	—	—
sym-Di-*o*-tolyl thiourea	—	166	—	—
sym-Di-*p*-tolyl thiourea	—	178	—	—
Thiourea	—	180	—	—
Thiosemicarbazide	—	182	—	—

Table IX, 44. Miscellaneous Phosphorus Compounds

PHOSPHATE	B.P.	M.P.	$d_{4°}^{20°}$	$n_D^{20°}$
Trimethyl	62°/5 (197°)	—	1·214	1·396
Triethyl	76°/5 (216)	—	1·070	1·405
Tri-isopropyl	84°/5	—	0·987	1·406
Tri-*n*-propyl	108°/5	—	1·012	1·416
Tri-isobutyl	117°/5	—	0·968	1·419
Tri-*n*-butyl	139°/6	—	0·977	1·425
Tri-isoamyl	143°/3	—	—	—
Tri-*n*-amyl	167°/5	—	0·961	1·432
Tri-*o*-cresyl	264°/20	—	—	—
Tri-*m*-cresyl	274°/17	26°	—	—
Triphenyl	245°/11	50	—	—
Tribenzyl	—	65	—	—
Tri-*p*-cresyl	—	78	—	—
Tri-2-naphthyl	—	111	—	—

PHOSPHITE				
Trimethyl	112°	—	1·052	1·410
Triethyl	157	—	0·969	1·414
Tri-isopropyl	60°/9	—	0·918	1·412
Tri-*n*-propyl	207	—	0·952	1·427
Tri-isobutyl	235	—	0·917	1·425
Tri-*n*-butyl	120°/10	—	0·923	1·432
Tri-*n*-amyl	123°/6	—	0·901	1·433
Triphenyl	228°/12	24°	—	—
Tri-*o*-cresyl	238°/11	—	—	—
Tri-*m*-cresyl	235°/7	—	—	—
Tri-*p*-cresyl	238°/7	—	—	—
Dimethyl hydrogen	72°/25	—	1·200	1·404
Diethyl hydrogen	66°/6	—	1·079	1·408
Di-isopropyl hydrogen	90°/25	—	0·996	1·407
Di-*n*-propyl hydrogen	92°/11	—	1·019	1·416
Di-isobutyl hydrogen	106°/12	—	0·976	1·420
Di-*n*-butyl hydrogen	119°/7	—	0·995	1·423

APPENDIX

A, 1 Laboratory Accidents and First Aid*

In case of accidents, always call or notify the demonstrator or teacher as soon as possible.

A **First Aid Box or Cupboard** should be kept in a readily accessible position in the laboratory and should contain the following articles clearly labelled:

Bandages (several sizes), gauze, lint, cotton wool, adhesive plaster, 'Elastoplast' or equivalent, and a sling.
Delicate forceps, needles, thread, scissors, and safety pins.
Fine glass dropper.
Two eye glasses.
Vaseline, Castor oil, Olive oil, Sal volatile, Boracic acid powder, Sodium bicarbonate powder, Chloramine-T powder, Sulphapyridine powder, Butesin picrate ointment.
Acriflavine jelly or emulsion (*e.g.*, 'Burnol').
Tannic acid jelly (*e.g.*, 'Tannafax').
One fireproof blanket—this is best stored in a special container near the First Aid Cupboard.
Bottles containing:
   One per cent acetic acid.
   One per cent boric acid.
   Saturated sodium bicarbonate solution.
   One per cent sodium bicarbonate solution.
   Rectified spirit.
   Glycerine.
   Light petroleum, b.p. 80–100°.
   A disinfectant, *e.g.*, 'Dettol' or 'T.C.P.'

A 'Laboratory First Aid Chart' ('Laboratory Emergency Chart'), which should be hung in a prominent position near the First Aid Box, is obtainable from British Drug Houses Ltd., and from the Fisher Scientific Company.

* For further information the following books may be consulted: D.S.I.R. National Chemical Laboratory, *Safety Measures in Chemical Laboratories*, Third Edition, 1964 (Her Majesty's Stationery Office); K. Guy, *Laboratory First Aid*, 1965 (Macmillan, London); H. A. J. Peters and J. W. Creyghton, *Safety in the Chemical Laboratory*, Second Edition, 1957 (Butterworths).
   Copies of these books should be placed in the First Aid Cupboard.

Eye Protection

The eyes are vulnerable to injury by splashing droplets of corrosive chemicals and flying particles of glass or other solid fragments. It is good practice to wear safety spectacles at all times in the laboratory. Safety spectacles and goggles are marketed in a number of styles and some provide protection for part of the face. Safety goggles should always be worn over the eyes during potentially dangerous operations, such as experiments involving large quantities of sodium or other alkali metals, distillation of large volumes of inflammable solvents, vacuum distillation, and handling of liquid nitrogen or other liquid gases.

Laboratory Apparel

Clothing should be protected from soiling and damage by chemicals and possible accidents of various kinds by wearing an inexpensive laboratory coat.

Burns

Burns caused by dry heat (*e.g.*, by flames, hot objects, etc.). For slight burns in which the skin is not broken, apply tannic acid jelly ('Tannafax'), acriflavine jelly ('Burnol') or butesin picrate ointment (butesin is *n*-butyl *p*-aminobenzoate).

For larger burns, or burns in which the skin is reddened or blistered, apply acriflavine jelly or crystal violet jelly without delay, and call for medical aid at once.

Acids on the skin. Wash immediately and thoroughly with a liberal quantity of water, then with saturated sodium bicarbonate solution, and finally with water. For a serious acid burn, follow this by applying a disinfectant, drying the skin and covering with acriflavine jelly.

Alkalis on the skin. Wash immediately with a large volume of water, then with 1 per cent acetic acid, and finally with water. For a serious burn, follow this treatment by applying a disinfectant, drying the skin and covering with acriflavine jelly.

Bromine on the skin. Wash the affected part immediately with a liberal supply of light petroleum, b.p. 80–100°, and then rub glycerine well into the skin. After a little time remove the superficial glycerine and apply acriflavine jelly or butesin picrate ointment.

Sodium on the skin. If a small solidified fragment of sodium can still be seen, remove it carefully with forceps. Wash thoroughly with water, then with 1 per cent acetic acid, and finally cover with gauze soaked in olive oil or acriflavine jelly.

Phosphorus on the skin. Wash well with cold water and treat with 1 per cent silver nitrate solution.

Methyl sulphate on the skin. Wash immediately and liberally with concentrated ammonia solution, and then rub *gently* with wads of cotton wool soaked in concentrated ammonia solution.

Organic substances on the skin. Wash freely with rectified spirit, then with soap and warm water.

Cuts

If the cut is only a minor one, allow it to bleed for a few seconds, see that no glass remains, apply a disinfectant (rectified spirit, 'Dettol', 1 per cent aqueous chloramine-T solution, or sulphapyridine powder) and bandage.

For serious cuts, send for a doctor at once: meanwhile wash with a disinfectant and endeavour to check bleeding by applying pressure immediately above the cut. Continuous pressure should not be maintained for more than five minutes.

Eye Accidents

In all cases the patient should see a doctor. If the accident appears serious, medical aid should be summoned immediately *while* first aid is applied.

Acid in the eye. If the acid is dilute, wash the eye repeatedly with 1 per cent sodium bicarbonate solution in the eye cup. If the acid is concentrated, first wash the eye with a large amount of water and then continue with the bicarbonate solution.

Caustic alkali in the eye. Proceed as for acid in the eye, but wash with 1 per cent boric acid solution in place of bicarbonate solution.

Bromine in the eye. Wash thoroughly with water and then immediately with 1 per cent sodium bicarbonate solution.

Glass in the eye. Remove loose glass *very gently* with forceps or by washing with water in an eye bath. Call for a doctor immediately.

Soreness which may follow minor accidents to the eye may be relieved by placing 1 drop of castor oil in the corner of the eye.

Fires

Burning clothing. Prevent the person from running and fanning the flames. Make the victim lie down on the floor, or throw him (her) down if necessary, and wrap the fireproof blanket firmly around the ignited clothes until the fire is extinguished.

Burning reagents. Turn out all gas burners and switch off all electric hot plates in the vicinity; remove everything which may ignite. The control of the fire depends upon its size and kind.

A small fire (for example, liquid in a beaker or flask, or an oil bath) may usually be extinguished by covering the opening of the vessel with a clean damp cloth or duster: the fire usually dies out from lack of air. For larger fires, dry sand may be employed. Buckets of dry sand should be distributed round the laboratory and should be *strictly reserved* for this purpose. Most fires on the laboratory bench can be smothered by the liberal use of sand. Sand once employed for this purpose should always be thrown away afterwards as it may contain appreciable quantities of inflammable, non-volatile substances (*e.g.*, nitrobenzene).

Although sand is usually very effective for extinguishing fires, it has the disadvantage that the compound or reaction mixture is usually lost and any glass apparatus around which the fire centres may be broken under the weight of the sand. Alternatively, *small* fires may be extinguished with carbon tetrachloride under high pressure of carbon dioxide (as contained for example, in the commercial Autelex extinguisher*); the mixture is directed on the fire and the 'blanketing' effect of the carbon dioxide and heavy carbon tetrachloride vapour will soon put out the fire. It must be noted particularly that:—

(*a*) carbon tetrachloride should not be used if sodium or potassium is present as violent explosions may result;

(*b*) the laboratory must be ventilated immediately the fire is extinguished in order to disperse the highly poisonous phosgene vapour which is always formed.

It is usually better to use a fire extinguisher charged with carbon dioxide under pressure*; this produces a spray of solid carbon dioxide

---

* Supplied by Read and Campbell, Ltd., 75 Victoria Street, London, S.W.1, etc.

upon releasing the pressure intermittently and is effective for extinguishing most fires in the laboratory.

For burning oil (or organic solvents), do not use water as it will only spread the fire: a mixture of sand and sodium bicarbonate is very effective. An excellent commercial 'Dry Powder Extinguisher' is available commercially*; the dry powder used (probably largely sodium bicarbonate) is expelled by a CO_2 charge. This fire extinguisher is suitable for fires caused by magnesium and metal hydrides.

Poisons

Solids or liquids

(i) **In the mouth but not swallowed.** Spit out at once and wash repeatedly with water.

(ii) **If swallowed.** Call a doctor immediately. In the meantime, give an antidote according to the nature of the poison.

(*a*) *Acids* (*including oxalic acid*). Dilute by drinking much water, followed by lime water or milk of magnesia. Milk may then be given but no emetics.

(*b*) *Caustic alkalis.* Dilute by drinking much water, followed by vinegar, lemon or orange juice, or solutions of lactic acid or citric acid. Milk may then be given but no emetics.

(*c*) *Salts of heavy metals.* Give milk or white of an egg.

(*d*) *Arsenic or mercury compounds.* Give an emetic immediately, e.g., one teaspoonful of mustard, or one tablespoonful of salt or zinc sulphate, in a tumbler of warm water.

Gases

Remove the victim to the open air, and loosen clothing at neck. To counteract chlorine or bromine fumes if inhaled in only small amounts, inhale ammonia vapour or gargle with sodium bicarbonate solution. Afterwards the patient should suck eucalyptus pastilles, or drink warm dilute peppermint or cinnamon essence, to soothe the throat and lungs.

If breathing has stopped, apply artificial respiration (for details see, for example, the chart on 'Treatment of Electric Shocks': this chart should be displayed in a prominent position in every laboratory).

* Supplied by Read and Campbell Ltd., 75 Victoria Street, London, S.W.1, etc.

Elementary Practical Organic Chemistry [A

A, 2. Reciprocals

	0	1	2	3	4	5	6	7	8	9	SUBTRACT DIFFERENCES								
											1	2	3	4	5	6	7	8	9
1·0	1·0000	9901	9804	9709	9615	9524	9434	9346	9259	9174	9	18	27	36	45	55	64	73	82
1·1	·9091	9009	8929	8850	8772	8696	8621	8547	8475	8403	8	15	23	30	38	45	53	61	68
1·2	·8333	8264	8197	8130	8065	8000	7937	7874	7813	7752	6	13	19	26	32	38	45	51	58
1·3	·7692	7634	7576	7519	7463	7407	7353	7299	7246	7194	5	11	16	22	27	33	38	44	49
1·4	·7143	7092	7042	6993	6944	6897	6849	6803	6757	6711	5	10	14	19	24	29	33	38	43
1·5	·6667	6623	6579	6536	6494	6452	6410	6369	6329	6289	4	8	13	17	21	25	29	33	38
1·6	·6250	6211	6173	6135	6098	6061	6024	5988	5952	5917	4	7	11	15	18	22	26	29	33
1·7	·5882	5848	5814	5780	5747	5714	5682	5650	5618	5587	3	6	10	13	16	20	23	26	29
1·8	·5556	5525	5495	5464	5435	5405	5376	5348	5319	5291	3	6	9	12	15	18	20	23	26
1·9	·5263	5236	5208	5181	5155	5128	5102	5076	5051	5025	3	5	8	11	13	16	18	21	24
2·0	·5000	4975	4950	4926	4902	4878	4854	4831	4808	4785	2	5	7	10	12	14	17	19	21
2·1	·4762	4739	4717	4695	4673	4651	4630	4608	4587	4566	2	4	7	9	11	13	15	17	20
2·2	·4545	4525	4505	4484	4464	4444	4425	4405	4386	4367	2	4	6	8	10	12	14	16	18
2·3	·4348	4329	4310	4292	4274	4255	4237	4219	4202	4184	2	4	5	7	9	11	13	14	16
2·4	·4167	4149	4132	4115	4098	4082	4065	4049	4032	4016	2	3	5	7	8	10	12	13	15
2·5	·4000	3984	3968	3953	3937	3922	3906	3891	3876	3861	2	3	5	6	8	9	11	12	14
2·6	·3846	3831	3817	3802	3788	3774	3759	3745	3731	3717	1	3	4	6	7	9	10	11	13
2·7	·3704	3690	3676	3663	3650	3636	3623	3610	3597	3584	1	3	4	5	7	8	9	11	12
2·8	·3571	3559	3546	3534	3521	3509	3497	3484	3472	3460	1	2	4	5	6	7	9	10	11
2·9	·3448	3436	3425	3413	3401	3390	3378	3367	3356	3344	1	2	3	5	6	7	8	9	10
3·0	·3333	3322	3311	3300	3289	3279	3268	3257	3247	3236	1	2	3	4	5	6	7	9	10
3·1	·3226	3215	3205	3195	3185	3175	3165	3155	3145	3135	1	2	3	4	5	6	7	8	9
3·2	·3125	3115	3106	3096	3086	3077	3067	3058	3049	3040	1	2	3	4	5	6	7	8	9
3·3	·3030	3021	3012	3003	2994	2985	2976	2967	2959	2950	1	2	3	4	4	5	6	7	8
3·4	·2941	2933	2924	2915	2907	2899	2890	2882	2874	2865	1	2	3	3	4	5	6	7	8
3·5	·2857	2849	2841	2833	2825	2817	2809	2801	2793	2786	1	2	2	3	4	5	6	6	7
3·6	·2778	2770	2762	2755	2747	2740	2732	2725	2717	2710	1	2	2	3	4	5	5	6	7
3·7	·2703	2695	2688	2681	2674	2667	2660	2653	2646	2639	1	1	2	3	4	4	5	6	6
3·8	·2632	2625	2618	2611	2604	2597	2591	2584	2577	2571	1	1	2	3	3	4	5	5	6
3·9	·2564	2558	2551	2545	2538	2532	2525	2519	2513	2506	1	1	2	3	3	4	4	5	6
4·0	·2500	2494	2488	2481	2475	2469	2463	2457	2451	2445	1	1	2	2	3	4	4	5	5
4·1	·2439	2433	2427	2421	2415	2410	2404	2398	2392	2387	1	1	2	2	3	3	4	5	5
4·2	·2381	2375	2370	2364	2358	2353	2347	2342	2336	2331	1	1	2	2	3	3	4	4	5
4·3	·2326	2320	2315	2309	2304	2299	2294	2288	2283	2278	1	1	2	2	3	3	4	4	5
4·4	·2273	2268	2262	2257	2252	2247	2242	2237	2232	2227	1	1	2	2	3	3	4	4	5
4·5	·2222	2217	2212	2208	2203	2198	2193	2188	2183	2179	0	1	1	2	2	3	3	4	4
4·6	·2174	2169	2165	2160	2155	2151	2146	2141	2137	2132	0	1	1	2	2	3	3	4	4
4·7	·2128	2123	2119	2114	2110	2105	2101	2096	2092	2088	0	1	1	2	2	3	3	4	4
4·8	·2083	2079	2075	2070	2066	2062	2058	2053	2049	2045	0	1	1	2	2	3	3	3	4
4·9	·2041	2037	2033	2028	2024	2020	2016	2012	2008	2004	0	1	1	2	2	2	3	3	4
5·0	·2000	1996	1992	1988	1984	1980	1976	1972	1969	1965	0	1	1	2	2	2	3	3	4
5·1	·1961	1957	1953	1949	1946	1942	1938	1934	1931	1927	0	1	1	2	2	2	3	3	3
5·2	·1923	1919	1916	1912	1908	1905	1901	1898	1894	1890	0	1	1	1	2	2	3	3	3
5·3	·1887	1883	1880	1876	1873	1869	1866	1862	1859	1855	0	1	1	1	2	2	2	3	3
5·4	·1852	1848	1845	1842	1838	1835	1832	1828	1825	1821	0	1	1	1	2	2	2	3	3

A, 2.   Reciprocals (*continued*)

	0	1	2	3	4	5	6	7	8	9	|| 1	2	3	4	5	6	7	8	9
											|| || 	SUBTRACT DIFFERENCES							
5·5	·1818	1815	1812	1808	1805	1802	1799	1795	1792	1789	0	1	1	1	2	2	2	3	3
5·6	·1786	1783	1779	1776	1773	1770	1767	1764	1761	1757	0	1	1	1	2	2	2	3	3
5·7	·1754	1751	1748	1745	1742	1739	1736	1733	1730	1727	0	1	1	1	2	2	2	2	3
5·8	·1724	1721	1718	1715	1712	1709	1706	1704	1701	1698	0	1	1	1	1	2	2	2	3
5·9	·1695	1692	1689	1686	1684	1681	1678	1675	1672	1669	0	1	1	1	1	2	2	2	3
6·0	·1667	1664	1661	1658	1656	1653	1650	1647	1645	1642	0	1	1	1	1	2	2	2	2
6·1	·1639	1637	1634	1631	1629	1626	1623	1621	1618	1616	0	1	1	1	1	2	2	2	2
6·2	·1613	1610	1608	1605	1603	1600	1597	1595	1592	1590	0	1	1	1	1	1	2	2	2
6·3	·1587	1585	1582	1580	1577	1575	1572	1570	1567	1565	0	0	1	1	1	1	2	2	2
6·4	·1563	1560	1558	1555	1553	1550	1548	1546	1543	1541	0	0	1	1	1	1	2	2	2
6·5	·1538	1536	1534	1531	1529	1527	1524	1522	1520	1517	0	0	1	1	1	1	2	2	2
6·6	·1515	1513	1511	1508	1506	1504	1502	1499	1497	1495	0	0	1	1	1	1	2	2	2
6·7	·1493	1490	1488	1486	1484	1481	1479	1477	1475	1473	0	0	1	1	1	1	2	2	2
6·8	·1471	1468	1466	1464	1462	1460	1458	1456	1453	1451	0	0	1	1	1	1	2	2	2
6·9	·1449	1447	1445	1443	1441	1439	1437	1435	1433	1431	0	0	1	1	1	1	1	2	2
7·0	·1429	1427	1425	1422	1420	1418	1416	1414	1412	1410	0	0	1	1	1	1	1	2	2
7·1	·1408	1406	1404	1403	1401	1399	1397	1395	1393	1391	0	0	1	1	1	1	1	2	2
7·2	·1389	1387	1385	1383	1381	1379	1377	1376	1374	1372	0	0	1	1	1	1	1	2	2
7·3	·1370	1368	1366	1364	1362	1361	1359	1357	1355	1353	0	0	1	1	1	1	1	2	2
7·4	·1351	1350	1348	1346	1344	1342	1340	1339	1337	1335	0	0	1	1	1	1	1	2	2
7·5	·1333	1332	1330	1328	1326	1325	1323	1321	1319	1318	0	0	1	1	1	1	1	1	2
7·6	·1316	1314	1312	1311	1309	1307	1305	1304	1302	1300	0	0	1	1	1	1	1	1	1
7·7	·1299	1297	1295	1294	1292	1290	1289	1287	1285	1284	0	0	0	1	1	1	1	1	1
7·8	·1282	1280	1279	1277	1276	1274	1272	1271	1269	1267	0	0	0	1	1	1	1	1	1
7·9	·1266	1264	1263	1261	1259	1258	1256	1255	1253	1252	0	0	0	1	1	1	1	1	1
8·0	·1250	1248	1247	1245	1244	1242	1241	1239	1238	1236	0	0	0	1	1	1	1	1	1
8·1	·1235	1233	1232	1230	1229	1227	1225	1224	1222	1221	0	0	0	1	1	1	1	1	1
8·2	·1220	1218	1217	1215	1214	1212	1211	1209	1208	1206	0	0	0	1	1	1	1	1	1
8·3	·1205	1203	1202	1200	1199	1198	1196	1195	1193	1192	0	0	0	1	1	1	1	1	1
8·4	·1190	1189	1188	1186	1185	1183	1182	1181	1179	1178	0	0	0	1	1	1	1	1	1
8·5	·1176	1175	1174	1172	1171	1170	1168	1167	1166	1164	0	0	0	1	1	1	1	1	1
8·6	·1163	1161	1160	1159	1157	1156	1155	1153	1152	1151	0	0	0	1	1	1	1	1	1
8·7	·1149	1148	1147	1145	1144	1143	1142	1140	1139	1138	0	0	0	1	1	1	1	1	1
8·8	·1136	1135	1134	1133	1131	1130	1129	1127	1126	1125	0	0	0	1	1	1	1	1	1
8·9	·1124	1122	1121	1120	1119	1117	1116	1115	1114	1112	0	0	0	1	1	1	1	1	1
9·0	·1111	1110	1109	1107	1106	1105	1104	1103	1101	1100	0	0	0	1	1	1	1	1	1
9·1	·1099	1098	1096	1095	1094	1093	1092	1091	1089	1088	0	0	0	1	1	1	1	1	1
9·2	·1087	1086	1085	1083	1082	1081	1080	1079	1078	1076	0	0	0	0	1	1	1	1	1
9·3	·1075	1074	1073	1072	1071	1070	1068	1067	1066	1065	0	0	0	0	1	1	1	1	1
9·4	·1064	1063	1062	1060	1059	1058	1057	1056	1055	1054	0	0	0	0	1	1	1	1	1
9·5	·1053	1052	1050	1049	1048	1047	1046	1045	1044	1043	0	0	0	0	1	1	1	1	1
9·6	·1042	1041	1040	1038	1037	1036	1035	1034	1033	1032	0	0	0	0	1	1	1	1	1
9·7	·1031	1030	1029	1028	1027	1026	1025	1024	1022	1021	0	0	0	0	1	1	1	1	1
9·8	·1020	1019	1018	1017	1016	1015	1014	1013	1012	1011	0	0	0	0	0	1	1	1	1
9·9	·1010	1009	1008	1007	1006	1005	1004	1003	1002	1001	0	0	0	0	0	1	1	1	1

A, 3.   Table of Relative Atomic Weights, 1961

Based on the Atomic Mass of $^{12}C = 12$

Element		Symbol	Weight	Element		Symbol	Weight
Aluminium	. .	Al	26·982	Manganese	. .	Mn	54·938
Antimony	. .	Sb	121·75	Mercury	. .	Hg	200·59
Arsenic	. .	As	74·922	Molybdenum	. .	Mo	95·94
Barium	. .	Ba	137·34	Nickel	. .	Ni	58·71
Beryllium	. .	Be	9·012	Nitrogen	. .	N	14·007
Bismuth	. .	Bi	208·980	Oxygen	. .	O	15·999
Boron	. .	B	10·811	Palladium	. .	Pd	106·4
Bromine	. .	Br	79·909	Phosphorus	. .	P	30·974
Cadmium	. .	Cd	112·40	Platinum	. .	Pt	195·09
Calcium	. .	Ca	40·08	Potassium	. .	K	39·102
Carbon	. .	C	12·011	Selenium	. .	Se	78·96
Cerium	. .	Ce	140·12	Silicon	. .	Si	28·086
Chlorine	. .	Cl	35·453	Silver	. .	Ag	107·870
Chromium	. .	Cr	51·996	Sodium	. .	Na	22·990
Cobalt	. .	Co	58·933	Strontium	. .	Sr	87·62
Copper	. .	Cu	63·54	Sulphur	. .	S	32·064
Fluorine	. .	F	18·998	Tellurium	. .	Te	127·60
Germanium	. .	Ge	72·59	Thorium	. .	Th	232·038
Gold	. .	Au	196·967	Tin	. .	Sn	118·69
Hydrogen	. .	H	1·008	Titanium	. .	Ti	47·90
Iodine	. .	I	126·904	Tungsten	. .	W	183·85
Iron	. .	Fe	55·847	Uranium	. .	U	238·03
Lead	. .	Pb	207·19	Vanadium	. .	V	50·942
Lithium	. .	Li	6·939	Zinc	. .	Zn	65·37
Magnesium	. .	Mg	24·312	Zirconium	. .	Zr	91·22

Index

Abbe refractometer, 20–23
Absorbance, 242, 243
Absorption maxima (ultraviolet), 243, 244, 246, 247
Acetals, 110, 189, 198
   reactions and characterization of, 110, 111, 189
   table of, 349
Acetates, 81, 93, 155, 156, 204, 205
Acetic anhydride, 81, 82, 155
Acetone semicarbazone, 118
Acetoxime, 115, 117
Acetyl chloride, reaction with alcohols, 72, 197
   reaction with amines, 155, 204
Acid amides: *see* Aliphatic amides; Aromatic amides
Acid chlorides of aliphatic acids, 126
   reactions and characterization of, 126, 127
   table of, 363
Acid chlorides of aromatic acids, 128
   reactions and characterization of, 128, 129
   table of, 365
Acid hydrazides, from esters, 135
Acyl phloroglucinols, 144
Acyloins, 196
Alcohols and ethers, class reactions for, 195–198
Alcohol-ethers, crystalline derivatives of, 79, 80
Aldehydes and ketones, differentiation between, 189, 190
   reactions of, 188–190: *see also* Aliphatic aldehydes; Aliphatic ketones; Aromatic aldehydes; Aromatic ketones
Aliphatic alcohols, 71
   crystalline derivatives of, 75–80
   differentiation between primary, secondary and tertiary (Lucas' test), 73
   oxidation with 'chromic acid', 73
   rapid method for distinguishing tertiary from primary and secondary, 74

Aliphatic—*contd.*
   reactions of, 71–75, 196, 197
   table of and derivatives of, 320–323
Aliphatic aldehydes, 106
   crystalline derivatives of, 109–110
   reactions of, 106–109, 188, 189
   table of and derivatives of, 347–348
Aliphatic amides, primary, 137
   characterization of, 138, 139
   reactions of, 137–138, 207
   table of, 377
Aliphatic amines, primary and secondary, 147
   crystalline derivatives of, 149–151
   reactions of, 147–149, 203, 204
   table of and derivatives of, 384–386
Aliphatic and aromatic amines, tertiary, 153
   crystalline derivatives of, 161–162
   table of and derivatives of, 394–396
Aliphatic carboxylic acids, 120
   crystalline derivatives of, 121–126
   neutralization equivalents of, 121, 203
   reactions of, 120–121, 202, 203
   table of and derivatives of, 357–358
Aliphatic esters, 129
   characterization of, 133–136, 190–194
   hydrolysis of, 129, 130, 131
   saponification equivalent of, 131, 132, 194, 195
   table of, 366–371
Aliphatic ethers, 102
   characterization of, 103–104, 195–198
   cleavage of, 103, 197
   reactions of, 102, 197
   table of, 343
Aliphatic halogen compounds: *see* Alkyl halides
Aliphatic hydrocarbons, saturated:

Index

Aliphatic—*contd.*
  see Saturated aliphatic hydrocarbons
Aliphatic hydrocarbons, unsaturated: *see* Olefinic hydrocarbons; Alkynes
Aliphatic ketones, 114
  crystalline derivatives of, 118–120, 188–190
  reactions of, 114–118, 188, 189
  table of and derivatives of, 352–353
Aliphatic nitriles (cyanides), 142
  conversion to amides, 143
  crystalline derivatives of, 144–146
  reactions of, 142–144, 208, 210
  reduction to primary amines, 145
  table of and derivatives of, 381–382
Aliphatic nitro compounds, 171
  characterization of, 172
  reactions of, 171–172, 206, 209
  table of, 400
Aliphatic sulphonic acids, table of, 403
Alkanes: *see* Saturated aliphatic hydrocarbons
Alkenes: *see* Olefinic hydrocarbons
Alkyl halides, 96, 186
  crystalline derivatives of, 97–100
  reactions of, 96–97, 186, 187
  table of and derivatives of, 334–336
Alkyl mercuric halides, 98
Alkyl nitrates, table of, 372
Alkyl nitrites, table of, 372
Alkyl sulphates, 213
  table of, 372
Alkyl sulphites, table of, 372
S-Alkylthiuronium picrates, 98
Alkyl 2,4,6-trihydroxyphenyl ketones, 144
Alkynes, characterization of, 65, 66
  mercurides of monosubstituted, 66
Aluminium chloride, 67
Amides, 121, 122
  hydrolysis of, 207
  hydroxamic acid test for, 207: *see also* Aliphatic amides; Aromatic amides
Amines: *see* Aliphatic amines; Aromatic amines
Amines, class reactions for, 203–205
Amines, separation by Hinsberg's method, 153–155
Amino acids, 162
  as dipolar ions, 162
  crystalline derivatives of, 165–168
  ninhydrin reaction for, 163, 164
  reactions of, 163–165
  table of and derivatives of, 397–398
α-Aminoalkylmercaptoacetic acid hydrochlorides, 145, 146
Amino-phenols, table of, 391
Analyzer, 26, 27
Anhydrides, class reactions for, 190
  hydroxamic acid test for, 190, 191
Anhydrides of aliphatic acids, 127
  characterization of, 128
  reactions of, 127, 128, 190, 191
  table of, 364
Anhydrides of aromatic acids, 129
  table of, 365
Anilic acids, 128
Anilides, 97, 121, 122, 123, 133
Anils, 159
Antimony, detection of, 41
Arenes: *see* Aromatic hydrocarbons
Aromatic alcohols, 80
  reactions of, 80, 195, 197, 198
  table of and derivatives of, 324–325
Aromatic aldehydes, 111
  crystalline derivatives of, 112–114
  reactions of, 111–112, 188, 189
  table of and derivatives of, 350–351
Aromatic amides, primary, 140
  hydrolysis of, 140
  reactions of, 140, 141, 207
  table of, 378
Aromatic amides, substituted, 141
  hydrolysis of, 141, 207
  reactions of, 141, 142, 207
  table of, 379–380
Aromatic amines, primary and secondary, 151
  crystalline derivatives of, 155–161
  reactions of, 151–153, 204, 205
  tables of and derivatives of, 387–391, 392–393
Aromatic amines, tertiary, 153
  crystalline derivatives of, 161–162
  reactions of, 153–155, 205
  table of and derivatives of, 394–396

Index

Aromatic carboxylic acids, 126
  reactions of, 126, 202, 203
  table of and derivatives of, 359–362
Aromatic esters, 136
  hydrolysis of, 136, 137, 190, 192
  table of, 373–376
Aromatic ethers, 104
  characterization of, 104–106
  cleavage of, 104, 197, 198
  table of and derivatives of, 344–346
Aromatic halogen compounds: see Halogenated aromatic hydrocarbons
Aromatic hydrocarbons, 66
  characterization of, 67–71, 186
  melting points of sulphonamides of typical, 67
  nitro derivatives of, 68
  oxidation of side chains in, 69
  table of and derivatives of, 318–319
Aromatic ketones, 120
  reactions and characterization of, 120, 188, 189
  table of and derivatives of, 354–356
Aromatic nitriles, 146
  conversion to amides, 146, 147, 208
  derivatives of, 146
  hydrolysis of, 146, 208, 210
  table of, 383
Aromatic nitro compounds, 168
  crystalline derivatives of, 170–171
  reactions of, 168–170, 206, 209
  reduction to amines, 170, 206
  reduction to hydroxylamines, 168, 169, 206
  table of, 399
Aromatic sulphonamides, 180
  derivatives of, 180
  hydrolysis of, 180, 211
  tables of, 404, 405
Aromatic sulphonic acids and their salts, 175
  crystalline derivatives of, 186–180
  fusion with caustic alkali, 175
  reactions of, 175–176, 211, 212
  table of and derivatives of, 402–403, 404
  p-toluidine salts of, 179
o-Aroylbenzoic acids, 67

Aryloxyacetic acids, 82, 83
Arsenic, detection of, 41
Atomic weights, table of relative, 420
Auxochrome, 245
Azines, 113, 114, 115
Azo compounds, reduction of, 207
  table of, 408
Azo dye, formation from primary amine, 151
Azoxy compounds, 207
  table of, 409

Barbiturates, table of, 407
Baeyer's test for unsaturation, 121, 185
Barfoed's reagent, 90
Bathochromic shift, 245
Beer–Lambert law, 241
'Beilstein', 222
Beilstein's test, 96
Benedict's solution, 90, 91
  preparation of, 90
  reaction with aldehydes, 107, 200
  reaction with carbohydrates, 90, 200
Benzal azine, 114
Benzal derivatives, 119, 159
Benzanilide, hydrolysis of, 142, 210
Benzenesulphonates, 149, 158, 159, 205
Benzenesulphonyl chloride, for separation of amines, 153–155
  reaction with amines, 158, 204, 205
Benzimidazole, 160
Benzoates, 77, 82, 88, 156, 165, 205
Benzoyl chloride, 82, 88, 89, 156
  reaction with alcohols, 77, 197
  reaction with amines, 156, 157, 204, 205
  reaction with amino acids, 165
N-Benzylamides of carboxylic acids, 134
  table of, 135
Benzylidene (benzal) derivatives, 119, 120, 159
S-Benzylthiuronium chloride, 125, 178
S-Benzylthiuronium salts of carboxylic acids, 125, 126
S-Benzylthiuronium sulphonates, 177, 178, 180
  table of, 404

423

Index

Bisulphite compounds, 108, 109, 116, 213
Biurea, 119
Biuret reaction, 140
Boiling point of a liquid, 14
Boiling points, determination of, 12–16
  by Siwoloboff's method, 14, 15
  correction for 10 mm. pressure difference, 15
Bond refractions, D-line, 25
Boric acid test for polyhydric alcohols, 87
Bromine, detection of, 38, 39
Bromine–carbon tetrachloride reagent, 62, 185, 202
Bromine water, 61, 62, 81, 85, 202
p-Bromoanilides, 122
Bromo derivatives, of aromatic ethers, 105, 197
  of phenols, 85, 202
p-Bromophenacyl esters, 123
Burns, 414
n-Butyl acetate, hydrolysis of, 129

Carbohydrates, 89, 199
  characterization of, 91–95
  reactions of, 89–91, 199–202
  table of and derivatives of, 333
Carbon and hydrogen, detection of, 34
Carbon disulphide reagent test, 148, 149
Carboxybenzoylation, 67
Carboxylic acids, equivalent weights of, 121, 203
  tests for, 120, 202, 203: *see also* Aliphatic carboxylic acids and Aromatic carboxylic acids
Carboxylic acids and phenols, class reactions for, 202–203
Carbylamine test, 148, 151, 152, 153, 205
  mechanism of, 148
Cellulose, 95
Chemical shifts, 287–290
  of some reference standards, 289
  parameter, 289
  tables of, 287, 288
Chlorine, detection of, 38, 39
Chlorosulphonic acid, 67, 100, 101, 104, 105
Chlorosulphonylation, 67, 100, 101

Chromic acid test for alcohols, 73, 197
Chromic anhydride, reagent, 74, 197
  test for distinguishing alcohols, 74
Chromophore, 244, 245
Class reactions, 2, 184–215
  summary of more important, 215–216
Cleavage of ethers, 103, 104, 197, 198
Copper derivatives, of enols, 86
  of amino acids, 163
Cuts, 415
Cyanohydrins, 114
Cyclohexanone, oxime, 117
  phenylhydrazone, 115, 117
  purification through bisulphite compound, 116

Density, determination of, 18–20
Derivatives, preparation of, 2, 217–220
  requirements of satisfactory, 217
  summary of the more useful, 218–220
  tables of, 316–412
Diazotisation, 151, 205
2,4-Dichlorophenoxyacetates, 167
2,4-Dichlorophenoxyacetic acid, 167
2,4-Dichlorophenoxyacetyl chloride, 167
1,2-Difluorotetrachloroethane, conformation of, 293
Dihalogenated aliphatic hydrocarbons, 100, 337, 338
1,3-Diketones, 86, 87
Diketene, structure, by mass spectrometry, 309
  by n.m.r. spectrometry, 292, 293
Dimedone, 109, 189
  derivatives, 109, 110, 112
  anhydrides of, 109, 110
3,5-Dinitrobenzoates, 75, 82, 165, 193
3,5-Dinitrobenzoyl chloride, 75, 76, 82, 174
  preparation from acid, 75, 76
  reaction with aliphatic ethers, 103
2,4-Dinitrochlorobenzene, 65, 84
  precautions in handling, 85, 160
2,4-Dinitrofluorobenzene, 165
2,4-Dinitrophenylhydrazine, 115, 188
  reagent, preparation of, 118, 189

Index

2,4-Dinitrophenylhydrazones, 109, 112, 113, 115, 118, 188, 189
2,4-Dinitrophenyl derivatives, of primary and secondary amines, 159
   of amino acids, 165
2,4-Dinitrophenyl ethers, 84
2,4-Dinitrophenylsulphenyl chloride, 64
   addition to alkenes, 64, 65
   addition to alkynes, 65, 66
   preparation of, 65
   melting points of adducts with alkenes, 65
   melting points of adducts with alkynes, 66
2,4-Dinitrophenyl-sulphides or -thioethers, 173
2,4-Dinitrophenylsulphones, 173, 174
3,5-Dinitrothiobenzoates, 174
Di-1-naphthylurea, 77, 78, 97, 98
1,5-Diphenyl-3-methylpyrazole, 86
Diphenylurethanes, 83
Dipolar ions, 51, 162
Disaccharides, 92, 200
Disulphides, 213
   table of, 210

Electrically-heated metal block, 9, 10
Electromagnetic spectrum, 239
   table of regions of, 240
Electronic spectra, 241
Elements, qualitative analysis for, 1, 34–43
Enols, 85
   copper derivatives of, 86
   table of and derivatives of, 331
   tests for, 85–87
Equivalent weight, 121, 132, 203
Esters, hydrolysis of, 129–132, 192, 193
   acid hydrazides from, 135
   acidic components of simple, identification of, 133, 34, 193
   alcohol components of simple, identification of, 133, 193
   N-benzylamides from, 134, 135
   hydroxamic acid test for, 191, 192: see also Aliphatic esters and Aromatic esters
Esters and anhydrides, class reactions for, 190–195

Esters of inorganic acids, tables of, 371, 412
Ester of a phenol, hydrolysis of, 193
Ethers, class reactions for, 195–198: see also Aliphatic ethers and Aromatic ethers
Ethers, detection of peroxides in, 102
   removal of peroxides from, 102
Ethyl acetoacetate, 86, 131, 251
Extinction, 242
   coefficient, molecular, 242, 243
Eye accidents, 415
Eye protection, 414

Fats, 131
Fehling's solution, 90, 107, 190
   preparation of, 90, 107
   reaction with aldehydes, 107, 190
   reaction with carbohydrates (sugars), 90, 200
Ferric chloride solution, 80, 85
   preparation of 'neutral', 85
   reaction with phenols, 80, 202, 203
Ferrous hydroxide test for nitro compounds, 169
Finger print region, 261
Fires, 416
First aid box, 413
Fluorescein test paper, 39
Fluorine, detection of, 40
Formyl derivatives, 160
Freezing point, determination of, 9
Fuchsin aldehyde reagent: see Schiff's reagent
Functional groups, identification, by infrared spectra, 273–274, 275–279
   by mass spectra, 303–309
   by ultraviolet absorption maxima, 247–252
Functional groups, reactions for, 184–214
   summary of more important reactions for, 215–216
Fusion with caustic alkali, 175
Fusion with soda lime, 34, 126

Galactose, oxidation to mucic acid, 200
Gases, 417
Girard-T reagent, 224
Glyceride, 131
Glycogen, 95

Index

Grignard reagent, 97, 98, 133, 134
Group and bond frequencies (infrared), table of, 274

Halogen compounds, reaction with ethanolic potassium hydroxide, 96, 100
  reaction with ethanolic silver nitrate, 96, 100, 187
  reaction with sodium iodide in acetone, 187, 188
  reactions of, 186–188: *see also* Alkyl halides
Halogenated aliphatic hydrocarbons, di- and poly-, 100, 186
  table of, 337, 338
Halogenated aromatic hydrocarbons, 100, 186
  crystalline derivatives of, 100–102
  reactions of, 102, 186
  table of and derivatives of, 339–342
Halogeno-aliphatic carboxylic acids, table of, 358
Halogeno-aromatic compounds, tables of: alcohols, 325
  aldehydes, 351
  carboxylic acids, 361
  ethers, 345, 346
  ketones, 335, 336
Halogeno-phenols, table of, 329
Halogens, detection of, 38, 39, 43
Hinsberg's method for separation of amines, 153, 154, 205
Hydrazides from esters, 135
Hydrazine, 115
Hydrazines, monoaryl, 204
Hydrazones, 115, 208
Hydrazo compounds, 207
  table of, 409
Hydrogen 3-nitrophthalates, 78
Hydrogen 3-nitrothiophthalates, 174
Hydrolysis, of amides, 140, 209, 210
  of benzanilide, 142
  of n-butyl acetate, 129
  of esters, 129–131, 192–194
  of esters of phenols, 193
  of nitriles, 143, 210
  of phenyl benzoate, 137
  of phosphates, 214
  of phosphites, 214
  of sulphonamides, 211

Hydroquinones from quinones, 183
Hydroxamic acid test, for amides, 207, 210
  for esters and anhydrides, 190, 191, 192
  for nitriles, 208, 210
Hydroxylamine, 115, 190
Hyperchromic effect, 246
Hypochromic effect, 246
Hypsochromic shift, 246

Ignition test, 33
Ignition tubes, 35
Imides, 208
  table of, 407
Infrared bands of common functional groups, 275–279
  acid anhydrides and acid halides, 277
  alcohols and phenols, 275
  aldehydes, 276
  alkanes, 275
  alkenes, 275
  alkynes, 275
  amides, 277
  amines, 278
  aromatic hydrocarbons, 275
  carboxylic acids, 276
  esters and lactones, 277
  ethers and peroxides, 275
  ketones, 276
  nitriles, 278
  nitrites, 278
  nitro compounds, 278
  organo-halogen compounds, 279
  sulphonamides, 279
  sulphones, 278
  sulphoxides, 278
  thiols, 278
Infrared spectra, typical, 265–273
  n-decane, 1-octene, 1-hexyne, 266
  n-propanol, propionic acid, acetone, 268
  di-n-butyl ether, n-heptaldehyde, n-butyl cyanide, 270
  n-butylamine, n-caproamide, L-α-alanine, 271
Infrared spectroscopy, 258–279
  characteristic bands of common functional groups, 275–279
  elementary theory, 258–261
  for determination of molecular structure, 262
  for determination of purity, 262

Infrared—*contd.*
  for identification of a compound, 161
  for identification of functional groups, 261
  group and bond frequencies, table of, 274
  instrumentation, 262–264
  sample handling, 264, 265
  selected bibliography, 279
  solvents for, 265
  uses of, 261
Inner salts, 51, 162
Inulin, 95
Iodine, detection of, 38, 39
Iodoform test, 198, 199
Isocyanide test: *see* Carbylamine test
Isothiocyanates, 214, 411
Isotopes, relative abundance of lower to highest, table of, 302

Keto-enol tautomerism, 251, 252, 295
β-Keto esters, 86, 131
Ketones: *see* Aliphatic ketones; Aromatic ketones
Kofler hot bench, 10, 11

Laboratory accidents and first aid, 413–417
Laboratory apparel, 414
Lactones, 190
Lanthanum chloroanilate, 40
Lassaigne's test, 35, 41
Liebermann's nitroso reaction, 152, 153, 205
Light absorption, law of, 242
Lucas reagent, 73, 197
Lucas test, 73, 74

Malaprade reaction, 88, 201
Mass spectra, 309–312
  n-butyraldehyde, 310, 311
  ethyl *sec*-butyl ether, 309, 310
  α-tetralone, 311
Mass spectometry, 298–312
  elementary principles of, 298, 299
  for determination of molecular weights, 301
  for determination of structure of α-tetralone, 311, 312

Mass Spectrometry—*contd.*
  for establishment of empirical formulae, 302, 303
  ionisation process, 300, 301
  instrumentation, 300
  of some classes of organic compounds, 303–309
  selected bibliography, 312
Mass spectrum, 309
Melting point, 3, 9
  baths for determination of, 6, 7
Melting point apparatus, 7, 9, 10, 11
Melting point capillaries, filling of, 5
  preparation of, 4, 5
Melting points, determination of, 3–12
  mixed, 11, 12
Melting points and solubilities of dibasic acids, 47
Mercaptans, 172
  crystalline derivatives of, 173–175
  reactions of, 172, 173, 212
  table of and derivatives of, 401
Mercaptoacetic acid, 145, 146
Mercury alkynides, 66
Mercuric iodide reagent, 66
Mercurides of monosubstituted alkynes, melting points of, 66
Mercury, detection of, 41
Mercury mercaptides, 175
  melting points of, 175
Methiodides, 161, 394, 395, 396
Methone: *see* Dimedone
Metho-p-toluenesulphonates, 161, 162, 394, 395, 396
Methylphenylosazones, 94
3-Methyl-1-phenylpyrazolone, 86
Microscope hot stage, 10, 11
Mixtures of organic compounds, qualitative analysis of, 223–238
  general discussion, 223–227
  preliminary examination of, 227–230
  separation of water-insoluble, 230–233
  separation of water-soluble, 233–236
  separation by physical methods, 236–238
Molecular refractivity, 24
Molecular weight, determination of, by mass spectrometry, 301
  by Rast's camphor method, 31
Molisch test, 89, 200

Index

Monosaccharides, 89, 91, 92, 199
Mucic acid, 200
Mulls, preparation of, 264, 265

1-Naphthalides, 97
1-Naphthylcarbamates, 77, 78, 83, 89
1-Naphthylhydantoic acids, 166
1-Naphthyl isocyanate, 77, 83, 84, 97, 166
1-Naphthyl isothiocyanate, 150
1-Naphthylthioureas, 150
1-Naphthylureido acids, 166
1-Naphthylurethanes, 77, 78, 83, 89
Nicol prism, 25, 27
Ninhydrin reaction, 163, 164
Nitriles, hydrolysis of, 208: *see also* Aliphatic nitriles; Aromatic nitriles
Nitro- and amino-aromatic compounds, tables of: alcohols, 325
aldehydes, 351
carboxylic acids, 362
ketones, 356
Nitro-aromatic ethers, table of, 346
p-Nitrobenzoates, 76, 82, 157
p-Nitrobenzyl esters, 124
Nitro compounds, reduction products of, 206, 209: *see also* Aliphatic nitro compounds; Aromatic nitro compounds
Nitro derivatives, of aromatic ethers, 186
of aromatic hydrocarbons, 68
of aromatic nitro compounds, 170, 171
of halogenated aromatic hydrocarbons, 100
Nitrogen, detection of, 35, 36, 37, 42
Nitrophenols, table of, 330
p-Nitrophenylhydrazones, 94, 113
3-Nitrophthalic anhydride, 78, 160
for derivatives of alcohols, 78, 79
for derivatives of amines, 160
for derivatives of mercaptans, 174
Nitrosamines, 152, 206, 209
Nitroso compounds, 206
table of, 408
p-Nitroso derivatives, 162
p-Nitrosodimethylaniline, 153
3-Nitrothiophthalates, 174, 175
Nitrous acid, reactions with, primary aliphatic amines, 147
primary aromatic amines, 151

Nitrous acid—*contd.*
secondary aliphatic amines, 148
secondary aromatic amines, 152
tertiary amines, 153
Nuclear magnetic resonance spectroscopy, 289–297
general principles of, 280–284
instrumentation, 284–286
selected bibliography, 296, 297
some applications of, 292–296
N.m.r., typical spectra, 294–296
acetylacetone, 294, 295
crotonaldehyde, 295, 296
isopropanol, 294
Nujol, 264

Olefinic hydrocarbons, 62
characterization of, 64
mechanism of addition of bromine to, 63
reactions of, 62, 63, 185
table of, 317
Optically active substances, 25, 26
Optical density, 242, 243
Optical rotation, molecular, 29
specific, 28
Optical rotatory dispersion, 29, 30
curves, 29, 30
Optical rotatory power, determination of, 25–29
Osazones, formation of, 91, 92, 200
plate of, *facing* p. 93
Oxidation of a side chain, 69, 101, 102, 170
Oximes, 112, 115, 119, 208

Periodic acid test, 88, 201, 202
Phenol and carboxylic acid, separation of, 136, 137
Phenols, 80
class reactions for, 202–203
crystalline derivatives of, 81–85
reactions of, 80, 81, 202
table of and derivatives of, 326–330
Phenylacetamide, from benzyl cyanide, 147
Phenyl benzoate, hydrolysis of, 137
Phenylcarbamates, 77
Phenylhydrazine, 112, 115
Phenylhydrazine reagent, preparation of, 113, 117
Phenylhydrazones, 112, 115

Index

Phenyl isocyanate, 77, 97
Phenyl isothiocyanate, 145, 149
p-Phenylphenacyl esters, 124, 125
Phenylthioureas, 149, 150, 161
Phenylurethanes, 77
Phosphates, alkyl and aryl, table of, 412
Phosphites, alkyl and aryl, table of, 412
Phosphorus, detection of, 40
Phosphorus compounds, 214, 215
Phthalic anhydride, 67, 79, 150, 168
Phthalimides, *N*-substituted, 150
Phthalyl derivatives, 168
Physical constants of organic compounds, 1
  tables of (including derivatives), 313–412
Picrates, 70
  of aliphatic amines, 150
  of alkyl 2-naphthyl ethers, 99
  of aromatic ethers, 195
  of aromatic hydrocarbons, 70
  of halogenated aromatic hydrocarbons, 102
  of tertiary amines, 161
S-alkylthiuronium, 98
Plane polarized light, 25
Poisons, 417
Polarimeter, 26
  half-shadow, 26, 27
  photoelectric, 26, 27
  tube, 28
Polarizer, 26, 27
Polyhalogenated aliphatic hydrocarbons, 100
  table of, 337–338
Polyhydric alcohols, 87, 199
  boric acid test for, 87
  crystalline derivatives of, 88, 89
  reactions of, 87, 88, 199
  table of and derivatives of, 332
Polysaccharides, notes on identification of, 95
Potassium hydroxide solution, ethanolic, 96, 97, 194
  preparation of, 97, 131
Potassium hydroxide in diethyleneglycol, 195
Potassium iodide-iodine reagent, 189
Potassium permanganate solution, 62, 63, 69, 185
Pressed discs, preparation of, 265

Primary and secondary aliphatic amines: *see* Aliphatic amines, primary and secondary
Primary and secondary aromatic amines: *see* Aromatic amines, primary and secondary
Prussian blue, 35
Pycnometer, 18, 19

Qualitative organic analysis, basis of, 1
  for the elements, 33–43
  of mixtures, 223–238
Quinones, 181
  characterization of, 183
  general properties of, 181
  reactions of, 181–183
  table of and derivatives of, 406
Quinoxalines, 182

Rast's camphor method, 31
Reciprocals, table of, 418–419
Reduction of nitriles to amines, 145
Reduction of nitro compounds, to amines, 170, 172, 209
  to hydroxylamines, 209
Reductive acetylation, 183
Reference works for qualitative organic analysis, 221–222, 237
Refractions, bond (D-line), 25
Refractive index, determination of, 20–24
Refractivity, molecular, 24
  atomic and structural constants (D-line), 24
Refractometer, 22
Rimini's test, 147
Rotation, molecular, 29
  specific, 28, 29

Salting out, 72
Saponification equivalent of an ester, 131
  determination of, 132, 194
Saponification of esters, 129–131, 192–194: *see also* Hydrolysis
Saturated aliphatic hydrocarbons, 61, 185
  characterization of, 62
  reactions of, 61, 186
  table of, 316–317
Schiff's bases, 159
Schiff's reagent, 108, 189, 201
  preparation of, 108

Index

Schotten–Baumann method of benzoylation, 82, 156, 157, 197
Semicarbazide hydrochloride, 116
Semicarbazones, 110, 112, 116, 118, 119, 208
Silver nitrate, ammoniacal, 106, 189
  preparation of, 106
  reaction with aldehydes, 106, 189
Silver nitrate, ethanolic, preparation of, 96
  reaction with halogen compounds, 96, 186, 187
Siwoloboff's method, 14
Soda lime, distillation with, 34, 126, 141
Sodium bicarbonate test, 80, 120, 202
Sodium bisulphite, adduct, 108, 213
  preparation of reagent, 109
Sodium carbonate-zinc method for the elements, 41–43
Sodium dithionite, 183
Sodium fusion test, 35, 36
Sodium, handling of, 36
Sodium iodide, in acetone, 187, 188
Sodium plumbite solution, 37
Sodium, reaction with esters, 196
  reaction with ketones, 196
Sodium test, 197
Solubilities of organic compounds, general discussion, 44–48
  determination of, in different solvents, for group tests, 57–60
Solubilities of stereoisomers in water and in ethanol, 47
Solubilities of the pentanols in water at 20°, 48
Solubilities, volatilities and steam volatilities of compounds, table of, 226
Solubility behaviour, summary of, 48–53
Solubility groups, 53–57
  classification of, 54, 55
  outline of solubility classification procedure, 56
  tables of, 55, 56
Spectropolarimetry, 29
Spectroscopic methods, 239–312
  infrared, 258–279
  mass spectrometry, 298–312
  nuclear magnetic resonance, 280–297
  ultraviolet, 241–257

Spectroscopic methods—*contd.*
  units for, 240
Spin–spin coupling constants, 292
  table of, 292
Spin–spin splitting, 290–292
Starch, 95
Styphnic acid, 70
Styphnates, 70
Sugars, 89, 199: *see also* Carbohydrates
Sulphates, dialkyl, 213, 372
  salts of monoalkyl, 213
Sulphides, 212
  table of, 410
Sulphinic acids, 212
Sulphites, dialkyl, 372
Sulphonacetamides, 178, 179
Sulphonamides, from sulphonic acids, 176, 177
  hydrolysis of, 208, 209
  of aromatic hydrocarbons, 67
  of aryl ethers, 104
  of halogenated aromatic hydrocarbons, 100, 101
  tables of, 404, 405
Sulphonanilides, 177
Sulphones, 213
  table of, 410
Sulphonic acids, 177, 178, 179, 211, 212
  alkyl esters of, 213: *see also* Aromatic sulphonic acids
Sulphoxides, 213
  table of, 410
Sulphur compounds, miscellaneous, 211
  table of, 410–411
Sulphur, detection of, 35, 37, 43
Sulphur dioxide test reagent, 176
Sulphuric acid, concentrated, 62, 63
  mechanism of reaction with alkenes, 64
  solubilities in, 52, 53, 56, 67
Sulphuric acid, esters of, 213, 372
Sulphuric acid, fuming, test, 186

Tables of derivatives, 316–412
  index to tables, 314–315
  preface to tables, 313
Tautomeric systems, ultraviolet spectra of, 251, 252
  n.m.r. spectra of, 294, 295
α-Tetralone, structure by mass spectrometry, 311, 312

Tetramethylsilane (TMS), 289
Thermometers, calibration of, 16–18
  reference substances for, 18
  stem correction for, 16
  with small bulbs, 17
Thiele acetylation, 183
Thiocyanates, alkyl, table of, 411
Thioethers, 212
  table of, 410
Thioglycollic acid, 145, 146
Thiols: see Mercaptans
Thiophenols, 172, 212, 401
Thioureas, table of, 411
Tollen's ammoniacal silver nitrate reagent, 106, 189
p-Toluenesulphonates, 84, 149, 158, 159, 166, 167, 411
p-Toluenesulphonyl chloride, 84, 154, 158, 167
  purification of, 158
p-Toluidides, 122, 123, 133
  from esters, 133
Transmittance, 243
Tribromophenol, 85
3,4,5-Triiodobenzoates, 79
  for crystalline derivatives of alcohol-ethers, 79, 80
1,3,5-Trinitrobenzene, addition compounds with, 71
2,4,7-Trinitro-9-fluorenone, 69
  adducts with aromatic and polynuclear hydrocarbons 69
  melting points of, 69, 70

Ultraviolet spectra, of ethyl acetoacetate in various solvents, 251
  of ethyl methyl ketone, 255
  of mesityl oxide, 255, 256
  of nitrobenzene, 256, 257
  of p-nitrophenol, 256, 257
  of quinoline dicyanides, 248, 249
Ultraviolet spectroscopy, 241–257

Ultraviolet—contd.
  absorption maxima of chromophoric groups, 244
  additivity principle, 245
  general considerations, 241–242
  general discussion of spectra of selected compounds, 244–247
  law of light absorption, 242, 243
  identification of functional groups by, 247–252
  instruments for, 252–255
  of cis and trans isomers, 250
  of conjugated systems, 245, 246
  of miscellaneous ring systems, 246
  of substituted benzenes, 247
  selected bibliography, 257
  solvents for, 243, 244
Ultraviolet spectroscopy, use in structure determination, of
  'carbothialdine', 249–250
  geometrical isomers, 250
  quinoline dicyanides, 247–249
  tautomeric systems, 251–252
Unsaturated hydrocarbons, 184: see also Olefinic hydrocarbons; Alkynes
Unsaturated esters, 131
Unsaturation, tests for, 62, 63, 184, 185
Urea nitrate, 139
Urea oxalate, 139
Urea, reactions of, 139, 140

Volatility in steam, 225, 226

Xanthydrol, 138, 140, 180
Xanthylamides, 138, 377
N-Xanthylsulphonamides, 180, 404

Zinc powder, distillation with, 182
Zinc powder–sodium carbonate mixture, 42
Zirconium–alizarin red S paper, 40
Zwitter ions: see Dipolar ions

547
V862e2
pt.2